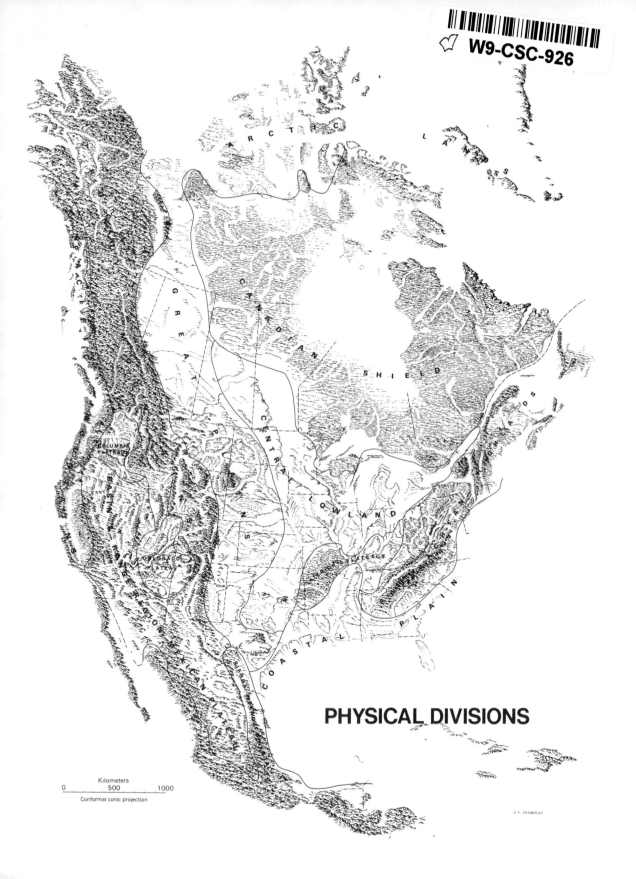

PHYSICAL DIVISIONS

Kilometers
0   500   1000
Conformal conic projection

J. P. TREMBLAY

Earth, Time, and Life

Earth, Time, and Life

An Introduction to Geology

Charles W. Barnes

Northern Arizona University

New York Chichester Brisbane Toronto
John Wiley & Sons

To Charlotte Elizabeth Barnes,
full partner in the search

This book was set in Times Roman by University Graphics.
It was printed and bound by Von Hoffman.
The drawings were designed and
executed by John Balbalis with the assistance of the Wiley Illustration Department.
Picture research was done by Kathy Bendo. Claire Egielski
supervised production. Cover and interior design by Angie Lee.
Cover photo: True-color LANDSAT imagery by U. S. Geological Survey,
Computer Branch, Flagstaff, Arizona.

Library of Congress Cataloging in Publication Data:

Barnes, Charles W   1934-
    Earth, time, and life.

    Includes bibliographical references and indexes.
    1. Geology. I. Title.
QE28.B24   550   79-17236
ISBN 0-471-05616-2

Printed in the United States of America

10 9 8 7 6 5 4 3 2 1

About the Cover

The image on the cover of this text is a mosaic of three satellite images recorded by the LAND-SAT-1 earth-orbiting satellite in October 1973 from an altitude of 570 miles (915 kilometers). The area included in the imagery is about 15,000 square miles of north-central Arizona, with part of the Grand Canyon in the upper left corner, the green tree-covered San Francisco Volcanic Field in the lower left corner, Meteor Crater in the lower center, the Petrified Forest and Painted Desert in the lower right corner, and Black Mesa Basin in the upper right quadrant.

The satellite records the scene beneath it as a series of digitized data points in several portions of the visible spectrum. The images from several parts of the spectrum are then combined into one scene after correcting for image distortion and scale variations by computer processing. Additional computer processing removed atmospheric haze and simulated this natural color version. The work was done at the U.S. Geological Survey's Image Processing Facility and Photographic Laboratory at Flagstaff, Arizona, a city that is barely visible in the lower left part of the image. This color image may be purchased from the U.S.G.S. Eros Data Center, Sioux Falls, South Dakota, 57198, as Public Affairs Office Image Number E-769-57CT.

Numerous other images are available at the same address. Advanced techniques of image processing provide one of many powerful modern tools in helping geologists to understand earth processes better and to search for new sources of mineral deposits, water, and energy.

Preface

"Science is the knowledge of many, orderly and methodically digested and arranged, so as to become attainable by one."
John Frederick William Herschel

This book introduces the fundamental concepts of geology to beginning college students who have had no background in college-level sciences, including geology. For most students, the course in which they use this book will probably represent their only exposure to geology. Therefore I have discussed the entire scope of geology—its historical and its physical aspects—with minimum use of unnecessarily technical language.

The text is based on a major recommendation from a committee created by the Geologic Society of America to offer suggestions for the improvment of geologic education in the late 1940s. The committee's suggestions are still appropriate today; at all levels of instruction "only those inferences be presented . . . for which the essential observational data and the logical steps leading to the inference have also been presented."

This book is one geologist's attempt to ex-amine briefly the history of many fundamental geologic ideas and present them in the context of human history. Since I believe strongly that geology is among the most human of all sciences, I think its fundamental ideas must be presented with human touches and with clear indications of how these ideas affect the daily lives of real people.

The approach throughout is historical; the development of each major geologic concept is traced. The sequence of content is traditional, but many chapters emphasize the dual nature of geologic inquiry, which often rests as much on practical needs as on human curiosity. For example, the chapters on minerals provide insights into the development of critical ideas about the nature of the crystalline world, with its repetitive order, and a study of the disorderly economics of mineral consumption.

Some scientists like to picture the world

as something that they explore as a neutral observer, as though they are outside the world. The science explored in this book is an intensely human activity *within* the world it describes; that activity is both limited and shaped by the world. Ideas, symbols, and imagination are the unique gifts of being human; ideas not only make us more human, but they spring from our humanity.

This sense of understanding what science—geological science—*is* forms my dominant theme. For too many people, science is something mysterious (something so mysterious as to be incomprehensible) that *other* people in white lab coats do. Many introductory science courses, with a morass of terminology, facts, classifications, and natural laws trotted out like divine truths, only reinforce that confusing view of the world of science. I believe that the vital connective tissue in *understanding* science is its history—its conceptual development as well as its chronology.

When science is seen in perspective, as one of many normal expressions of what it means to be human, the mystery falls away. Science is an expression of our humanity; it involves little more than curious people yearning to understand the world within which they live. Their chief tool is the human mind, that most marvelous of all instruments; they daily employ imagination, symbols, ideas, and rational thinking. Science seen in this perspective is an extraordinarily rich story of people like ourselves, with all of our shortcomings and potential for greatness.

Each teacher may use this book in a variety of formats to serve diverse introductory courses. Throughout the book there are frequent references to allied material in other sections. Each chapter contains a series of questions, many of which have no single, obvious answer; these questions highlight modern, controversial areas of geology. A glossary of all terms in **boldface** and appendices on mineral and rock identification, chemical principles in geology, classification of life forms, and understanding geologic and topographic maps are provided at the end of the book.

The illustrations have all been conceived exclusively for this text, and many of the photographs and other illustrative materials date from the previous four centuries of geologic thought. Together they illustrate the historical sweep of our widening curiosity about the earth.

The careful development of any good text requires the generous assistance of many people. In particular, I am indebted to many people who contributed ideas, information, criticism, and opinion as the book progressed. I am particularly grateful to Marjorie Dalecheck for her continued assistance during one summer's work in the photo archives of the U.S. Geological Survey and to Marcia Goodman for her invaluable assistance during two summers' work at the History of Science Collections at the University of Oklahoma Libraries. Discussions there with Ken Taylor, Duane Roller, and Dave Kitts were particularly fruitful. Ed Teasdale, Cities Service Company; Gil Hill, Patrick Petroleum; Archie Hood, Shell Development Company; Bob Kemper and John Irwin, Northern Arizona University Libraries; D.A. Brown, Australian National University; Patricia Hill, geophysicist, U.S. Geological Survey; Bob Houston, University of Wyoming; Michael Collier, my geologist-photographer colleague in Flagstaff, Arizona; M. Teetz, Oakland Museum; Bob Dott, University of Wisconsin; the late Lewis M. Cline and Stan Tyler, University of Wisconsin; Mike Carr, U.S. Astrogeology

Center; Gordon Swann, Ivo Luchitta, George Ulrich, and Ed Wolfe, U.S. Geological Survey; Rolland R. Reid, University of Idaho; Elso S. Barghoorn, Harvard University; E.S. Leskowitz, United Nations; Trevor Ford, University of Leicester; and my colleagues at my home university will all recognize their contributions to this total effort. Connie Erickson was particularly helpful in numerous details and was largely responsible for manuscript typing. None of these people are accountable for any misstatements or obscurities; obfuscation of the obvious is the author's sole responsibility.

Anyone who has written knows how crucially important the combined skills of professional reviewers and editors are. I am particularly grateful to Anne Reid and Don Deneck, who jointly saw me through the five years of preparation of this textbook, and to Eleanor Wiles, whose kind but trenchant criticism was fundamental to any success it may enjoy.

Finally, no effort of this magnitude would have been possible without the forbearance and enthusiasm of my family; we have jointly shared in both the exhaustion and exhilaration as this book enveloped our lives.

Charles W. Barnes

Flagstaff, Arizona
January, 1980

Note to Students

Open before you is the result of the combined efforts of several hundred people and five years of work. A few hints about the way the book is organized and its underlying viewpoint will make your use of it more fruitful.

Each chapter considers two distinctive kinds of ideas, since this is first a book about ideas. One kind of idea is *what* we know; gaining an understanding of concepts is fundamental to becoming educated. A second kind of idea is understanding *how* we know; this knowledge brings vitality to the process of education.

The ideas are chiefly geologic, of course but, because ideas spring from humans living in one period of time, the ideas are very much a part of the environment of the people who proposed them. This book discusses the history of many geologic ideas, or where the ideas have come from.

Many chapters also develop ideas that affect your daily life—insights on events as simple as the roll of a pebble downslope or as complex as the eruption of a volcano. Geology is an intensely *practical* science; geologic knowledge can enhance your travel anywhere, can help you to appreciate how dependent we all are on products from the earth, and just might keep you from losing your property or even your life.

Our energy, mineral, and water resources are becoming front-page news as well as painful economic realities. Geologists, as never before, are being asked to find more resources, evaluate more potential construction sites, provide for more water, and recommend intelligent policies for conservation in a world of diminishing resource-to-population ratios. In a world placed more and more under stress by the needs of a constantly increasing population, some knowledge of geology is simply fundamental to being an informed citizen and to making sound decisions.

I believe that science springs from our humanity, and that scientific curiosity is, in the best sense of the word, natural. Geological science, like all other sciences, is an intensely human endeavor that develops from the society of the time as surely as art, politics, literature, or any other expression of what it means to be human.

Geology is a particularly fertile vehicle from which to examine the history of scientific ideas; it provides us with a better understanding of where our water, minerals, energy, landscapes, and many hazards to both life and property come from and also suggests where *we* come from and where we may be going.

Chapter One offers a philosophical perspective on developing human perceptions of the earth and suggests the twin viewpoints that we have always taken in regard to the earth. The earth was to be USED, and it was to be UNDERSTOOD. The study of minerals (Chapter Two) is a first example of this duality. The history of our developing understanding of the nature of minerals is a classic example of the architecture of an idea. Humans discovered order *within* minerals; the *use* of minerals is a study in disorder.

The study of rocks, which are composed of minerals, is next; rocks furnish a not-so-mute testimonial to the internal and external energies that affect the earth. In Chapters Three to Five, people begin to understand the stories in the rocks, and they begin to grapple with the concept of an earth of unbelievable antiquity.

In Chapter Six, earthquakes furnish a glimpse into chaos and also into the developing field of earthquake prediction, which is certain to have major social, legal, and ethical ramifications. An unexpected order in the worldwide distribution of earthquakes allows us to step back and consider the earth through the lenses of a new theory. An earth composed of colliding continental and oceanic fragments, chattering, and overriding one another, in time becomes accepted reality, over thunderous objections (Chapter Seven).

A brief discussion of landforms and their influence on our lives follows in Chapter Eight. Each bit of scenery has its past; in a population that travels as much as we do, one of the great cultural values of an introductory geology course is the enhanced enjoyment it can bring to the next trip anywhere.

Energy (Chapter Nine) is a topic of increasing importance to us all; energy is what makes us run, and the current supply and demand situation is making us more and more vulnerable. Water is a companion topic to energy; in Chapter Ten we discuss where and how this equally vital resource is found, how it is treated, and the legal systems that have been developed to settle disputes over its use and abuse.

The concept of time (Chapter Eleven) introduces the last third of the text, which reviews major questions about the origin and development of life and the series of changes in location and environment that we collectively call historical geology (Chapters Twelve to Fifteen). As the last pages are turned, humans arrive and take up their inheritance—the treasures, both material and intellectual, furnished by study of the earth.

The whole is a story briefly told, because useful books must hold to reasonable lengths. No geologist, including myself, will find all their favorite subjects or ideas here, but the book is constructed so that every teacher can develop a special way of sharing the earth with you.

If you should want to read further, each chapter provides up-to-date references that will extend your knowledge well beyond what is available here. Most of the references are easily available in college and public libraries, and studying them will carry you as far as you wish to go.

If, after working with this book, you have comments, questions, or suggestions, please write to me in care of Northern Arizona University, Flagstaff, Arizona 86011. I will do my best to answer any questions and will respond constructively to suggestions.

C.W.B.

Contents

Earth, Time, and Life

Dawn in the Grand Canyon. (Photograph by Michael Collier.)

Chapter One
A BEGINNING

''The most beautiful thing we can experience is the mysterious. It is the source of all true art and science.''
Albert Einstein

You and I are from the earth. We carry its substances in our bones, in our flesh, and in our blood. We are the culmination of ceaseless centuries of biologic trial and error and of thousands of years of cultural development and learning. We cannot erase our kinship with the earth, because our origin contains the key to all that we may become. Our future is in understanding our planet, over which we have a more and more uncertain dominion.

A HUMAN PERSPECTIVE

Early humans several million years ago knew that they were from the earth, but they did not know the earth we know; they were creatures of glacial climates. We, in contrast, live in a relatively warm and gentle time and find it difficult to imagine a time when the climate in Kansas was more like that of northern Canada. Our immediate ancestors were nomadic; they moved south as the glaciers advanced and returned north as the climate warmed. In the caves of southern Spain are cave paintings that show that 50,000 years ago, the culture of the area was much like that of the modern Eskimo.

Today southern Spain is a sunny, warm resort area.

Along with fire, humanity's second great discovery was the manufacture and use of tools to extend their capabilities. People began to use stone implements several hundred thousand years ago, during Paleolithic times; 15,000 years ago they mastered the intricate working of homogeneous, rocky materials (Figure 1-1) such as obsidian and flint into useful and beautiful objects.

Early people were geologists; they knew which earth materials in their vicinity made the best tools. Their curiosity about the nature of things is the hallmark of any good scientist, and their use of earth materials as tools and weapons persists today.

Tools were *needed*, because early humans faced the harsh realities of energy balance common to all life—consume more energy from the quarry than you expend in the hunt. Stone tools dramatically extended the reach of a single hunter, just as socialization into hunting parties increased the *size* of the quarry that could be successfully hunted. Organized hunting parties could provide food for many people; thus, the wooly mammoth was a common hunter's goal in the subarctic climate. All was not work, however; mammoth hunters in what is now

1-1
Modern projectile points. Early people also took advantage of the flaking property of similar rocks by flaking them to a sharp edge. (From J. W. Dawson, 1880, Fossil men and their modern representatives, Fig. 25, courtesy of History of Science Collections, University of Oklahoma Libraries)

Czechoslovakia piped music on bone flutes over 20,000 years ago.

EARLY HUMANITY AND MINERAL WEALTH

Neolithic times, beginning about 10,000 B.C., brought us into still closer husbandry with the earth's resources. Besides working stone implements, Neolithic people began intensive agriculture, mining, and quarrying. The harsh, dry countries of the eastern Mediterranean seem to us an unlikely place to begin an agricultural revolution but, again, we must remember that 10,000 years ago northern Europe was enveloped by glaciers, and the eastern Mediterranean would have enjoyed a warm, rainy, agricultural endowment.

Our use of the earth, in time, became ever more sure and, with both luck and backbreaking labor, the earth may have seemed an endless horn of plenty. Pottery was another Neolithic triumph; some pottery dates back more than 9000 years. What a triumph this first merging of clay with fire must have been! Mining and quarrying came next; the earliest mining began an incredible 7000 years ago. Flint, for tools, was among the earliest of the mineral commodities mined. Copper mining began shortly thereafter on the island of Cyprus, whose Greek name means "copper." Bronze objects were being made in Thailand by 3600 B.C., and extensive underground mining dates back to the time of the Pharaohs of the nineteenth dynasty (about 1400 B.C.).

Copper mining and smelting were not uniquely an old-world activity; early Americans mined copper in what is now modern Michigan around 2000 B.C. These early min-

1-2
Copper in Keweenaw rock. The bright spots are bits of shiny copper enclosed by the rock. Specimen is about 6 inches (15 centimeters) in diameter. (Photograph by N. K. Huber, U.S. Geological Survey.)

ers dug thousands of pits, built roaring bonfires inside the pits, and poured cold water on the simmering rock to split it into fragments. Next, copper (to be used for ornamental purposes) was pounded out of the shattered rock with stone hammers. These ancient residents of Michigan left their copper pits about 1000 B.C. and vanished as an indentifiable culture. The copper they left behind in the ancient rocks of the Keweenaw Peninsula of northwestern Michigan (Figure 1-2) is now (4000 years later) only a minor copper reserve.

ENGINEERING THE EARTH

Stonehenge, the greatest Neolithic monument to the art of quarrying and stonemasonry, still stands on the Salisbury Plain of southern England. Stonehenge is an array of massive stone slabs and lintels, each weighing up to 50 tons (50,000 kilograms), set in circular precision on a featureless plain (Figure 1-3). Clever geologic detective work has allowed us to trace the source of the stone to a quarry 25 miles (40 kilometers) away. Quarrying and erection of these monoliths would be a sizable engineering feat today; radiocarbon dating (see Chapter Ten) of the antlers that these ancient Britons used as tools indicates that construction began around 2700 B.C. and lasted for over 1000 years.

The quarrying of the stone slabs and the erection of this ceremonial site ranks as one of the engineering marvels of all time; the site is a dedication to our sense of kinship with the stars. Stonehenge is an astronomical observatory, laid out with high standards of precision. Estimates of the labor required suggest approximately 18 million man-hours. Think of the skills required to sustain a quarrying and construction operation for over 1000 years to near-modern levels of mathematical precision, and we will share a different view of our Neolithic ancestors.

Our first encounters with the earth produced an order of things based on *usefulness*. The earth was possessed and its riches were used, but its secrets remained. We can imagine that early humans wondered why some stones could be worked to an edge and others could not, but there was no way for them to unravel the riddle. An ordering of things by merit had been created and the earth yielded an endless store of useful items, but the earth remained an unpredictable resource. Early humanity's sense of the earth was that of consumer; their store of earth knowledge enveloped a single concern: Is it useful?

MINERAL WEALTH AND CIVILIZATION

Our *cultural* history begins about 10,000 years ago, a time that coincides with the end of the last Ice Age. Humans began to dominate the earth, cultivate its plants, and domesticate its animals. As the earth warmed from the last Ice Age, families settled in villages, tended their flocks, and tilled the earth. Living together in villages was a social revolution; it offspring were leisure time and the ability to specialize one's activities in an interdependent society. Planting and working the same soil each year was an agricultural revolution; its offspring was hybrid wheat, which needed to be threshed to separate the grain from the stalk. From these

1-3

These stone monoliths, which weigh many tons (metric tons), still stand on the Salisbury Plain, testifying to the skill and imagination of humanity. They also testify to another side of us; they have recently been fenced with barbed wire so that further vandalism by unthinking twentieth-century people will not destroy them. (Photograph courtesy of the British Tourist Authority.)

parallel revolutions came the revolution of technology, which is the child of science.

We had ceased to *accept* the world as it was and began to *transform* the natural world. Irrigation ditches needed to be dug, and new sources of water had to be found. The plow, another example of people using tools to extend their capacities, was invented; this was followed by discovery of the wheel and the axle. An earth transformed became an *exploited* earth.

A growing familiarity with the planet Earth also bred a growing utilization of the earth's *mineral resources*. Our history is one of successful exploitation of our planet beginning, geologically, with the use of found stones and then of shaped stones, and culminating in the mining of minerals and their smelting into useful metallic substances. This exploitative history continues today; the availability of cheap iron and steel and plentiful power has revolutionized our modern world.

We may think of minerals as something combined with vitamins in a pill or perhaps as the sparkling crystals in a museum display case. Both images are included in a geological understanding of what constitutes a mineral; some natural elements in some minerals are nutritionally useful, and some minerals may form sparkling crystals. A complete discussion of what a mineral is appears in Chapter Two; early civilized people regarded nearly *anything* of value dug from the earth as a mineral, and they built new cultures based on mineral wealth. Indeed, the word *mineral* can be traced back to Celtic origins, and it describes that which is taken from a mine.

The grandeur of Greece rested partly on the labor of slaves in the silver mines of Lorean. The average life expectancy of these early slave miners was 4 years. The bronze swords of the Grecian armies at the Battle of Marathon tore through Persian leather armor and, thereafter, one civilization slumbered while the other prospered. The gold from Mount Pangaeus financed the conquests of Alexander the Great, who conquered the known Western world.

Implicit in stories of civilizations supported by mineral wealth is a sobering note. Mineral supplies are *exhaustible*. Phoenicians mined the tin fields of Cornwall in Britain centuries before Christ, and those same tin fields provided England with great wealth into the nineteenth century. Now the supplies of tin minerals are exhausted. If the affluence and influence of nations are founded largely on exploitation of exhaustible resources, what is the nation's future?

For the Greek Empire, the decline in silver production led to the decline of a civilization. For Great Britain, the lack of adequate resources led to colonialism and war. For Japan, the oil of Indonesia and the wealth of China were the targets of World War II; for Germany the oil fields of Romania and the coal and iron of Alsace-Lorraine provided the means to an ugly end. The rich resources of South Africa today give it a degree of political independence from pressures to change its social structures, just as the rich natural resources of the northeastern United States helped to preserve our union over 100 years ago.

MINERALS IN OUR LIFE

In 1974, the U.S. Geological Survey estimated the average value of mineral resources recovered from all the mines within the conterminous United States as about $250,000 per square mile (square kilometer). The *total* value of mineral resources produced in the 3 million square miles (7⅘ million square kilometers) of the United States is then approximately $750 billion, *one-third* of which was produced in the *last* 25 years. Mineral resources are among our most thoroughly *disguised* industrial commodities; we are rarely aware of the direct value of mined products in our life.

Many Americans have never seen a mine; less than 1 percent of the land surface has ever been mined. The raw materials of the earth are usually processed before we see them, and we are unaware of their source. Ask a chemist where bottles of chemicals come from; the answer is often a stockroom or a supply house. Copper pipes come from a plumbing store, light bulbs from a grocery store, insulation from a contractor, fertilizers from a garden store, and automobiles from a car lot. These glib responses are illusions, because everything listed comes ultimately from the earth and is then processed into usable commodities for further retail sale.

The clothes we wear are made mostly from natural fibers grown with mineral fertilizers or from synthetic fibers made from coal or petroleum. Like early peoples, we use minerals for weapons (nuclear or conventional) or for adornment (cosmetics and jewelry). Buildings are made of sand, gravel, stone, bricks, cement, steel, aluminum, asphalt, and glass. Our furniture is made more and more from metals and plastics and is finished with paints, stains, polishes, and varnishes drawn from the earth. The paper on which these words are printed (by machines made from metals) is "filled" with a fine clay to make the surface smoother for higher-quality printing.

In almost every facet of our daily life, we use minerals without knowing it, so hidden are their uses in a complex, industrial society. Not recognizing our mineral consumption makes us even more vulnerable to three inexorable laws governing minerals. Mineral supplies are *exhaustible, irregularly distributed,* and *irregularly used.* Ninety percent of the world's molybdenum comes from a single mine near Climax, Colorado, while the United States, with only one-sixth of the world's population, consumes one-half of all extracted materials.

Patterns in supply and demand have changed radically in the last 25 years. In 1940 the United States produced and consumed about one-half of the world's mineral supplies; by 1975 we produced only one-quarter of the total. In the same time interval, world consumption of 18 basic mineral commodities has increased six times, while U.S. consumption has not quite doubled. Developing countries, increasing affluence, and burgeoning populations are placing increasing demands on limited, nonrenewable mineral items.

Figure 1-4 shows the mineral commodities of major industrial importance consumed by an average American student in a year. Can you fathom why it required 430 pounds (200 kilograms) of *salt* to keep you alive this year? Where did it all go? Like many minerals, its use is thoroughly disguised in the finished products we use. You eat less than 5 pounds (2⅕ kilograms) of salt each year.

SCIENCE FOR HUMANITY

Like any discoverers, early humans perceived what their preconceptions allowed, and their images preconditioned those who followed. To earliest people, the earth must have been at once benevolent and fearsome, because *everything* was unknown. Each

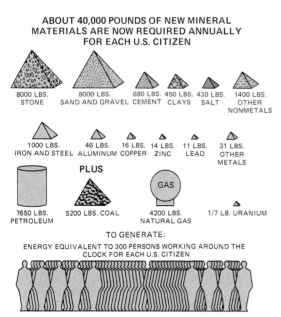

ABOUT 40,000 POUNDS OF NEW MINERAL
MATERIALS ARE NOW REQUIRED ANNUALLY
FOR EACH U.S. CITIZEN

8000 LBS. STONE

8000 LBS. SAND AND GRAVEL

680 LBS. CEMENT

450 LBS. CLAYS

430 LBS. SALT

1400 LBS. OTHER NONMETALS

1000 LBS. IRON AND STEEL

46 LBS. ALUMINUM

16 LBS. COPPER

14 LBS. ZINC

11 LBS. LEAD

31 LBS. OTHER METALS

PLUS

7650 LBS. PETROLEUM

5200 LBS. COAL

GAS
4200 LBS. NATURAL GAS

1/7 LB. URANIUM

TO GENERATE:
ENERGY EQUIVALENT TO 300 PERSONS WORKING AROUND THE
CLOCK FOR EACH U.S. CITIZEN

1-4

Per capita consumption of earth materials by U.S. citizens. (Illustration courtesy of the U.S. Bureau of Mines.)

rock and each landscape were portents, but of what? If the earth was free of constraints, anything could happen. If the earth is capricious, everything is possible.

If the earth is fickle, ordered, scientific inquiry into the nature of things is impossible. Things have no nature, stones are mute, and wisdom consists not of challenging preconceptions, but of bending to them. The earth is to be held in great reverence. An ancient Sanskrit prayer expresses this concept: "O, Mother Earth, ocean girdled and mountain breasted, pardon me for trampling on you."

Native Americans have long shared a reverent association with the earth. Chief Joseph is quoted as saying " . . . I never said the land was mine to do with as I chose."

Another northwestern Indian leader more than a century ago said "The Great Spirit, in placing men on earth, desired them to take good care of the ground, and to do each other no harm." Willa Cather, quoting Father Latour, remarks that " . . . it was the Indian's way to pass through a country without disturbing anything; to pass and leave no trace, like a fish through the water, or birds through the air."

By contrast, Western tradition since the Middle Ages, has insisted that the earth can be understood and that it can be exploited for the benefit of those who "own" the land. This subtle, but critical, shift in our view of the earth springs from the fundamental assumption that the earth is *orderly. If* the earth is orderly, *things found together in nature are together for a reason.* An orderly earth can be *understood* by patient and careful observation combined with our power to reason, to test, and to comprehend.

James Hutton and Uniformity

Curiosity about our earth stretches back many thousand years, but modern geologic thought about the earth awaited the patient work of a Scots farmer whose ideas were published in 1788. The Scot was *James Hutton;* his gift to our science was an appreciation of the orderliness of the earth and of the *processes* and *rates* with which changes take place.

Hutton was drawn to the study of soil formation, an obvious concern for a farmer. He realized, after intensive observation and study, that rocks change *gradually* into soil, which is *slowly* washed into the sea, where rocky particles *slowly* become hard rock again, only to be uplifted and exposed to the elements once again and crumble back into soil. He believed that the natural world was not only orderly, but *cyclic,* and that rates of change in the natural world were often *impossibly slow in human terms.*

Hutton's gift to the future was a vision of an earth that was dynamic and ever changing, cyclic, and *uniform in process over very long periods of time.* His ideas have been summarized as the **principle of uniformity— the present is the key to the past;** careful observation of earth processes operating *today* will allow us to *interpret* the PRODUCTS of those same processes that operated in the past.

Note that Hutton's ideas are *assumptions* on the nature of the natural, rocky world. As Hutton, in 1788, phrased his idea, " . . . the uniformity of nature, *even if not strictly true* (emphasis added), is necessary for our clear conception of the system of nature."

A New Way to See

We can now examine the earth from a new perspective, because an assumption of orderliness and uniformity of process yields a view of the earth that is *totally* different from the view that early humans held. *If* the processes that shape our earth toil at rates of change that·are often too slow for us to recognize, the earth *is* old beyond our imagination. With an ancient earth that is armed with a multiplicity of processes, once again, anything is possible.

The exchange of views was not an even trade. Modern, educated people know that we live on an ancient earth that is capable of many things, but is always capable of being understood, an earth whose processes may even come to be predictable and alterable. Understanding a natural process inevitably leads to human intervention and to a view of the universe as something that can be bent to our will. Unfolding discovery (Figure 1-5) and unending exploitation have followed, replacing the ancient fear of and reverence for the earth. Science is both an expression of our growing curiosity and of our desire to intervene.

Geology, the science of the earth, like all sciences, is founded on the assumption that the universe is orderly and therefore capable of being understood. Process and product in the natural world share a *cause* and *effect* relationship; each process is parent to an observable product. The giant boulder in an Iowa cornfield, the vaulting strata at the

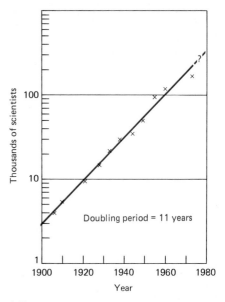

1-5
Rate of increase in numbers of American scientists since 1900. (*Source. American Men and Women of Science,* first edition published in 1906, fourteenth edition published in 1979. Permission of the R. R. Bowker Company. Copyright © 1979 Xerox Corporation.)

Garden of the Gods in Colorado, the consummate grandeur of the Grand Canyon of Arizona—all these have *meaning*. They are the result of natural processes that are still operating today, as they have for billions of yesterdays.

KNOWING

We have *exchanged* the mystery of a chaotic earth, together with the fear and reverence it engendered, for the mysteries provided by a scientific view of the earth. Understanding brings with it greater, not lesser, mysteries because there is much about the earth that is presently inexplicable. Karl Pearson, in the book *Grammar of Science,* phrased these ideas extraordinarily well nearly 100 years ago.

Does science leave no mystery? On the contrary, it professes mystery where others profess knowledge. . . . There is mystery enough here, only let us clearly distinguish it from ignorance within the field of possible knowledge. The one is impenetrable, the other we are daily subduing.

Reasoning

Modern people "subdue ignorance" in two somewhat different modes of reasoning. **Deductive reasoning** calls for making reasonable generalizations and then testing their logical *consequences* to see if they accord with observation. Suppose that I establish that students are honest as a generalization. I then test my assumption by tossing a coin to the class while I am blindfolded and ask the lucky student to return it anonymously after

class. If the coin generally comes back, I *may* have proved my original assumption.

But suppose I threw out a $100 bill! Would the result still be the same? Suppose I announce the result to the class the next day; would the results be the same? Very often the problem is knowing what is *really* being tested.

Inductive reasoning operates in the reverse; it requires extensive observation, and then testing and classification of the resulting information. Finally, the grand *generalization* that satisfactorily explains many seemingly unrelated fragments of information is arrived at. Newton's *law of gravity* is such a sweeping generalization about mass relations that holds only as long as space is flat and time is absolute. However, these generalizations may fail as new bits of information arrive; for example, we now know that both time and space are curved or relative!

Theories as Lenses

Generalizations that are less thoroughly tested are known as *theories;* those that are even more tenuous are *hypotheses.* Many hypotheses and theories are advanced originally as highly speculative models. As such, these models clarify ideas, provide substance for observation, experiment, and calculation and, finally, are a source for newer speculative models that agree more closely with what is real. Frequently, facts do *not* speak for themselves. Facts remain just that, cold and immutable, until they are looked at in a new light.

One of the more interesting examples of an old theory focusing on new perceptions comes from our views on continental permanence. Three centuries ago, Europeans, looking at world maps, suggested that sometime in the past Europe and Africa had been torn away from the Americas; their suggestion was based on the shapes of the Atlantic coastline of each continent. In 1912, Alfred Wegener, a German meteorologist, summed up the evidence that pointed to the reality of continental motion. His theory spotlighted an immediate stumbling block: how to drive the thin, rigid continents through solid oceanic rock?

The necessary research into the nature of the rocky floor of the oceans had to wait until after World War II for either the acceptance or rejection of Wegener's ideas, but the concept of continental drift focused our perception on what data were critical. The new facts from the ocean floors were dramatic confirmation of the theoretical model that revealed them (see Chapter Six).

GEOLOGY AND PEOPLE

All science springs from *human curiosity,* making the average 1-year-old child a supreme example of a good scientist. For a young child, everything is new and is to be tested, organized, connected with everything else, and thus understood. That simple, yet powerful, curiosity about how the world works is the driving force behind the science of geology. Emerson phrased it eloquently: " . . . men love to wonder and that is the seed of our science."

The study of the earth also requires intensely *practical* research. Where may a successful dam be built? How may earthquakes be predicted, even prevented? Such practical research often gives geology its unique flavor as a science that touches directly on the lives of people. Nor are the curiosity-directed and need-directed types of inquiry antagonistic. A century of academic curiosity about the origin of volcanoes supports today's practical research that is directed toward using subterranean volcanic heat as a supplementary source of energy.

Geology, which is the study of the complex physical and biological system than we call earth, is a uniquely interdependent science that draws heavily on the techniques and understandings of all the natural sciences. Consider the eruption of an undersea volcano, a modern process that geologists study intensively. Models of the eruptive process might deal heavily in stress analysis, which is an aspect of physics and engineering. Models of the formation of lava deal with liquid-solid relations at high temperatures and pressures; this is an aspect of physical chemistry. The study of the newly developing life on the flanks of the dormant volcano is the province of marine geologists and paleontologists, who use techniques common to the biological sciences.

Geologists use ideas from all the natural and physical sciences in studying our earth, but many of the concepts and techniques used are uniquely geologic. A *seismograph* is an instrument used to display ground motion during an earthquake. The geologic analysis of seismographic data to tell us more about our trembling earth has resulted in detailed knowledge on the nature of the earth's interior and the origin of earthquakes and, recently, in the ability to detect underground nuclear explosions half a world away.

Perhaps the greatest gift of geology is an appreciation of the immensity of *time*. Among the first written speculations on the age of the earth, Theophilus of Antioch, in approximately A.D. 180, stated that the world was created in 5529 B.C. For centuries thereafter, other people speculated on the age of our earth; estimates, based on the rate of intermittent earth processes, yielded ages of about 100 million years by the turn of this century. In 1905 Ernest Rutherford (later Lord Rutherford) suggested that the study of the ratio of the quantity of offspring (atomic decay products) to the quantity of radioactive parent remaining (see Chapter Ten) would provide the first accurate age of the earth. These techniques require us today to comprehend an earth approximately 4.7 billion years old.

The idea of an earth 47 million centuries old comes not only from Lord Rutherford and the thousands of geologists who followed his lead, but also from James Hutton. Well over 100 years before the age of the earth became firmly established by radioactive means, Hutton correctly surmised that the slow, almost imperceptible, rate of many earth changes required an earth of great antiquity.

An ancient earth is a dynamic earth, but it is not constantly a catastrophic earth. In an *ancient* earth, streams may cut their own valleys grain by grain, inch by inch (centimeter by centimeter), century by century. In an earth only a *few thousand years old,* cataclysmic events are required to split the earth's surface; streams later occupy the gigantic chasms that result.

This argument over the origin of stream valleys is an old one and highlights the debate between the *catastrophists,* who necessarily believe the earth to be very young, and the *uniformitarians* (followers of *Hutton*), who believe in *uniformity* of process and surmise that the earth is old. The controversy over the origin of stream valleys lasted until the beginning of the nineteenth century, when John Playfair, Hutton's close friend, noted that tributary streams join master streams at common elevations; this is an exceedingly unlikely occurrence *if* streams occupied valleys formed by great earthquakes. *If* earthquakes formed valleys, valley intersections would occur at a great variety of heights, and waterfalls would be the rule, not the scenic exception. Thus Playfair's canny observation and inference, now termed the **Principle of accordant stream junctions,** helped to subdue the argument between the uniformitarians and the catastrophists.

Today geologists recognize that although the processes that alter the earth are unchanging through time, the intensity and mix of processes have varied greatly from one time and place to another. As an example, glaciers have sporadically been a major climatic and geologic agent through most of our several million years on earth but, today, we are free of glacial intrusion except at the highest latitudes. The process of glaciation continues, but its impact on the earth is minor *at this time.*

Inherently, geology is a historical science, concerned with understanding the earth today and with probing deeply into the vestiges of its past. The historical flavor of the science of geology is unique; no other science shares our concern with the earth's ancient past or our concern with predicting its future, particularly for predicting events that directly affect us, such as landslides, earthquakes, and volcanic eruptions.

Geology also plays a unique role in our economic life, so that economic concerns and gentle curiosity are often intertwined in many geologic investigations. Economic concerns with the earth fall into two categories: (1) the location and exploitation of the earth's energy, water, and mineral resources, with minimum environmental damage, and (2) the prediction, prevention, or mitigation of the geologic hazards to human life, including earthquakes, landslides, and volcanic eruption. As Will Durant, the American philosopher, remarked, "Civilization exists by geologic consent . . . subject to revocation at any moment."

SUMMARY   Early humans revered the earth, both for the store of earth materials that allowed them constantly to extend their dominion, and as a fearful and unpredictable place where anything was possible. Modern humanity, on the basis of experience, *asserts* that the world is an orderly, understandable place and proceeds to study nature and to subdue and alter the natural world. Using our senses, which are now vastly extended by scientific apparatus, and our unique intellect, knowledge subdues ignorance and recognizes new mystery.

Geology, the science that expresses our curiosity about the earth, wields the tools of all sciences to study a complex earth and to win from it the mineral, energy, and water resources that are fundamental to our modern economy. Better understanding of the geologic hazards that beset us has also been recently attained; unfortunately, this information is too little used.

Although economic-directed and curiosity-directed research are the foundation of geologic inquiry, our understanding of the earth's past is based on modifications of Hutton's *Principle of uniformity,* which insists that the earth processes have remained the same throughout 47 million centuries of tumultuous time, but that their intensity, duration, and location have varied. This concept of uniformity allows us to reconstruct events long before our arrival; it also allows us hesitant predictions about the earth's future.

Geology is an uniquely historical, natural science; it makes major contributions to the affluence of humanity. Cause and effect rationality and uniformity of process are its most powerful intellectual tools: without the former there is *no* science; without the latter there is *no* past.

EXERCISES   1. As we continue to mine more mineral wealth from the earth, predict what major obstacles must be overcome before a metallic mineral commodity, such as aluminum cans, becomes recyclable.
2. What evidence could have been used by intelligent people before Hutton to prove that the earth was very *young?*
3. Imagine that you lived during Paleolithic times in the midst of a glacial advance. Would you have *any* evidence that the world had ever enjoyed a past climate unlike the one in which you lived?

4. Who has had a greater impact on your life-style, Hutton or Napoleon? Why?

5. Earth materials were first categorized by their *usefulness*. Now geologists also classify mineral deposits by their mode of *origin*. What shifts in viewpoint does that classification imply?

6. What difference can you suggest between the demands made on the earth by a nomadic population versus those made by a village culture?

7. If understanding the earth leads to manipulating the earth and to a loss of respect and kinship with the earth, what are the values of understanding more of the earth's processes? Alternatively, does understanding lead to greater respect, as others would argue?

SUGGESTED READINGS

Leveson, David, 1971, *A Sense of the Earth,* Garden City, N.Y., Doubleday, 176 pp.
The most thoughtful statement of our kinship with the earth and our discovery of the earth. An incredibly moving book.

Skinner, Brian J., 1976, *Earth Resources,* 2nd ed., Englewood Cliffs, N.J., Prentice-Hall, 152 pp.
Excellent summary of the sources and problems relating to mineral and energy resources. Authoritative, modern, and well written.

Whitehead, Alfred North, 1953, *Science and the Modern World,* Toronto, Ont., Collier-Macmillan Canada, 212 pp.
Read the first two chapters for a deeper understanding of the origins of all science and the rest of the book for a deeper understanding of yourself.

Young, Keith, 1975, *Geology: the Paradox of Earth and Man,* Boston, Houghton Mifflin, 526 pp.
A provocative look at the geologic impact of a mushrooming population—you and I, but more of us.

KEY CONCEPTS

Prescientific humans
  Useful, but fearful, mystical earth.
Scientific humans
  Earth is rational, therefore understandable; cause and effect reasoning; inductive and deductive reasoning; principle of uniformity; comprehension of time.
Geology
  Curiosity about how things are and how things were; intelligent use of earth resources; diminish geologic hazards to life and property.

Glistening crystals of *quartz,* the most common mineral on earth. (Photograph by W. T. Schaller, U.S. Geological Survey.)

Chapter Two

MINERALS

"Science is built up with facts, as a house is with stones. But a collection of facts is no more a science than a heap of stones is a house."
Jules Henri Poincare

The word *mineral* is among the most adaptable of nouns. To druggists, minerals are combined with vitamins. To rock hounds, minerals are attractive and may be hard enough to polish. To prospectors, minerals are of potential dollar value. Early people referred to *anything* mined from the earth as a mineral. Geologists are satisfied only with a much stricter definition. *A* **mineral** *is a naturally occurring, inorganic, crystalline solid, with a chemical composition and physical properties that vary within narrow limits.* How did this definition evolve?

MINERALS—A STUDY IN ORDER

The stages in our understanding of minerals furnish fascinating insights into the process of understanding that is often called the **scientific method.** Those stages in understanding require *observation, classification, testing,* and *interpretation;* each stage involves a delicate interplay among all the stages. Examine with me *how* humans came to understand minerals; when we are through, we will see from where that imposing definition in the previous paragraph came.

We will also breifly discuss chemical concepts that may be familiar to you from your science background. If the concepts and ideas are a bit unclear or if you have never studied chemistry, read Appendix B, which is a review of the basic ideas we will be utilizing.

Observation and Classification

Early peoples observed which rocks were capable of being worked with tools and which were not. They must have been puzzled, even frustrated, at the contrast, but they had taken *two* critical steps in under-

standing. They had observed, and they had classified. Some rocks could be worked; others could not.

As the Stone Age passed into the Bronze Age, humanity's quickening understanding of metallic earth materials allowed at least a fourfold classification: (1) masses of native copper surrounded by other rock; (2) copper (and tin) minerals that must be smelted (heated) to remove the metals; (3) masses of gold in rock; and (4) all else.

Classification follows observation, the *most critical* first step in any scientific investigation, and reflects our viewpoint and the depth of our knowledge. Classification is a halfway house toward full understanding and is logically followed by abstractions, often expressed in mathematical notation, that bind together our classified information into a coherent, understandable whole. A classic example of this kind of advancing knowledge is provided in a brief look into our understanding of minerals.

As the early use of minerals expanded, jewelry and cosmetics (powdered, colorful minerals) were added to our inventory, as were additional metals, including iron, lead, and silver. Additionally, minerals were used as medicines and talismans (charms), often thought to possess magic powers. Dozens of minerals were *named,* a step in classification that suggests that knowledgeable persons could now *separate* one mineral from another, based entirely on appearance.

Alphabetical lists of minerals were compiled by the Middle Ages (Figure 2-1). Utilitarian classifications (tool; not-tool) gave way to alphabetical lists; we classify items alphabetically when we know nothing about them or see *no relation* between them.

Aristotle (384-322 B.C.) had classified minerals, metals, and fossils in a single group, a concept that was to confuse mineral classi-

TABULA COMBINATORIA,

In qua breviter omnium lapidum pretioforum formæ & virtutes exhibentur, Alphabetico ordine difpofita.

Nomina.	Forma, Color, Natales Loci.	Virtutes & proprietates.
ADAMAS.	Omnium gemmarum præftantiffimus, duritiei indomabilis, diaphanus; In India crefcit verus & geminus.	Introfumptus venenum eft, ob cauſticam vim; portatus dicitur gemma reconciliationis, fortitudinis & conftantiæ, fed perperam, uti alias diximus
ÆTITES.	Ab Aquila fic dictus, eò quod in nidis eorum inveniri dicatur; In utero fuo alium portat diffolutum.	Varia funt genera, quæ tamen omnia alio prægnantia funt: maxime laudatur applicatus fœminis difficulté partus laborantibus.
ACHATES.	Variis figuris fpectabilis gemma coloribus differentibus imbuitur. In India, Europa variis locis invenitur, & paffim in Germania.	Venenis peftiferis, viperarum atque fcorpionum ictibus adverfari dicitur; febrientium æftus fedat, oculis prodeft.
ALABASTRUM.	Eft marmor fplendidum, varii coloris, eft album nigrum, mellei coloris; in Ægypto, Sicilia, Hetruria, reperitur.	Uftus & refinæ mixtus duritiem refolvit, cum cera mixtus ftomachi dolores fedat, cum lacte potum dyfenteriæ medetur.
AMETHISTUS.	Violacei coloris eft, variafque differentias fortitur, pro varia conditione locorum, ubi reperitur.	Ebrietati putatur refiftere, à qua & nomen fortitur: Superftitiofi quoque eum ingenium principiumque conferre putant.
ASTERIA feu ASTROITES.	Nomen habet à ftellulis, quibus totum ejus corpus depictum eft; in varias fpecies dividitur, & variis in locis Italiæ invenitur.	Aceto fuperaffufa hinc indè propria fponte fe movet. Variolis medentur creditur pueris alligatus.
BALANITES.	A glandis figura fic dicta; duo funt genera, fubvirides & fubflavæ; variis locis inveniuntur.	Dicuntur vi aditringenti pollere, atque adeo diarrhœæ mederi.
BASALTES.	Ad marmora refertur, eo quod exactiffime poliatur. Unde & inter Lydios lapides refertur, auro & argento probando aptos.	In Mifnia prope Drefdam magna copia eruitur, & Lydii lapidis munere paffim fungitur.
BELEMNITES.	Sic dictus à fagittæ figura, quam refert: varii coloris reperitur, vocatur & Lyncurius; ex lata radice in cufpidem crefcunt.	Pulvis vulnera curat, calculos frangit, & nocturnis phantafmatis refiftere dicitur.

2-1

A typical alphabetical list of "minerals," including rocks (*Basaltes*), fossils (*Belemnites*), and minerals (*Amethistus*). Basalt (*Basaltes*) is a common volcanic rock, belemnite (*Belemnites*) is a common fossil of an ancient, squidlike animal, and amethyst (*Amethistus*) is a semiprecious gem mineral, a purple-colored form of quartz. (List from A. Kircheri, 1665, courtesy of History of Science Collections, University of Oklahoma Libraries.)

fication for nearly 2000 years. The *lapidaries,* encyclopedic books about minerals (Figure 2-2) published during the Middle Ages, are largely collections of distorted fact and impossible fancy about minerals—*anything* dug from the earth.

In lapidaries, one finds that rocks and minerals were believed to be capable of reproduction, and there are "eyewitness" accounts of the birth of diamonds from other diamonds by a miracle of nature. Rotund, highly colored minerals were thought to be female; male minerals were both slimmer and drabber. Such comic tales were the stuff

2-2

Frontispiece from *De Mineralibus,* printed in 1518, only 50 years after the invention of printing. *De Mineralibus* is a classic among the lapidaries of its time; its author is Magnus Albertus. (Courtesy of History of Science Collections, University of Oklahoma Libraries.)

Minerals—A Study in Order   **19**

of medieval life; they suggest that science, founded on observation of the *real* world and classification of facts, was at a low ebb.

Mineral Testing—A Brief History

George Bauer (1494?–1555), better known by his Latinized name, *Georgius Agricola,* typified sixteenth-century science at its best; he is often called the "father of modern mineralogy." His serious and thoughtful studies of the earth resulted in major contributions to mining and mineral science. His work, *De*

2-3
Mining scene from *De Re Metallica,* by Georgius Agricola, printed in 1556. The people working underground worked by the light of tallow lanterns—dim and dangerous work. (Courtesy of History of Science Collections, University of Oklahoma Libraries.)

Re Metallica, is a classic in the history of mining (Figure 2-3) and was translated into English by the late Lou Henry Hoover and Herbert Hoover. In *De Natura Fossilium* (the nature of fossils, as minerals were then identified), Agricola described the known minerals in objective detail and classified them on the basis of visible, *testable* properties such as opacity, color, and weight. Once again, people had turned to reason and experience.

What Agricola was to mineralogy in the sixteenth century, Danish physician Niels Stens, commonly Latinized to *Nicolaus Steno* (1638–1686), was to the seventeenth century. Steno, by careful observation, measured the angles between the prismatic faces of quartz crystals from many localities and found that the angles were *identical* (Figure 2-4) between like pairs of faces. These early experiments, since repeated thousands of times on many different minerals from around the world, have been codified as the **Principle of constancy of interfacial angles.**

Observation. Interfacial angles for any one type of mineral are *constant*.

Inference. There is *order* to the inorganic world. Crystals are remarkably rigid and repetitive.

Question. Having found *repetitive order,* what causes it?

The twentieth-century mind may quickly find an answer through reasoning by analogy. If we see hundreds of tract homes on a hillside, each home precisely like the one next door, they were clearly built to an identical design over a common frame. What gives them their shape? Their rigid, wooden *frame*. Mineral crystals must also have their

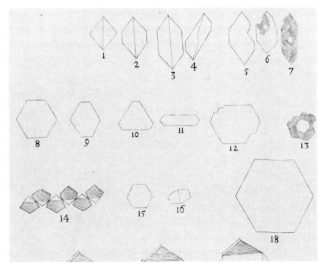

2-4
Plate IX from *Prodromus,* by N. Steno, printed in 1669. Sketches 1 to 13 illustrate *symmetry,* the balanced disposition of faces around an axis, plane, or point. Notice that for sketches 2 to 13, the ANGLE BETWEEN THE FACES REMAINS CONSTANT, although the *length of each face is different* in each sketch. (Courtesy of History of Science Collections, University of Oklahoma Libraries.)

shape, because they have a *rigid internal framework.*

The next step is almost as easy; minerals are chemical compounds (Appendix B), so the framework is one of *atoms, locked together in rigid geometric arrays by the attractive forces between them.* Now we use words not to state observable facts, but to describe conceptual images. X-ray diffraction cameras can photograph the rigid arrays of atoms we glibly describe, and they remind us that reality agrees with inference.

We have leaped ahead. Watch, instead, the eighteenth-century mind solve the same problem without recourse to atomic theory; atomic theory came from the insights of mineralogists, not the other way around.

In 1783, Rome de l'Isle, a French mineralogist, published *Cristallographie,* an outgrowth of extensive measurements of interfacial angles. de l'Isle took Steno one step further, *beyond* observation and classification, to abstraction. The faces on any given mineral are related to each other by simple mathematical relations. Internal order is reflected in external order; external form reflects internal form.

de l'Isle's famous countryman, Abbé René Just-Haüy (1743–1822), finally solved the puzzle of crystal order. Haüy, building on the concepts of de l'Isle, envisioned crystals as composed of minute "integral molecules." Faces were the planes *produced* when large numbers of these "molecules" were stacked together in rigid order, a concept illustrated in one of Haüy's original figures (Figure 2-5). Furthermore, Haüy, in his *Essai d'une Theorie sur la Structure des Crystaux* (Essay on a Theory of Crystal Structure), established that crystals *changed* shape *slightly* as variations in chemical composition occurred.

He further recognized the **symmetry** of crystals, the property of crystals whereby crystal faces always bear a rigid geometrical relation to one another and so *reappear at precise angular intervals on rotation of a crystal.* You may want to test this yourself; pick up an ordinary wooden pencil and rotate it slowly about an axis that is parallel to

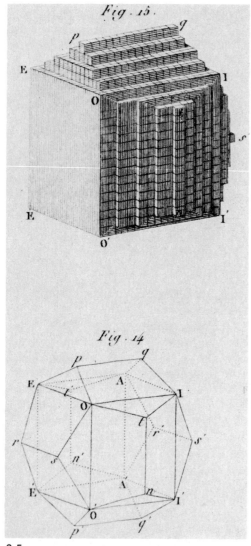

its length. Every 60 degrees of rotation, a new "face" appears that is identical to the one that preceded it and identical to the one that follows with a *further* rotation of 60 degrees; the pencil has a sixfold rotary symmetry. The human body exhibits slightly imperfect mirror symmetry, because the right side of the body is nearly the mirror image of the left side (Figure 2-6).

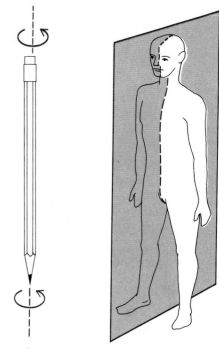

Symmetry about an axis   Mirror plane symmetry

2-5
These two figures, taken from R. J. Haüy, 1803, *Traité Élémentaire de Physique,* Pl. 2, illustrate the concept of building symmetrical crystal shapes by the symmetrical addition of "integral molecules." The crystal shape in the lower figure was envisioned as produced by the addition of many tiny cubes to one another, as shown in the upper figure. (Courtesy of History of Science Collections, University of Oklahoma Libraries)

2-6
Examples of two different kinds of symmetry. The pencil is symmetrical about an *axis* parallel to its length; the human body is approximately symmetrical about a vertical *plane* that bisects the eyes. The dashed part of the human figure is the mirror image of the other half. Each of the six sides of the pencil is identical to all other sides and face the viewer consecutively as the pencil is rotated 60 degrees about an axis parallel to the pencil length.

Interpretation

Crystals are unmasked. The first generalizations stated that mineral crystals were a form of ice, frozen so hard that they could no longer melt (the word crystal comes from the Greek *krystallos,* meaning ice). Agricola, Steno, de l'Isle, and Haüy, century by century, observed, classified, inferred, observed again, speculated, and then leaped to the abstract generalization that crystals are an expression of an ordered world, but a microcosmic one, where "integral molecules" fill space in repetitive patterns of sublime symmetry until they run out of atomic nutrition.

Historically, *atomic* is a poor word choice, since the atomic theory came 50 years *after* the work of Haüy; however, Haüy's vision of tiny units locked together in repetitive arrays (Figure 2-5) was remarkably prophetic and profoundly influenced John Dalton, the founder of modern atomic theory.

Curiously (as often happens in science), while substantial progress was being made in understanding the inorganic nature of minerals, an aberrant classification scheme, based on the principles of biology, became common. Carolus Linnaeus (1707–1778), who gave biology its binomial, or *Linnaean taxonomic,* system, proposed a similar system for minerals, replete with Latin names (Figure 2-7). Abraham Gottlob Werner, perhaps one of the most inspiring geology teachers of all time, suggested a similar hybrid Linnaean-chemical classification in 1774.

Modern Mineral Classification

Friedrich Mohs (1773–1839), a German mineralogist, proposed another Linnaean-type system in 1820 and then went on to become

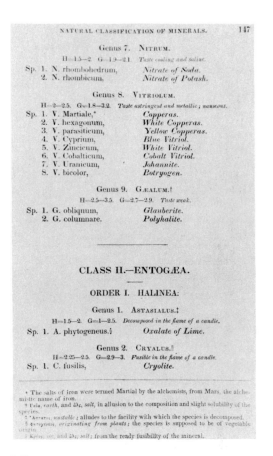

2-7
This page, taken from James Dwight Dana's first edition of *A System of Mineralogy,* published in 1837, illustrates the BIOLOGIC classification of minerals (see Appendix F). Thirteen years later, this scheme was abandoned in favor of grouping minerals by chemical subdivisions (see Appendix A), which is the scheme still used today. (Courtesy of History of Science Collections, University of Oklahoma Libraries.)

famous as the inventor of a scale of mineral hardness that is still commonly used today (Table 2-1). In 1841 John Jakob Berzelius, a Swedish chemist, published the first classification of minerals based on many *chemical*

Mohs Hardness Values for Common Materials

Material	Mohs Hardness
Talc	1
Gypsum	2
Fingernail, rock salt	2.5
Calcite, copper penny	3
Fluorite, dolomite	4
Apatite	5
Ordinary glass, nail	5.5
Feldspar, pocket knife	6
Pyrite (fool's gold), streak plate	6–6.5
Quartz	7
Topaz	8
Corundum (ruby, sapphire)	9
Diamond	10

analyses; this classification, somewhat modified, is used today (Appendix A).

The change from a view of minerals as something other than akin to biological units took a long time to come about. As one example, the most comprehensive and authoritative compilation of mineral data today is James Dwight Dana's *System of Mineralogy,* now in its seventh edition. The first and second editions used Linnaean-style classification; the third edition reflected a shift to a system of classification of minerals as chemical elements and compounds.

PHYSICAL PROPERTIES OF MINERALS

We know that there are about 88 elements (Appendix B) that occur naturally in varying amounts within our earth. Of these, only 8 elements, oxygen, silicon, aluminum, iron, calcium, magnesium, sodium, and potassium, occur in an average rock in amounts greater than 1 percent. The other 80 elements *combined* occur as *less than* 1 percent of our rocky earth.

Among the elements in this elusive and elite group are the staples of modern civilization such as chromium, lead, silver, gold, zinc, copper, molybdenum, titanium, tungsten, and tin. Where do these seemingly abundant commodities in our civilization come from, if they occur in such minute quantities? What makes some minerals valuable and others worthless?

In order to understand these questions, we must return to our growing knowledge of what a mineral is. We have said that minerals are inorganic, naturally formed crystals that are composed of repetitive geometric arrays of an element or elements locked together by electrical forces. As such, they are mostly chemical compounds whose elemental proportions may vary within narrow limits, although a few minerals are composed of

2-8

This, the earliest drawing of a snowflake, is taken from *Micrographia,* by Robert Hooke, and was published in 1665. Hooke was among the very first to use the newly invented microscope to study the natural world. The hexagonal symmetry of a snowflake is obvious. (Courtesy of History of Science Collections, University of Oklahoma Libraries.)

only one element (gold is an elegant example). Other exceptions to our classification are the **mineraloids,** a small group of minerals that lack well-defined crystalline structures.

A snowflake, then, is a mineral, because it is a naturally occurring, crystalline chemical compound of two elements, hydrogen and oxygen. Indeed, some *mineralogists*—geologists who specialize in the study of minerals—have studied the properties of the many forms of ice quite carefully. Let us retrace their research.

Crystallinity

If we examine a snowflake under a magnifying glass, the first thing we will notice is its six-rayed, starlike crystals; this is an indication that when water freezes, the crystals that form are commonly the result of hydrogen and oxygen atoms locking themselves into rigid, repetitive *hexagonal* arrays. No two snowflakes out of millions are ever exactly alike, but they all share the same six-way *symmetry* (Figure 2-8); geologists classify ice as belonging to the *hexagonal* system, one of six major subdivisions of all natural crystals. Examining ordinary salt under a magnifying glass would have led us to different conclusions; salt crystals are perfect cubes (the result of an array of sodium and chlorine atoms locked together), and salt is classified into the *cubic* system (Figure 2-9). Ice is hexagonal; table salt is cubic.

First Observation. *Internal atomic order is expressed as external crystalline order,* and the shapes and symmetry of any natural solid can be classified into one of six crystal systems.

Hardness

Another physical property that we can readily check is the **hardness** of ice. Hardness reflects both the strength and symmetry of the electrical attractive forces within the crystal. For this test we cannot use our snowflake, so let us use hail or even an ice cube instead (even though, technically, an ice cube is no longer a mineral, since it was not naturally formed). In order to test its hardness, we need test specimens of known hardness. Some of these we can easily find

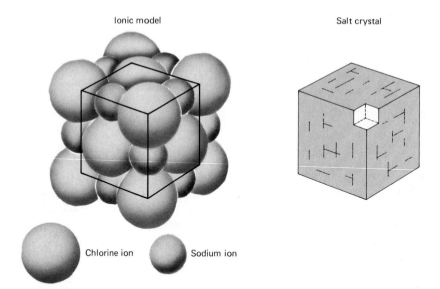

Ionic model

Salt crystal

Chlorine ion   Sodium ion

2-9

The packing arrangement of sodium and chlorine ions in common table salt compared to a sketch of salt crystal. The external form of the crystal reflects the internal arrangement of ions, which can only fit together in one arrangement that accommodates both their size and the requirements of electrical charge between the ions. The salt crystal is slightly imperfect, as one corner has been cleaved away.

(see Table 2-1). Friedrich Mohs, the German mineralogist mentioned earlier, gave us just such a scale over 100 years ago. He arranged 10 common minerals in order of *relative* hardness; talc, the softest, was assigned the number 1, and diamond, the hardest, was assigned number 10.

In fact, newer hardness tests show that each mineral in the Mohs scale (up to number 9) is about 1.2 times harder than the preceding one. The scale is thus approximately logarithmic from hardness number 1 to hardness number 9; however, diamond, at number 10 is about *five times* as hard as corundum, which has hardness number 9. The Mohs scale thus represents a total range of true hardness values of about 40 units compressed into 10 units of relative hardness.

Using each of the specimens in the Mohs hardness scale in turn, we try to scratch our specimen of ice and discover that talc will not scratch ice, but gypsum will.

Second Observation. Ice has a hardness of 1.5 on the Mohs scale (see Table 2-1).

Interestingly, the hardness number we determine will vary with the temperature of our specimen, since ice becomes *much* harder as temperatures drop well below its freezing point. The hardness of most minerals varies only slightly as a function of temperature, so ice is unusual in displaying so much variation. The phenomenon of hardness variation with temperature is familiar to anyone living in a cold climate; chipping ice on a bitterly cold day is rugged work, because the ice itself is now remarkably hard.

Color and Streak

Having determined the crystal form and hardness of ice, other properties are easily determined. Its **color** is clear; if the water is pure and free from dissolved gas and we attempt to powder it against a piece of unglazed porcelain (called a *streak plate*), we will discover that its **streak** is also colorless. The color of the powdered mineral (its *streak*) is usually that of the whole mineral. Some minerals display dramatically different streak colors than their color in mass; for these minerals, streak is a particularly diagnostic property. For minerals whose hardness exceeds that of the streak plate (see Table 2-1), *no* streak results. Instead, one has a grooved streak plate, and we have *also* completed a hardness test.

Luster

Luster is the appearance of the mineral in reflected light; our specimen of ice reflects light in a manner similar to glass or china; therefore ice has a *glassy* or *vitreous* luster. Tightly packed atoms of nonmetallic elements cause very large amounts of light to be reflected from a still-transparent mineral; the most striking example is diamond, which is composed of tightly packed, strongly bonded carbon atoms. If many of the elements in the mineral are metallic, *all* light is reflected, and the mineral is *opaque*. Opaque minerals usually exhibit one of two types of luster, *metallic* or *earthy*. Massive varieties of the common iron mineral *hematite* are dull or earthy; coarse crystalline forms are metallic and reflect light like polished metal surfaces.

Magnetism and Taste

Numerous other tests suggest themselves, including a test for **magnetism** with a hand magnet. For ice, the test is negative. There are very few magnetic minerals, and only one, *magnetite,* is common. The **taste** test is also negative, since ice is simply cold and tasteless. If we try a taste test with a crystal of table salt (mineralogists call it *halite*), the result is predictable: a salty taste. Many clays taste earthy and stick gently to your tongue; some minerals, such as *thenardite,* will make you pucker for days.

Specific Gravity

The weight, or density, of minerals relative to one another is another property that is worth testing. The test we use is approximately 22 centuries old; Archimedes of Syracuse first used it to test (without melting it) his king's crown in order to be sure that the jewelers who made the crown had used pure gold. As he stepped into a full tub of water for his bath, he noted that water overflowed in a *volume* equal to the volume of his body. The *weight* of the water would likewise bear a constant proportion to his body weight. His deduction was that if *equal weights* of two *different* substances of differing density were added to a brimming container, the *volumes* of water displaced would differ.

A dramatic test before the court followed. A 1-pound (453-gram) bar of silver displaced $1/_{10}$ pound (45 grams) of water; clearly, silver was 10 times as heavy (as dense) as an *equal volume* of water. One pound (453 grams) of gold displaced $1/_{19}$ pound (24 grams) of water; gold is 19 times as dense as an *equal volume* of water (Figure 2-10). Now came the critical test. The king's golden crown was slowly lowered into a vessel brimming with water,

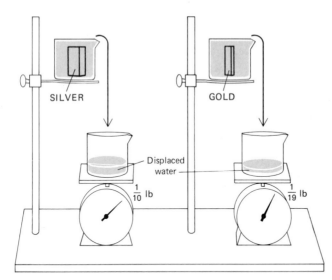

Sketch of completed experiment. One-pound (½-kilogram) bars of gold and of silver have been lowered into beakers that were brimfull of water; all displaced water has been trapped in beakers beneath. The *ratio* of the weight of the metal to the weight of the displaced water is the *specific gravity* of the metal. The DENSITY, in contrast, is mass (weight) per volume; for silver the density is about 625 pounds per cubic foot (10 grams per cubic centimeter). Gold is nearly twice as dense.

and the overflow water was weighed; the trembling jeweler stood convicted. The proportion between crown weight and water weight was slightly *more* than it should have been; as the wretched jeweler later confessed, the gold had been adulterated with silver. The death of a jeweler followed the birth of an idea, and kings thereafter wore heavier crowns.

We can use a modification of Archimedes' test to find the *specific gravity* of any mineral, because the **specific gravity** *is the weight of a mineral compared to an equal volume of water.* The specific gravity of gold is 19.3 while that of silver is 10.5. We must first know the *weight* of the *mineral,* which is easily determined with any kind of balance. Next we must know the *weight* of an *equal volume* of water, and here we use a modification of Archimedes' idea. A mineral immersed in water is partially buoyed up by the water and hence weighs *less* than it does when it is surrounded by air; the *difference* in weight equals the weight of the volume of

water displaced by the mineral. To obtain specific gravity, the mineral is first weighed in air and is weighed again while suspended in water by a fine thread. Expressed as a formula:

$$\text{Specific gravity} = \frac{\text{weight of mineral in air}}{\text{weight in air minus weight in water}}$$

The specific gravity of ice is approximately 0.92, a fact that is obvious to anyone who has noticed ice cubes floating with about one-tenth their volume out of water and the other nine-tenths submerged. Ice is a peculiar solid in many ways; most solids are heavier or denser then the liquid from which they are formed. If the situation were reversed, what a strange world it would be; icebergs would sink (a boon to mariners), but lakes would freeze from the bottom up (a bane to those who ice fish and to skaters).

The specific gravity of many minerals ranges between 2 and 3, with a range from

2-11
Crystals of *cerrusite,* a heavy mineral that is a compound of lead. The crystals, shaped like matchsticks, radiate slightly from a common center of growth. (Photograph courtesy of the U.S. Geological Survey.)

aragonite, which has a specific gravity of nearly 3. Identical in internal structure to aragonite is *cerussite* (Figure 2-11), or *lead* carbonate; its specific gravity is over 6. Clearly, heavy elements make heavy minerals, and we might reasonably expect any mineral containing significant amounts of heavy metallic elements to yield a high specific gravity.

An example of two minerals of *identical* chemical content is *graphite* and *diamond;* both are composed of pure carbon. The carbon atoms in graphite are weakly bound in one direction, so that its Mohs hardness is 1, the softest of minerals, and its specific gravity is a bit over 2 (Figure 2-12). In diamond, the carbon atoms are tightly bound, with little space between them; the resulting mineral is the hardest natural substance on earth (10 on the Mohs scale) and has a specific gravity of 3.5, *almost twice* that of its chemical twin, graphite. Heavy minerals obviously are fully packed, while many lightweights are composed mostly of empty space.

Fracture

Two somewhat related properties of minerals remain to be tested. Each involves partial or complete destruction of the specimen, but the destruction yields valuable information. If the attractive forces acting between atoms are approximately the same in all directions, striking the specimen with a hammer will cause it to **fracture,** or break, along randomly oriented, curved, or uneven surfaces. Attacking our ice cube with a hammer will always yield the same result—a spalled or curved fracture that is *conchoidal* (shaped like the inside of a clamshell). This type of fracture (Figure 2-13) is familiar to everyone, since this is the way all homoge-

less than 1 for ice to more than 19 for gold. This wide range in a measurable physical property requires an understanding of the *source* of variation; the specific gravity of a mineral, like its luster, depends on the *weight* of atoms within the mineral and the manner in which the atoms are *packed* together (Appendix B).

To illustrate, compare two similar minerals. You may be familiar with one, *calcium* carbonate, as a constituent of clamshells, where it often occurs as the mineral

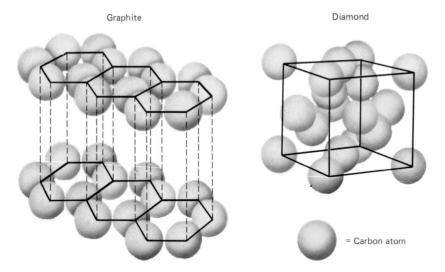

Graphite

Diamond

= Carbon atom

2-12

In graphite, as shown in the model on the left, carbon atoms are arranged in sheets that are composed of interlocking hexagons. The attractive force among atoms *within* the layers is strong, while the attractive force *between* layers is weak; hence, graphite readily cleaves into sheets and is used as a lubricant. In diamond, as shown in the model on the right, carbon atoms are tightly bound in a dense array that forms a cubic structure; diamond cleavage can only occur by cleaving off the eight corners of the cube.

neous substances break, including window glass (remember your experiences with a BB gun?), most fine-grained rocks and, of great importance to early people, flint and obsidian. Working flint and obsidian by repeating many conchoidal fractures until they merge into a sharp edge was a basic tool-building skill many thousands of years ago and is still practiced today as a hobby by "rock knappers."

Cleavage

Other minerals, when struck, will separate cleanly along repetitive, smooth, *flat* planes; this property is called **cleavage.** Cleavage results when the attractive forces acting be-

tween atoms vary as a function of direction within the crystal. When struck, the mineral readily splits where the binding forces are weak, and *flat* planes of breakage, called *cleavage planes,* result.

From one point of view, cleavage planes represent defects in the internal structure that are analogous to building a home without joining the walls to the floor or the roof to the foundation. One earthquake later, the components separate, and the home is no more. From another point of view, cleavage may be a very desirable property; the easy cleavage of *graphite* makes it an excellent dry lubricant. The cleavage in graphite is one directional, causing the mineral to cleave easily into thin plates. If you use graphite powder in your door lock, every

2-13
Natural volcanic glass fractures readily into a *conchoidal* fracture pattern, typical of many homogeneous substances. (Photograph by C. Milton, U.S. Geological Survey.)

time you open the lock, thousands of graphite sheets are torn from their neighbors and slip easily away. If you write with a lead pencil, the same principle is true; the lead in the pencil is a mixture of graphite and clay, and writing consists of leaving millions of tiny graphite flakes behind.

The cleavage of the mineral group *mica* is similar to that of graphite, and micas are occasionally used (so-called white graphite) as a lubricant. In earlier days, clear micas were sometimes used for windows, and even today many potbellied wood furnaces have mica windows (*isinglass*). Flaky mica also adorns the inside of toasters, where its resistance to heat and electricity make it an ideal natural insulator and its one-directional cleavage makes sheets of it easy to install.

Ordinary ice does not display true cleavage, just conchoidal fracture. Other minerals display an uneven fracture in some directions and a flat cleavage in other, weaker directions. Still other minerals have so many planes of weak bonding that they do not fracture at all, but cleave readily in multiple directions when struck.

Cleavage ease, direction, and number of planes vary from mineral to mineral; this is an easily tested property, even though the test *is* destructive. Even Steno (author of the Principle of constancy of interfacial angles) was guilty of overexuberant testing. He once deliberately cleaved an enormous specimen of calcite (Figure 2-14) *loaned* to him, into thousands of little rhombic shapes (the typical cleavage product of calcite), and thereby learned more about the constancy of *intercleavage angles,* while the hapless owner no doubt learned not to lend Steno any more minerals.

Physical Properties—A Summary

Our list of tests on the physical properties of minerals is nearly complete; tests into the crystal structure and chemical composition of minerals beyond the levels described can only be undertaken using specialized equipment. The systematics of mineral identification are further described in Appendix A. A few simple and inexpensive tools are required, but the chief tools are a keen eye and an inquiring mind.

Various combinations of these physical properties make some minerals more valua-

2-14
Cleaved crystals of calcite. Calcite cleaves or splits into *rhombic* shapes that look like distorted cubes. (Photograph by Michael Collier.)

ble than others. We value some minerals for their hardness (abrasives) and others for their softness (dry lubricants). Other minerals are valued for their combination of color, luster, and hardness (gemstones) or for their color alone (pigments). Still others may be valued for their high specific gravity, such as certain minerals that are used in drilling muds to prevent violent blowouts during deep drilling operations. Early magnetic compasses used magnetite (*lodestone*) needles to keep mariners on course; this duplicated in function an even earlier Viking use of *andalusite,* whose unique optical properties allowed sailors to determine latitude from the sun and thus led to the earliest European discovery of America.

The *taste* of one mineral, halite, or rock salt, is critically important to our food, and salt formed a major trade and barter item in much earlier times. The word *salary* literally means salt-money; many people were once paid in salt, because the commodity was so precious to food preservation and taste.

What about the minerals that we call gemstones? Their unique physical properties illustrate more forcefully than any other minerals one role that minerals have always played in human life.

GEMSTONES

Since the beginning of civilization, people have been fascinated by gemstones; they have represented human hopes and dreams from their first recorded history. Earliest people regarded pretty pebbles as worthy of wearing, and natural stones drilled for use in pendants are among the oldest anthropologic treasures. Many kinds of mineral and rock have been called gemstones, but precious stones all share three attributes. Gemstones are *rare, hard,* and *beautiful.*

Rarity is perhaps the most critical factor; how can something be precious if everyone has one? *Amethyst,* a lavender-colored form of the common mineral quartz was once among the most precious of gems. Amethyst was for royalty, dignitaries, and church officials. Queen Elizabeth I counted an amethyst necklace among her most highly prized possessions. Then, in the nineteenth century, enormous deposits of gem-quality amethyst were discovered in Brazil; its price is now so low that is is often used in costume jewelry. Fashion may also dictate the value of a gem; the price of *opal* fluctuates with our changing tastes and superstitions as to its allegedly unlucky nature. *Turquoise*, a common semiprecious stone used in southwestern Indian jewelry, became fashionable in the 1970s; prices for turquoise have risen tenfold in a decade. Rarity remains a major part of the definition of a gemstone; the desire to possess something that no one else can have is an indelible part of human nature.

Hardness is the second common ingredient for a gemstone. Most gems are polished to bring out their color and luster, and soft material will neither polish well nor retain a polish under use. Slightly softer material may be suitable for a brooch or pendant, which will receive little wear, but materials for a ring must withstand daily batterings and still continue to look their best. The majority of first-rank gem minerals have Mohs hardness numbers above quartz, that is, above 7. *Emerald*, the gem form of the common mineral *beryl*, has a hardness near 7.5, making it among the softer of the premium gem minerals. Its relative softness is overshadowed by the magnificent color associated with true emeralds and by the rarity of clear, faultless specimens. *Aquamarine* is another form of beryl (Figure 2-15), but it is usually regarded as a semiprecious stone because of its great abundance.

The queen of the gems is, of course, *diamond*, the hardest natural substance known (Mohs hardness of 10). Next only to diamond in hardness are *ruby* and *sapphire*, both gem forms of the more common *corun-*

2-15
Crystals of *aquamarine,* a blue-green form of the common mineral *beryl.* Like quartz, aquamarine forms six-sided crystals. (Photograph courtesy of the U.S. Geological Survey.)

dum, which is used as an abrasive. Ruby and sapphire share a hardness of 9. Diamond, emerald, ruby, and sapphire are the four most highly prized gems.

Beauty is the third constituent of a gem's definition; this is its most critical and yet least definable property. Beauty may mean great brilliance and clarity (diamond) or deep color and transparency (ruby). Unusual optical properties such as the silky appearance of *cat's-eye* the internal sunburst of *star sapphire,* and the irridescence of *precious opal* may be important. Opaque material may be valuable for both its color and its moderate hardness, as jade was when jade carving was a Chinese art 5000 years ago. Not all gem material is even a mineral by geologic definition; *amber* (fossilized tree resin), *coral* (the calcareous homes of marine animals), and *jet* (a variety of coal) have all been used for ornamental purposes over the ages.

Gemstone Use

Our use of minerals has followed a predictable pattern, and similar patterns prevail in the use of gemstones. The earliest materials used were simply pretty pebbles from a stream but, as tools developed, natural bone materials, jade, jet, turquoise, amber, and *lapis lazuli* were intricately carved and polished. These are all relatively soft, abundant, and homogeneous materials and could be worked without recourse to abrasives harder than quartz. By the twelfth century B.C., inlaid gold jewelry with colored gemstones was buried with the Pharaohs. By the first millenium B.C., powdered garnet and corundum were available as abrasives, and the gem forms of quartz, including *onyx, agate, cornelian, jasper,* and *bloodstone,* could be worked. By Greek and Roman times, the use of gold and silver with unfaceted gems was common, and cameo and intaglio carving was a highly developed art.

The polishing and faceting of the hardest gems—diamond, ruby, sapphire, and emerald—remained a technological impossibility until the late Middle Ages, when diamond powder was finally introduced as an abrasive. Polishing of the hardest gems proceeded forthwith and, by the seventeenth century, the full brilliant cut we associate with diamonds and other gems was discovered.

Along with an appreciation for the beauty in gems there has always been a sense of mysticism. The earliest recorded uses for gems include offerings to the gods or talismans to protect one from forms of evil. In a time when less was known, there was more to be feared, and mysticism and magic became inextricably entwined with gemstones. *Hematite,* the dark red iron ore, is near the color of venous blood; in the Middle Ages

hematite was believed to be capable of stopping the flow of blood from a wound. Since it also supposedly made one invulnerable to wounding, many warriors rubbed it over their bodies from head to toe. Hematite also allegedly brought one success in legal matters.

Malachite, a brilliant green copper ore, kept children from harm and combated not only evil spirits by day, but kept away the terrors of the night. *Agate* and diamond made one lucky in love, strong, and fearless. Emerald enabled one to prophesy, banish witches, strengthen one's memory, and blind poisonous snakes; when placed under the tongue, emerald made one a powerful, eloquent speaker.

Ruby made one stay young forever, guarded fruit trees, preserved health, and settled disputes. Some talismans combined a number of different jewels into a single setting; the bearer of such a potent device was protected from everything, including snakebite, demons, witches, quarrelsome mates, and pestilence! Each stone provided its own protections; the stones were also said to reinforce each other, bringing the best of times to the wearer in any conceivable setting (Figure 2-16).

A surviving remnant of this tradition is the use of birthstones, each standing for a zodiacal sign or birth month. Although we wear birthstones mostly as a pleasant ornament, our ancestors believed that they drew special powers from the heavens to one's body and provided certain forms of protection from witchcraft. Medieval people regarded *onyx* as among the most dangerous of stones, because it stood for all manner of evil. Today onyx is still absent from our commonly accepted list of birthstones for the same reason.

Among the most interesting technological

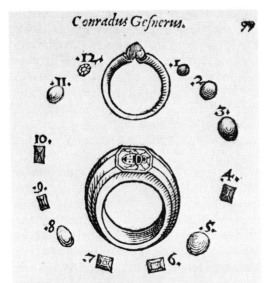

Conradus Gefnerus.   99

Annulus cum Callimo lapillo, du-
plici facie humana infigni, infrà pone
tur cap. II.

2-16
An early (1565) sketch of suggested
birthstones taken from *De Rerum Fossilum*
by Conrad Gesner. Each stone brought its
wearer its own form of security. (Courtesy of
History of Science Collections, University of
Oklahoma Libraries.)

developments of the twentieth century is our
newly founded ability to form synthetic
gems in the laboratory. Rubies and sapphires are formed by melting aluminum
oxide powder at temperatures near 2000 degrees Celsius. Chromium oxide is added if
rubies are desired, and titanium and iron oxides are added to produce sapphires. A still
later modification of this process enabled an
American corporation to produce star rubies
and sapphires that rival natural stones in
beauty. Synthetic emeralds are a product of

the last 40 years. Diamonds were first produced by General Electric in 1955.

Synthetic diamonds are made from pure
carbon, held at very high temperature and
pressure. The end results would not please
one's eye; the diamonds are small and
opaque and are intended for use as industrial
abrasives. The pressure involved is roughly
equal to supporting the Empire State Building on your little toe, and the temperature
necessary to complete the crystallization is
near 3000 degrees Celsius. In 1970, a few
gem-quality diamonds of around a carat each
were manufactured as a demonstration; they
cost much more to make than comparable
natural diamonds would cost. Apparently
the gem diamond market need have no fear
of synthetic diamonds, for a while at least.

Gemstones reflect the internal order
within minerals in a remarkably beautiful
way; their glistening crystals have been our
highest mineral prize. The *use* of minerals,
including gemstones, reflects not order, but
a deepening chaos. We now discuss patterns
of mineral *consumption* for a view of a strikingly *disordered* world.

MINERAL CONSUMPTION—A STUDY IN DISORDER

Suppose you have a savings account that
yields 7 percent compound interest and, in
that account, you deposit a spare $1 million
that you do not need. Each year you leave
the account alone; in only 10 years, you will
have $2 million in your account, because the
interest you earned each year was added to
the account, and interest was earned the
next year on the original amount *plus* the
interest. Mathematicians refer to such
growth as *exponential*; a *doubling time* of
10 years is the result of 7 percent growth.

(To find the approximate doubling time for any compound interest, divide the interest rate into 72; the result is the doubling time in years.)

Mineral consumption patterns for the world, as well as for the United States, exhibit the same sort of growth that your hypothetical $1 million did; *mineral demand is exponential.* Our annual demand for fertilizers grows at 7 percent; 10 years from now we will be using twice as much as we use today, if the trend continues. Our consumption of steel has an annual growth rate of about 2 percent, corresponding to a doubling time of about 30 years; for gold the annual growth rate is 4 percent, yielding a doubling time of about 18 years.

The cumulative effect of doubling rates is always startling; even at small rates, doubling provides greater numbers to be doubled the next time. It has taken an estimated 30 doublings in *all* of time since the first human creature walked upright to reach the current human population. At current rates of population increase (2 percent worldwide), the population will double every 35 years. This rate of increase—hundreds of times the rate common throughout all of history—has been the result of modern medical practice, which extends life and enhances newborn safety in a manner unknown 100 years ago.

If the present rate were to be maintained, in the year A.D. 2680 there would be one human standing next to another human on every space on earth. There would literally be no room to lie down. By A.D. 3100, humanity would weigh more than the earth.

Mineral Needs—the Future

Exponential growth rates in mineral consumption have two unrelated components,

population growth and rising affluence. Our total, worldwide consumption of minerals must, therefore, double every 35 years simply to keep pace with our reproductive success. If we look at worldwide production of a dozen critical mineral commodities, the doubling time observed over the last 40 years is approximately 12 years; worldwide energy demand shares a similar doubling time.

The gap between the rising demand caused by rising population and the remainder of demand is obviously the result of rising *expectations* around the world—the demand for a more affluent life-style. More and more people demand more and more from the earth, and therein lies a problem. As we will see, mineral resources are not only exhaustible, irregularly distributed, and irregularly consumed—they are *finite.*

The earth's store of mineral wealth is fixed, having been formed slowly over billions of years by natural earth processes. The earth's rate of formation of new deposits is some minute fraction of 1 percent of current world demand, so *what we have left now is all we have.* With supplies fixed in size and demand rising, there can only be one outcome. *Regardless of the size of the resource,* demand will eventually exceed supply. Imagine what a doubling time of 12 years will mean when extended for only a few centuries. In 1975, estimated world production of mineral commodities is 15 billion tons ($13\frac{3}{5}$ billion metric tons). With a doubling rate of 12 years, by 2075 world production would need to be about 4 trillion tons ($3\frac{3}{5}$ trillion metric tons). Two centuries more at this rate and we will have mined *every speck of land above sea level.*

In place of the absurd patterns of growth just described are a series of fascinating possibilities. *Substitution* of another resource for one grown scarce provides a short-term solution, although the substitute will also be exhausted in time. Aluminum is being substituted more and more for copper wiring; even though aluminum is a less desirable electrical conductor, it is cheaper than its scarcer competitor, copper. *Mining the oceans* has also been suggested, but the oceans are also a finite resource, and recovering the highly disseminated elements from seawater will require prodigious amounts of energy, which is also currently in short supply.

Recycling is yet another way to extend our supply, but even if we recycled *everything* we used, we would still be dependent on new mineral supplies from the earth; no recycling process is 100 percent efficient and, of course, recycling could not possibly satisfy the demands of exponential *growth*. The economic desirability of recycling rises with the cost of the commodity. About one-quarter of our domestic copper needs are currently met from scrap; perhaps 15 percent of our aluminum beer cans and soft-drink cans are recycled, and nearly one-half of U.S. gold needs are met from reclaimed gold.

A Forecast

Over the next 100 years only one course of action is really open. In a world that depends heavily on mineral resources, the worldwide *expectation* that standards of living will constantly rise *will fade;* living standards will be forced to stabilize and probably decline. Our reproductive success, coupled with enormous medical advances, will become our curse; the earth will not support our mushrooming population, and population will level or decline under a combination of social and political pressure, new birth-control technology, and famine. Recycling will be the standard, and those who follow us will wonder at our profligate use and subsequent dispersal of the earth's rich harvest.

MINERAL OCCURRENCE

We have previously reflected on the role of mineral resources, noting that they are exhaustible and irregularly distributed and consumed, but how do they occur? What are ore deposits anyway? They are not difficult to describe. **Ore deposits** are occurrences of *naturally concentrated* elements that can be mined at a *profit*. Notice that there are two parts to this definition: a geologic reference to their *occurrence* and an economic statement about their *profitability*. Let us examine each of these.

Rocks and Ores

The majority of the metals that we consume occur within the upper mile of the earth's surface as combinations of elements in mineral forms. Of all of the elements known to occur naturally within the earth, *only eight* are present in an average rock in amounts greater than 1 percent. These eight elements must make up most of the minerals of our crust. Taken together, they comprise nearly 99 percent of the elements available to us; the other elements all together comprise approximately 1 percent.

As noted in Figure 2-17, oxygen is the most abundant of the elements; it comprises, by weight, nearly one-half of all rocks. Oxygen is a lightweight element, so that it occupies nearly 92 percent of solid rock by volume. This oxygen does not occur as does the gas we breathe, but as an ionized (charged) atom (see Appendix B) bound to metal atoms through electrical attraction. A

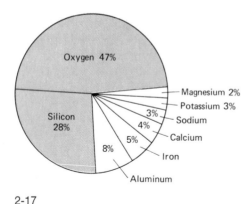

2-17
Major elements in the outer shell of the earth, shown by weight percent. All other elements not shown *total* less than 1 percent. If a similar chart were prepared for *volume* percent, oxygen alone would account for 92 percent of the crust's total volume. By *weight,* oxygen and silicon comprise three-quarters of an average rock.

mental image of most minerals as a latticework of oxygen atoms with much smaller metallic atoms in between is reasonable and explains why most common minerals have specific gravity values only two or three times that of water.

Silicon and aluminum are the most plentiful metallic ions, so most minerals are **silicates**—compounds of silicon and oxygen— or **aluminosilcates**—compounds of aluminum, silicon, and oxygen. Silicate and aluminosilicate minerals are extremely ample in most surface rocks, and they are minerals characterized by powerful internal electrical forces.

The extraction of desirable elements from minerals involves *extraction* (mining), *separation* of the desired mineral(s), and *liberation* of the desirable elements from their minerals. The expenditure of energy is needed at each stage. Separating the elements found within silicate and aluminosilicate minerals requires the expenditure of large amounts of energy to break the powerful electrical forces that hold them together. Thus the silicate and aluminosilicate minerals that form most of our earth are *not* used as sources for metals because the recovery method is so expensive.

Therefore ordinary rock will hardly do as a source for ore; extraction is expensive in energy costs, and average rock contains *less than 1 percent total* of elements such as gold, silver, lead, zinc, and chromium. Ore deposits represent *unusual* places within our earth where natural processes have concentrated the desirable elements many times over their average abundance long before we arrived. A profitable zinc mine, for example, must mine ore where zinc is already *300 times* its *average* concentration in the earth. Chromium ore is 1500 times its average concentration, and lead ore is 2500 times its average percentage. Such enriched deposits are *rare* occurrences that are formed by *uncommon* concentrating processes. The minerals in an ore deposit must be those where the desirable element is heavily concentrated with respect to average rock and occurs in a chemical compound with rather weak internal electrical forces, making separation of the desirable element from the mineral less expensive in energy costs.

Geologists seek these unusual geologic occurrences as storehouses of mineral wealth and, as population and life-style expectations grow, exponentially increasing pressure is being brought to bear to find more of these rare resources. How do they form, and how much remains?

Many of the scarce metals are deposited in natural concentrations of more easily refined minerals by waters that circulate from underground reservoirs of melted rock. As hot water in contact with melted rock leaves the area, it may carry away small amounts of metals from the melt in complex solution. The next step occurs in higher, cooler parts of the earth's crust, where these metal-bearing waters must be naturally channeled into fracture networks and their metals in watery solution are precipitated into insoluble minerals. Further enrichment may occur later by solution and redeposition.

Not all metallic ore deposits are concentrated by such complex means, but the processes described are typical of many metallic deposits. Other processes as diverse as gravity concentration of heavy metals such as gold into *placers* (natural concentrations of heavy minerals), evaporation, rock weathering, and underground solution also operate to make ore deposits. All of these processes are characterized by their complexity and infrequency of occurrence. Ore-forming processes are intricate, *rare events,* yet we reap their harvests with exponential intensity.

The remaining reserves represent assets for the future, and their supply can be reasonably well predicted; in spite of their intricate origin, the reserves of each element bear a linear relation with their abundance in the earth's crust. Generally, the reserves of thoroughly searched-for elements are limited by crustal abundance, as shown in Figure 2-18, so that the rarest elements have diminutive reserves.

Two other features of ore deposits can likewise be quantitatively evaluated. For many metals, as the percent of the elements in a rock diminishes, the amount of lower-*grade* ore available for mining increases; mathematicians would describe the relation as *log normal,* which simply means that rich deposits are rare, but leaner deposits are more and more common. The same log normal relation holds with the *size* distribution of deposits; the smaller the deposit, the more frequently it occurs (Figure 2-21).

Economics of Ore Deposits

A mineral deposit may be scientifically interesting, but an ore deposit *must be profitable.* Increases in the price of gold during the mid-1970s have caused the reopening of many old gold mines, just as changes in mining and ore treatment technology have widened the profit margin and kept many mines alive. As long as prices paid for commodities continue to rise, the mine operator can mine lower- and lower-grade ore, *if it is available,* in spite of its higher per-unit cost in energy. For almost any commodity, the price we are willing to pay depends on the availability of cheaper substitutes; there are few attractive substitutes for the uses to which we put our most expensive metals, gold and platinum.

The use of a mineral commodity is greatly governed by cost which, in turn, is governed by its abundance and susceptibility to substitution. Let us compare the consumption of metals to their abundance, which is related directly to reserves. As noted in Figure 2-19, we tend to consume many metals in approximate proportion to their crustal abundance, or reserves. Scarce metals such as gold, mercury, silver, tin, lead, and copper tend to be overused, while moderately abundant metals such as aluminum, magnesium, and titanium are somewhat under-consumed.

Focusing on one commodity of critical importance, *copper,* will highlight the problems ahead. Copper, like many metallic ore deposits, occurs in otherwise barren rock as

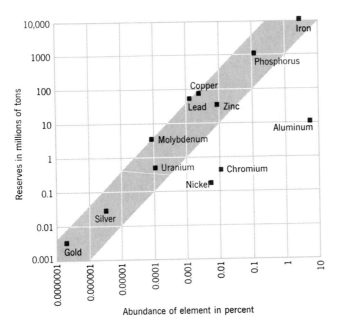

2-18

The amount of metal *ultimately* available for mining is proportional to the abundance of the metal within reach of mining techniques; rare metals have small reserves. The shaded area encloses the metals whose reserves [in tons (metric ton)] are greater than 1 million times their abundance (in percent). Aluminum is an especially unusual metal on the graph; although it is quite *abundant*, its *reserves* are relatively low. Most aluminum is tied up in the minerals of ordinary rocks, where the high bonding energy makes the aluminum difficult to extract economically. Thus, aluminum is abundant, but economic deposits are not in proportion to its position as the third most abundant element. (Data taken from U.S. Geological Survey Professional Paper 820, 1973.)

compounds of copper with sulfur or, primarily, oxygen; it is recovered by mining the ore-bearing rock, crushing it to a fine powder, recovering the copper-bearing minerals by flotational processes, and melting the concentrated copper minerals in a furnace to produce molten copper (Figure 2-20). The slabs of raw copper produced are usually further refined by electrical means, and we see the end product as electrical wire or as copper plumbing materials.

Mineral Production

A 1975 study by the National Academy of Sciences identifies the southwestern United States, mainly Arizona, as one of the most heavily mineralized copper regions in the

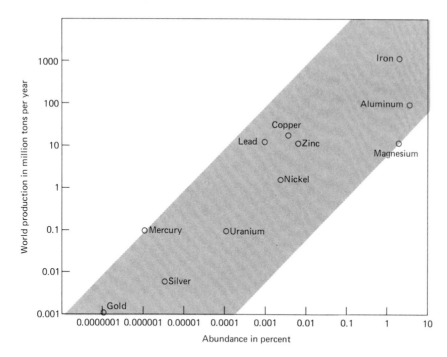

2-19

The world *production* of metals is roughly proportional to abundance, although metals such as gold, silver, mercury, lead, copper, and zinc are currently being produced in such large amounts in terms of their abundance that they may become metallic curiosities long before relatively underused metals such as aluminum and magnesium. (Data taken from U.S. Geological Survey Professional Paper 820, 1973.)

world. Within this copper-rich region, the area known to contain copper deposits of currently subminable grade is still no more than *one-hundredth of 1 percent*. Mineral deposits are rare!

Mineral deposits must be mined and processed where they occur, in whatever location natural processes have left them (Figure 2-21). It is difficult to move a 100 million-ton (90 million metric ton) accumulation of ore minerals and rock to a convenient place before mining and processing the ore. However, some voices suggest just that; in a time

of burgeoning demand and diminishing supply, an area of public land equal in size to all of the states east of the Mississippi River is no longer accessible, under federal Law, for mineral exploration.

Although environmental concerns are surely appropriate in a world of exponential demand, many thoughtful geologists wonder from where resources for the future will come. Often 20 years and millions of dollars separate initial exploration efforts in a region and the subsequent flow of processed mineral resources.

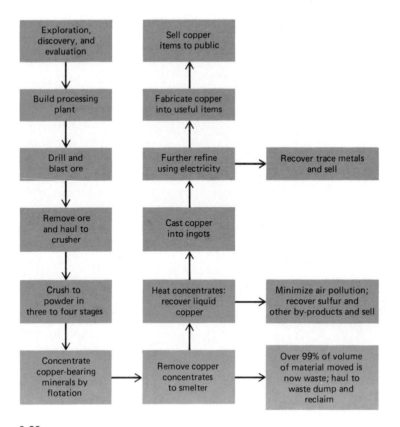

2-20
Flowchart of stages in the production of metallic copper in a typical "copper porphyry" mine operation. Such operations consume 1 pound (½ kilogram) of alloy steel in crushing operations for every 1 pound (½ kilogram) of copper produced and also consume large amounts of water and energy. More than 99 percent of the material handled is waste rock. Total time elapsed from discovery to sales is 10 years or more.

The 1975 estimate of the National Academy of Sciences suggests that worldwide reserves plus past production currently amount to about 3 percent of the world's ultimate copper yield. Within the United States, reserves plus past production are about 16 percent of the estimated U.S. ultimate yield. Both 3 and 16 percent seem small, but remember what exponential growth means; with a demand doubling approximately every 12 years, copper will be in critically short supply by the year 2000

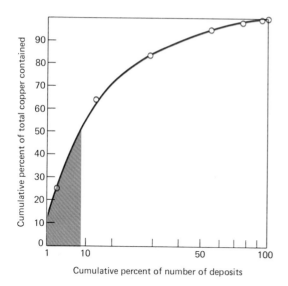

2-21
Frequency distribution of world copper deposits. One-half of the world's copper is contained in less than 10 percent of its mines (shaded area). (Reproduced from *Mineral Resources and the Environment*, page 165, with permission of the National Academy of Sciences, Washington, D.C.)

and might well be regarded by our grandchildren as a rare metallic curiosity (Figure 2-22).

The future for finite mineral resources consumed by exponential growth is plain. Elements other than the abundant eight face transition into scarce or rare commodities within 100 years; recycling will be the norm, and production of new metal from the earth will steadily decline as ore grades fall. After a time, the grade of ore will become so low that ore will cease to be a meaningful word, since all the natural *concentrations* will be gone. At that time, the scarce metals will

have to be gotten from average silicate rocks, in which they are tightly bound in minute quantities. The energy costs and associated environmental problems of such extraction will be enormous, placing the costs for many scarce commodities beyond practical reach. We will be forced back to using aluminum and iron as our primary metals, because they are the only elements whose earthly supply will support our needs into the future.

The Wealth of Nations

If mining of ore deposits has a predictable future, what can be said about the role of ore deposits in the growth of civilizations? The golden age of Greek civilization is somewhat misnamed; their silver mines gave them their wealth and power. Gold from the Americas in part allowed Spain to dominate the fifteenth and sixteenth centuries, and the fabulous mines of Cornwall promoted the flourishing British civilization of the seventeenth through the nineteenth centuries. Our high standard of living in the United States in the twentieth century is predicated on the *prodigious* consumption of both energy materials and minerals; we have *used during the last thirty years more mineral fuels and minerals than all the rest of the world has used in all of recorded history.*

One way to illustrate the dependence of any country on its mineral supplies (and its energy resources) is to plot the national output of goods and services per capita against energy consumption per capita and mineral consumption per capita. Figures 2-23 and 2-24 are graphs of this type; the data are from the United Nations statistical yearbook. The

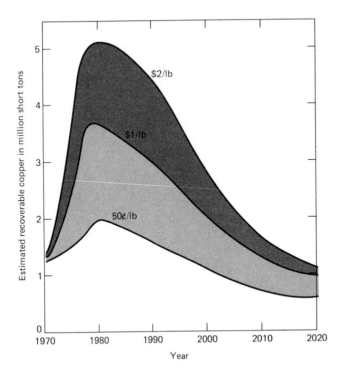

2-22
Potential U.S. copper production as a function of price to the year 2020. Note that doubling the price paid does *not* double the estimated recoverable copper. (Data from the U.S. Bureau of Mines.)

figures for energy consumption per capita are especially startling; the United States, which comprises one-sixth of the world's population, consumes one-third of its energy supplies and thereby produces one-third of the world's total output of goods and services. The figures for steel production and consumption are equally revealing, since steel is perhaps the most basic industrial commodity in the modern world.

The quality and availability of one's energy and mineral supplies are critical factors in the economic growth of nations, because life-style is directly related to resource consumption. Modifying a concept first expressed by Dr. Vince McKelvey of the U.S. Geological Survey in 1972, the following qualitative equation represents the role of minerals and fuels in our life.

$$L = \frac{R \times E \times F \times I}{P}$$

L represents life-style, R raw minerals consumed, E energy consumed, F food resources available, I all forms of ingenuity and education, and P the total number of people who share in the product.

As pointed out by McKelvey, these factors are highly interrelated; it is the availability of energy that makes the use of raw minerals possible and the availability of fertile soil and temperate climate that make our agriculture base, and it is ingenuity and cap-

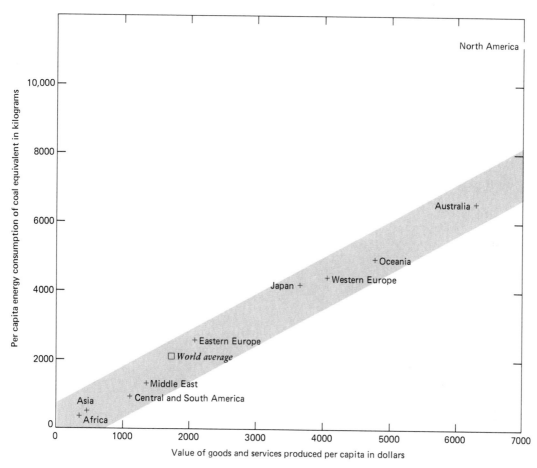

2-23

Per capita energy consumption for selected world areas compared to value of goods and services produced. Shaded area includes most of the world, with the exception of North America. (Data taken from *Statistical Yearbook*. Copyright © 1976, United Nations. Reproduced by permission.)

ital that makes it all work. Ingenuity and capital are the most important multipliers; *drive, dollars, education,* and *cleverness* make social systems work. As suggested by McKelvey, the equation is simply a restatement of the classic economic theory that na-

tional output is the product of capital times labor. Capital, in this view, is far more than money; it is raw material, food, energy resources, and political and managerial ingenuity. Labor is more than human toil; labor's contribution is vastly magnified by

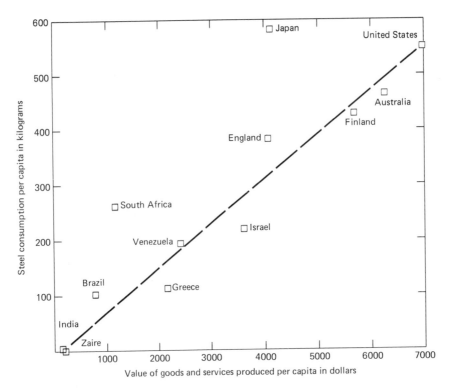

2-24
Per capita steel consumption compared to per capita total production for selected countries. The relation is roughly proportional, with the countries left of the dashed line using somewhat more steel in the production of less value per capita than the United States, while those to the right of the dashed line use somewhat less steel in the production of greater value per capita than the United States. (Data taken from *Statistical Yearbook:* Copyright © 1976, United Nations. Reproduced by permission.)

machines that consume energy and produce products. We humans are hardly vast resources of physical energy; our maximum output will just keep one 100-watt light bulb burning (Figure 2-25).

If metal production is a sure indicator of the wealth and power of nations, what of the future? As Figure 2-26 indicates, there are predictable trends in the history of mining. Many of the most thoroughly explored countries have relatively small reserves of mineral resources, since most of their mineral wealth is mined out. New countries, characterized by relatively little exploration of mineral resources, have a large potential for production. The United States stands between these two extremes, still in the heyday of its mineral production, but importing a higher percentage of raw materials each year.

2-25
What is the energy equivalent of 1 "personpower?" We can keep one 100-watt light bulb burning at a sustained pace. For obvious reasons, power is usually expressed in terms of horsepower.

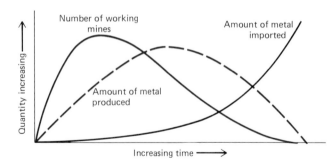

Number of working mines

Amount of metal imported

Amount of metal produced

Quantity increasing →

Increasing time ——→

2-26
For any one country, the historical development of mineral resources moves generally from left to right on this graph; thus, the position of the country through time shifts from far left to far right on this graph. Currently, the United Kingdom is on the far right, the United States in the center, and the Soviet Union is on the far left. Each country occupies the position of its predecessor several decades earlier. (*Source.* B. J. Skinner, "A Second Iron Age Ahead?" *American Scientist, 64,* 1976.)

SUMMARY   The use of minerals for adornment, tools, cosmetics, and weaponry preceded an understanding of their inorganic origin by thousands of years. Gems, characterized by rarity, hardness, and beauty, were already important in the pre-Christian era and were soon regarded as mystical substances. The origin of gems remained in dispute through the Middle Ages, when fanciful tales of their medicinal, reproductive, and protective powers were a part of the quasi-science of that day.

Patient detective work through the last 40 years that culminated in the use of X-ray cameras allows us to visualize all minerals as rigid latticeworks of atoms, bound together in repetitive arrays by interatomic, electrical forces. One measure of the strength and symmetry of those forces is the mineral's *hardness,* or its resistance to having parts of those arrays torn away.

Specific gravity, or the relative weight of minerals, allows us to infer the packing density of the atoms and reflects the relative weight of the atoms themselves. Planes of electrical weakness within crystals are readily displayed when the mineral is struck; *cleavage planes* form in the mineral. Crystals whose internal bond strength is relatively uniform in all directions *fracture* instead of cleave; conchoidal fracture is typical of many homogeneous substances, whether crystalline or noncrystalline.

Ore deposits represent rare natural concentrations of useful elements in mineral forms that are amenable to reduction to the elemental form at relatively low cost. Our need for ore deposits accelerates with each passing year, as a combination of growing populations and rising affluence cause exponentially increasing demands on finite resources. Elements other than the abundant eight will become scarce by the end of this century, and metallic curiosities by the end of the next century, although recycling and substitution may slow down their demise. Increased exploration of the more remate parts of the earth will undoubtedly turn up many new ore deposits, but the reserves of any element are in direct ratio to its crustal abundance, and the abundance of all metals, other than aluminum and iron, *aggregates* less than 1 percent of all rock.

Mineral wealth has figured prominently in the rise and decline of civilizations, because the constructive use of earth resources is a major part of national output. At the same time that our resource demands are skyrocketing, environmental concerns are preventing further mineral exploration in enormous areas, forcing our mineral demands onto a world whose rate of mineral consumption accelerates at doubling rates that are far higher than our own.

Minerals form the foundation of any modern economy; they serve us as fuels, abrasives, pigments, cosmetics, filters, insulation, fertilizers, explosives, gemstones, building materials, detergents, insulators, and as the only known source for the variety of metals that touch every aspect of our life. Because of its size, mineral resources, soils, climate, and the labor and ingenuity of its people, the United States stands today as first among nations, a role played by many civilizations before us.

EXERCISES   1.   What kind of symmetry is exhibited by a starfish, a soda cracker, a bicycle wheel, and an ice cube?

2. One frequent observation is that minerals of low specific gravity tend to be soft. Can you explain why?
3. Expose a clear crystal of quartz to an X-ray beam for a time, and it becomes smoky colored. Heat the crystal of smoky quartz in an oven, and it becomes clear again. What must be causing the color of smoky quartz?
4. Some minerals exhibit both cleavage and fracture. How could that be?
5. The surface of a specimen of graphite feels greasy. Why?
6. Look around you. Is there anything in the room that did not come from the earth?
7. What is the difference between a rock and a mineral? Between an ore deposit and a mineral deposit?
8. We have observed that there are only a few large, rich ore deposits, but more and more smaller, leaner ore deposits. Why?
9. It has been said that every mineral commodity has a substitute; in the case of copper, increasing amounts of aluminum wire are used to carry electricity. What factors limit the substitution of one metal for another?
10. What factors limit recycling of a single metal?

SUGGESTED READINGS

Cameron, Eugene N. (ed.), 1973, *The Mineral Position of the United States, 1975–2000,* Madison, University of Wisconsin Press, 159 pp.
A review by eight professionals written for the layperson. Frank, forthright, and sobering.

Ewing, Rodney C., February 1978, "The Elegant Symmetry of Crystals" in *Natural History,* pp. 65–71.
Natural History, published by the American Museum of Natural History in New York, is always enjoyable. This article is one of the reasons why.

Marsden, Ralph W. (ed.), 1975, *Politics, Minerals, and Survival,* Madison, University of Wisconsin Press, 86 pp.
The social side of mineral use and overuse.

Skinner, Brian J., 1976, *Earth Resources,* 2nd ed., Englewood Cliffs, N.J., Prentice-Hall, 116 pp.
The best summary of minerals and what they mean to our daily lives. Delightfully written by a leading scholar in the field, this is a must book.

KEY CONCEPTS

Scientific method
Observation, classification, testing, interpretation.

Law of constancy of interfacial angles

Minerals

Chemical compounds, natural; crystalline; physical properties invariant or within narrow limits.

Physical properties

Ten characteristics easily tested; make some minerals more valuable than others

Gemstones—hard, rare, beautiful.

Mineral consumption

Exponential demand.

Increasing affluence;

increasing population.

Resource base finite.

Recycling;

substitution;

ore deposits—*natural concentrations, size and richness log normal.*

This is a place where a volcano once was but is no longer. All that is left is radiating fractures and the central vent, both filled with congealed lava, and beauty. Aerial photography near Shiprock, New Mexico. (Photograph by Michael Collier.)

Chapter Three
IGNEOUS ACTIVITY

"Everything that exists is in a manner the seed of that which will be."
Marcus Aurelius

Rocks have often been called the language of the earth, because they yield stories of the earth's early days to those patient enough to learn their language. As any good book may be composed of thousands of words, rocks may be composed of any among several thousand minerals; however, perhaps only a dozen varieties make up over 99 percent of all rocks.

Books and words are like rocks and minerals: each whole is made up of many parts. Elements join to make minerals, minerals join to make rocks, and rocks join together to make a landscape, which is the library of geology.

THE CYCLIC EARTH

Another series of questions is related to our persistent curiosity about the age of our earth. What is the oldest rock like? Where is the oldest rock found? Where do the rocks come from, anyway? Current answers to these questions at first sound quite straightforward. The oldest rocks in the universe come either from the moon, courtesy of our Apollo program, or as free samples from space that are called *meteorites;* they were formed as long ago as 4.5 billion years. No rocks of this antiquity are known from earth; our oldest rocks were formed 3.5 to 4 billion years ago. These ancient rocks come from several different areas on the earth. The oldest one (close to 4 billion years old) was found in Greenland. These specimens are of either *igneous* or *metamorphic* origin, which means that they formed from melted rock material or from altered, solid rock material. From where, then, do rocks come? They come from *older* rocks.

If rocks form from other rocks, there is truly nothing new on this earth, and the search for the "first" rock is doomed, because it long ago was changed to another rock. Each rock is both offspring and ancestor, just as you and I are future parent and former child. Each rock contains a key to its past and limits to its own future.

Perhaps the most enduring lesson of geology is that the earth is endlessly cyclic, changing the form and substance of matter back and forth between and within the inorganic and organic worlds. Rock is just rock for a fleeting moment in earth history; its soluble substances eventually become part of everything we eat and drink and thus become part of trillions of living cells. Death returns our bodies to dust, and our physical substance may be reorganized into a beaver, a brick, or a grain of sand. Nothing physical on this earth is permanent; change is the order of the natural world.

The water cycle furnishes a familiar example of incessant change. The rain or snow that fell today was evaporated from rivers, lakes, and oceans by solar energy (Figure 3-1) only a few days before. Water falls on the land and runs off to the sea, but the sea does not fill up, because the water brought in equals the water evaporated.

This concept, beautifully expressed in Ecclesiastes 1:7, yields an intellectual dividend: the water you drank today once may have been part of a volcanic eruption, an invasion of glaciers, or a blade of grass. Water is ageless, since it must be as old as the earth itself. Even the water trapped miles down within the earth eventually returns to the surface, most often as spectacular outbursts that we call volcanic eruptions. Ancient volcanic eruptions were probably the source of the earth's water supply, which is the absolute necessity for all forms of life. Yet eruptions may also take life.

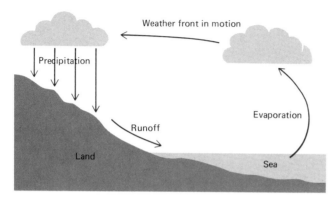

3-1
Water is constantly in motion from land to sea and back again. Driving this constant motion is the radiant energy from a rather ordinary star, about 93 million miles (110 million kilometers) distant.

VOLCANIC VIOLENCE

Anyone watching a volcanic eruption (from a safe distance) must be bothered by the same questions that occurred to earliest peoples. What causes volcanoes? Can they be predicted? Are they of any use to us, or are they simply a natural curse to be endured? Earliest humans lived with volcanoes; the Mediterranean cradle of civilization has been a scene of intense volcanism throughout much of our brief tenure on the earth. This volcanism seems to have been responsible for the destruction of one of the oldest European civilizations in the Mediterranean area.

The sudden collapse of the Minoan civilization, which was centered on the island of Crete, after more than 1000 years of prosperity has always puzzled anthropologists. Recent combined geologic and archeologic studies have unraveled the following tale of the death of a civilization. In 1470 B.C. the volcano Santorin (Figure 3-2) on the island of Thera, about 120 miles (200 kilometers) southeast of Athens, began to rumble with violent earthquakes. Pumice was blown out of the Santorin cone and carried southeasterly by prevailing winds 60 miles (100 kilo-

meters) to Knossos, the Minoan capital on Crete.

Terrified residents of Thera evacuated the island, leaving almost everything behind. Offerings of the pumice were made to the Cretan earth goddess at many shrines on Crete. A catastrophic volcanic explosion soon blew the entire Santorin cone away; next, the remnants of Santorin collapsed into the sea. What is left today is a lagoon more than 1000 feet (400 meters) deep: a ring of land encloses a roughly circular crater that is underneath the ocean. A lofty mountain was gone and, with it, a civilization. The deserted island of Thera was deeply buried under ash and pumice, while prevailing winds blew the erupted ash, pumice, and cinders hundreds of miles (kilometers) to the southeast, creating a deadly fall of pumice and ash on Crete that destroyed crops, plugged wells, dammed streams, and caused mass starvation of people and grazing animals. Earthquakes overturned lamps and braziers in many Cretan buildings, thus setting entire communities on fire. From the sea came massive walls of water that were produced by the spreading shock waves from undersea earthquakes.

These big earthquake-generated ocean

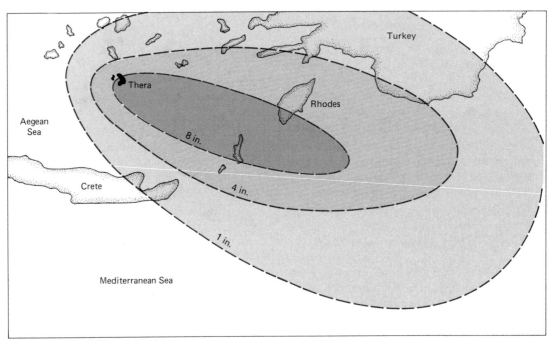

Turkey

Thera

Rhodes

Aegean
Sea

8 in.

Crete

4 in.

1 in.

Mediterranean Sea

3-2

Setting of a disaster. The colored lines connect points of equal ash (from Santorin) thickness as determined from cores of the ocean floor taken on a research cruise in 1975. (Adapted with permission from *Natural History Magazine,* April 1978. Copyright © 1978, American Museum of Natural History.)

waves, or **tsunamis,** rose 40 to 50 feet (12 to 15 meters) high as they crashed onto the low coasts of Crete in savage, hammering waves that destroyed fleets of trading vessels and warships and drowned thousands. Thera was utterly devastated, eastern Crete suffered severe damage, and Knossos was partly destroyed. Survivors moved to western Crete or left the area. An advanced Bronze Age civilization that had lasted nearly 1500 years was gone; invading Mycenaean Greeks soon took over the pitiful remnants of the Minoan civilization.

Even Egypt, several hundred miles (kilometers) downwind, felt the effects. Egyptian records describe days of darkness and massive coastal floods and the cessation of trade with the Minoans on Crete. The foundering and destruction of Thera may well have been the source for the ancient Greek legend of Atlantis, the "lost" continent. An event such as this, which destroyed a thriving civilization in a few days, would obviously have made a lasting impression and a story that bore retelling, and expansion, many times.

For the hapless Minoans, the earth was not cyclic, but incomprehensibly catastrophic. A civilization at peace with the earth for well over 1000 years could not see its destruction as simply a punctuation mark in the ongoing story of the earth, nor could they understand the violence that overtook them, snuffed out their lives, and destroyed everything that they cared about. Geologic violence is a human perspective; to the earth, the end of a civilization is a matter of complete indifference.

Three thousand years later, we understand some of the reasons why volcanism overtook the Minoans. We are taking the first tentative steps toward appraising the volcanic hazards that exist around the world in our own daily lives. The first step in unraveling the riddle of volcanism is the first step in understanding any natural phenomenon. We must look around and organize what we see; we must search for order.

VOLCANOES—AN ORDERLY ENIGMA

Plotting the distribution of volcanoes around the world reveals distinctive patterns. A glance at Figure 3-3 suggests that the world's volcanic activity occurs chiefly in narrow zones. Most of the world is relatively free of volcanic activity, but the margin of the Pacific Ocean Basin has been called the Ring of Fire; fully three-quarters of the world's active volcanoes cluster on the Pacific rim.

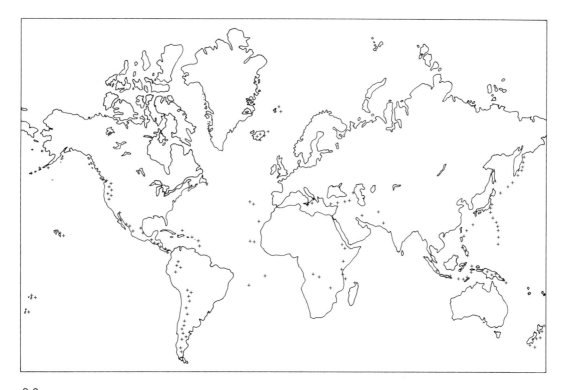

3-3
The crosses mark the sites of volcanic eruptions within the last few thousand years. (Data gathered from numerous sources.)

The remainder cluster in the Indonesian and Mediterranean-Himalayan area, with scattered volcanism associated with the Hawaiian Islands, eastern Africa and the Red Sea, the Caribbean, Iceland, the Galapagos, the Azores, and the southern Atlantic Ocean (Figure 3-3).

How can we understand an ordered violence on an ancient earth? The existence of narrow zones of volcanism suggests that volcanic belts may represent major breaks in the earth's rocky crust and that intervening areas are free from disturbance. A cursory examination of earthquake data confirms this; earthquakes also occur mostly in narrow zones, and these zones commonly *coincide with volcanic belts*. Evidently earthquakes and volcanoes are associated on our earth, although we cannot push this association too far. Not all earthquakes occur in volcanic areas, and not all volcanoes are associated with earthquake belts. Yet the common association of volcanoes and earthquakes in space and time could hardly be entirely fortuitous; perhaps the exceptions have their own unique answers.

Earthquakes provide additional information on the origin of volcanoes. A part of the energy that is released in earthquakes will only travel as waves through solids, and these waves pass without hindrance through the outer 1800 miles (3000 kilometers) of the earth.

Inference. The outer half of our rocky earth is solid, at least when it is affected by high-energy, high-frequency earthquake waves.

Now the origin of volcanoes is obscured again. How can a *solid* earth make *molten* rock at all, and why does it make molten rock only in certain zones?

The distribution of temperatures within the earth may partially answer the questions. Referring to Figure 3-4, we can see that temperatures within the earth are sufficiently high to melt many kinds of rock well within the upper few miles (kilometers) of the earth's solid crust.

Question. If temperatures are high enough, why isn't the earth a few miles (kilometers) beneath our feet one giant puddle?

Earthquake wave information tells us that the outer half of the earth is solid, while temperature distribution suggests that the rock is *above* its melting point only a few miles (kilometers) down. What is wrong here?

A study of Figure 3-5 suggests the answer. Rock only a few miles (kilometers) down is under many tons (metric tons) of pressure from the weight of the overlying rock, so that even when rock is above its surface

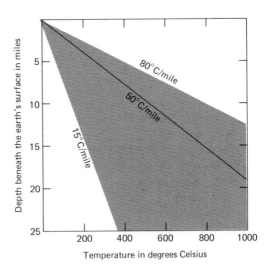

3-4
Range of temperature gradients within the earth. The worldwide average is near 50 degrees Celsius per mile (80 degrees Celsius per kilometer).

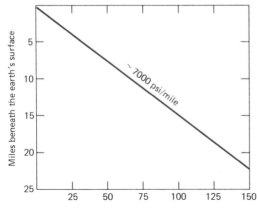

3-5

Pressure versus depth within the earth. The pressure on a rock is proportional to the density and extent of overlying rock; pressure increases linearly with depth and is shown here for a rock of average density (2.8 grams per cubic cenimeter). Expressed in metric terms, the pressure gradient averages 0.3 kilobars per kilometer, where 1 bar equals 14.7 pounds per square inch.

melting temperature, it still does not melt. Melting of a solid normally involves an increase in volume, but expansion is impossible under the prodigous pressures that rocks enjoy only a few miles (kilometers) beneath the surface. The rise of the boiling point of a liquid under pressure is a familiar phenomenon. Our car radiators and pressure cookers in the kitchen both operate under moderate pressure levels; this raises the boiling point of water a few tens of degrees. We benefit from this by way of shorter cooking times and radiators that will not easily boil over. The same effect operates when solids are placed under pressure, because their melting point also rises with pressure.

How, then, does nature make liquid rock from solid rock? Over 500 active volcanoes on the surface of the earth argue convincingly that the earth *can* do it, no matter what our charts and graphs tell us. If rock heated well above its melting point underwent a loss of pressure, it would melt; alternatively, if rock at a constant pressure (depth) level were locally strongly heated, melting might ensue.

At first glance, the moderately common association of earthquakes with volcanic areas might seem to provide an easy answer to our questions. Surely earthquakes might bring about the loss of pressure in localized areas and this would cause melting. Our speculations lead us nowhere, however; it seems improbable that low-pressure zones could be *maintained* for any length of time within the earth, and many earthquake zones are devoid of time-equivalent volcanism, just as many volcanic areas do not display contemporaneous earthquake activity.

Perhaps the heat produced during radioactive decay (Chapter Eleven) plus that produced as large blocks of the earth slide past one another (Chapter Seven) may be sufficient. Debate and more study continue.

The origin of liquid rock within the earth remains an enigma to many geologists. Whatever the process or processes of formation, the products generally occur in the narrow zones of the earth that are associated geographically with earthquakes, but the *time* association with earthquakes is far more irregular. It is also difficult to imagine any earthly process that *concentrates* heat in local zones, so this solution is equally unlikely.

IGNEOUS ROCKS

Whatever its origins, geologists call pressured *liquid rock* (combined with gas) *within*

3-1
Igneous Rock-Forming Minerals

Name	Chemical Composition	Appearance
	Dark-Colored Minerals	
Olivine	Iron-magnesium silicate	Bottle green to yellowish greenish brown, glassy, stubby, fractured crystals or granules
Pyroxene	Complex iron, magnesium, calcium, sodium silicate, or aluminosilicate	Very dark green to black, dull, stubby crystals or granules; right-angle cleavage
Amphibole	Similar to pyroxene	Very dark green to black, shiny, prismatic needles
Biotite mica	Complex iron-potassium aluminosilicate	Greenish brown to reddish, bronze, or chocolate brown shiny flakes
Calcic plagioclase feldspar (anorthite)	Calcium-sodium aluminosilicate	Dark gray to dark greenish gray rectangular to lathlike crystals, minute stractions on some cleavage faces, occasionally irridescent
	Light-Colored Minerals	
Sodic plagioclase feldspar (albite)	Sodium-calcium aluminosilicate	Light gray to cream-colored rectangular to lathlike crystals, minute striations on some cleavage faces
Orthoclase feldspar	Potassium-sodium aluminosilicate	Salmon pink to creamy white rectangular crystals
Muscovite mica	Potassium aluminosilicate	Clear, sparkling flakes
Quartz	Silicon dioxide	Clear to cloudy white glassy fragments; conchoidal fracture, no cleavage; look like glass fragments in the rock

the earth **magma.** No one (by definition) will ever *see* magma; when it pours out on the earth's surface, the molten material is called **lava.** The rocks resulting from the cooling (freezing) of either magma or lava are called **igneous,** a word derived from the Latin word for fire. Igneous rocks are *those that form from the freezing of molten rock,* either by slow cooling of magma beneath the surface or by rapid cooling of lava on the earth's surface.

Igneous rocks are the best candidates for the "original" material of the earth; several lines of evidence (see Chapter Twelve) converge to suggest that the earth's earliest history was that of a solid, then molten, body of matter. The composition of igneous rocks reflects the abundant eight elements described in the previous chapter (see Figure 2-17); igneous rocks are composed almost entirely of *aluminosilicates* of iron, magnesium, calcium, sodium, and potassium, plus the mineral quartz, which consists of only silicon and oxygen in a 1:2 ratio. About nine groups of minerals make up over 99 percent of all igneous rocks; their names and identifying properties are listed in Table 3-1.

The freezing of *mineral* crystals within magma or lava eventually forms a *rock* that is composed of intergrown crystals. Crystals grow in the liquid as temperatures drop below their melting point in a manner analogous to the freezing of ice crystals from water on a cold window. As cooling continues, crystals grow at the expense of the fluid, and soon the fluid is entirely a solid, composed of a mass of intergrown crystals. Figure 3-6 illustrates a texture common to many igneous rocks; the rock is a mass of randomly oriented crystals. Our analogy is once again obvious; if igneous rocks were books, intergrown mineral crystals would be the words that form the manuscript.

Bowen's Reaction Series

In order to imagine what occurs as fluid rock begins to cool, we must remember, first, that each mineral within the solid rock has its own characteristic physical properties (see Chapter Two). Among the physical properties unique to any one mineral is its *melting point* or *freezing point*—two different terms that describe the temperature at which a solid crystalline lattice array falls apart (melts) or forms (freezes).

Since each mineral melts at its own unique temperature, when a molten rocky fluid cools, each mineral's crystal lattice reappears (forms) when the temperature of the melt drops *below* the mineral's unique melting/freezing point. Each mineral, then, delays formation of its crystals in a melt until the temperature is sufficiently cool to allow it to form (freeze or crystallize) a stable crystal. Thus, as magma cools, each mineral component forms *in sequence*—from those with high melting/freezing points down to those with low melting/freezing points.

However, one problem remains; the crystals that form in the cooling magma also *react* with it. This is a subject of much geo-

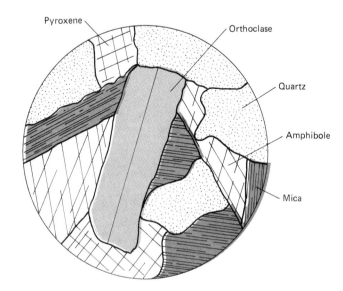

Pyroxene

Orthoclase

Quartz

Amphibole

Mica

3-6
Texture of a "typical" igneous rock. Intergrown crystals are shown somewhat enlarged to aid in recognition.

logic interest today; N. L. Bowen was among the earlier geologists to tackle this problem with both thermodynamic theory and high-temperature laboratory experimentation. Bowen was an American geologist and chemist whose attention, early in this century, was drawn to the problem of crystal formation and reaction in cooling magmas. In the course of his studies, which spanned nearly 50 years, Bowen was able to recognize two distinct kinds of magma-crystal reaction: continuous reaction and discontinuous reaction.

Continuous Reaction. If we consider the feldspar group first (see Table 3-1), we are dealing with three end members of a chemically partly homogeneous series.

1. Anorthite, the plagioclase feldspar rich in calcium and aluminum.
2. Albite, the plagioclase feldspar rich in sodium and silica.
3. Orthoclase, the orthoclase feldspar rich in potassium and silica.

Bowen observed that when a magma cooled, the first feldspar to form (at the highest temperature) was always rich in calcium and aluminum. As temperature dropped and crystallization continued, the earlier crystals were gradually transformed into those progressively enriched in sodium. At somewhat lower temperatures, orthoclase, the potassium-enriched feldspar, began to form as a separate mineral.

What Bowen saw was a nearly **continuous reaction** of the crystals with the hot liquid surrounding them such that their chemical composition changed and maintained chemical equilibrium with the surrounding melt. Clearly, the feldspar crystal lattice requires calcium and aluminum from the magma to provide the combination of small size and high electrical charge necessary to hold a crystal together (form a solid) at temperatures near 1500 degrees Celsius. As temperatures drop, progressive enrichment in sodium provides larger and larger atoms of lesser electrical charge that are now capable of holding a crystal together at lower and lower temperatures (see Figure 3-7).

Discontinuous Reaction. Bowen observed that the darker minerals (such as olivine), the pyroxenes, the amphiboles, and biotite (see Table 3-1) followed a somewhat different path of crystallization. Each of these mineral groups is separate from the others, so they cannot show the gradual, nearly continuous changes already observed among the plagioclase feldspars. Instead, as magma very slowly cools, olivine commonly crystallizes first; then, as temperature drops, pyroxene begins forming *at the expense of olivine* and also forms new crystals of its own. In time, the olivine, if enough silica is available, may be totally converted to pyroxene. As temperature drops still lower, the pyroxene may react with the melt to form amphibole which, at still lower temperatures, may react to form biotite (see Figure 3-7). Such a series of "jumps," in which one distinct mineral reacts to form a totally new mineral group, is called the **discontinuous reaction series.** The dark minerals react within a cooling magma by chemical conversion to one another at specific temperatures; in contrast, the plagioclase feldspars react continuously, changing their composition ever so slightly as temperature drops a bit more.

Fractional Crystallization. Suppose we start with a rock containing a mixture of an-

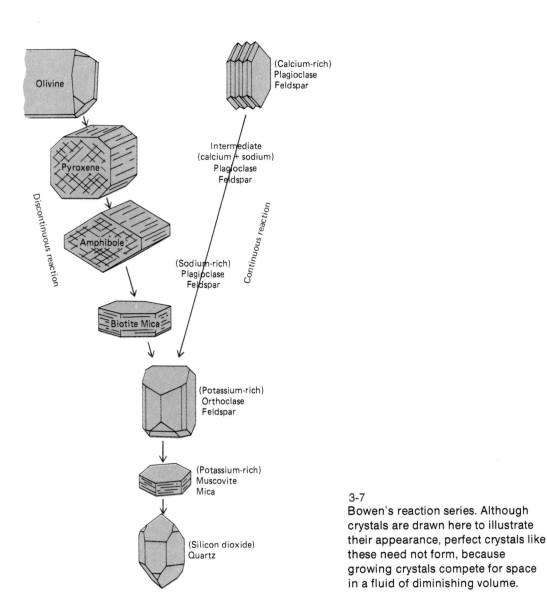

Olivine

(Calcium-rich) Plagioclase Feldspar

Pyroxene

Intermediate (calcium + sodium) Plagioclase Feldspar

Discontinuous reaction

Continuous reaction

Amphibole

(Sodium-rich) Plagioclase Feldspar

Biotite Mica

(Potassium-rich) Orthoclase Feldspar

(Potassium-rich) Muscovite Mica

(Silicon dioxide) Quartz

3-7
Bowen's reaction series. Although crystals are drawn here to illustrate their appearance, perfect crystals like these need not form, because growing crystals compete for space in a fluid of diminishing volume.

orthite, albite, and amphibole. Let us melt it and watch it slowly cool. If, during cooling, all the crystals that form remain in contact with the magma, calcium-rich feldspars will form first but will change gradually into an intermediate form, that is, into a feldspar whose composition is a mixture of albite and anorthite. Olivine might form first among the dark minerals, but it eventually dissolves to become pyroxene and then dissolves or reacts once again to become amphibole. At the end of our experiment, we have *exactly* what we began with—a rock containing a feldspar that is a mixture of anorthite and albite and that also contains the mineral amphibole. Nothing has changed; the process is analogous to melting an ice cube and then refreezing it.

Suppose we change the ground rules. Let us imagine an experiment with the same rock where each crystal, as it forms, is *not* free to react with the liquid and change its composition and form. This could occur, for example, if the magma cooled so quickly that there was not enough time for the described chemical changes to occur.

In still another scheme, the early crystals have a greater specific gravity than the later ones; suppose that the early crystals, as they formed, settled down to the bottom of a large "vat" of magma.

Or perhaps earth forces might squeeze the liquid-crystal mush, and the liquid might be forced through fractures in its container to continue crystallizing somewhere else.

Each of these three imaginary schemes has one thing in common; the crystals that form do not have a chance to react continuously, or discontinuously, with the melt. The result of separation of crystals from remaining melt is change, remarkable change.

The melt that remains is quite different in overall composition from the original molten material, because it has lost part of its substance to the crystals. The crystals, meanwhile, can no longer react, and they represent *one unique stage in the cooling history* of the melt. One fraction of the melt (the crystals) has been separated from the other fraction (the liquid). The process of **fractional crystallization**—crystallization in which the crystals no longer react with the melt—can form mineral crystals (and, therefore, rocks) *whose composition is totally different from the overall composition of the original magma.*

Chemical Differentiation. These are fascinating ideas, but are they real? Can a cooling magma differentiate or separate itself into rocks unlike its original chemistry? As is so often the case, the answer must be found in the rocks themselves.

Our target is Kilauea, an intermittently active volcano on the eastern margin of the island of Hawaii. Hawaii is the southeasternmost of a chain of volcanic islands stretching 1500 miles (2,400 kilometers) northwestward. In November 1959, a summit eruption of the Kilauea volcano began; within a month Kilauea had erupted slightly less than 50 million cubic yards (38 million cubic meters) of dark lava into a lava lake that is approximately 365 feet (110 meters) deep. Here was a ready-made lava "vat"; within a few months after the eruption, intrepid geologists from the U.S. Geological Survey began drilling into the cooling crust. At that time, temperatures above that of the boiling point of water were common only a few inches (centimeters) beneath the surface; frequent rains produced huge clouds of steam as the rain sizzled on the lake crust.

Samples of the recently cooled crust, the liquid-crystal mush at the base of the crust, and the melt beneath it were taken over an interval of several years. The drilling operations encountered problems. Penetration of the drill bit and rod into the melt—at temperatures near 1000 degrees Celsius—often resulted in melt freezing onto the slightly cooler drill bit. Unless removal was rapid, the tungsten carbide bits, and steel drill rods were simply dissolved by the hot, corrosive magma.

By studying the framework of the crystals that grew with the progressive cooling of the magma lake, these geologists were able to follow the **chemical differentiation** process just described. Three processes were observed.

1. Gravitational settling of denser crystals.
2. Pressing of the liquid from the crystal mush or framework into adjacent fractures.
3. Concentration of silica and potassium near the top of the liquid phase.

Conclusion. Chemical differentiation of magma occurs through various forms of fractional crystallization.

The offspring differ from the parent, and the parent magma is also changed, because the crystal fraction no longer reacts with the parent liquid.

Other kinds of evidence exist that favor chemical differentiation of magmas. Many very dark, plutonic rock bodies have textures that suggest that their crystals were compressed and battered—an unlikely occurrence had they remained surrounded by fluid. Some volcanoes begin by erupting very dark magnesium–iron-rich, silica-poor lavas but, in time, they erupt lavas of more intermediate and even silicic composition. Many dark-colored intrusive bodies have zones of olivine accumulation at the bottom and progressively lighter-colored silica-, sodium-, and potassium-enriched minerals going upward—just what would be expected if the heavier early minerals sank to the bottom.

Bowen found order in a delicate crystallization within the earth's fiery furnace; even at temperatures greater than molten steel, there was a natural imperative.

A Caution. Bowen's idea has withstood the test of use; it explains many of the observed diverse occurrences of the bewildering variety of igneous rocks. But theories can be seductive in their power, and the reaction principle is a seductive idea. Geologists expected Bowen's idea to explain somehow all the problems they encountered in understanding igneous rocks.

But the origin of some igneous rocks cannot be explained by fractional crystallization. The dark rocks of the ocean floor, which covers more than one-half of the earth, are apparently little changed from their parent magma. Other masses of light-colored igneous rock are bounded by and intertongued with metamorphic rocks, so that many seemingly igneous rocks probably form from extensive alteration at high temperature and pressure of still-solid rocks.

Plutonic Rocks

Imagine for a moment that an area of many cubic miles (cubic kilometers) of rock melted deep underground, pushed upward, and then slowly cooled in place. The resulting mass of solid rock, now called a **batholith,** would be composed entirely of trillions of crystals, most no larger than your fingernail. If the rock overlying the rock mass were slowly worn away by natural erosional processes, we could *see* a batholith. Therefore, by definition, a batholith is a mass of coarsely crystalline igneous rock whose *exposed* area exceeds 40 square miles (100 square kilometers).

The igneous rock, formed as the result of slow cooling, is made up of visible (Figure 3-8) intergrown crystals and is called **plutonic,** after Pluto, the Roman god of the under-

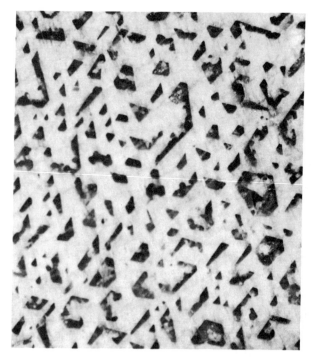

3-8
This plutonic rock's texture is unusual in that only two crystals—quartz and orthoclase—crystallized from the magma. In the competition between the two crystals as they grew, they formed this texture, reminiscent of hieroglyphic writing; hence, the rock is termed graphic granite. (Photograph by W. T. Schaller, U.S. Geological Survey.)

world. There are many places within the United States where one can see batholithic masses of plutonic rocks. The largest of these areas is the Sierra Nevada of California; imagine an entire mountain range made up entirely of interlocking crystals! Other areas include central Idaho, the Green and White mountains of New Hampshire and Vermont, the Laramie Range of Wyoming, the Black Hills of South Dakota, Stone Mountain in Georgia, Pike's Peak in Colorado, much of northern Minnesota and Wisconsin, the Wichita Mountains of Oklahoma, and parts of the Cascade Range in Washington.

The margins of many batholiths suggest that the magma moved into overlying cooler rock, baked it, tore it up, and shouldered it aside (Figure 3-9). Fragments of the bordering rock are often found near the margins of these intrusive batholiths; the fragments were torn away and carried along much like logs in a river that were trapped when the river froze. Other batholithic margins are gradational, suggesting that the rocks formed in place, greatly *altering* the surrounding rocks but not *forcefully* intruding them. Between these two types of margins are those that seem to be partly gradational and partly intrusive, perhaps reflecting a magmatic body that moved upward only a short distance into already altered rocks.

The varying nature of batholithic margins was recognized more than 100 years ago. This touched off an acrimonious debate about the origin of crystalline rocks in plutonic settings that is an interesting part of the progress of geology. Whatever origin is ascribed to plutonic rock, geologists now realize that there are many different modes of

3-9
Light-colored plutonic rock invading dark-colored rocks near a batholithic margin. (Photograph by J. R. Stacy, U.S. Geological Survey.)

origin for cyrstalline, seemingly igneous rocks.

Modern studies suggest that many batholiths are roughly tabular in shape and form many miles (kilometers) down within the continental crust. The rock overlying cooling magmatic masses must become heated and altered; ore deposits are one result (see Chapter Two) of a complex series of alteration events. If the pressure from the magma forces open fissures that reach up to the earth's surface, a volcano will be born.

Volcanic Rocks

Many geologists agree that volcanism at the surface is simply the visible evidence of the accumulation of magma beneath. Whether volcanism is *always* related to subsurface batholithic activity is an open question among geologists these days, although it is clear that in some areas, notably the Yellowstone National Park area, surface volcanism and geyser activity are related to a magmatic body cooling not far beneath the tourists' feet.

Volcanic rock is distinguished from plutonic rock in two particulars; one is observational, and the other is an inference from the observation. **Volcanic rocks** are those that are either fine grained or glassy; they *must* form by rapid cooling on or near the earth's surface. The *size* of crystals is related to cooling rate. Slow cooling allows time for large crystals to grow; therefore, coarse crystalline rock can *only* form deep within the natural insulation provided by the earth. Experience with modern lava flows verifies this; silica-rich flows that cool within a few hours tend to yield **obsidian** (see Figure 2-13), a natural volcanic *glass* that is devoid of crystals. Obsidian forms when there is no time for crystals to get their lattice arrays together in the rapidly thickening fluid. Lava flows that cool for months or years are composed of fine crystals, most too small to be seen without a mangifying glass. Generally, the longer lava takes to cool, the larger the resulting crystals will be.

Classification

Having learned something about the mineral content of igneous rocks and the influence of cooling rate on crystal size, we can now

MINERAL CONTENT

	Largely quartz and ortho-clase. Minor dark minerals.	Quartz minor or absent. Sodic plagioclase and amphibole abundant.	Quartz absent. Calcic plagioclase and pyroxene dominant. Olivine absent to common
Glassy	Obsidian - - - - - - - - - - - - -		
Frothy	Pumice	Scoria -	
Finely crystalline	Rhyolite - - - - - Andesite - - - - - - - - - BASALT		
Medium crystalline	Aplite - - - - - - - ⌐		Diabase - - - - - - - - - - - -
Coarsely crystalline	GRANITE - - - Diorite - - - - - - - - - Gabbro		

(Left vertical axis: TEXTURE AND ORIGIN — PLUTONIC——VOLCANIC)

AVERAGE ROCK COLOR	Commonly light colored	Intermediate color	Commonly dark-colored
AVERAGE ROCK CHEMISTRY	Rich in silica, aluminum, potassium, and sodium		Rich in iron, calcium, and magnesium

NOTES

1. *Porphyritic* may be used to modify the name of any rock displaying widely ranging crystal size; for example, *porphyritic basalt.*
2. *Pegmatitic* is a modifying adjective for extremely coarse-grained rocks, such as *pegmatitic granite.*
3. Names of *most* common rocks are capitalized.

3-10
Classification chart for common igneous rocks.

classify all igneous rocks. Classification is based on *observable* properties, and the most obvious properties of igneous rocks are their *mineral content* and their *texture,* or the size, shape, and arrangement of crystals (Figure 3-10).

The texture of a rock is analogous to the texture of cloth. If all the threads are uniformly small, the texture is fine, or smooth, and individual threads cannot be seen by the naked eye. If some threads are coarse and the others are finer, we say that the material has a nubby, or uneven, texture. Geologists classify rocks that display a few crystals that are coarser than the rest as **porphyritic,** an adjective used to modify the rock name. Porphyritic rocks must have a composite history. Some crystals grow during a slow cooling deep within the earth; this is followed by a sudden eruption of the mush of crystals and liquids onto the surface, which allows rapid cooling of the remaining liquid.

Material composed entirely of coarse threads is uniformly rough in appearance; each thread is visible to the eye, just as the large crystals of plutonic rock are. Figure 3-10 is a typical classification chart for igneous rocks of either plutonic or volcanic origin.

VOLCANOES—THE IDEA

Roman mythology identifies Vulcan as the god of fire and blacksmith to the other gods. Even though Vulcan's name has been somewhat eclipsed by that of his more famous wife, Venus, his prowess at the forge provided one early explanation for the origin of volcanoes. Smoking mountains were simply identified as chimneys for Vulcan's forge,

far beneath the earth. When Vulcan struck his anvil, working red-hot metal, explosions and showers of sparks ensued. The island of Vulcano, near Sicily, received its name as the principal forge site of Vulcan, and we have called thundering, smoking mountains volcanoes ever since.

Our understanding of volcanoes changed little between Greco-Roman times and the nineteenth century, when modern investigations of volcanic rocks and active volcanoes began. Stories about volcanoes as imprisoned winds, the activities of the underworld gods, and similar myths (Figure 3-11) are faithfully traceable to Aristotle and others, 300 years before Christ's birth. Listen to Shakespeare repeat them as the current understanding of the seventeenth century in *Henry IV*.

> Diseased nature often times breaks forth
> In strange eruptions; oft the teeming earth
> Is with a kind of colic pinched and vex'd
> By the imprisoning of unruly winds

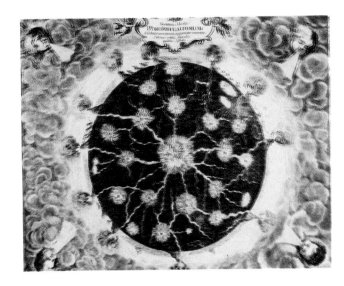

3-11
This seventeenth-century engraving accurately represents the knowledge of the time. Great fires raged within the earth; volcanoes were their "chimneys." (Courtesy of History of Science Collections, University of Oklahoma Libraries.)

Within her womb: which for enlargement
Striving shakes the old bedlam earth, and
Topples down steeples and moss-grown towers.

The eighteenth century saw as clear a fight between authority and experience in geology as the sixteenth century had seen in establishing the Copernican (sun-centered) model of the universe.

Abraham Gottlob Werner, professor at the Freiberg School of Mines in Saxony, was on the side of authority as well as simplicity. On the side of experience (and complexity) was James Hutton. Werner began with preconceptions, as we all do; they formed the basis of a lifetime of dynamic, inspiring teaching that made him a commanding figure among European geologists and students. His school became famous, and students came from all over Europe to study with him. That much of what he taught about rocks was shown to be wrong during his lifetime did not bother him, because he thought he had the truth, and simplicity, on his side.

Werner's preconceptions, common to his time, were that (1) the earth was homogeneous; that is, its history was the same at every spot on the earth; (2) the Noachian flood was a recent, historical event; *all* rocks formed from *this* ocean, which had covered the earth; and (3) volcanism was an unimportant, recent process, caused by the burning of underground coal. The fact that both French and Italian geologists had studied basalts elsewhere and recognized their volcanic origin before Werner began to teach did not matter to him, nor did the problem of where to *put* all that water, which must have covered the highest mountain peaks of the earth.

Simply, Werner believed that all rocks, including basalt, precipitated from a worldwide ocean. These notions, often called the *Neptunist theory*, astound us today, but they were taught as fact to generations of young geologists in Saxony.

Often in the history of science dogged defense by authorities of a demonstrably erroneous idea has resulted in a burst of new research from those eager to attack either the person or the idea. Sometimes the idea is vindicated instead; Chapter Seven discusses an idea that North American geologists regarded as improbable in the 1950s that is now the central theme of modern geologic thought.

At other times the idea serves as a stimulus and is then abandoned. Nicolas Desmarest, one of Werner's students, was among the first to challenge him; after studying the basalts of the Auvergne region of southern France, Desmarest concluded that basalts were of volcanic origin. For those who challenged his rashness at attacking Werner's authority, he had a reply that is at the heart of modern science—*go and look for yourselves.*

James Hutton also attacked Werner's ideas and again appealed to the rocks themselves to yield their story; Hutton believed that crystalline rocks were of igneous origin. *Two* lines of proof were needed to complete this theory: (1) evidence that crystalline rock had once been perfectly fluid, and (2) evidence that the fluid had been hot. At Glen Tilt in Perthshire, Scotland, he found them *both,* together. There veins of a reddish granite intrude a pale limestone and thoroughly bake and alter the adjacent limestone. Hutton became so excited when he found his evidence that those with him thought he had discovered gold. There was no gold, but there *was* truth. The rocks yielded their story and Neptunism declined, but it did not die easily; Werner was convinced of the veracity of his own ideas to his last day.

People have always enjoyed living near volcanoes, because they are very beautiful and because altered volcanic. rock often makes excellent soil. It is an undeniable part of their legacy that unexpected volcanic eruptions have caused hundreds of thousands of deaths (Figure 3-12); perhaps the first geologic martyr was Empedocles of Agrigentium. Legend suggests that his death in about 435 B.C. occurred when he came too close to Mount Etna's crater while attempting to observe an eruption. Pliny the Elder paid the same price at Vesuvius in A.D. 79. His nephew, Pliny the Younger, described this eruption, which buried both Pompeii and Herculaneum under volcanic ash and mudflows; his letter constitutes the first accurate description of a volcanic eruption.

VOLCANOES IN ERUPTION

A volcanic eruption produces three components, gases, liquids, and solids, in varying mixtures. All three are a normal part of the magma beneath the surface. As the magma rises, pressure on the magma diminishes. Dissolved gases and liquids, which may expand explosively into gaseous form as pressures are diminished, provide what is necessary for eruption, since many eruptions are driven by vast volumes of escaping gas. Indeed, we should also think of many volcanoes as sites where the earth blows water and other volatiles back into the atmosphere.

The most abundant gas, which emerges during and after a volcanic eruption, is simply water vapor. Carbon dioxide is a distant second, and sulphurous gases, including various sulphur oxides, and hydrogen, argon, copper, lead, boron, mercury, flourine, bromine, chlorine, iron, and zinc, are third. Deep wells drilled in modern volcanic areas often recover small amounts of the chemical compounds of these same elements from the water and provide an intriguing look into the process of making ore deposits.

Some volcanic areas are devoid of volcanic rocks; essentially the only volcanic product there is gas. These areas of gas re-

3-12
An eruption of Vesuvius in 1631. As this old engraving suggests, Vesuvius has caused human misery many more times since A.D. 79. The bridge is choked with people fleeing the devastation of Naples. (Courtesy of History of Science Collections, University of Oklahoma Libraries.)

lease contain **fumaroles** or **solfataras,** openings in the earth from which only steam and other volcanic gases issue. One interesting area in the United States is The Geysers, an area 50 miles (80 kilometers) north of San Francisco, where the escaping steam is used to drive turbines that generate several hundred megawatts of electrical power.

As magma nears the surface, the expansion of the gases within it provides much of the energy for a volcanic eruption. The expansion of gases is familiar to anyone who has ever carelessly opened a soft drink bottle; the resulting frothing overflow (and perhaps eruption on one's clothing) is analogous to the events in a magma as it approaches the surface. If large amounts of gas are present in the magma, the eruption may be exceedingly violent. One such eruption, that of Krakatoa, a small island near Sumatra, in 1883 was similar to that of Santorin, discussed earlier.

Most of the island was blown away, leaving a circular basin in the seafloor 1000 feet (300 meters) deep. The *sound* of the explosion was heard 4 hours later in the Indian Ocean, nearly 3000 miles (5000 kilometers) away. The explosion-induced pressure wave in the atmosphere was read by barographs halfway around the world. Sea waves up to 130 feet (40 meters) high that were also caused by the explosion ravaged the coasts of Java and Sumatra. Over 30,000 people died, mostly by drowning; a Dutch warship was thrown more than $\frac{1}{2}$ mile (1 kilometer) inland from its anchorage. Ash was blown nearly 60 miles (100 kilometers) into the air; for 125 miles (200 kilometers) downwind, the sun was blotted out for a day of complete darkness. The fine ash suspended in the atmosphere gave the earth glorious sunsets and bitterly cold winters for several years, because the ash blocked about 13 percent of incoming solar radiation, and the average temperature of the earth dropped several degrees. Our expression "once in a blue moon" recalls this time; for years the air was so laden with ash that the moon seemed to be blue.

The catastrophic eruptions of Santorin and Krakatoa have much in common. They were both the result of expanding gas accumulation under what seemed to be a dead volcanic cone. The force of the expanding gas blew many cubic miles (cubic kilometers) of solid material high into the air. Leakage of seawater into the red-hot magma chamber may have been the final event that set off both catastrophes. After the eruption was complete—usually a matter of a few days—all that remained was a large, roughly circular pit called a **caldera** (Figure 3-13).

The word *caldera* comes from the Spanish word for cauldron (a large kettle) and describes a roughly circular area caused by some combination of violent explosion and subsequent collapse of the area once occupied by magma beneath the volcano. Caldera-forming explosions are so violent that many volcanoes literally blow their own foundations away, and the resulting massive collapse greatly enlarges the original (explosive) caldera. Calderas exhibit quite a range in size, from $\frac{1}{2}$ mile (1 kilometer) to perhaps 50 miles (80 kilometers) across. Among the largest calderas known on earth are those in the Yellowstone Park and in the nearby Island Park area in Idaho. A caldera of much smaller size occupies what is left of the former Mount Mazama in Oregon; we know it as Crater Lake. Calderas are also known on other planets; Olympus Mons on Mars has a caldera about 40 miles (60 kilometers) across.

Still another combination of gas and solids yields a different form of eruption. Known

3-13
In this aerial view, a dark lava flow has oozed its way across light-colored plains north of Flagstaff, Arizona.Numerous volcanoes dot the horizon. (Photograph by Michael Collier.)

as fiery ash cloud eruptions (sometimes called by the equivalent French term, *nuée ardente*), these are among the least predictable and most violent of all eruptions. Their unpredictability is well illustrated by the 1902 eruption of Mount Pelée on Martinique, in the Caribbean. On May 8, a prodigous explosion on the side of Mount Pelée was instantly followed by the discharge of white-hot gas and tons of ash, suspended in the gas like silt in a raging stream. This heavy emulsion of ash and gas swept down the side of the mountain, destroying the village of Saint Pierre, which was in its path, and all but a few of the 28,000 inhabitants.

Among the 28,000 who died in the boiling inferno of gas and ash was Professor Landes of Saint Pierre's College. Only the day before, he had advised the residents, who were already alarmed by a month of earthquakes and minor eruptions, that they had nothing to fear from Mount Pelée. The local government had likewise assured people that there was no danger and, to help calm the jittery citizens, the governor brought his family to live in Saint Pierre. Among the few who lived was a prisoner who survived the maelstrom of ash and gas in a deep underground dungeon. According to one version of the story, after his rescue he went to work for a traveling circus sideshow, a pardoned and grateful man. Another version has him hauled safely out of his dungeon and executed for the previous crimes he had committed!

The power of such a glowing avalanche of gas and ash is difficult to comprehend. At Saint Pierre, the avalanche moved downslope at velocities in excess of 100 miles (160 kilometers) per hour; internal temperatures ranged between 600 and 1000 degrees Celsius. Destruction of the city was total; the incandescent cloud was capable of carrying sizable boulders distances of several miles. The weight of material involved is impressive; typical volcanic ash has a specific gravity nearly three times that of water. The day of the Saint Pierre eruption, one of the surviving ships in the harbor, the steamer *Roddam,* staggered out of the harbor with 120 tons (109 metric tons) of ash on her deck. These fiery avalanches are capable of energetic erosion and can leave grooves in solid rock to record their passage, much as glaciers do.

From a distance, a *nuée ardente* is a scene

of some beauty. Curiously, the glowing avalanche is essentially soundless, because each glowing particle of ash is suspended between other particles in expanding gas. Electrical effects are common; they are caused by friction in the convoluting emulsion and lead to giant lightning flashes, boiling globe and ball lightning, and powerful thunderclaps. It is probably the internal electrical activity that makes the glowing clouds so cohesive; these avalanches may sweep along for many miles as a well-defined mass, just like a giant mudflow (see Chapter Eight).

Many of the incredibly violent phenomena described owe their ferocity to some combination of two factors: the inadvertent admittance of water to a highly pressurized magma cauldron, as at Krakatoa, or the plugging up of a vent area by congealed, viscous lava, as at Mount Pelée. Either natural situation carries with it the promise of violence, because expanding, superheated gases possess extraordinary energy. Not surprisingly, many explosions caused by vent plugging occur in volcanoes that are composed mostly of silicic, light-colored rock, because lava of rhyolitic composition tends to flow much *less* readily than lava of basaltic composition. Rhyolitic lavas often contain more water vapor than basaltic composition. Rhyolitic lavas often contain more water vapor than basaltic lavas, so the potential gas content is also higher.

However, basaltic and andesitic magmas also are capable of explosive activity, either because of water having access to the magma or because of an abundance of gas being dissolved in the magma. The former state leads to the formation of a **maar** crater, and the latter results in a **cinder zone** (Figure 3-14). Each of these landforms consists of fragments of volcanic rock, collectively called **pyroclastics** (literally, fire-formed

3-14
The rounded conical form of this cinder cone northeast of Flagstaff, Arizona, is fairly typical; the cone is little more than a pile of cinders dumped on the earth's surface. (Photograph by G. K. Gilbert, U.S. Geological Survey.)

fragments). Pyroclastics come in all sizes, ranging from ash so fine that it may remain suspended in the atmosphere for years to blocks of frozen lava that weigh many tons (metric tons). The word **cinders** describes intermediate-sized granular material, while fist-sized material and larger material are often referred to as **bombs.** Bombs result from lava spatter blown high into the air that cools and solidifies as it falls, often assuming streamlined, spindle shapes, similar to those of raindrops (Figure 3-15).

Intermittent eruption of pyroclastics, followed by quiet eruption of flowing lava followed, in turn, by another explosive eruption, builds **stratovolcanoes,** or **composite cones.** These mountains are among the most beautiful objects of the natural world (Figure 3-16); Fujiyama, for example, has affected Japanese art for centuries.

3-15
A volcanic bomb, streamlined and frozen during the passage of lava through the air. The bomb is about 2 feet (⅗ meter) long. (Photograph by H. T. Stearns, U.S. Geological Survey.)

Many composite cones are formed from lavas and pyroclastics of andesitic composition in rudely alternating layers. They commonly document gas buildup under a dormant volcano, followed by explosive, pyroclastic eruptions. Gas pressures diminish, and fluid lava flows take the place of pyroclastic eruptions. Finally, all volcanic activity ceases, and the stratovolcano sleeps again, as internal gas pressures increase.

Some stratovolcanic eruptions are roughly cyclic; Stromboli, the "lighthouse of the Mediterranean," has been erupting every 30 minutes or so since prehistoric times. Mount Etna erupts approximately every 7 years, while Mount Vesuvius has erupted approximately every 40 years in recent times. The early history of Vesuvius, however, was far more erratic, because in A.D. 79 there was no known Roman or Etruscan record of volcanic activity on Mount Vesuvius. Vesuvius was considered a long-extinct volcano. This belief abruptly changed on August 24, A.D. 79. That fatal day saw the eruption of thousands of tons (metric tons) of cinders, ash, and pumice that buried the town of Pompeii, 6 miles (10 kilometers) downwind. Only 10 percent of Pompeii's 20,000 citizens remained behind after the early part of the eruption. Those who stayed behind still lie there. Their bodies formed molds in the ash that suffocated, poisoned, and buried them. Roofs collapsing under the weight of ash caused the deaths of others. Modern excavation has revealed a perfectly preserved scene of what it was like to be a Roman 1900 years ago.

Towering clouds of ash and steam billowing above Vesuvius touched off torrential

3-16
This old photograph of Mount Mayon, in the Philippines, displays the classic shape of a stratovolcano. (Photograph by H. Gannett, U.S. Geological Survey.)

Volcanoes in Eruption   **75**

rains, a phenomenon common to many modern volcanic eruptions. The rain on the thick deposits of ash, barren of vegetation, caused large masses of a rocky, ashy substance to form; this substance began a rapid descent down the steep slopes in a manner similar to that of an ordinary mudflow. These volcanic mudflows, called **lahars,** swept everything before them as they gained size and speed. Lahars are yet another of the hazards associated with volcanism; for the residents of Herculaneum, a village due west of Vesuvius in A.D. 79, death came by burial under acrid piles of seething mud.

The watery laharic material, about 20 yards (18 meters) thick, dried to a natural cement; the modern excavation of Herculaneum required essentially quarry methods. Everything is once again as it was in A.D. 79 when the villas became tombs, and the ruins of the city lay forgotten under the consolidated mud for nearly 1900 years.

If gas plays a still lesser part in volcanic activity and if the escaping lava is basaltic and therefore rather fluid, **shield volcanoes** result. These volcanoes are little more than roughly circular masses of lava, somewhat thicker near the vent. Since the explosive activity of this form of volcanism is either mild or absent, we at last have a volcano whose activity may be studied at close range. Kilauea is one of many shield volcanoes on the island of Hawaii, and it is probably the most intensively studied volcano on earth.

All of the Hawaiian Islands are simply the tips of shield volcanoes that have grown from the ocean floor. The island of Hawaii is made of clusters of basaltic shield volcanoes whose aggregate diameter exceeds 90 miles (160 kilometers). Hawaii rises higher above the seafloor [6 miles (10 kilometers)] than Mount Everest does above sea level. The total volume of extruded lava required to form Hawaii exceeds 10,000 cubic miles (40,000 cubic kilometers), all accumulated on the ocean floor within the last 1 million years. The greatest of these clusters is Mauna Loa (Figure 3-17), prodigious giant among all active volcanoes; its neighbors are Kohala, Hualalai, and Mauna Kea. Collectively, these four massed shield volcanoes form the island of Hawaii, the easternmost, youngest, and largest of the Hawaiian Islands. Yawning on the east slope of Mauna Loa is the Kilaueau caldera, home of the U.S. Geological Survey's Volcanological Observatory. Kilaueau is dotted with instruments that deftly record the activity beneath it and make Kilauea and its parent, Mauna Loa, the most thoroughly studied and best understood volcanoes on earth.

3-17
Mauna Loa, Hawaii, from the air. Mauna Loa is a classic shield volcano whose summit, here above the clouds, stands 13,680 feet (4200 meters) above sea level (U.S. Air Force photograph.)

Volcanic activity in the Kilauea caldera is nearly continuous, usually as gentle eruptions of steam and smoke, or larger outpourings of liquid lava or, even more rarely, fountains of lava blasting into the air to heights of 200 yards (180 meters). Mark Twain, in *Roughing It,* provides his own irreverent description of what it is like to watch the craters and lava lakes (Figure 3-18) of the Kilauea area at night.

. . . here was a vast, perpendicular, walled cellar, nine hundred feet deep in some places, thirteen hundred in others, level-floored, and *ten miles in circumference!* Here was a yawning pit upon whose floor the armies of Russia could camp, and have room to spare. . . . The greater part of the vast floor . . . was as black as ink . . . but over a mile square of it was ringed and streaked with a thousand branching streams of liquid and gorgeously brilliant fire! It looked like a colossal railroad map of the State of Massachusetts done in chain lightning on a midnight sky. Imagine it—imagine a coalblack sky shivered into a tangled network of angry fire! . . . The smell of sulphur is strong, but not unpleasant to a sinner.

Earthquakes associated with the eruption of basaltic lava suggest that the magma source for Kilauea is about 35 miles (60 kilometers) beneath it. As the magma works its way upward, it accumulates in a shallow chamber beneath Kilauea, causing the summit of the crater to inflate, swell, and tilt as the pressure rises. Finally, cracking of the stretched, tilted surface is signaled by swarms of small earthquakes, sometimes as many as 1000 a day. A rapid increase in earthquake number and intensity indicates an impending eruption. The summit deflates

3-18
Halemaumau crater at night, 1961 eruption. As you can see, Mark Twain described it well. (Photograph by D. H. Richter, U.S. Geological Survey.)

and shrinks during the eruption and, after the eruption is complete, the volume of lava extruded equals the amount of summit subsidence.

Such a well-understood model might apply to all volcanoes, but few volcanoes can be safely studied at close range like Kilauea, and there is little assurance that all volcanoes follow the eruptive pattern just outlined. Some generalities are, however, clear.

Volcanoes are usually roughly conical hills, formed by everything from fluid, basaltic lava flows to cinders and bombs, ash, and mixtures of all these materials. A fairly circular vent provides the common opening for the release of material coming from within the earth. Occasionally, as loose cinders are readily washed away, the inner plumbing system is exposed. As a volcano dies, magma congeals in its conduit to form sturdy, hard rock. The remnant, after ero-

3-19
Shiprock, an outstanding example of a volcanic neck. The ridges radiating away from the former vent area are lava-filled fractures that once fed the now-eroded volcanic pile. (Photograph by Michael Collier.)

sion of the erupted material, forms a resistant plug or pipe, usually called a **volcanic neck.** A volcanic neck is like tattered plumbing, dangling in the air, after the house has burned down. Shiprock (Figure 3-19), a landmark in northwesternmost New Mexico, is a well-known example of such a neck.

Some **lava flows** record the welling of basaltic lava from numerous, often interconnected, fissures. The lava is so fluid that no hills or cones are erected; instead, the lava stretches out over many miles (kilometers) as a syrupy sheet of black rock (Figure 3-20). The surfaces of the most fluid flows

3-20
A lava flow on the Uinkaret Plateau in northwestern Arizona. The dark flow fills in a valley in the rolling, light-colored plateau surface. (From a sketch by W. H. Holmes, U.S. Geological Survey.)

3-21

Pahoehoe surface on a lava flow from Kilauea, Hawaii. (Photograph by R. T. Holcomb, U.S. Geological Survey.)

have ropy, rippled structures (Figure 3-21) that are called by their Hawaiian name, *pahoehoe* (pronounced *pah-hoy-hoy*). Colder, more viscous flows move as cascading blocks and jumbled masses of congealed

lava. The Hawaiian name for these rough surfaces is *aa* (pronounced *ah-ah*).

Some lava flows spring as flank eruptions from the sides or base of cinder cones (Figure 3-22), while larger, extensive flows may cover parts of several states. One such area in the United States is the Columbia Plateau region of the Pacific Northwest. Here flows from many fissures blanket parts of five states, covering nearly 200,000 square miles (500,000 square kilometers) to depths of 1 mile ($1\frac{3}{5}$ kilometer) or so. The volume of lava erupted is roughly *eight* times that of the island of Hawaii. Such areas of numerous lava flows are called **lava plateaus,** because they form the largest flat areas on the face of the continents. Lava plateaus are made from coalescing lava flows, stacked one atop the other over some length of time. Often the length of time between flows is sufficiently long that soils and vegetation form, only to be buried by the next flow (Figure 3-23).

The lava brought to the surface must cut its way through whatever rocks lie beneath; such exposed volcanic plumbing is called a **dike** when a tabular magma body has rammed its way through rock, crosscutting

3-22

This symmetrical cinder cone near Flagstaff, Arizona, was also the source of a somewhat quieter eruption of fluid lava from its base. The lava flow spilled out across the countryside for several miles (kilometers) as a sluggish river of lava. (Photograph by Michael Collier.)

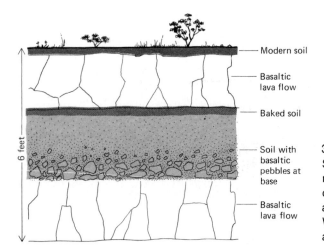

Modern soil

Basaltic
lava flow

Baked soil

Soil with
basaltic
pebbles at
base

Basaltic
lava flow

6 feet

3-23
Sketch from field notes of an area
near Walla Walla, Washington. An
overlying basaltic lava flow buries
and bakes an underlying soil zone.
Within the unbaked soil, leaf fossils
are visible.

any preexisting layering (Figure 3-24), or a
sill (Figure 3-25) when the magma has
wedged the intruded rock apart parallel to its
layering. Dikes and sills form an important

part of many deeply eroded areas of the
earth (Figure 3-26) and remind us of the possibilities that may lie deeply buried beneath
our feet.

3-24
Sketch of dikes near Mount Etna, on Sicily.
This sketch is taken from Charles Lyell's
Principles of Geology, first edition, published
in 1883. It was the first textbook of geology.
(Courtesy of History of Science Collections,
University of Oklahoma Libraries.)

VOLCANOES AND HUMANITY

Volcanoes have been sources of mixed awe
and terror from our earliest beginning. Major
volcanoes of the world are the object of religious veneration and, until recently, places
of human sacrifice in attempts to appease
the gods. The myth and folklore of volcanoes can, and does, fill books; only within
the last 200 years has ignorance been partly
replaced with understanding.

Still, hundreds of thousands of people
have died miserably as the result of vol-
canic-induced sea waves, ashfalls, lahars,
nuée ardente eruptions, lava flows and cascades, suffocation, gas poisoning, and starvation after crop destruction (Figure 3-27).
However, volcanic activity has its beneficial
side as well.

The atmosphere we breathe is the product
of ancient volcanic eruptions, highly modi-

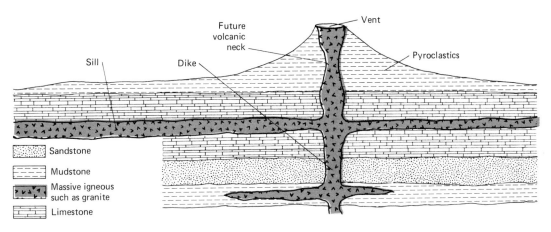

Sandstone

Mudstone

Massive igneous
such as granite

Limestone

3-25

A schematic cross section through the earth beneath a volcano. The vent is
fed through a plumbing system that may reach down 25 miles (40 kilometers)
or more. Magma flowing upward under pressure not only cuts across the
layering of overlying rocks to form a *dike,* but may also wedge rock layering
apart and form a *sill* that approximately parallels the layering in older rock.
Notice that the sill, unlike a lava flow (Figure 3-23), will bake rocks both above
it and below it. If the loose pyroclastic material on the surface is worn away,
the upper part of the plumbing is exposed as a volcanic neck (Figure 3-19).

fied by oxygen respiration from early bacteria and blue-green algae (see Chapter Twelve). The water we consume is a gift of those same early volcanoes. The natural, nonpolluting energy of underground steam is being employed more and more, and the valuable industrial chemicals that are recovered are an important by-product. Thousands of square miles (square kilometers) of new land surface, much of it highly fertile, have been created by volcanism. One flow in the Columbia Plateau has been traced for over 200 miles (300 kilometers) and covers more than 20,000 square miles (50,000 square kilometers). If such a flow originated today in Chicago, an extremely unlikely occurrence, it would destroy a major city and much of the fertile cropland of Illinois. The same flow in an uninhabited tropical area would be a potential benefactor; only a few tens of years later, the surface of the flow might well have changed into fertile soil, rare in an environment where intense rains tend to wash the nutrients out of soil through time (see Chapter Four).

The problem with volcanism rests partly with geography; volcanism in populated areas equates with disaster, while volcanism elsewhere may simply give us more land to till or may build a beautiful mountain for us to enjoy. People love to live near volcanoes precisely because they are often high, beautiful mountains and because altered volcanic rocks of many types make exceptionally fertile soil. How can we and volcanoes get along with each other?

Appraising the Hazard

We can live with volcanoes if we know the answers to two distinct questions:

3-26
These dikes, near Alamosa, Colorado, are more resistant to erosion than adjacent rock; the dikes therefore make vertical rock walls marching across the Colorado landscape. (Photograph by G. W. Stose, U.S. Geological Survey, 1901.)

1. What are the approximate hazards of living here?
2. How much, and how precise, a warning of an eruption will I receive?

Evaluation of the hazard of living near a particular volcano is related entirely to its history of eruption. If the volcano is termed **extinct,** there has been no eruption in historic time, and *presumably* there will be no further eruptions. But Vesuvius was considered an "extinct" volcano in A.D. 79 and then brought death to thousands with little warning. Evidently, appraisal of volcanic hazards depends on the cyclical nature of the volcano's eruption. If the volcano *is* periodic, its future is reasonably predictable for the same reason that we can predict it will be cold in January. The future is predictable only when the past has been equally so.

A few active volcanoes are cyclical in pattern, but the majority are not. It is not the active volcanoes that concern us; no one would move next door to Vesuvius while pumice whipped the air. How can one appraise the hazard of **dormant** volcanoes, those that have not erupted within one's lifetime, but that have erupted within historic times? One can only assume that if eruptions occur again, they will be similar to those of the past and will pose similar hazards. The basic assumption is tenuous, because many modern eruptions are not exactly like those of the past, but history is all we have with which to work.

A 1975 study of the volcanic hazards of the Cascade Range in Washington and Oregon is an example of what can be done. The Cascade Range is a series of stratovolcanoes that stretch from Mount Baker in Washington south to Mount Lassen in northern California (Figure 3-28). Lahars and ashfalls both have been common within historic times; what are the hazards of living in this beautiful and richly volcanic part of the world?

One potential disaster would be the eruption of ash and pumice from any one of the cones in a manner similar to that of Mount Mazama about 7000 years ago. Crater Lake is the remnant of Mazama's eruption; what would happen if Lassen suffered the same style of eruption? The dispersal of the resulting ash and pumice is easily predictable, given our knowledge of prevailing winds and the extent of the ashfall from Mount Mazama. What is suggested as a result of Lassen's eruption is the total destruction of the cities of Alturas and Susanville, much like that of Pompeii. A similar event with Mount

3-27
Destruction of vegetation by ashfall from Irazú volcano, Costa Rica, 1964. Imagine what such an ashfall does to water sources, grazing animals, and agriculture—in short, all the necessities of life. Now look back at Figure 3-2 and imagine what Santorin meant to the Minoan people.

Hood would devastate The Dalles, a city in Oregon, and Yakima, Washington (Figure 3-28).

Mudflows, or lahars, from Mount Rainier have stretched northwest toward Puget Sound within the last few hundred years. A modern lahar down the White or Puyallup rivers would wreak damage beyond our imagination and could conceivably transform Tacoma into a modern Herculaneum. A stubborn question arises. Should I move, and what are my chances?

Geologists would currently insist that neither Yakima, Alturas, or Tacoma should be abandoned, because we all live with risks of some sort no matter where we live, and the volcanic risks near the Cascades are perhaps similar in magnitude to those of being struck by lightning or contracting bubonic plague. But the risk persists nevertheless, and it should be a *known* risk, with political and scientific actions taken to lessen the risk, modify its consequences, and enhance the accurate prediction of catastrophe.

There is little that can be done to modify the consequences of the violent eruptions of ash and pumice that ravage the land downwind. Mudflows are equally not amenable to human intervention although, like ashfalls, their path, down modern stream courses, is *predictable*. Sizable dams across susceptible streams might trap the flow, but the resulting reservoir would need to be immense and *devoid of large volumes of water* when the mudflow arrived. A mudflow cascading into a full reservoir would create a double disaster, causing first a calamitous flood as the reservoir water overtopped the dam and, second, dam collapse; this would be followed by the pent-up mudflow. Diversionary dams or barriers might shunt small flows out onto uninhibited areas; major flows would overtop them and drag them along as part of the flow.

Predicting the Hazard

If there is little that can be done to lessen the destruction, once volcanic events are under

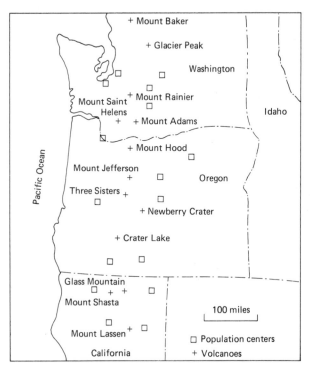

3-28
Sketch map of population centers and volcanoes in the Pacific Northwest. Communities with a few miles (kilometers) of major volcanoes may experience lahars, mudflows, lava flows, flooding, and *nueé ardênte* flows. By recent estimates, if large ash eruptions occur, prevailing westerly winds may deposit 1 to 3 feet (up to 1 meter) of ash on communities up to 50 miles (80 kilometers) east of the volcanic source area. (Data largely from U.S. Geological Survey Map MF-786, 1976.)

way much can be done to lessen the loss in lives and property with adequate prediction. The prediction of volcanic events is difficult, as the fate of Professor Landes at Saint Pierre's College should remind us. The prediction of volcanic events rests on detailed knowledge of the past history of the volcano and of far more detailed knowledge of the inner workings of a volcano than we are ever likely to obtain. A large body of data may eventually allow successful prediction of eruptions and, for a few thoroughly studied volcanoes, prediction is possible at this time.

Among the features observed to herald volcanic eruptions are changes in the temperature of hot springs, fumaroles, and crater lakes. These temperatures may be taken directly or may be monitored by repetitive measurements from infrared cameras that are mounted on either aircraft or space satellites. Doming and tilting of the ground surface near the eruptive site is a common precursor to volcanism, although neither swelling, radical temperature changes, or ground tilting *always* precedes uplift. On some occasions all three have been observed in concert; then the volcano deflates and nothing occurs or an eruption breaks out miles (kilometers) from the site of change.

Careful measurement of the earth's magnetic field, which locally should be changed by the movement of large volumes of liquid rock, has allowed some warning to be given, although the change may occur only hours or even minutes before the eruption. The howling and erratic behavior of dogs and other farm animals is a common precursory event, but one to which most humans rarely pay attention. Horses have been observed to run in frantic circles, trying to escape; dogs howl and dig as if trying to bury themselves. Evidently, many animals are far more sensitive to impending disaster than we are, since similar erratic behavior of farm animals occurs just prior to a major earthquake (see Chapter Six).

Small earthquakes, perhaps too small even to be detected by sensitive instruments, may be one of the phenomena that domestic animals react to, since earthquake activity often preceded eruption by days, weeks, or years. Local harmonic tremor is a unique type of trembling that is associated with impending eruption, as are certain other types of very shallow earthquakes within volcanic cones, yet no type of earthquake activity is an ironclad prognosticator; some volcanoes erupt without any earthquake warnings, while others quake for decades, but never erupt. The forces within the earth are complex and difficult to predict in an area of tumultous magmatic intrusion, gas expansion, internal shattering and engulfment of rocks, steam and water leakage, and tilting and bulging of the earth's surface—all common phenomena near the earth's several hundred active volcanoes.

The difficulties of volcanic prediction should not leave us despairing; very accurate predictions for highly instrumented, well-understood volcanoes such as Kilauea are now a part of everyday life. There is much more to be learned, but prediction of volcanic events near population centers would be greatly enhanced in the future by widespread instrumentation of dangerous volcanic areas that are near population centers. Additional work with topographic maps (see Appendix D) could define areas of potential disaster for various kinds of volcanic eruption, because the hazards from pumice and ashfalls, as in Pompeii, are distributed very differently than those from *nuée ardente* eruptions or volcanic mudflows. Tiltmeters might be a second line of defense on particularly dangerous peaks, as would monitoring the temperatures of any fumarolic discharge, volcanic lakes, or hot springs. Airborne aeromagnetic surveys might likewise be useful, as would measurement of local variations in the electric field potential near volcanoes. No *one* piece of information allows us currently to predict volcanic eruptions, but relatively modest levels of earthquake instrumentation in areas where volcanic peaks and populations interface might give us the potential to bring trained teams and portable equipment to areas of developing danger to refine our predictions further.

Nothing is really lacking today except the will and, with the will, the money to support increased levels of volcanic monitoring. That the yearly costs of even such a modest program would be substantial is beyond question, but the benefit-to-cost ratio may be high. If *you* were a resident of Tacoma, what would it be worth to you to know that the rumblings of Mount Rainier were being watched by someone who cared?

SUMMARY

Volcanoes are an intermittent step in a cycle of rock change, because all rocks come from other rocks. Volcanoes occupy linear zones on the face of the earth; these zones are commonly also areas of earthquake activity.

Such order in the production of magma within an otherwise apparently solid earth suggests that the same forces that cause large blocks of the earth's outer shell to shudder against one another (see Chapter Seven) assist in turning solid earth to molten mass, but the enigma of magma generation continues as one of the most challenging questions in geology.

Once formed, magma can only seek its way to the surface, forming volcanic features, or remain buried and cool over many million years. With slow cooling, plutonic rocks form; their myriad variety is partly due to the process of fractional crystallization, which may act to separate the original chemistry of the magma into an array of igneous offspring. The masses of granitic batholiths and the basaltic ocean basins seem, however, to have undergone little chemical differentiation; a fuller understanding of their origin will come after studying later chapters (such as Chapter Seven).

Our curiosity about volcanoes must stretch back to our earliest encounters with them. Unpredicted volcanic fury is violence beyond human comprehension; we just now are taking the first hesitant steps toward appraising and predicting volcanic hazards. Volcanoes are not all bad, however; volcanic products include building materials, rich new soil, new land, and mountains of every size and form. Earlier gifts included our atmosphere and water; these ideas are developed further in Chapter Twelve. Volcanic activity also yields geysers, hot springs, and a minor source of energy. Igneous processes yield one other value; the molten fury beneath our feet reminds us, as the philosopher Will Durant has observed, that "civilization exists by geologic consent."

EXERCISES

1. Scientists have observed that, in general, the lower the lava's silica content, the more fluid the lava. What kind of rock should compose shield volcanoes, then?

2. Explain why the *same* kind of lava that builds shield volcanoes also forms steep-sided cinder cones. What makes the difference?

3. The caldera at Santorin provides evidence suggesting that the initial explosion hurtled blocks from the source area at speeds exceeding 1200 miles (2000 kilometers) per hour. *How* could this information have been obtained?

4. Lava Hot Springs, near Pocatello, Idaho, is so mineral rich that bathers float high in the water. What controls which minerals might be present in solutions? Could hot springs make an ore deposit?

5. The largest shield volcano on Mars, Olympus Mons, if placed on earth would cover the state of New Mexico and would be nearly three times as high as Mount Everest. Would the source of magma for this

awesome shield volcano have been deeper or shallower than those on earth that are less than one-fifth its size? Why? What is the relative strength of the Martian versus Earth crust? Would the height of Olympus Mons allow you to speculate on the pull of gravity on Mars, compared to Earth?

6. The average rate of eruption on Hawaii is 1.2 cubic miles (4 cubic kilometers) of basalt per century. Using the volume data given earlier in this chapter, how long has the earth taken to create Hawaii? The estimated volume of Olympus Mons, on Mars, is 250 times that of Hawaii. *If* the rate of volcanic extrusion on Mars and Hawaii were the same—at first a dubious assumption—how long did it take Martian volcanic processes to make Olympus Mons? Interestingly, your answer will agree with a date derived from an entirely different line of reasoning.

SUGGESTED READINGS

Bullard, Fred M., 1976, *Volcanoes of the Earth,* Austin, University of Texas Press, 441 pp.
The lore of volcanoes, superbly done.

Green, Jack, and Short, Nicholas M., 1971, *Volcanic Landforms and Surface Features: A Photographic Atlas and Glossary,* New York, Springer-Verlag, 519 pp.
Elegantly illustrated, this is a fine visual and educational treat.

MacDonald, Gordon A., 1972, *Volcanoes,* Englewood Cliffs, N.J., Prentice-Hall, 510 pp.
The authoritative book on volcanism, particularly within the Hawaiian Islands.

Vitaliano, Dorothy B., 1973, *Legends of the Earth: Their Geologic Origins,* Bloomington, Indiana University Press, 305 pp.
Witty, provocative, and thoroughly researched, this is must reading for anyone who delights in the earth.

KEY CONCEPTS

Plutonic rocks
Coarse crystals, slow cooling, chemical differentiation common, intrusive, exposed only after miles of covering rock are stripped away; may be connected with overlying volcanics by dikes and sills; batholiths—margins range from forceful intrusion to gradational.

Fractional crystallization

Process of continual (?) separation of crystals and liquid; observed in modern, cooling lava lakes; observed by crystal separations in many darker rocks; observed in progressive change in lava chemistry from beginning to end of some eruptive cycles.

Volcanic rocks

Fine-grained, rapid cooling, extrusive; produced in belts of volcanic activity and earthquakes; provide both benefits and hazards to us.

Magma

Source several tens of miles (kilometers) within the earth; heat provided by radioactive change and friction of moving earth blocks—our best, tentative theory; formed on many other planets.

A shattered oak near Paso Robles, California, displays beauty in decay. (Photograph by Michael Collier.)

Chapter Four
WEATHERING
the earth in decay

"What greater folly can there be than to call gems, silver, and gold precious, and earth and dirt vile?"
Galileo

The rotting wood, the rusting pipe, the peeling paint, and the shattered street—all these attest to the power of sun, water, and ice to alter everyday things. Whether the alteration is good or bad depends on where you come from; the same farmer that curses the peeling paint gains a living from weathering's child, the soil.

Indeed, soil is one of our greatest national assets; it is the bridge between the world of food and the mineral world. With the exception of seafood, everything we eat comes, in some way, from the soil. Energy is expended in making soil, and energy flows through soils to plants and animals, including humans.

This, then, is a chapter about energy, but not the energy that binds atoms in orderly array (Chapter Two) or the fiery energy of volcanoes (Chapter Three). It is about the energy from the sun, which slowly alters glittering rock to crumbling soil. As suggested earlier, change is part of the natural world.

PERSPECTIVES ON WEATHERING

Our earth is, in its own way, a living entity that responds and transforms from day to day and year to year, just as we do. From our beginning moment, we grow and we metamorphose, or change, and the restless earth beneath our feet is always in revolution. Sometimes the changes are very slow, such as rock crumbling into sand in Death Valley. Sometimes changes are swift, and entire civilizations suffer.

The concept of a cyclic earth suggests that nothing physical is permanent. Each product is the result of a process and the source of an altered future. Weathering of rock is a major process; rates of change may only be visible during a lifetime or may be nearly

invisible over the whole course of human history. Whatever the rate, the process is predictable, because weathering takes place only on the earth's surface and is amenable to study.

One perspective on weathering comes from a twentieth-century French chemist (Henri Louis Le Chatelier), who proposed the following principle to explain many chemical reactions: *a system at equilibrium, if disturbed, reacts so as to regain equilibrium under the new conditions.* At first, this fundamental chemical principle seems simply to govern reactions in someone's test tube, but the earth's rocky surface is also a laboratory.

Le Chatelier's principle applies to *any* system: those who disturb the equilibrium of a wasps' nest are soon made painfully aware of the wasp's effort to minimize the disturbance. The surface of the earth is a scene of unending conflict among the *atmosphere,* the gaseous envelope around the earth, the *hydrosphere,* the water that flows on and within the earth, and the *biosphere,* a collective term for all that lives. Taken together, the combined assault of life, and also that of the omnipresent water, slowly reduce the most impregnable rock to soil. Rock, *a system of minerals,* has been disturbed; soil, a system of new minerals, results. A tree is nature's way of converting the soil into something edible—such as the apple—and we are nature's way of converting the apple to animal flesh. Thus we not only come from the earth, but we also *are* the earth—converted into another of its endless forms. Cyclic change continues.

Weathering is the response of rocky materials to exposure at the earth's surface; the end product is a mantle of loose rock and soil material that is in equilibrium with the surface environment. Le Chatelier predicted the process, because challenge is followed by change. The minerals of rocks formed at higher temperatures and pressures are unstable when exposed to water and life, but their *products,* formed by weathering, are stable on the earth's surface. An old equilibrium was destroyed; a new equilibrium reigns.

The word *weathering* suggests that the process is strongly related to weather and that perhaps the chief controls on weathering intensity and process are directly related to climate, or average weather. Observation of rock weathering suggests that *two controls, temperature and moisture, are dominant.* Temperature yields *two* striking effects. A 10 degree Celsius increase in temperature usually *doubles* the *rate* of any chemical reaction, including the chemical reactions that are a part of weathering on the earth's surface. The organic content of soil also *rises exponentially with temperature,* which leads to increased biochemical activity, since microorganisms gain their nutritional needs directly from the soil's mineral fragments. Water facilitates both mechanical and chemical changes, and each effect enhances the other.

The central theme of weathering is twofold. Weathering is one of many examples of Le Chatelier's principle in geology, because weathering involves a shift in equilibrium as rocks find themselves at the interface between the atmosphere and the rocky crust of the earth. The chief agent in the shifting equilibrium is water; below some threshold value of moisture, weathering does not occur (Figure 4-1). Not only is water a strikingly effective agent of chemical change, but it is also a devastatingly effective agent of mechanical shattering within climatic regions experiencing freeze/thaw cycles.

Mechanical Weathering

Mechanical weathering, the breaking of solid rock into smaller fragments, takes many

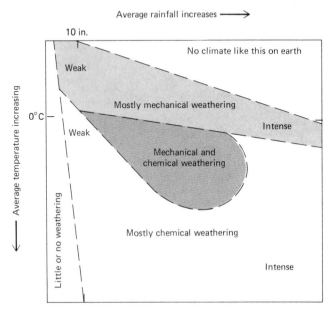

4-1
Weathering types as a function of climate. Notice that the intensity of weathering is controlled more by the amount of liquid water available than by temperature. Mechanical and chemical weathering (the lightly colored area) are jointly effective when temperatures average slightly above freezing in a moderately rainy environment.

forms. Four major categories are (1) shattering of rock by *frost wedging;* (2) rock expansion caused by *unloading;* (3) rock expansion caused by solar *heating, fire,* or *water intake;* and (4) rock shattering caused by *crystal growth.*

Frost Wedging. Imagine a cube of water, 10 inches (25 centimeters) on a side. The total volume is 10^3 inches (16,400 cubic centimeters). Now freeze that cube of water. The freezing results in almost 11^3 inches (21,600 cubic centimeters) of ice! Water is a liquid that has many remarkable characteristics, including its characteristic of expanding when it changes to a solid, unlike any other liquid. Let that water expand in an enclosed space, and the pressures are measured in tons per square inch (metric tons per square centimeter). Water in rock cracks is seldom completely confined, but even a small part of this pressure may exceed the crushing strength of the rock and may cause the rock to shatter on a bitterly cold night. **Frost wedging,** the shattering of solids by growing crystals of ice, is a familiar maintenance problem on streets and curbs. *Frost heaving,* the irregular expansion of soil as ice crystals grow within it, may cause much damage to building foundations, driveways, and roots of plants.

The result of frost wedging is smaller, angular chunks of otherwise unmodified rock. Like other natural forms of weathering that act to break up solid rock (Figure 4-2), frost wedging is one kind of *mechanical weathering.*

Unloading. Ordinary rock is an elastic solid, a fact attested to by anyone who has ever bounced a rock off a solid surface. As an elastic substance, rocks can be compressed into units of lesser volume when sufficiently high forces are employed. Rocks

4-2

Observe the power of a root, here wedging a granite boulder. (Photograph by G. K. Gilbert, U.S. Geological Survey.)

formed deep within the earth experience the weight of overlying rocks from the time of their formation. As the overlying rock is removed by natural erosive processes, the underlying rock expands. Much of the expansion, which is caused by unloading, is taken up by fracturing; this is the only method available near the earth's surface to substances as brittle as rock. These fractures, or cracks, usually roughly parallel the surface of the earth; the spacing between cracks decreases as the earth's surface is reached. Such *sheeting,* or spalling, of rocks (Figure 4-3) near the surface is common and is an effective shattering agent in homogeneous rocks that are undergoing pressure release. In some quarries, as rock is quarried out, expansion of newly exposed rocks is so rapid that "rock bursts" occur and quarry personnel are subjected to rock shrapnel. Rapid removal of load in quarries has repet-

4-3
Unloading fractures in granite,
Yosemite National Park, California.
(Photograph by H. W. Turner, U.S.
Geological Survey.)

itively and dramatically demonstrated the reality of unloading fractures as a major form of mechanical weathering of massive rock.

The concept of unloading fractures is an old one, traceable back to a turn-of-the-century study of the origin of the spectacular granite domes in Yosemite National Park by the American geologist, G. K. Gilbert. Although not everyone today would agree that granite domes are formed by curving sheet joints caused entirely by unloading, the majority of near-surface, subhorizontal fractures in massive rocks are simply sheet joints that reflect the expansion of rock toward the sky.

Volume Change. Still another way to cause rocks to disintegrate naturally may be to heat them during the day by solar radiation and cool them at night, because heat is radiated back into the atmosphere. This concept has received little support from laboratory attempts to duplicate the natural envi-

ronment of diurnal heating and cooling. In the laboratory, rocks subjected to cyclic heating and cooling are apparently unfazed by the experiment, although one experiment showed that they more readily absorbed a dye on their outer surface after such treatment. Perhaps the effect is to promote the entry of water. When water was used as the cooling agent, the effect was far more dramatic, with only a few years of diurnal cycling yielding disruption. Laboratory data suggest that diurnal temperature changes have little effect on natural rocks *unless* moisture is present. Dark-colored rocks may undergo substantially more thermal stress than their light-colored, reflective cousins, so that diurnal temperature cycles can still not be ruled out as a factor that eventually leads to the cracking and disintegration of some rock.

A more dramatic example of disintegration of rock as a result of uneven heating is furnished by rocks exposed to fire. No camper would build a fire directly on mas-

4-4
Disintegrated granite near Midlothian,
Virignia, 1897. (Photograph by J. B.
Woodworth, U.S. Geological Survey.)

sive rock more than once. The rock will soon begin to spall off into knife-edged fragments; the process is near explosive as thin, circular fragments are heated intensely and they explosively expand. The same process on a much larger scale is true of forest fires, where large areas may be intensely heated. Examination of a recently burned-over area will reveal a surface littered with thin, circular rock slivers. Although forest and brush fires seem catastrophic and rare, they were, before we attempted to control them, usually caused by lightning and moderately common, and they burned over huge areas before burning themselves out.

A third method of expansion in rock volume results from **hydration,** the addition of water to the chemical structure of minerals, producing a new mineral of greater volume. The net effect of hydration is to cause the old mineral to swell in size while a new, larger mineral replaces it. Constrained as any mineral is by the other minerals around it, the swelling of minerals causes shattering and displacement of nearby minerals. The result may be a solid rock changed to loosely connected minerals; the material still looks like rock, but any impact completes the process and causes only a granular aggregate to remain. **Granular disintegration** (Figure 4-4) is an early stage in rock weathering and is a bane to those who like to climb rocks, because the rock surface is now loose, crumbly, and covered with natural ball bearings (mineral fragments). The granules are innocent products of chemical weathering, which causes mechanical weathering.

Another effect of hydration of minerals is to promote sheet jointing; water enters the near-surface cracks readily and further enhances the separation of rocks into thin, curving sheets. A term used to describe the collection of processes that cause rocks to spall off into thin, curving layers is **exfoliation** (Figure 4-5). Exfoliation processes may literally be likened to those that cause the earth's surface to peel off like the layers of an onion; they probably include spherical weathering around fractures, expansion caused by unloading, and expansion caused by mineral hydration as major contributors. Whatever the collection of processes, the results remain the same—thin, slabby sheets of loose rock lying on the rock surface.

Crystal Growth. Ice is not the only crystal whose growth causes the destruction of rock. Ordinary rock salt and its soluble associates may crystallize within cracks and pores of rock near the surface, and the effects will be like those of ice. Salt weathering has been described in coastal areas,

4-5
This boulder is slabbing away as result of the addition of water, causing minerals to swell near the surface. (Photograph by J. R. Stacy, U.S. Geological Survey.)

where crystals of salt from seawater help wedge rocks apart, and from arid areas as diverse as Arabia and Antarctica.

Mechanical weathering enhances the other role of water, that of chemical agent, leaching and changing the chemical composition of the minerals that water contacts. One of the simplest methods of increasing the rate of chemical reaction is to break up the reactant into smaller chunks, thus increasing exponentially the surface area that is exposed to attack. For example, break a cube 1 (2½ centimeters) on each side into cubes $\frac{1}{10}$ inch (¼ centimeter) on each side. The surface area exposed *increases 1000 times.* Mechanical weathering, by shattering the rock into many smaller pieces, thus promotes **chemical weathering,** the name given to a group of processes that *change the chemical composition of a rock* in predictable ways. Chemical weathering mostly involves the *addition of water* to the altering minerals within the rock and the concurrent *removal* of various *metals in solution.*

Chemical Weathering

Chemical weathering is dependent on *three* independent variables: *temperature, topography,* and *water. Temperature* increases accelerate the rate of chemical reactions but, at the same time, retard reactions by evaporating water that would have otherwise leached through the zone of weathering. *Water promotes chemical reactions* both by acting as a solvent and a natural acid, but *only* the water that percolates down into the rock material of the earth participates in weathering. Runoff water affects weathering, however, because it erodes and carries away loose, weathered material, always exposing fresh rock to further attack.

Topography is a third variable in chemical weathering. Only in areas of some slope can water constantly carry away the products of weathering while exposing new material to the attack of the elements. In contrast, flat, low areas may receive abundant moisture but, if drainage is sluggish and the products of reactions tend to remain, further breakdown is inhibited.

Chemical weathering consists of a series of chemical processes whose products and reactants can best be expressed in generalized chemical equations. As in any chemical change, for the process to *continue,* the *products* of the reaction must be continually *removed* from the site of reaction. If the products of the reaction are not removed, weathering continues until a mantle of soil is built up; then weathering essentially ceases, because the soil material exposed to the atmosphere is now in equilibrium with the atmosphere, and the potentially reactive rocks beneath are buried under their own alteration products.

A useful concept in analyzing chemical weathering is the **weathering zone,** the part of the exposed rock that is affected by chemical weathering processes. In arid areas, in areas of perpetual below-freezing weather, and on very steep slopes, only a few inches (centimeters) of rock may be slightly altered. Deep, thick weathering zones are more typical of areas of tropical climate, abundant rainfall, and little slope, and soils here may be many yards (meters) thick. The loose blanket of material within the weathering zone may be called **regolith,** or **soil,** to distinguish it from the unaltered bedrock beneath it.

Hydrolysis, solution, and *hydration* (see p. 96) are the three principle modes of chemical weathering; each involves water as the major agent of change. Hydrolysis is a chemical reaction that mostly involves the *exchange* of *metals* in mineral structures with the *hydrogen* of the water. Water may seem to us an innocuous substance and an absolute necessity for all life but, to many rock minerals, it is an agent of change. Extensive, intense weathering needs nothing more than water, rock, warmth, and time.

Hydrolysis. Consider the following series of reactions, given in generalized form, as illustrative of the change of a rock such as granite, which is rich in orthoclase feldspar, to a mound of nearly inert aluminum oxide, which is the product of intense tropical weathering. The reactions are shown in stages. Pure water is the only thing added, and all *soluble* compounds are italicized in the equations. Both mineral names and chemical formulas are given. Note the interchange between the hydrogen (H) of the water and the potassium (K) in the orthoclase feldspar and succeeding minerals.

(1) orthoclase + water $\longrightarrow$
illite + silica and potassium *in solution*
$$3KAlSi_3O_8 + 2H_2O \longrightarrow KAl_2(Al,Si_3)O_{10}(OH)_2 + 6SiO_2 + 2KOH$$

In this first sequence, orthoclase has been changed to a micalike clay, *illite,* and both silica and potassium are removed from the weathering site in solution.

(2) illite + water $\longrightarrow$
kaolinite + potassium *in solution*
$$2KAl_2(Al,Si_3)O_{10}(OH)_2 + 5H_2O \longrightarrow 3Al_2Si_2O_5(OH)_4 + 2KOH$$

The next stage is alteration of illite to *kaolinite,* a clay devoid of potassium, as potassium was removed from the weathering site in solution. Kaolinite is a stable mineral, unless moisture supply is continuous and temperatures are tropical. Under these conditions, the following reaction is completed.

(3) kaolinite + water $\longrightarrow$
gibbsite + silica *in solution*
$$Al_2Si_2O_5(OH)_4 = H_2O \longrightarrow 2Al(OH)_3 + 2SiO_2$$

All that is left is *gibbsite,* which is one of several aluminous oxides and hydroxides in **bauxite,** the world's only current source of aluminum ore.

In the preceding reactions, repetitive changes occur. *Hydrogen atoms replace potassium atoms; both potassium and silica are placed in soluble form and leave the weathering zone.* If they cannot leave because drainage is poor, the soluble products remain, and further stages in weathering are precluded. One can imagine a tropical region with gibbsite (bauxite) on the tops of ridges, kaolinite on hillslopes, and illite in the swamps, where everything from above is being washed in.

Hydrolysis always involves hydrogen as the "invader" that exchanges places with metals such as potassium, sodium, calcium, iron, and magnesium, which leave the weathering zone in solution.

The concentration of hydrogen within the weathering zone is the most fundamental measure of the rate at which hydrolysis may occur. The concentration of available hydrogen within an environment is known as *acidity,* usually expressed as the *pH,* the negative logarithm of hydrogen ion concentration in an environment. The pH number is the inverse of concentration; therefore lower numbers reflect greater concentration, which is typical of acidic environments. We are all familiar with acids, ranging from the powerful acid in car batteries to the sharp taste of vinegar in salad dressings. Vinegar is a weak acid whose pH is not far from that of chemically pure water (pH = 7) and whose name literally means "sour wine."

Clearly, one way of promoting active hydrolysis is to make the environment more acidic; then even more hydrogen is present than when we start with pure water. Nature provides many sources of natural acids, including humic acids, sulfuric acid, and carbonic acid. *Humic acids* are produced when rainwater trickles through decaying vegetation; the resulting complex organic acids may yield pH values as low as 4, which is moderately strong, and leaching (hydrolysis) under a mat of decaying pine needles or oak leaves may be intense. Equally strong acids may be generated by the reaction of water with natural sulfide minerals such as pyrite, as shown in the following equation.

pyrite + water + oxygen $\longrightarrow$
ferrous sulfate and *sulfuric acid*

(4) $2FeS_2 + 2H_2O + 7O_2 \longrightarrow$
$2FeSO_4 + 2H_2SO_4$

Pyrite and its allied sulfides are fairly common minerals, and their exposure to the atmosphere in regions of mining activity may cause stream water to yield pH values near 4. Such high concentrations of hydrogen lead to rapid hydrolysis, intense weathering, and the formation of large volumes of metal-depleted clays.

A third source of natural acid is carbon dioxide, a gas that is naturally present in small amounts in the atmosphere and also produced by rotting vegetation. Rain incorporates carbon dioxide as it falls, *carbonic acid* results, and all rain is thus weakly acidic (pH = 5.7). Carbonic acid is a weak acid that is found in all carbonated soft drinks and beers, and it is the most common acid within the weathering zone. Its chemical activity is low, but carbonic acid is present in large amounts, and its cumulative effect may surpass that of stronger acids.

Although most sources of materials that make rain somewhat acid are natural—including especially the "air pollution" that results from volcanic eruptions (Chapter Three)—a recent study suggests that humans may contribute up to half the potentially corrosive materials in rain. The average acidity of rain has been increasing in recent years over the entire United States; rainfall in Pasadena, California, measured in 1976–1977, yielded average pH values of 3.9. That is approximately 80 times more acid than normal rain measures. Recent studies in the Adirondacks of New York show that pH values in lakes have fallen dramatically in only a few decades; over one-half of the Adirondack lakes restudied now have pH values less than 5. The problem is worldwide; average rainfall pH values between 4 and 4.5 now are common in Europe.

No one can be certain as to the effects of

increasingly acidic rain, but fish kills, damaged vegetation, algal blooms, and severe weathering of buildings have all been described to date. The effects on human health are, quite simply, unknown, but the effects on plant nutriton, element availability from soils, and plant reproduction are all negative.

The source of more and more acidic rain is easy to find. A complex of manufacturing processes adds material to the air that simply was not there a century of "progress" back. The chief villains seem to be the various oxides of sulfur and nitrogen that come, inevitably, from the increased burning of fossil fuels such as coal, oil, and gas (see Chapter Nine). Whatever the cause, we have unknowingly set in motion yet another worldwide environmental change, and the raindrops that fall now are not as pure as they used to be.

Plutarch called the Parthenon, the temple built atop the Acropolis 24 centuries ago, "a spirit impervious to age . . . dressed in the majesty of centuries." For those 24 centuries, Plutarch seemed to be right. Although Romans turned it into a brothel, Christians into a church, and Turks into a powder magazine that blew up in 1687, little seemed to faze the Parthenon. After resisting human onslaughts for 24 centuries, the Parthenon is now crumbling under the automobile exhaust and factory smokestacks of Athens. *Nothing* has equalled the damages of the last 50 years of air pollution and of its gift—acid rain.

The details of sculpture on many faces of the temple whose "spirit is impervious to age" are almost gone; the marble of the Parthenon quite literally drained away in the acid rains. Things were worsened when an earlier attempt at restoration used iron bars for reinforcement; their corrosion hastened the decay of one of our greatest artistic treasures. UNESCO, an agency of the United Nations, is attempting to raise the millions of dollars needed for a wholesale restoration; the price will be only a small token of the worldwide cost of polluting our air.

Solution. Solution of some rock material may be the dominant weathering process. Measurements of the rate at which various metals are taken into solution by hydrolysis suggest that calcium, sodium, and magnesium are the most soluble of the common metals found in ordinary minerals. Potassium is a close fourth, although once it is released from its host mineral by hydrolysis, potassium tends to be strongly *trapped by clay minerals,* where its size and electrical charge cause it to be bound to the surfaces of the clay crystals.

Although sodium and potassium are present in most rocks in roughly equal amounts and are released from minerals in approximately equal quantities, the sea contains 10 times as much sodium as potassium. Sodium enters rivers in their voyage to the sea; potassium is trapped in clay minerals on the land. For humans, the consequences of this fact are fortunate; if potassium were removed by rain as readily as sodium, we would endlessly need to apply potassium fertilizer, only to see it washed away. In the natural world potassium remains with the clays, waiting only for the powerful micro-chemistry of a plant rootlet to snatch it away for the plant's nutritional needs.

Silica (SiO_2) may remain as an essentially insoluble compound in the weathering zone unless water volume and alkalinity are high. Only under intense tropical weathering does silica become soluble, and it enters the streams as dispersed colloids. Iron joins silica in resisting solution, because only in fairly acid, oxygen-free environments will a form of iron become soluble. The ubiquitous presence of oxygen within the weathering zone leaves the iron insoluble; the reddish, orange, and brownish colors of many rocks reflect the rusty colors of oxidized iron. Even though iron is a moderately common element in an average rock, little of it reaches the stream except in acid, stagnant areas. Iron is soon precipitated from the stream as it begins to flow, and we know iron from the rocks around us mostly as a colorful stain.

Aluminum is the most insoluble of all the abundant natural metals; it requires extremely acid or extremely alkaline environments in order to become soluble as a gel or colloidal hydroxide. In normal weathering environments aluminum stays behind after everything else is washed away. In tropical climates temples built of blocks of **laterite,** an alumimous soil, may last for centuries; one example is Angkor Wat in northwestern Cambodia. Structures built of native stone in the same area crumble into decay in a lifetime.

Other forms of solution include the rapid dissolving of deposits of natural rock salt and the less rapid removal of layers of gypsum and limestone. The solution of limestone, a common sedimentary rock, is a particularly important process, because limestone is abundant and frequently exposed at the earth's surface. The solution of limestone requires the presence of carbon dioxide gas in circulating water, a condition that is, as previously observed, quite common. This form of solution has received its own name, **carbonation,** to reflect its importance as an agent of chemical weathering. A typical example of the chemical solution of the mineral calcite, which is the common mineral constituent of the rock limestone, follows.

$$\text{(5)} \quad \begin{aligned} &\text{calcite + carbon dioxide + water} \longrightarrow \\ &\text{soluble calcium bicarbonate} \\ &CaCO_3 + CO_2 + H_2 \longrightarrow \\ &Ca(HCO_3)_2 \end{aligned}$$

Limestone solution is perhaps most familiar to us as the process that forms most caves, but solution is an important process in a variety of different domains. The water we drink may be called "hard"; this reflects the dissolved limestone, as well as other substances, that are objectionably present. Caliche or hardpans in soils are impediments to construction in many arid and semiarid areas; they are also formed by the solution of limy materials and their redeposition by evaporation.

Solution becomes a more and more important agent of chemical weathering as total rainfall rises, because in humid areas the streams may carry more material in solution—the results of *chemical* weathering—than they do insoluble rock and mineral fragments—the products of *mechanical* weathering. Thus the clear stream may be quarrying away the land more rapidly than the muddy one. The clear stream operates by stealth and carries away the land atom by atom, while its muddier cohort puts on a showier display.

A LESSON FROM LE CHATELIER

In many ways, scientific activity can be thought of as creating concepts. Each concept holds together a body of experience, and each concept gives order and a deeper meaning to that experience. As already suggested, science is far more than just a collection of facts; it is an *activity* of finding order among facts. As such, the ordering concepts are creations of the human mind; science is rationally organized experience.

Consider, then, the power of an idea previously discussed. Based on thousands of pieces of human experience, Le Chatelier stated that a system at equilibrium, if disturbed, will react so as to regain equilibrium under the *new* conditions. This guiding principle has allowed us to see weathering as a *response,* not as a fact. Rocks (systems of minerals) *react* when exposed to the atmosphere. The direction of reaction is predictable, using Le Chatelier's model. The rocks will react so as to absorb water and gain volume in the wet, low-pressure environment of the earth's surface.

Now answer the following challenging question. Which minerals, in a rock composed of many minerals, will be *most* reactive? Restated, the question is as follows. If minerals respond to a changed environment, what would make one mineral react more vigorously than another? We now know what we *need* to know—the important first step to an answer.

In a group of minerals that are all the same size and exposed to the same amount of water at the same temperature (notice that a lot of important variables are eliminated), what would make one mineral more unstable than another? This is a still more powerful way of asking the original question.

A tentative idea, based on the phrase "more unstable," comes to mind. If minerals are no longer in equilibrium with their environment, are there *degrees* of disequilibrium or instability? Of course, there are. Both minerals and humans may display a wide *range* of stability or equilibrium.

Therefore, if Le Chatelier's summation of human experience is well founded, the *most* unstable mineral is the one *furtherest* from equilibrium, or the one that is the *most disturbed.* Hence, *it will react first,* because it is the one most "out of step" with its environment.

And what minerals are most "out of step?" Precisely the ones formed at highest temperature, highest pressure, and in the absence of water; in other words, the minerals *formed* and *in equilibrium with* an environment *most unlike the earth's surface* should be the most unstable *on* the earth's surface.

Remember that ideas *are* seductive, and this is a very tentative idea that we have reasoned our way through. To test it we go back to the only real source of authority— the rocks themselves.

We first examine granite, a common igneous rock, in various stages of weathering and disintegration. Slightly weathered granite has turned a bit "chalky," because the feldspars are slowly turning to clay. The micas look considerably more ragged; a pervasive iron stain rings the areas around each flake of biotite. The quartz looks absolutely untouched. Look carefully at granite that is in a more advanced stage of decay; the micas are gone, because long ago they turned to clay and soluble products (see reaction 2). Orthoclase has likewise turned mostly to clay (see reaction 1), and quartz is freed from the minerals that once imprisoned it and forms grains of sand.

Next we will examine *gabbro* and watch its reaction under the *same* conditions that our granitic example endured. Long before the granite even looks chalky, gabbro is in a bad way. Olivine clearly goes first; in its place there is a little clay and some rusty iron stain, and nothing else. The calcium-rich plagioclase feldspars likewise react quickly, forming clay and soluble calcium compounds.

As we expected (and Le Chatelier pre-

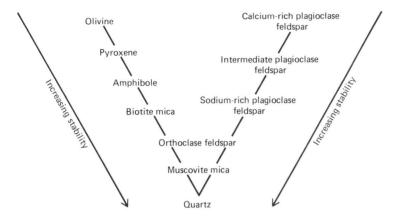

Olivine

Pyroxene

Amphibole

Biotite mica

Calcium-rich plagioclase
feldspar

Intermediate plagioclase
feldspar

Sodium-rich plagioclase
feldspar

Orthoclase feldspar

Muscovite mica

Quartz

Increasing stability

Increasing stability

4-6

Stability of minerals when exposed to the weathering environment. In general, the more silicon the mineral contains, the more stable it is. Quartz, pure silicon dioxide, is most stable of all. Compare with Figure 3-7.

dicted), there *is* a stability series of minerals in relation to chemical weathering. An American geologist, Samuel Goldich, first worked this out, and he published his results in 1938. Figure 4-6 summarizes that work. The form of the diagram is like Bowen's reaction series (Chapter Three); the last minerals to form at the lowest temperature are the least reactive—or most stable—on the earth's surface.

Table 4-1 lays out the "output" side of weathering and answers questions about the products of weathering. As can be seen, the dominant weathering product is clay, a name given to a complex *group* of minerals that are all sheetlike in structure, low in density, rich in aluminum, and often contain some water within their structure. Weathering of any rock containing feldspars, micas, pyroxenes, amphiboles, or olivine always yields the same result—floods of clay, some iron oxides and hydroxides that stain things in shades of yellowish brown or rusty red, and metals *in solution*. If the parent rock con-

tains quartz crystals, sand grains are added to the output.

It is curious that the weathering of complex rocks yields such simple, everyday results—floods of clay, a little iron stain, some quartz sand grains, and soluble metals—and nothing more.

The insoluble minerals produced by chemical weathering are now stable; they persist on the earth's surface. The most abundant—clay—may be picked up by running water and carried away in muddy streams. The clay, which is eventually spread out in layers, makes a *sedimentary* rock called *shale* (see Chapter Five). Quartz grains are also carried along and are slowly abraded and rounded, but they persist chemically unchanged for long periods of time. Layered quartz grains, cemented together, form the *sedimentary* rock called *sandstone* (see Chapter Five). The sand on our beaches usually consists of quartz grains that were set free by the weathering of granitic rocks.

Thus **sedimentary rocks** (that is, rocks

4-1

Products of chemical weathering of common minerals. Notice that clay is the dominant product, while quartz is unchanged. Iron hydroxides are slowly converted to various forms of iron oxide, a strong pigment. The soluble metals, with the exception of most of the potassium, wind up in the world's oceans. Calcium, through both organic and inorganic means, forms limestone. sodium combines with chlorine to make salt; the sea is salty because of the weathering of sodium minerals on the land.

Mineral	Insoluble Product	Soluble Product
Calcium-rich plagioclase feldspar	Clay	Calcium
Intermediate (calcium + sodium) plagioclase feldspar	Clay	Calcium + sodium
Sodium plagioclase feldspar	Clay	Sodium
Orthoclase feldspar	Clay	Potassium
Biotite mica	Clay + iron hydroxide	Potassium
Muscovite mica	Clay	Potassium
Olivine, pyroxene, and amphibole	Clay + iron hydroxide	Magnesium
Quartz	Quartz persists	

composed mostly of grains deposited in layers, usually by water) are one of the *major* products of weathering, and they form part of the basis for Chapter Five. Weathering yields other products. A select group of rather rare minerals also survives weathering as quartz does and persists through great lengths of time; among them are gold, diamond, platinum, and ore minerals of titanium and tin. These select minerals are all extremely stable and extremely dense and, therefore, may be concentrated in eddy currents in running water to form **placers,** which are ore deposits or concentrations produced by the high density and stability of certain rare minerals.

Economically far more important than all the world's gold, diamonds, or platinum, however, is weathering's greatest gift to us—*soil.* Galileo Galilei, perhaps the sixteenth century's greatest physicist, caught the spirit of soil's value in the partial quotation, that opened this chapter. Consider Galileo's views in full.

What greater folly can there be than to call gems, silver, and gold precious, and earth and dirt vile? Do not these persons consider that if there should be as great a scarcity of earth as there is of jewels and precious metals, there could be no prince but would gladly give a heap of diamonds and rubies and many wedges of gold, to purchase only so much earth as should suffice to plant a jasmine in a little pot?

WEATHERING'S ENDOWMENT—SOIL

Weathering seems to us to be a destructive process, because everything that is material fades away with time. Weathering makes a mockery of the phrase " . . . as solid as a rock!" Yet the processes of rock decay yield an unparalleled endowment—soil. Soil is perhaps our most undervalued resource, as the expression " . . . as dirt beneath our feet" makes clear. Soil, like its rocky parent, is simply omnipresent, taken for granted, and ignored.

An evocative phrase better describes soil as the placenta of life. The placenta of higher animals is the organ that acts as a filter and nutrient donor between a mother and her offspring. Soil fills the same role for all continental life, because it forms at the interface between the inorganic mineral world and the world of life. Soil is formed partly by life, contains much that lives and still more that has lived, and is the fundamental resource that supports all that we eat, with the exception of seafood. Soil is at the base of the continental food chain; we are at its peak.

Life is an effective soil-forming agent, and plants are the major contributor. The apparently lifeless encrusting *lichen* is in reality a remarkable pairing of fungus and an alga, which draw their nutrition directly from the rock by secreting acids. Bacteria have been suggested as an important source of chemical decay, as have blue-green algae and diatoms. Mosses often follow lichens, accelerating the rate of soil production and preparing the way for higher plants such as the grasses. The amount of microflora in the soil is surprising; it averages 1 ton per acre (1 metric ton per 4000 square meters) in the upper 4 inches (10 centimeters) of a productive soil in a temperate region. The microorganic world breaks down the dead organic matter that is added naturally to the soil; the result is *humus,* or decayed organic matter. The process of decay is also rebirth; the complex proteins, lipids, and carbohydrates of living matter are broken down again into simpler inorganic compounds and are made available to feed new life. Another function of humus is to cause the soil structure to aggregate and become crumbly; this results in increased aeration and water flow through the soil.

Larger plants, established on a base of soil produced by lichens, mosses, and their kindred lower plants, further modify the soil zone. Large roots penetrate cracks in the underlying rock and wedge the rocks apart; this is a form of mechanical weathering known as **root wedging** (Figure 4-2). Roots add carbon dioxide to the soil; producing carbonic acid which, combined with other acids, stimulates mineral decomposition. Roots also provide channels into the soil for air and water and derive the nutrition for the plant from soluble metals in soil minerals, from the soil water, and from various organic complexes. Plants act to cycle elements from the soil to the earth's surface; the inorganic becomes organic for a time. If the plant is not removed, the elements are recycled back into the soil as humus after the plant's death. If the plant is removed, the animal that takes it away gains some of its nutritive value. If a larger animal eats the first one, the plant's nutrition is passed along again. Human beings stand on top of this chain of food; we eat, but we are not eaten. Nutritional needs may, of course, be satisfied much more directly; the cereal grains and vegetables are, worldwide, our most critical food.

Soils come in many forms, and the term *soil* has different meanings for engineers, farmers, foresters, geologists, and bankers. To the engineer, soil raises problems in slope design and foundation planning; to the farmer, soil is dirt that supports plants; to the forester, soil is the substrate for a renewable resource; to a geologist, soil may just be weathered rock; and, to a banker, soil is an asset whose value is expressed in dollars per acre (square meter). Soil, like rock, has both scientific and pragmatic concerns, and our classifications reflect those viewpoints.

Geologists and soil scientists recognize two major subdivisions of soils, the azonal and zonal soils. **Azonal soils** include two subgroups: (1) *transported soils,* which are either recently washed into place as, for example, soils adjacent to modern rivers, or (2) *immature soils,* which are composed of little-modified rock material. Azonal soils thus represent rocky material that is essentially unmodified by weathering processes or materials that are carried in from a previous site of weathering. As the name implies, azonal soils exhibit little change when examined in a vertical cut; they are almost the same at the top as at the bottom.

Zonal soil groups, in contrast, exhibit changes in appearance from top to bottom—changes produced by the net effect of water, which leaches material from the top layers of the soil and redeposits the leached, soluble material in the underlying layers. Each layer is called a **soil horizon,** this is a zone of relatively homogeneous chemistry, mineralogy, texture, and appearance that is separated from the zones above and below it by measurable changes in the soil's properties. An example of a zonal soil is shown in Figure 4-7; unaltered bedrock is termed the D horizon, moderately altered bedrock is the C horizon. The B horizon represents the *zone of accumulation,* where soluble and insoluble material from the layers above it accrue. The surface horizon is termed the A horizon and represents the *zone of leaching* or loss of both the insoluble clays and the more soluble metallic compounds to the horizons below. The A horizon also may contain large amounts of organic matter, both living and dead; organic matter, formed by the decaying residue of plant and animal life, is strongly concentrated near the surface.

Zonal soils merge imperceptibly with azonal soils, because recently exposed rock

A horizon.
Upper part, very dark brown, rich in humus and clay. Lower part sandy and pale gray. Boundary transitional to horizon beneath.

B horizon.
Yellow-brown, blocky clay. Occasional limestone fragments up to $\frac{1}{2}$ in. Drainage fair, boundary transitional.

C horizon.
Limestone fragments to 3 in. with interspersed deep-orange clay. Boundary transitional.

D horizon.
Mottled, thin-bedded limestone, pale yellow gray. Some $\frac{1}{4}$ in. seams of brownish clay near upper boundary.

4-7
A typical soil profile for a podzol. Notice the transitional boundaries between horizons. (Sketch taken from field notes; area is in southern Dane County, near Madison, Wisconsin.)

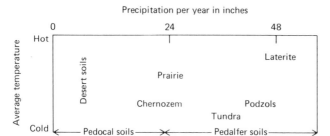

Precipitation per year in inches

4-8
Relation between climate and dominant zonal soil type. Approximately two-thirds of the world's soils are either desert or laterite soils. Both present formidable handicaps to conventional agriculture.

may yield thin soils with only an incipient development of distinguishable zones. The influence of the bedrock is particularly striking in these poorly developed, or immature, soils. Limestone bedrock will yield limy soils, and quartz-rich rocks will yield sandy soils. Soils gain maturity and well-developed zonation after prolonged exposure to the dominant climate, and the influence of the chemistry of the parent bedrock is subdued with time, even though the influence is not erased. Given sufficient time, the development of zonation in soils becomes more striking, and soils formed under the same climate on unlike rock types are similar. The soil is said to be more mature, meaning that its characteristics reflect the climate that formed the soil. Soil maturity is visually reflected in clearcut soil zonation, a sign of modification from an originally homogeneous parent material.

Figure 4-8 illustrates six major zonal soil groups and their relation to climate. Many soil classifications have been proposed; this one is broad and generalized. A still more generalized soil classification breaks soils into only two groups. The **pedalfers** are strongly leached soils composed largely of iron and aluminum oxides; they are characteristically acid and are formed in regions that receive more than 24 inches (60 centimeters) of rain each year. The **pedocals** are soils in which carbonates and sulfates are

dominant; they reflect alkaline conditions and a lack of leaching and are formed in environments that receive less than 24 inches (60 centimeters) of rain per year.

Desert soils are immature soils that consist mostly of mechanically weathered rock fragments. Their environment is one of strong oxidation, little organic matter is present, and iron and manganese deposits, in their oxidized state, provide reddish to brownish surface "varnish" (Figure 4-9) on

4-9
Desert varnish often served as "blackboard" for rock graffiti of all kinds. Here, an early explorer of the West left his mark near Hell Roaring Canyon, Utah. Nearly 150 years later, the inscription, scratched through the old desert varnish, remains unchanged in an arid environment. The rate of varnish formation must be incredibly slow. (Photograph by K. Sawyer, U.S. Geological Survey.)

exposed rock surfaces. Since rainfall averages less than 10 inches (25 centimeters) a year, little leaching occurs; the soil is alkaline and contains soluble alkali metals. The effect of parent material is obvious. Desert soils extend from the equator to the pole; the single distinguishing feature is the paucity of water. Desert soils are too rich in soluble alkalis for most types of plant growth; only salt-tolerant plants may survive. Desert soils are naturally "overfertilized."

Prairie soils are strongly zoned soils that span the boundary between pedocal and pedalfer soil types. In North America, the soils of large parts of the central United States are of the prairie type. As the name implies, these are grassland soils; they have a well-developed, thick, dark, organic-rich A horizon that overlays a clay-enriched light brown B horizon. Both warmth and moisture have been responsible for removing accumulations of calcium carbonate from the soil; this is the major characteristic that sets prairie soils apart from their close associates, the *chernozems*. Chernozems occupy a slightly drier, cooler climatic belt. The soil profile is much like that of a prairie soil, but carbonates are always present in the B horizon. Leaching in chernozems is less complete than in prairie soils. Calcium carbonate is leached from the soil layers above, mostly as the soluble bicarbonate, but it is *redeposited* in the deeper soil layers instead of being flushed all the way through the soil, as in more humid regions.

The zone of carbonate precipitation within the soil reflects incomplete leaching, so the depth to the carbonate horizon—often called the **caliche** zone or **hardpan** layer—is directly related to average rainfall (Figure 4-10). As areas more arid than those in which chernozems soils occur are encountered, the

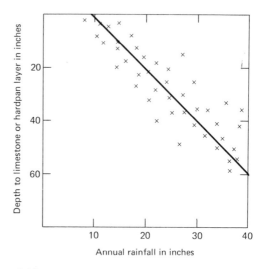

4-10
Relation between average rainfall and depth to top of zone of lime accumulation. Note that in arid areas, the hardpan is near or at the surface; that makes construction difficult. (Adapted from Hans Jenny and Frank Leonard, 1934, *Soil Science, 38,* 363–381, with permission. Copyright © 1934 The Williams & Wilkins Co., Baltimore.)

carbonate layer is found closer and closer to the surface and is joined by more and more soluble salts, including gypsum, and eventually by sodium and potassium salts, which are among the most soluble of all substances. The transition we have described is from the chernozems, which are soils typical of areas of moderate rainfall, to the more and more alkaline soils, to the alkali soils, which are typical of the most intense desert environments.

Both chernozems and prairie soils are widespread soil types; they form in zones of low to moderate rainfall in temperate climatic zones worldwide. The native vegetation over most of these two soil types is grass; they are the most productive soils for farming purposes, because they are only moderately leached, fairly well drained, neither particularly acidic nor alkaline, and contain moderate amounts of organic matter in the A horizon.

In contrast with the prairie and chernozem soils, all the other zonal soils reflect climatic extremes. Desert soils reflect an excess of solubles because of the lack of leaching, *laterite* soils reflect intense leaching in areas of very high rainfall, *podzols* reflect intense *surface* leaching as a result of the acid leaf litter furnished to the soil surface by tree cover, and *tundra* soils reflect soil immaturity in an environment where cold limits chemical weathering rate and waterlogging, because of permafrost beneath the soil, limits the movement of water.

Tundra soils develop in subarctic regions where the ground is not permanently frozen at the surface but where, at some depth down, the ground *does* remain frozen. The result is acid, azonal, waterlogged soil, peat bogs and marshes, and major construction problems in trying to find a stable foundation for buildings in an environment where the soil turns to mush every summer. Arctic areas, perpetually below freezing are, of course, arid areas, so there is no fluid water. The resulting soils are *polar desert soils,* and they are very similar to the soils of Death Valley.

Podzols form in many environments of moderate to high rainfall and are strongly zoned, mature soils. The chief requirement for their formation is abundant, although not tropical, rainfall, good drainage, and trees above the soils to furnish acid tree litter to the soil surface. The resulting soil is characterized by a bleached, nearly white A horizon underlying a mat of partly decayed tree leaf/needle litter on the surface. The B horizon is characterized by a well-developed central zone of abundant iron oxides and aluminous clays of yellow brown to reddish brown color. Podzols are typically thick, strongly zoned, intensely acid soils, best developed on porous parent rock, and closely tied in origin to the trees that grow in the soil that they modify. Podzol is a Russian term, best translated as *ash soil,* which is a descriptive term for the intensely leached and bleached part of the A horizon.

Laterite soil derives its name from the Latin word *later,* a brick, and aptly describes the properties of this soil when it is dry. As previously mentioned, lateritic soils have been cut into blocks and used as building materials in the tropics with great success. Laterites develop in climates characterized by high rainfall, intense leaching, and a strong oxidizing environment. Leaching is so intense that all of the soluble metals are washed away and silica is carried away in solution. What is left behind is the most insoluble of natural materials, iron and aluminum oxides. These are the most intensely leached soils on earth and, therefore, are poor soils for farming. Although not all tropical soils are laterites, large areas of lateritic soil are common in the tropics and form the base of an impoverished agricultural economy. The A horizon is thin and is often composed of concretions of iron and aluminum oxides, the B horizon is thick and composed of concretionary clay, and the underlying C horizon is composed of mottled and bleached zones that grades imperceptibly at many tens of yards (meters) into solid rock. Lateritic soils where the parent rock was rich in feldspar may be nearly pure aluminum oxide; such deposits are mined as aluminum ore.

Soils deserve more than just an occasional

complaint about the dirt beneath our feet; it is the rich, fertile soil of our temperate zone that enables America to feed itself exceptionally well and to export food to the rest of the world as well. If large parts of America were composed of desert soils, tundra soils, or lateritic soils, we would be a nation trading whatever *other* resources we had for food from other countries. Soil is our most basic material resource; for a country to grow into an industrial economy and thereby spread massive amounts of capital among ordinary people, its native soils must be capable of feeding the population after being tended by only a small part of it, the farmers. If we note that the advanced countries of the world are countries devoid of large areas of either desert, laterite, or tundra soils, the "dirt" beneath our feet acquires a value that we may have failed to appreciate fully.

SUMMARY

This chapter is about the radiant energy of our sun, interacting with a water-filled atmosphere and a life-filled rocky crust. Wherever in the natural world there is an *interface*—a contact between unlikes—there is change. As our thin, outer, rocky skin is assaulted by sun, water, growing ice, and clawing life, reaction occurs. The solid products that result are smaller, less dense, metal depleted, and occupy greater volume than their parent material.

Mechanical weathering reduces big rocks to little ones; the ensuing increase in surface area promotes chemical attack. Water entering a crystal may cause it to swell; the result is one form of mechanical weathering. Thus, chemical and mechanical weathering work hand in hand; their chief agent is water since, in the absence of water, there is essentially no weathering.

Weathering, too, is a process of chemical differentiation that is somewhat similar to the chemical differentiation described by N. L. Bowen in Chapter Three. Mechanical weathering, by itself, makes *no* changes in the chemistry of the weathered product, but chemical weathering sends calcium and sodium to the sea while potassium is largely held by clay flakes on the continent. Chemical weathering also sends enormous volumes of clay and somewhat lesser volumes of quartz sand to the sea. Much smaller amounts of oxides and hydroxides of iron are produced; they form powerful pigments in shades of rusty reds, golds, yellow browns, and purples.

Weathering also creates economically valuable deposits that range from placer deposits of glittering gold, diamonds, and platinum to ore deposits of many other metals. In economic terms, the chief product of weathering is soil, whose composition chiefly reflects climate, given a lengthy period of weathering. Soils range from immature desert soils that are overenriched in soluble materials to intensely leached laterites that are overdepleted in soluble materials. It is the soils of the middle ground—the temperate climates—that provide the basic agricultural resource with which the world's hungry can be fed.

Weathering, seen as a response to change, also allows us to predict the stability of minerals; logic and observation both tell us that minerals formed at low temperatures are most stable near the earth's surface, while minerals formed at high temperatures react rapidly. Mineral stability is to weathering, then, the inverse of Bowen's reaction series.

The rate of chemical weathering, worldwide, is accelerating as the products of our industrial revolution fill the sky with acid-producing compounds; the costs of this unthinking experiment are only beginning to be recognized.

EXERCISES

1. Since the moon has essentially no atmosphere, what kinds of weathering could occur on the moon? Which of the three major groups of rock—igneous, sedimentary, and metamorphic—*must* make up the surface of the moon?

2. pH is the common measure of the acidity or alkalinity of any solution, including rain. The pH number is an exponent, which means that a solution at pH = 6 is 10 times as acid as one at pH = 7, the value for pure water. Approximately how many times more acid than pure water is the rain that falls on Pasadena, with an average pH value near 4?

3. The pH value in your stomach may reach 2—so acid that it is capable of dissolving meat. If your stomach routinely digests meat, why doesn't it digest itself? (Ask a doctor!)

4. In a pile of weathered rock debris, predict which minerals, mica, quartz, or amphibole, would form somewhat spherical grains. Why?

5. Some beach sands in Hawaii are composed almost entirely of olivine, yet the climate is tropical, and olivine should be quite unstable. Explain the apparent contradiction.

6. Assuming a desire to be immortalized for as much of forever as is humanly comprehensible, what kind of tombstone should you instruct your heirs to order?

7. As erosive processes remove the uppermost part of a soil, isn't the parent material for the A horizon really the B horizon? Discuss.

8. One geologist called soils "shale factories." Can you suggest the reason for this view?

9. Newly quarried granite increases its strength by fully one-third after being set aside for only 6 months. Can you suggest a reason why?

10. The marble of the Parthenon is an elegant pale pink; rock quarried today from the same quarry that the marble used to build the Parthenon came from is pure white, but contains very small amounts of an iron carbonate mineral. Explain the color change.

SUGGESTED READINGS

Carroll, Dorothy, 1970, *Rock Weathering,* New York, Plenum Press, 203 pp.
    Thorough, readable discussion of chemical weathering and soils.

Goldich, Samuel S., 1938, "A Study in Rock Weathering," *Journal of Geology, 46,* pp. 17–58.
    A detailed study of the chemical changes occurring during weathering; led to concept of stability series.

Keller, Walter D., 1962, *The Principles of Chemical Weathering,* Columbia, Mo., Lucas Bros., 112 pp.
    Understandable discussion of the broad topic by a master teacher.

Loughnan, Frank C., 1969. *Chemical Weathering of the Silicate Minerals,* New York, American Elsevier, 154 pp.
    More technical than the rest and loaded with fine reference material.

Ollier, Cliff, 1969, *Weathering,* New York, American Elsevier, 304 pp.
    Thorough treatment, particularly good discussion of mechanical and biotic weathering.

Winkler, Erhard M., 1973, *Stone: Properties, Durability in Man's Environment,* New York, Springer-Verlag, 230 pp.
    Thorough summary of weathering of worked stone; delightful reading, written by a scientist who has (see his preface) "genuine personal affection for commercial stone."

KEY CONCEPTS

Weathering

A response process.
    Products bulky, of low-density, and water rich.

A chemical differentiation
    Makes the sea more alkaline, the land more acid

Rate of process depends on:

Water availability and acidity; temperature; freeze/thaw cycling; and slope—removal of weathered regolith.

Mineral stability, the reverse of Bowen's reaction series, reflects increasing number and strength of silicon-oxygen bonds in more and more stable minerals.

Soils

Character shaped by bedrock, climate, and time.

Given sufficient time, climate the prevailing influence.

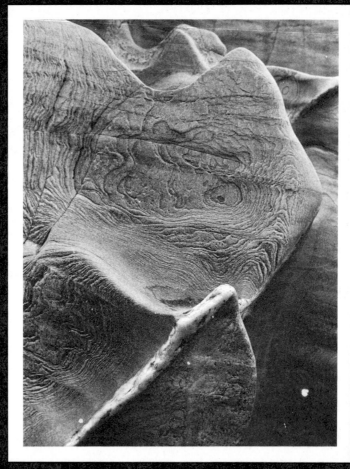

Eighteen million centuries ago, this rock was metamorphosed. Exposed and polished by time and running water into ageless forms, it is still becoming. (Photograph by Michael Collier.)

Chapter Five
SEDIMENTARY AND METAMORPHIC ROCKS

"A handful of sand is an anthology of the universe."
David McCord

Several miles (kilometers) within the earth rocks that are under high temperature and pressure lose their strength and flow like terrestrial taffy; we describe such changes as one kind of *metamorphism.* Many miles (kilometers) above, weathered debris from the continents settles down in a low place and quietly is made into *sedimentary* rock. Each of these changes—at first so unalike—record the earth's endless transformations of its own substance.

Each of these rock-making processes leaves behind many clues in the rocks that are formed; each rock testifies to its own beginning. We will now learn to read these "stories in stones."

ROCKS AT REST

The combined assault of erosive forces bring about 20 billion tons (18 billion metric tons) of material from continent to sea every year. This material is dumped mostly on the **continental shelves,** which are broad, very gently sloping submerged extensions of the continent; their average width is 35 miles (60 kilometers). Water depth over the shelves ranges up to 650 feet (200 meters), and the undulating plain beneath has an average slope of much less than 1 degree.

Waves and currents churn and redistribute the **sediment,** the loose insoluble debris brought to the sea, in layers that are horizontal, or nearly so. In a general way, coarser material remains close to shore, while finer and finer material is carried further out to sea where, in deeper water it, too, may settle to the shelf in horizontal layers and find temporary rest. The path from land to sea may be very long; there are many interruptions as particles are stranded in lakes, sandbars, and other deposits on the continent for pe-

riods of a few seconds to hundreds of thousands of years. One recent estimate of the length of time required for a grain of sand to travel the Mississippi River from Minnesota south to the Gulf of Mexico suggested 2 million years as an average time!

Erosion is the term used to describe *all* the processes that bring weathered debris generally down to lower places on the earth. All of the forms of natural transportation—the agents of erosion—move weathered material from high places to low, so the net motion of sediment is always down, eventually to the oceans.

Sedimentary rocks result from the accumulation and consolidation of both the suspended and dissolved loads that are delivered from the continents to the sea. Sedimentary rocks may be thought of as rocks at rest; they are the product of weathering and erosion acting on the continental rocks above them, and they usually form in the shallow waters of the continental shelf domain. The formation of sedimentary rocks *begins* where weathering and erosion *stop,* when sediment has reached its lowest point.

Smaller amounts of sedimentary rock also form on the continents, but continental sediments are notably transient, exposed as they are to yet another cycle of weathering and erosion. Sites of continental sedimentation include areas near volcanoes, where sedimentary rocks composed largely of volcanic ash, cinders, bombs, and other volcanic debris may form by natural cementation of volcanic fragments. Such hybrid rocks are collectively known as *pyroclastic* (see Chapter Three) rocks, or rocks composed of rock and mineral fragments of volcanic origin, deposited in almost horizontal layers. Other areas include freshwater lakes, where deposits such as *marl,* a type of clay-rich limestone formed where calcium compounds in solution are precipitated by a combination of both organic activity and solar water hearing, may form. Evaporating bodies of seawater and desert alkali lakes form sediments as varied as *borax*, salt *(halite)*, and *gypsum* deposits. Swamps collect partially decayed organic matter; we call the result of many centuries of this accumulation and alteration *peat;* peat may then slowly be altered to *coal*. Glaciers leave behind distinctively modified gravel, sand, silt, and powdered rock deposits that may be cemented into a rock named *tillite*. Many other distinctive continental environments produce a rock that faithfully records their story, both in the appearance, texture, and mineral content of the rock and in the kind of preserved ancient life (**fossils**) that it may contain.

Sedimentary rocks represent the weathered, transported debris of older rocks that are brought to a site of rest and transformed from loose sediment and soluble chemical compound into hard, layered rock. Like igneous rocks, formed from melted older rocks, sedimentary rocks form from weathered, eroded older rocks. How rapidly other rocks of all kinds are converted into sedimentary rocks may be easily estimated.

Recycling the Earth

Inspection of very large areas of the continents will reveal that approximately *two-thirds* of all rocks *exposed to view* are of sedimentary origin. The remaining one-third is divided equally into igneous and metamorphic groups, and the igneous group once again is divided equally into volcanic and plutonic subgroups. Sedimentary rocks are formed on the surface and are also very exposed to view.

Another interesting relation is obtained when one plots the exposed area of sedimentary rocks of different ages (Figure 5-1). The relation between amount of sedimentary rocks exposed and the age of the rock is exponential; the doubling time corresponds to approximately 130 million years. In other words, one-half of all *exposed* sedimentary rock is younger than 130 million years. Of the one-half remaining, one-half of those rocks are between 130 and 260 million years old. Of the one-quarter now remaining, one-half of those rocks are between 260 and 520 million years old. The data present a consistent picture since, in only 130 million years, one-half of all exposed sedimentary rocks is

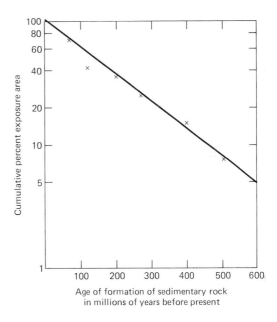

Relation between age of deposition of the sedimentary rock and the amount of it currently exposed. (Adapted from Harvey Blatt and Robert Jones, 1975, *Geological Society of America Bulletin*, p. 1085, with permission.)

recycled into other sedimentary rocks of younger age. The *older* the rock, the *less* its exposed volume, as each 130 million-year cycle gnaws its one-half out of what was left by the previous cycle.

Sedimentary rocks older than 600 million years may be regarded almost as geologic curiosities, because only about 3 percent of exposed rocks of this age are of sedimentary origin. There is another interesting way to look at this information; notice the consistency over 600 million years of earth history of the processes of weathering, erosion, and the formation of sedimentary rocks. Averaged over approximately 130 million years, the "bite" from older rocks has remained, on the average, the same. One-half of older rocks is recycled each long cycle. Hutton's principle of uniformity (see Chapter One) predicted that processes should remain the same all through earth history, but it is surprising to find that the *rate* of process has apparently remained relatively stable throughout a significant portion of geologic time.

Plutonic and metamorphic rocks exhibit an *inverse* relation between exposure area and rock age, as exposure percentage *increases* with progressively older rocks. In contrast with the paucity of sedimentary rocks older than 600 million years, the great *majority* of plutonic and metamorphic rocks are of this venerable age and much older. Since events older than 600 million years comprise nearly seven-eighths of geologic time (see Chapter Eleven), it is not surprising to observe that more than three-quarters of all plutonic and metamorphic rocks falls within that ancient time span. The rate of formation of magma averaged over great lengths of time also seems to remain constant, as does the rate of metamorphic change, which will soon be discussed.

Curiously, *one-half* of all volcanic rocks exposed are *less than* about 70 million years old. Obviously, volcanic rocks often form steep, high slopes of chemically reactive rock and are soon recycled into sedimentary rock. Their plutonic counterparts exhibit the *reverse* relation—plutonic rocks are less and less common among younger rocks. This relation must reflect the great length of time required for erosive agents to strip away the miles (kilometers) of overlying rock that once covered plutonic rock as it cooled.

The fate of rocks becomes a bit more obvious; those poured out on the surface by fire, water, or wind are rapidly (in geologic terms) recycled into other rocks. Those formed deep beneath the earth await millions of years of erosion to lay them open to public view. Bodies of cooling magma are *perhaps* as common now as they ever were, but we see only the volcanic activity far above the cooling magma. Our distant descendants will see the buried "cause" for all the surface displays we see at Yellowstone National Park today.

Classification

Classification of items within the natural world normally implies that we see a "connectedness" between the items. Classification of sedimentary rocks begins with *two* great groups of rocks: (1) those composed mostly of *fragments cemented* together by chemical and organic material, and (2) those composed mostly of chemical and organic material *crystallized* together into rock. These two major groups are transitional to one another.

Rocks composed predominantly of insoluble fragments of minerals, rock fragments, shells, and other organic debris are known as **clastic** rocks (from the Greek *klastos,* which means broken). The fragments are cemented together by various combinations of finer clastic material, chemical substances, and organic material.

Rocks composed mostly of minerals precipitated from water may be thought of as rocks composed of cement, with few clastic fragments to dilute the cement. These rocks are known as **chemical** rocks, and they are held together by interlocking mineral crystals in the same way and for the same reason as the interpenetrating crystals of igneous rocks. In both igneous and chemical sedimentary rocks, crystals precipitate from a fluid; in one case the fluid is hot, in the other it is not.

But we said that classification implies connectedness. Where is the connection between clastic and chemical sedimentary rocks? Both are usually formed in water, and both faithfully reflect the environments in which they form. Clastic sediments reflect sediment brought to a lower point of elevation; chemical sediment reflects the end point of chemical energy, expended on the continents in weathering processes. Both kinds of sedimentary rock represent low points in the cycling of energy on the earth. Once formed, they can only await a change in their position: movement upward brings recycling through weathering and erosion; displacement downward means higher temperatures and pressures and changes that we call either igneous or metamorphic.

Clastic rocks are classified on the basis of dominant grain size; the composition of the individual fragments and the cement are reflected either in modifying adjectives, as calcareous sandstone, or in distinctive names, as in *coquina* (see Table 5-1). Limestones are a challenging group to classify, because

their origin commonly is a mixture of organic and inorganic chemical processes and physical processes that involve the settling out of fragments of carbonate minerals and shells. Tables 5-1 and 5-2 suggest a convenient classification chart for both the clastic and chemical rocks; notice that limestone is present in both charts.

Limestone is the third most abundant sedimentary rock group; the term includes a varied assemblage of rocks whose common ground is composition. All limestones are made of the mineral *calcite* (see Appendix A), which is composed of calcium carbonate. The oceans of the world are close to being saturated with calcium carbonate; this statement simply suggests that ocean water contains about all the calcium bicarbonate (the soluble form) material it can hold. The oceans are close to equilibrium; add more calcium bicarbonate from the rivers of the world, and calcium carbonate will be precipitated from the seawater to settle as limy mud on the shallow ocean floors of the continental shelf. Now the system is back at equilibrium; Le Chatelier's principle has again described a portion of our natural world.

Although this neat picture is true, it does not tell the whole story; calcium carbonate deposition in the sea does not usually occur using the process just described. Both animals and plants extract large volumes of calcium carbonate to build both their skeletons, if they have one, and their homes; after they die, these broken hard parts may also form limestone. Warm, tropical seas are presently the areas of extensive carbonate deposition, although some limestone is being formed in cooler water. The tropical zone is a zone of slight carbonate supersaturation; that is, the seas contain slightly more calcium carbonate than is truly stable in ocean water, and the

5-1

Classification of clastic sedimentary rocks. Terms in parentheses are modifying adjectives for any rock name shown in capital letters.

Dominant Grain Size	Dominant Mineral or Fragment					
		Quartz	Orthoclase	Plagioclase	Calcite	Dolomite	Clay
	Volcanic Rock or Mineral Fragments	(Quartz-ose)	Granitic Rock Fragments (Arkosic)	Dark Volcanic Rock Fragments (Graywacke)	Shell Material (Calcareous)	Shell Material (Dolomitic)	(Argillaceous)
Boulder (256 mm)	Volcanic breccias and agglomerate ↑	Fragments of this size rarely consolidate and form rock. The only significant exception is *tillite,* consolidated glacial debris.					
Gravel (2 mm)	Lapilli	CONGLOMERATE (if fragments are rounded) BRECCIA (if fragments are angular)			COQUINA ↑ (shell hash)		No such rocks
Sand (¹⁄₁₆ mm)	Tuff	SANDSTONE			Calcarenite		
Silt (¹⁄₂₅₆ mm)	Ash	SILTSTONE					
Clay	Ash	No such rocks					CLAY-STONE or SHALE
(¹⁄₂₅₆ mm)					Micrite ↓		

(Pyroclastics — LIMESTONE — DOLOSTONE labels run vertically between columns)

plants and animals are able to remove *calcite* and, more often, its less stable mineral form, *aragonite,* with ease. Plants involved in calcite removal range from algae to thick-leaved aquatic grasses; a similar function is accomplished in freshwater lakes by plants such as the *stonewort.* Animals span the spectrum from microscopic zooplankton to corals, oysters, clams, starfish, and many other invertebrates.

Vertebrates usually remove calcium for use in their skeletons and mostly in the form of calcium fluoro- and hydroxylphosphates—the materials that compose our own bones and teeth. The fluorophosphate is slightly harder than the hydroxylphos-phate; this explains why water with a small amount of fluorine present strengthens our teeth against decay by converting the weaker hydroxylphosphate to the tougher fluorophosphate.

Among the clastic rocks, thinly laminated **shales** and more massive **mudstones** (rocks composed of clay) dominate; clays represent the major insoluble product of weathering (see Chapter Four). These enigmatic rocks are the most plentiful and least well understood of all sedimentary rocks. Their extremely fine grain size makes mineral identification difficult, but it also fosters excellent preservation of any plant or animal debris left buried in the mud. Shales and mudstones

5-2

Classification of chemical and organic sedimentary rocks. In order not to make this table too complex, minor occurrences outside of common environments have been ignored.

Environment of Formation	Dominant Mineral or Minerals							
	Calcite	Dolomite	Gypsum	Halite	Organic Matter	Hematite and Magnetite	Silica	Phosphates
Open ocean	Limestone					Banded iron formation	Diato-mite	
Restricted ocean	Limestone	Dolostone			Rock phosphate			Rock phosphate
Evaporating lagoon		Dolostone	Gypsum					
Intense evaporation			Gypsum	Rock salt				
Freshwater lake	Marl and tufa						Diato-mite	
Swamp					Coal			
Waterfalls and springs	Traver-tine							
Caves	Stalac(g) mites and dripstone							
Hot springs	Traver-tine						Geyser-ite	

are usually formed near the outer edge of the continental shelf, or in deep marine or continental basins—anywhere where currents are weak and fine material can settle out. Not surprisingly, grain size is roughly proportional to current velocity.

Sandstones, clastic rocks that are composed of sand-sized grains, are far more helpful in reconstructing the earth's history. Shales and mudstones tell us that the water in which they formed was little disturbed, but sandstones suggest a far more vigorous environment; their coarser relatives, the **conglomerates** and **breccias** (see Table 5-1), if they formed in the sea, suggest storm conditions and vigorous wave attack. Conglomerates and breccias also suggest a nearby source, and the rock fragments clearly identify the kind of source rock. Sandstones likewise testify as to their parent; a sandstone composed of quartz and orthoclase feldspar grains must have come from a granitic rock, while one composed of dark-colored volcanic rock debris suggests a more basaltic source (see Table 5-1). Coquinas and calcarenites (see Table 5-1) suggest waves crashing against a reef or beach rock, while a sandstone composed exclusively of quartz grains suggests intensive weathering in the source area so that only quartz remained and the clays that were produced were carried much further offshore. Some sandstones are composed entirely of volcanic cinders and ash; we have called these hybrid volcanic-sedimentary rocks *pyroclastics* (see Chapter Three). Pyroclastic rocks fit into no classification scheme easily, but their presence advertises a former volcano, perhaps nearby.

SEDIMENTARY TEXTURES

In the same way that composition of a sedimentary rock yields keys to its ancestry, the textures of sedimentary rocks may provide partial keys to their environment of deposition. Consider a sandstone that is composed entirely of grains of quartz, with each quartz grain essentially the same size as its neighbor. Such a rock could only be formed where the currents that moved and deposited each sand grain were uniform, because logic suggests that the *size* of grains (of equal density) being deposited is a function of the velocity of water or wind.

Where in nature could we find sand with each grain essentially the same size? For anyone who has frolicked on a sandy beach, one answer is obvious; a sandstone composed of grains of equal size (geologists would say the sediment was *well sorted*) might well have formed on a beach. If we examined our sandstone still more carefully and found fossils of burrowing clams, worms, and similar shore creatures, our proposal for the source has gained even greater confidence.

If we add a simple magnifying glass to our arsenal of weapons, we can search for evi-

5-2
The layers in this rock record the annual changes in the chemistry of an ancient freshwater lake (Photograph by W. H. Bradley, U.S. Geological Survey.)

dence on another level of information. Knowledge of a beach environment tells us that waves, crashing on a beach, roll the sand grains around and around. We should somehow expect the sharp corners of the grains to be knocked off in all the turmoil, and inspection of modern beach sand reveals that every grain has been rounded and abraded a bit. Let us look at the individual sand grains in our well-sorted sandstone; perhaps we can be still more confident in our interpretation that the sandstone in our hand was once part of a beach that was exposed to the rolling wave.

A look through our magnifying glass reveals glistening grains of quartz, each grain a bit rounded on its edges and polished somewhat by the natural polish we might have expected in a surf zone. We have read the past; our rock contained history. A well-sorted sandstone, composed of gently rounded and polished grains of quartz, with occasional fossils of burrowing organisms typical of the beach, can confidently be thought of as a fragment of an ancient beach.

Among the other features we notice about our former beach sandstone is the arrangement of layers of sand grains. Again our knowledge of a modern beach suggests what might be seen; as the waves attack the shore daily at slightly different angles and with varying power, the beach swash should lay sand grains in first at one angle and then at another. The layering (Figure 5-2) of grains (geologists call such layering **bedding**) trends first one way and then another. Such confused layering is usually called **cross-bedding** (Figure 5-3), which is a common bedding form in many different varieties of sedimentary rock.

SEDIMENTARY STRUCTURES

Therein lies a caution. **Sedimentary structures** (that is, unique arrangements of layering and layering surfaces) are formed by *processes* and *not by environments*. Unfortunately, similar processes can occur in very different environments and yield similar structures. Consider just cross-bedding; in the natural world cross-bedding is formed near delta (river mouth) margins by underwater sand waves, beach swash, river currents, and wind, to name only a few different environments. Careful analysis of cross-bedding, particularly where three-dimensional views may be obtained, may allow tentative environmental interpretations, but the rocks rarely leave their message that clearly written. More often it is the combination of study of the mineral composition, rock texture, fossils, and structures that may allow us to reason with some confidence our way to an understanding of rock history.

Consider a few more examples. Suppose again that we deal with a well-sorted sandstone, one where fossils, except for a few

5-3
Cross-bedding in modern sediment.
(Photograph by H. E. Malde, U.S.
Geological Survey.)

5-4
Cross-bedding in ancient wind-deposited sandstone forms a cliff in Zion National Park, southern Utah. (Photograph by Michael Collier.)

lizard tracks, are absent. The layering type is again cross-bedding, but now the layering sweeps across the horizon (Figure 5-4) in great swirls; each layer is stacked in at a high angle with respect to the adjacent layer. Examination of individual grains with a magnifying glass reveals that each grain is roughly spherical and that its surface is thoroughly frosted and pitted. What now?

Where in nature can we find piles of well-sorted sand with each grain pitted and frosted? Where can we find an environment where lizards scamper? Those who have lived in deserts have the upper hand in finding an answer; the situation we have de-scribed is typical of modern sand dunes (see Chapter Eight). The great sweeping sheets of sand tell of desert winds, shifting, churning, and playing with the sand that now forms the towering walls of Zion National Park (Figure 5-4).

Examine a few other common sedimentary structures; what could **ripple marks** (Figure 5-5) mean? Anyone who has ever watched a creek flow or wind blow sand around has seen ripples; they usually form as sediment is moved by wind or water from one place to another. But what else do they mean? Analysis of their orientation allows us to tell what direction the wind or water flowed, and detailed analysis may even tell us a bit more about what the transportation agent was and how fast it moved.

Among the more common structures in

5-5
Ripple marks in a former beach sandstone, Jefferson County, Colorado. (Photograph by J. R. Stacy, U.S. Geological Survey.)

5-6

Mudcracks in modern mud. Surface also displays raindrop craters. (Photograph by N. K. Huber, U.S. Geological Survey.)

modern sediment are **mud cracks** (Figure 5-6). These form wherever homogeneous material loses volume; in the case of mud, mud cracks form as muddy sediment dries out. These particular mud cracks record still another event—*raindrop imprints*. Such features are positive proof that the sediment was deposited in a continental environment and consolidated under drying conditions. Curiously, in the absence of raindrop imprints, mud cracks lose most of their environmental meaning, because they have been observed in muddy sediments beneath miles (kilometers) of seawater. Here the mud is often *colloidal* (that is, it forms a natural gel, much like a gelatine dessert), and colloids have the unique property of expelling water even when covered *by* water. You have perhaps noticed this if a gelatin dessert stays

uncovered in your refrigerator; in time, its surface will form "mud" cracks, even if it is covered with water.

FIVE KEYS TO THE PAST

Sedimentary rocks are matchless storytellers. They may speak of ancient seas, towering cliffs, gentle, warm reefs in tropical seas, rushing rivers, stagnant, rotting swamps, grinding glaciers, and desert lakes as easily as you and I can describe what we did a few years ago. The sequence of stories, stacked one on top another, makes a column of rock, which is a vertical newspaper (Figure 5-7) chronicling change, the central theme of the earth's story.

A column of rock seems to be mute, yet

Burrows

There are a few rather well-preserved clam fossils in this white, well-sorted sandstone. Thin-bedded laminar bedding, interrupted by burrows. Sand grains somewhat rounded.

Contact between units gradational.

White, well-sorted sandstone. High-angle cross-bedding. Sand grains well rounded, and surface is frosted. One set of tracks observed on bedding surface.

5-7

Modified from a sketch drawn of a road cut in central Ohio. The rocks are about 450 million years old. After examining the vertical change seen in this column of rocks, describe what was happening here 4.5 million centuries ago.

the keys to millions of centuries of earth history are recorded in columns of rock around the world. As A. N. Whitehead once said, *"it takes an unusual mind to undertake an analysis of the obvious."* Five grand generalizations from a series of unusual minds that analyzed columns of rocks (what could be more obvious than a column of rocks?) allow us to infer the sequence and character of events imprisoned within sedimentary rocks.

The first three generalizations came from Nicolaus Steno, one of the most ingenious minds in geology, as he wondered about the meaning of the constancy of interfacial angles among one type of mineral. Steno also wondered about rocks and, late in the seventeenth century, pointed out three relationships among layered sedimentary rocks that can be thought of as axioms, or obvious truths: *continuity, superposition,* and *original horizontality*. The **principle of continuity** states that sedimentary rocks in three-dimensional view are thin layers that either grade laterally (Figure 5-8) into other sedimentary sheetlike deposits or into areas of nondeposition or eroded source areas.

The **principle of original horizontality** argues that these sheets of loose sediment must have been *deposited* in near-horizontal layers (Figure 5-9), since water-saturated sediment will not stand up on much of a slope. Finally, the **principle of superposition** argues that, demonstrably, the oldest layer in a stack of sheetlike layers is the bottom one (Figure 5-10).

These are simple ideas. What is not obvious to us is their vast break with tradition, because we live in the twentieth and not the seventeenth century. For Steno's contemporaries, these ideas were an extraordinary new analysis of the obvious. How obvious facts are greatly depends on the theories that shape our observation. To Steno's contemporaries, mountains formed when wind blew sand into heaps or giants dropped their accumulated rock collections. Still another contemporary ascribed mountains to the

5-8
This old woodcut illustrates the principle of continuity. The same layer extends from pinnacle to pinnacle off into the distance. Scene near the junction of the Green and Colorado rivers, 1882. (Woodcut by W. H. Holmes, U.S. Geological Survey.)

5-9
Sedimentary layers such as these reflect the operation of three distinct events: (1) deposition of all layers as horizontal sheets of sediment; (2) their consolidation; and (3) tilting of the consolidated layers. (Lithograph from F. W. H. von Trebra, 1785, courtesy of the History of Science Collections, University of Oklahoma Libraries.)

earth soaking up water like a sponge and expanding. In a time of questioning and magic (the Renaissance), Steno's analysis of the obvious demanded patient observation as a substitute for fanciful speculation.

In the eighteenth century James Hutton offered the fourth of our basic principles, the **principle of uniformity** (see Chapter One). Uniformity of process is a fundamental guideline in understanding the earth; it suggests that the products of earth change are related to process as effect is to cause. With

5-10
This woodcut, published in 1882, illustrates the principle of superposition. The darker layers at the base of the pinnacle were deposited before the middle lighter layers, which are, in turn, older than the darker, then lighter, layers above them. (Woodcut by W. H. Holmes, U.S. Geological Survey.)

Hutton's powerful analysis of the obvious, a history of the earth became our heritage. Without uniformity, all we have is uncertainty.

Georges Chrétien Léopold Frédéric Dagobert Cuvier, one of the most remarkable scientists of all time, illuminated the nineteenth century with the fifth great principle applicable to sedimentary rocks. Cuvier was a genius who devoted his busy, organized life to the study of zoology and anatomy. He was an imposing figure with a gigantic head; his brain was a full one-third larger than that of an average person. In 1796, he stunned the world with an announcement of finding fossil *elephants* in the sedimentary rocks near Paris. One set of vertebrate remains was much like, although not identical with, the modern pachyderms, and was found in the river deposits. Another group of remains was found in the underlying gypsum quarries, but these remains were *distinct* from those found in the river valleys. There was a *sharp break* between the groups of fossils found one above the other.

Cuvier had early recognized what later came to be called the **principle of faunal assemblages;** that is, *each layer or strata contained groups of fossils* (called *fauna*) *unique to itself.* In layers of some antiquity, the fossils were unlike modern species but, in layers deposited only recently, the fossils are much like living forms. How did animals change with time?

To answer this puzzling question, Cuvier began studying the rocks around Paris with geologist Alexandre Brongniart, who had succeeded Haüy as professor of mineralogy at the Paris Museum of Natural History. In studying the rocks of the Paris Basin, Cuvier and Brongniart recognized an alternation of marine (deposited in the ocean) and nonmarine beds. The marine limestones were richly fossiliferous, while the freshwater lake sediments contained freshwater clamshells and the bones of vertebrate monsters. Other clay beds were devoid of fossils. Again, each bed had a distinctive assemblage of fossils, and the fossils of younger beds were more like modern life than those of older beds. The principle of faunal assemblages held. But HOW did the animals change through time?

Cuvier had recognized that there was an *order* to vertical change, that fossils that *differed most* from modern life were found in the deepest, hence *oldest,* formations. But why had old species disappeared, never to return? How did new species appear in younger deposits?

What follows is a fascinating example of a man of reason struggling with revolutionary ideas. To believe about 50 years before Darwin and Wallace that species had evolved would have conflicted with what the world believed about the origin of life. Cuvier observed orderly change, but he rebelled at the inference. In 1825, he proposed his own answer. Catastrophe after catastrophe had occurred through the ages, destroying all life. The Noachian flood had been the latest catastrophe, but perhaps not the last. After each deluge, new species of animals had been divinely created, only to be destroyed by the next flood. The world, inundated under roaring seas, was a world of violent change. The world changed; animals did not.

Cuvier's life highlights the struggle between faith and reason in the nineteenth century, much as the lives of Copernicus and Galileo had in the sixteenth century. After noting the possibility of evolution, or orderly change, he denied its existence. Cuvier's animals were the products of revolution, not evolution. His views opposed those of his contemporary, Lamarck, but Cuvier's prestige won him support; a well-founded explanation of evolutionary change in life was first developed about 30 years later by Darwin.

In spite of his refutation of the evolution theory, Cuvier is still remembered as one of the giants of nineteenth-century science. With Brongniart he had tramped the hills and quarries; he recognized that certain fossils were always associated with certain layers and that each layer could be identified by the fossils they contained. Moreover, the *relative* age of each layer could be found by careful study of the fossils they contain, because older layers contain fossils that are progressively distant from their living relatives. This concept, enshrined as the principle of faunal assemblages, gave geology its first clear tool for deciphering both the environment of rock deposition and the relative age of the rock.

The story of the earth could now be told layer by layer. No one could say when the story began, because there were no signposts along the way; it remained for twentieth-century investigations of the phenomenon of radioactivity to give geology the precision of chronologic dates. Cuvier's contribution was a nineteenth-century stepping-stone for those who were curious about the earth. Cuvier and Lamarck had founded the science of **paleontology,** the branch of geology that deals with understanding ancient life.

Geology had received another enduring principle; Steno, Hutton, Cuvier, and Brongniart explored the hills and analyzed the obvious. Cuvier described his method as follows.

These fossils are generally the same in corresponding beds, and present tolerably marked differences of species from one group of beds to another. The char-acteristic fossils of one bed become less abundant in the bed above, and disappear altogether in the others, or are gradually replaced by new fossils which had not previously appeared. It is a method of recognition which up to the present has never deceived us.

Geologists still agree with this 150 years later.

Much like Darwin and Wallace, Cuvier and Brongniart had a contemporary who groped his way to an independent but identical conclusion in England while they studied the rocks of the Paris Basin. *William Smith* (Figure 5-11) was a contemporary of Cuvier, but he was unlike him in nearly every way. Smith was a surveyor of canals; he was mostly self-taught and was not accustomed to mingling with the men of science of his day. Instead, he explored the English hillside, surveying canals and examining the strata (layers of rock) that they crossed. His study of the rocks led him to the same concept as Cuvier—"Each stratum contained organized fossils peculiar to itself." In 1815, he financed and published the first geologic map of England. A year later he published his *Strata Identified by Organized Fossils,* a book of careful line drawings of fossils printed on paper that was the color of the rock unit that normally contained them (Figure 5-12).

Smith worked alone and without financial support. The publication of his pioneering map and fossil catalog left him destitute. His priceless collection of British fossils was auctioned off and his house was sold to pay the printer. What remained was a stunning contribution by a man of great ability, modesty, and intensity. Cuvier and Brongniart had the best of French science at their disposal; Smith had only his notebook and an

5-11
William Smith. Frontispiece from *Strata Identified by Organized Fossils,* published in 1816. Trained as a civil engineer, Smith was particularly interested in the use to which each of the rock layers might be put. (Courtesy of the History of Science Collections, University of Oklahoma Libraries.)

among stratified (layered) sedimentary rocks.

The principles of *superposition, continuity, faunal assemblage, original horizontality,* and *uniformity* are the underlying assumptions in the history in sedimentary rocks. The rocks were mute before there were reasoning humans. Only people could examine a limestone and read the epitaph. Only a person could study grains of sand and hear the pounding waves. Only unique human beings would analyze the obvious.

METAMORPHISM—SOLIDS AS FLUIDS

The stories written in sedimentary rocks are not difficult to comprehend; the processes that form them and the modern environments of their formation are open to anyone's inspection on the surface of the earth. Intuitively as well as by laboratory demonstration, one can imagine loose sediment buried under many miles of sand, mud, and lime and slowly changed by pressure and natural cement into hard rock, a process of rock making that goes on today. The change from loose sediment to coherent rock is gradual, and sedimentary material may be found in all stages of change from recent sedimentary rock, which can still best be handled with a shovel or pick, to rock that yields only to a sledgehammer and steel.

What happens if sedimentary material is buried still deeper in our unsettled earth? The changes that take place are literally out of our sight and our minds. One change is obvious, however; somewhere, somehow, deep within the outer shell of the earth, rock material is melted (see Chapter Three), and some of the *igneous* (melted) material is fed to the surface of the earth as lava. *Weath-*

inquiring mind. They came to the same conclusion and published their results within a few years of one another. It is doubtful that the French scientists and the self-taught canal engineer ever met, but they jointly published geologic maps and recognized an obvious, powerful idea. In Smith's own words, "the same species of fossils are found in the same strata, even at a wide distance." Smith was the founder of the science of **stratigraphy,** the branch of geology that deals with both time and space relations

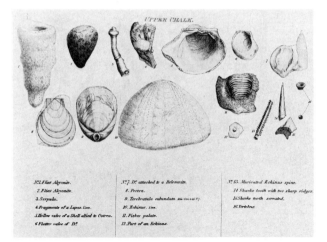

ering, erosion, sediment, and *soil* are a few of the names that previously identified changes in solid rocks near or on the surface. **Metamorphism,** a new word, describes changes in solid rocks within the earth as they respond to pressure and temperature regimes well above those required to make them sedimentary rocks and below those required to melt them (Figure 5-13).

Classification

Metamorphic rocks come in many guises, since many kinds of change may be called metamorphic. Rocks sheared and granulated along major zones of earth movement adopt a smeared and streaky appearance (Figure 5-14) and constitute a minor group of metamorphic rocks known as *cataclastic* rocks. Another type of cataclastic change known as *shock metamorphism* occurs around meteorite impact areas, for example, where new, abnormally dense minerals are formed during a brief episode of extreme pressure.

Contact, or *thermal, metamorphism* (Figure 5-13) occurs when magma intrudes reactive preexisting rocks; the resulting rock is baked into a natural brick, and minerals develop that are more stable at the higher temperature the rock endured. In each of these minor kinds of metamorphism the rock is changed and the agent of change leaves an unmistakable stamp. Sheared and granulated rocks, shocked rocks, and baked clinkery rocks tell their story easily and are often found adjacent to the source of the energy that changed them.

A third type of metamorphism is more enigmatic; *burial metamorphism* produces changes in rock by the application of high pressure in an environment of comparatively low temperature. High-pressure, low-temperature environments within the earth were difficult to understand until the concept of *plate tectonics,* discussed in the next two chapters, allowed us to view old information in a new light. The rocks produced are characterized by a bluish amphibole; they are often collectively termed *blueschists.* These colorful rocks establish an unusual environ-

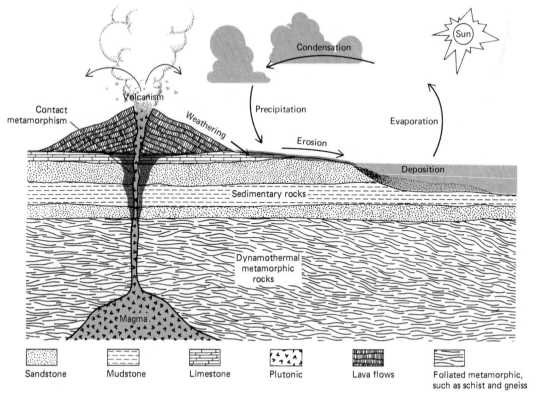

Labels within figure:
Volcanism
Contact metamorphism
Weathering
Condensation
Sun
Precipitation
Evaporation
Erosion
Deposition
Sedimentary rocks
Dynamothermal metamorphic rocks
Magma

Legend:
Sandstone
Mudstone
Limestone
Plutonic
Lava flows
Foliated metamorphic, such as schist and gneiss

5-13
Summary of the major rock-forming processes.

ment that we will discuss again in Chapter Seven.

The majority of metamorphic rocks that we see are produced by *regional* or *dynamothermal metamorphism;* the former emphasizes the observation that these rocks are observed over large areas, and the latter suggests that they are formed by the application of both heat and pressure. Dynamothermal rocks occupy a position within the earth's outer crust midway between sedimentary activity at the surface and igneous activity many miles down; they are also intermediate between the high temperatures whose ef-

fects we know as contact metamorphism and the high pressures whose effects we see as burial metamorphism (Figure 5-15).

Texture

As we have seen, the texture of a rock is the size, shape, and arrangement of the particles or crystals that compose a rock. The texture of an igneous rock is usually crystalline, and it is the interlocking of mineral crystals that make igneous rocks hard and resistant to breakage. Crystalline sedimentary rocks,

5-14
A cataclastic gneiss. Notice the streaky, "smeared" appearance, typical of cataclastic rocks. Ruler is 6 inches (15 centimeters) long; gneiss is exposed in Haywood County, North Carolina. (Photograph by J. B. Hadley, U.S. Geological Survey.)

locking crystals of calcite and is used in building as an ornamental stone, for table-tops and wall paneling, for monument stones, and for ashtrays, is the most common.

Careful study of a marble will reveal that we cannot carry our textural comparison with igneous or chemical sedimentary rocks too far; although all three groups of rocks are composed of interlocking crystals, the calcite or dolomite (a magnesium-rich calcite) crystals in the marble all seem to have formed and grown *at the same time*. In plutonic igneous rocks, early minerals compete for space as they crystallize from a fluid. Early minerals exhibit well-formed crystal shapes; later minerals simply take whatever space is left. Similar events may occur in the formation of chemical sedimentary rocks as various minerals crystallize from colder

like some limestones and many evaporites, form when crystals precipitate from a fluid and interlock. Clastic textures characterize the majority of sedimentary rocks and are the result of fragments cemented together by natural cement.

Metamorphic rocks, like their chemical sedimentary and igneous kin, also exhibit textures typified by interlocking crystals that also often make these rocks tough and resistant to breakage. The rock is a mixture of random crystals that are intergrown with one another. Such a rock is called **nonfoliated** if it is of metamorphic origin; the name describes a rock that does not exhibit any kind of alignment of crystals but, instead, is massive and homogeneous. Many kinds of nonfoliated metamorphic rocks are familiar to us. *Marble,* which is composed of inter-

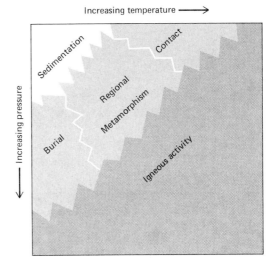

5-15
Domains of sedimentary, igneous, and metamorphic activity. All boundaries are gradational.

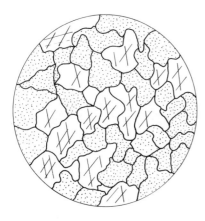

5-16

Sketch of texture common to many nonfoliated metamorphic rocks. This example is a marble; notice that all of the crystals of calcite are of approximately equal size and that every crystal interpenetrates its neighbors so that the overall texture is something like that of a jigsaw puzzle. This texture is the result of crystals growing at the same time and competing for space among themselves. Compare with Figure 3-6.

fluids. In nonfoliated metamorphic rocks, most of the crystals are of the same size and exhibit interpenetrating, mutual boundaries (Figure 5-16). How, then, does marble form?

The answer, again, is found in studying the earth itself. By the end of the eighteenth century, Giovanni Arduino, professor of mineralogy at the University of Padua, had suggested that marble was limestone " . . . endowed by heat with peculiar properties." Others recognized that marble seemed to be altered limestone; in some areas a careful observer could trace a layer of limestone and watch it change gradually into glistening, crystalline marble. In the mid-eighteenth century Hutton, in Scotland, had repeatedly recognized the profound changes taking

place in rocks adjacent to igneous intrusions and correctly interpreted contact metamorphism as evidence of the heat and fluidity of igneous rocks. Many nonfoliated metamorphic rocks gain their crystalline texture by little more than the application of heat; others adopt similar textures under the influence of both heat and pressure.

The answer to the mystery of metamorphic textures is found in simple principles of chemistry and physics that are newly applied. We all know that finely ground material is more chemically reactive than the same material in much coarser chunks, and sedimentary rocks are made largely of finely ground material. Add heat, or heat and pressure, and a generous helping of naturally occurring water, and reactions begin to occur between the mineral grains of the rock WHILE THEY REMAIN SOLID. Finely divided material is naturally reactive; heat and pressure provide the energy to cause new minerals to form and grow when the pressure and temperature stability limits of the old mineral are exceeded. The process of crystal growth in a solid substance is not a familiar one to us, and we must turn to the science of metallurgy for an example; here the process of *annealing* mimics its natural analog. Geologists call crystal growth in solids **recrystallization**.

Heating powdered metal causes the shredded grains to begin reacting (annealing) with one another; the rate of reaction decreases as size increases. Grain runs into grain, mutual boundaries are established and, as the source of heat energy slowly dies away, a new equilibrium is established. Once again, process is parent to product; recrystallization produces a rock composed of crystals that have grown larger, but fewer in number—crystals that have fought among themselves for room and established territorial boundaries mutually acceptable to the energy needs of each crystal.

Foliated metamorphic rocks may form under the same environment as nonfoliated rocks but, as the name implies, foliated rocks *exhibit alignment of crystals* as masses of sheetlike or rodlike minerals. The layering that is produced is analogous to the bedding or stratification of sedimentary rocks, but sediments are layered under the influence of gravity, while foliated rocks are layered under the influence of forces brought about by disturbances within the earth that presumably are related to uneven heating and cooling of rock masses.

Such forces brought to bear on rocks whose composition causes them to yield only minerals such as feldspar, quartz, olivine, and pyroxene produce random orientations of these box-shaped minerals in a *nonfoliated* crystalline rock. If the original rock is rich in the constituents that might form micas, amphiboles, or similar flaky or needlelike minerals, the basis is there for the formation of *foliated* rocks.

Foliated rocks form when growing minerals align themselves roughly perpendicular to the dominant pressure. The alignment is predictable, because less energy is expended by the minerals growing at 90 degrees to the dominant force; however, minerals experiencing the full effect of the force become unstable (Figure 5-17). The observation that solids alter under pressure is, again, not a common one, at least at first. An experiment is necessary to illustrate, only by analogy, the phenomenon. Take a large block of ice that is at least the size of your hand and set the heaviest weight you can find on top of it. Place the ice and weight away from any source of extra heat or wind, and come back

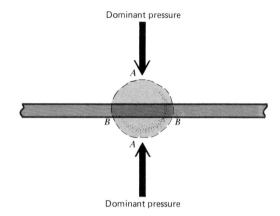

Dominant pressure

Dominant pressure

5-17
Under high pressure a mineral—shown with dashed line boundaries—dissolves at points A (the areas of highest pressure). The dissolved mineral material is redeposited in the areas of lowest pressure—points B. As this process of pressure solution and redeposition continues, the "old" mineral gradually assumes the form shown in color. Repeated many times with each mineral grain, the result is a foliated rock.

in ½ to 1 hour. The weight will have melted its way into the ice; given enough time, it may melt its way all the way through the opposite side of the block.

Table 5-3 is a common classification of metamorphic rocks. Perhaps the only surprise in the table is that granite is listed again; it was classified as an igneous rock in Chapter Three. Like many pyroclastic rocks, granite is also a hybrid. As previously described, in some areas granite makes abrupt contacts with the surrounding rocks, tearing them up and baking them into contact metamorphic rocks. These effects led Hutton to conclude 200 years ago that granite is an igneous rock; the same observations in other places lead to the same conclusions

5-3
Classification Chart of Common Metamorphic Rocks

Texture	Composition and Parent Rock Material				
	Clay-Rich (shales)	Quartz-Rich (sandstones)	Orthoclase-Rich (arkose)	Calcite-Rich (limestone)	Dark Volcanics or Graywacke
NONFOLIATED					
(Thermal)	Andalusite hornfels	Quartzite	—	Marble	Pyroxene hornfels
FOLIATED					
Slaty	Slate	—	—	—	Talc schist/ greenschist
Schistose	Phyllite/ mica schist	—	—	—	Blueschists at high pressure
					Epidote amphibolite
Gneissose	Gneiss	—	Gneiss	—	Amphibolite
Granulose	Granite	—	Granite	—	Pyroxene granulite

today. In other areas it is much less clear that granitic rocks were ever wholly fluid, since they may grade slowly into normally foliated metamorphic rocks. These granites seem to have formed at great depths through changes that took place mostly in the solid state and, thereafter, never moved.

The question of the origin of granite is a lively controversy within the science of geology and has been so for a century or more but, as geologist H. H. Read said in *The Granite Controversy* (1948), it simply seems that "there are granites and there are granites." Each exposure of granite must be carefully examined for evidence of fluidity and forceful intrusion. If both criteria are found, the granite is, by definition, undoubtedly igneous. If both criteria are absent, the granite is, by definition, an example of a remarkably intense metamorphism. If only one criterion can be found or if the evidence for each one is poorly developed, we have a controversy, one what sustains many field

and laboratory discussions among modern geologists. Perhaps we would be much better off if we had accepted the original definition of granite by Caeselpinus in 1596; he simply defined it as *"a grained rock,"* which is what the name granite *literally* means.

Another controversial rock in Table 5-3 is *slate*. Slate is a strongly foliated rock composed mostly of a flaky, claylike mineral called *illite* (see Chapter Four) and of poorly formed micas. Its mineral content hardly suggests metamorphism, since the minerals in a slate are typical of those in many sedimentary rocks. The change seems to have been *largely* textural, with little recrystallization or mineral change. Carefully documented field studies from many parts of the world indicate that slates seem to form when pressure is exerted on muddy sediments that contain a great deal of water. As the sediment is compressed, large volumes of water are lost, and the flaky minerals within slate are aligned as the water leaves. Slate, then,

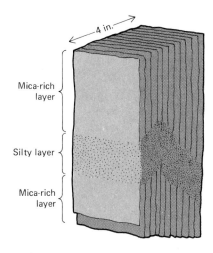

Mica-rich layer

Silty layer

Mica-rich layer

5-18

An example of slaty cleavage. This sketch, taken from field notes, is of some slightly metamorphosed sedimentary rocks, known as the Knife Lake group, that are exposed near Ely, Minnesota. Notice that the planes of slaty cleavage, which are vertical in this sketch, offset formerly horizontal *relict* (original) sedimentary bedding. The bedding must have originally been alternating layers of siltstone and shale. Slaty cleavage is well developed in the mica-rich layers but nearly absent in the silty layers.

has acquired a new texture under environments more characteristic of the compaction and water-loss processes that are typical of many sedimentary rocks. Thus, slate, too, is a hybrid but is conventionally described as a metamorphic rock, not a sedimentary one, because the formation of the new foliated texture obliterates part or all of the stratified or bedded texture that preceded it.

We take advantage of the strongly foliated texture of slate to split it into thin sheets and use it as roofing, flooring, blackboards, and foundations for pool tables. Slate readily breaks, or cleaves, parallel to its newly

found texture (Figure 5-18); slate displays **rock cleavage** or **slaty cleavage.** Both terms imply that slate, the rock, has within it planes of easy breakage that are comparable to the mineral cleavage discussed in Chapter Two. Rock cleavage is, of course, parallel to mineral cleavage in this case and is caused by the strong alignment of uncounted numbers of clay and mica flakes whose *mineral* cleavages are parallel planes of *rock* cleavage.

The minerals within contact and regional metamorphic rocks reflect the power of earth forces, which may cause them to grow in orientations normal to the forces, and the chemical content of the parent rock and the pressure and temperature environment that formed the new assemblage of minerals. Each assemblage of minerals in a metamorphic rock is as diagnostic of both the chemistry of the parent rock and the environment of metamorphism as are the assemblages of fossils in sedimentary rocks. Metamorphic mineral assemblages, like fossils, accurately reflect their environment to those who are able to interpret them.

The *foliation* of metamorphic rocks that are coarser grained than slate has received a special name, **schistosity,** to set both its appearance and its mode of origin apart from slaty cleavage. The schistosity of *phyllites* and *schists* (Appendix C) and the coarse schistosity of *gneisses* (Table 5-3) form from true recrystallization of old minerals into new ones that are strongly aligned perpendicular to the dominant pressure (Figure 5-19). There is much evidence that these schistose rocks flowed while they were solid (Figure 5-20) in a direction normal to pressure, much as modeling clay or silicone "Silly Putty" will slowly flow away horizontally from pressure exerted vertically on it. Again, our experience with solids that flow

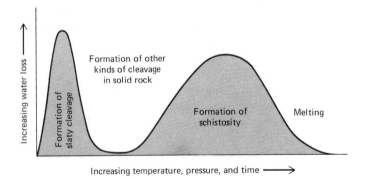

5-19
Environments for the formation of slaty cleavage and schistosity. The buried sediment is capable of responding as a fluid *three* times during its burial: (1) as the sediment loses water; (2) as the material is recrystallized while solid; and (3) as it is melted. All flowage taking place under the melting point results in aligned minerals—a texture called *foliation.* (Modified from John Maxwell, 1962, Fig. 12, *Geological Society of America Bulletin.*)

like fluids is minimal, and the concept of a fluid solid seems to be a contradiction. We once again look to the natural world for an example.

What Is a Solid?

The expression "slow as molasses in January" instinctively suggests that the rate of flow of a fluid diminishes as temperature drops. The next point is difficult to make because we have been taught since grade school that as temperature drops *below freezing,* all fluid motion in material stops, and we call the material a *solid.* Solids do not flow; fluids do. But what *is* a solid? A block of ordinary canning paraffin is a solid. If you drop it on the floor it will either bounce or break; both reactions are characteristic of solid things. But hold paraffin in

your hands, warm it a bit, and work gently with it; solid paraffin is soon deformed into folded paraffin, and a solid has flowed.

Other solids that flow in our experience include asphalt roads on hot, summer days, glaciers, glass, and even rock, the epitome of solidarity. Glaciers are simply frozen rivers of ice that move majestically down valleys a few yards (meters) a year. Thick glass windowpanes are thicker at the bottom than at the top after many years, a phenomenon that is observable in nearly any house more than 50 years old. The expression "solid as a rock" has also been nullified. Look at a marble bench in an old cemetery, an old campus, or an old public building; they all have sagged under their own weight. Rock salt flows so readily under the weight of overlying rocks that is has made *intrusive* domes in the soft sedimentary rocks of our Gulf Coast areas (Figure 5-21) and shattered the overlying rocks exactly as an igneous

5-20

Here is an example of a gneiss whose origin is a hybrid of igneous and metamorphic processes. The gneissic foliation is somewhat contorted; the rock may have been partially molten. (Photograph by J. B. Hadley, U.S. Geological Survey.)

intrusive would. The only difference is the flowing salt is cold, while magma is obviously above its freezing point. Gypsum rock has made extrusive "volcanoes" in parts of Utah and Iran; every element was there except any evidence of heat. The gypsum flowed while it was solid and cold.

What is a solid? It is something that does not flow DURING OUR EXPERIENCE WITH IT. A new element, TIME, enters our understanding of a solid.

We experience many examples of solid fluids. Ordinary wall paint is just one example. If paint were a true fluid, as soon as you put it on a vertical wall, it would run right off the wall under the influence of gravity. If paint were a solid, we would not be able to get it on the wall in the first place. Is paint a fluid or a solid? You decide.

Perhaps the most familiar example of the variable behavior of materials is furnished by Silly Putty. Dropped on the floor, it will bounce; it is an elastic solid. Left on the floor, it flows; it is a viscous fluid. Struck

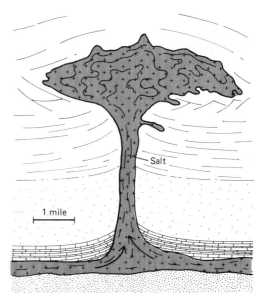

5-21

A cross section of a hypothetical area containing a salt dome. The bedded salt is of lower density than the surrounding sedimentary rocks. When placed under sufficient pressure, the salt heads upward and behaves like any other intrusive mass, except that it is well below its melting point. The layering preserved in the upper part of a salt dome is highly convoluted, reminding one of the whirling patterns formed in scum on a slowly flowing river.

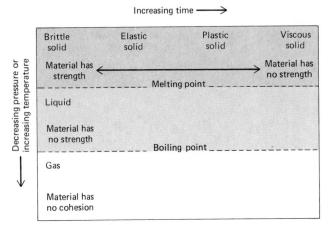

Increasing time ⟶

	Brittle solid	Elastic solid	Plastic solid	Viscous solid
Decreasing pressure or increasing temperature	Material has strength	⟵	⟶	Material has no strength

Melting point ‒ ‒ ‒ ‒ ‒ ‒ ‒ ‒

Liquid

Material has no strength

Boiling point ‒ ‒ ‒ ‒ ‒ ‒ ‒ ‒

Gas

Material has no cohesion

5-22
The behavior of matter. We are accustomed to thinking of material in terms of thermal boundaries (at constant pressure); these boundaries are reflected in the horizontal lines on the graph. Our speech also incorporates these boundaries; even a small child knows that ice is a solid, water a liquid, and steam a gas. Examine this graph for a minute, and surprising ideas occur. For example, expose ordinary water to a high-frequency vibration (very *short* stress duration) and it should *behave as a solid* according to this chart. In fact, it does; it *shatters.* You can do the experiment yourself in a well-equipped physics laboratory. (Graph much modified from S. Warren Carey, 1954. Published with permission of Geological Society of Australia Incorporated.)

with a hammer, it shatters; it is a brittle solid. What *is* Silly Putty? Notice that our terms solid and fluid describe *behavior* and, as with people, behavior changes with the way we are treated. The only thing we have changed with Silly Putty is the RATE at which we applied force. Rapid changes (a hammer blow) bring brittle behavior, while very slow changes cause the behavior to be fluid. There is a spectrum of behavior in materials; the changes from one form of behavior to another are marked by temperature and also by rate (time).

Figure 5-22 suggests a new classification of the way we view matter; it also suggests that we can now understand why metamorphic rocks exhibit evidence that they flowed even when they were solid. The concept of a solid behaving as a fluid under long-enduring pressure is a critical concept in geology; the next two chapters amplify this concept

and use it to explain the origin of earthquakes and continental motion.

METAMORPHISM AND WEATHERING— A STUDY IN CONTRAST

The central theme of the last few chapters is that the result of change always contains clues to the agent of change; that is, product reflects process. Among the agents of change that we have discussed, two, weathering and metamorphism, help to illustrate this relation. In the earlier part of this century weathering was simply regarded as one kind of metamorphism that involved the change of rock under low pressure and temperature; the other type of metamorphism required elevated temperature and pressure. Early geologists recognized that BOTH changes were metamorphic; that is, they involved *changes* in the mineralogy and texture of the rock.

Today the study of weathering is a science on its own (Chapter Four), and the process is studied by both geologists and *pedologists* (soil scientists). The field of metamorphic study has likewise narrowed to include only the processes that operate at higher temperatures and pressures. This reflects the normal evolutionary course of any science. An area of inquiry is established that results from the curiosity of human beings about how things work. The obvious is analyzed, beginning with an observation and description of the way things are. Classification follows as facts and observations are grouped together in a search for repetitive relations. Insights and inferences are developed, and abstractions, often stated in mathematical terms, ensue.

All science follows the same orderly developmental route. We have watched people as diverse as Steno, Hutton, Cuvier, and Smith struggle with the complex questions posed by the rocks and minerals of our earth. They encountered false starts, lucky accidents, flashes of genius, dead-ended research, and stubborn clinging to demonstrably untrue ideas—all the normal reflections of human nature behind the intensely human activity we call science.

Lucky accidents, followed by shrewd observation, abound. Sir Alexander Fleming discovered penicillin after leaving a petri dish covered with nutrient solution open in the laboratory; he then recognized that some strange mold was destroying the staphylococcus colony that was growing in the dish. The discoverer of streptomycin was studying poultry mouth diseases; sulfa drugs were discovered in the search for a better dye; and cortisone was the result of a secret intelligence investigation into the dietary consumption of enemy pilots. Our potential ability to modify earthquakes hinges on the recognition by a seasoned geologist, Charles Evans, that earthquakes in Denver occurred when contaminated waste water was pumped under high pressure into rocks deep beneath an Army proving ground.

Our investigation of the earth moves fitfully, but the preceding pattern can always be recognized. A study begins with, and is followed by, observation and classification. These early descriptive stages are followed by attempts at generalizations to explain large masses of descriptive information; one such example of a grand generalization is the plate tectonics model described in Chapter Seven. As the available information grows, another trend is discernible: each science splits into smaller subfields of inquiry as the information available exceeds the capacity of individuals to comprehend it all. We live today in the midst of the greatest explosive growth of scientific knowledge in human history; more than one-half of the scientists who have ever lived are alive today (Figure 1-5). The fragmentation of scientific knowledge is inevitable, and the split between those who study weathering processes and those who study metamorphic processes within the earth was a normal part of the increase in the quantity of scientific knowledge.

Compare the *products* that result from these two opposing processes, and the relation between result and agent is illuminated (Table 5-4). Each rock, each mineral, each bit of soil tells a story of unending reconstruction of what came before.

Consider a rock composed of coarse, glittering flakes of mica aligned in densely packed, crumpled rows; it yields stories of

5-4
Comparison of Weathering and Metamorphism

Measurable Quantity in 1 Cubic Inch of Rock	Effect of Weathering	Effect of Metamorphism
Total rock volume	Increases	Decreases
Average rock density	Decreases	Increases
Average grain size	Decreases	Increases
Average metal content	Decreases	Increases
Average water content	Increases	Decreases
Grain surface area exposed	Increases	Decreases
Overall rock texture	Random	Foliated
Agents of Change	*Inference from Altered Product*	
Pressure	Low pressure, as rock is increased in volume	High pressure, as rock is increased in density
Temperature	Low temperature, as water is added to minerals; little reaction among grains	High temperature, as water is driven off, with abundant reactions among minerals
Chemical change	Hydrolysis, with metals removed in watery solutions	Hydrogen and hydroxyl ions replaced by metals, as water is driven off

temperatures and pressures beyond human experience, but not beyond human comprehension. Educated people see the gnarled parade of mica and envision the power within an ancient earth. Early peoples saw only a pretty rock, its twisted convulsions perhaps a portent to something fearful. Someone once said that "to be educated is to become more human." Can you see why?

THE ROCK CYCLE

If product reflects process, then rocks have an inheritance. The grains of sand in a child's sandbox are the crystalline children of mountains and the parent to future cliffs of sandstone. All of this implies that rocks are transient visitors on the earth; they mir-

ror their past while they adjust to their future. The seeming permanence of rock only reflects our brief life span; if we were to live 1 million years, rock would seem less eternal, and if we were to live for many millions of years, the earth might seem a place of constant rebirth.

A good place to begin a summary of our knowledge of rocks is with a deeper view at yet another earth cycle—**the rock cycle.** Consider a rock—any rock—that is exposed at the surface of our earth. Weathering and erosive processes pick it apart, change its composition, and flush the offspring out to sea. There waves and currents wash the sediment and sort it by size, while animals dig in it, nest in it, and make new sedimentary rock. Its bedding, or stratification, testifies to an earth with the power to destroy its own mountains but gather up its children. If sedimentary rock were buried even more deeply, the crushing forces and searing heat within the earth form newly metamorphosed objects: glistening crystals are woven into rocks whose foliation reflects the forces that molded them.

Bury the metamorphosed material still more deeply, and atom is torn from atom as crystals yield to temperatures such as those that melt steel. Magma results, and plutonic igneous rocks wait deep within the earth for the forces of erosion that are gnawing away at the earth miles (kilometers) above them. Or perhaps the seething magma finds its way to the surface and spills down the side of a volcano in restless fury. The cycle is closed, because now we are describing surface rock, which awaits wind, rain, ice, and the tug of gravity to transform it once again (Figure 5-23).

The concept of a rock cycle is a satisfying summary of the processes and products discussed in these first few chapters. Each rock comes from another one, and the cycle yields "no vestige of a beginning—no prospect of an end."

Two centuries ago James Hutton saw the rock cycle as an expression of the "economy of nature." Everything is reused. Feldspar yields floods of clay to the rolling sea. The floods of clay may yield foliated mica, while still higher temperatures transform the micas back into feldspar.

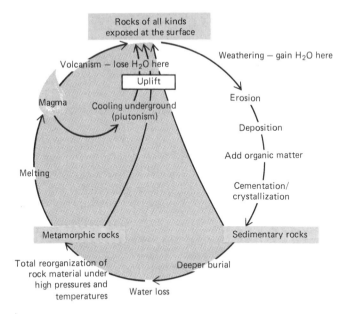

5-23
Schematic diagram of the rock cycle concept. Processes are in color; products are in black. The unshaded portion of the diagram includes all the processes driven by the sun's energy; all these processes involve adding water to material and creating products of low density and higher volume. The shaded portion of the graph includes all processes that occur within the earth; all of these processes involve loss of water and heating under pressure. The products are dryer, denser, and of lower volume. The cycle, shown by the outermost circle of arrows, is frequently interrupted by renewed uplift, which returns material to the earth's surface to "start" the cycle again. The energy received at the surface from the sun is more than 5000 times that escaping from the earth's interior by conduction through the rocks beneath our feet, yet it is the tiny trickle of heat beneath our feet that is the probable cause of earthquakes (Chapter Six) and of the opening and closing of the ocean basins of the earth (Chapter Seven).

Quo Vadis?

It was on the Appian Way, near Rome, that Peter was asked a powerful question: *Quo Vadis?* Whither goest thou? That same question can be asked within our concept of a tidy water cycle (Chapter Four) and an equally tidy rock cycle. Let us also ask it of the earth.

Cycles have much about them that fascinate human nature. They seem to combine the excitement of incessant motion with the comfort of retaining the status quo. Renewal always comes from decay—a comforting thought to the only animal that knows it must die.

The rock cycle, too, is a satisfying concept that provides a grand scheme within which to fit major geologic processes. Two centuries ago, this grand scheme not only seemed to combine all the "loose ends" of geologic thought but, in a world then intoxicated by the power of machines, the rock cycle seemed the mightiest machine of all "where the same instruments are constantly employed." The machine was seen as a perpetual motion machine, a sort of self-winding clock that never ran down. There was also another level of satisfaction—the machine had *purpose*. In Hutton's words " . . . the whole presents a machine of peculiar construction by which it is adapted to a certain end." The purpose of the machine was straightforward and comforting: to produce and replenish a *habitable world*.

In the terms in which the rock cycle is generally used, the answer to the question—whither goest thou?—is *nowhere*. Material is simply converted endlessly from one form to another but, over long periods of time, the earth is unchanging in form, process, or product.

The rock cycle is an old idea that originated when little was known about the interior of the earth. All of the processes were seen as an essentially closed system, operating within the outer few miles (kilometers) of the earth. Those processes were seen as operating with little change through immense periods of time; that is, the earth was a perpetual motion machine. Its materials were always in motion, but the motion went nowhere, and the purpose of all this rushing about was to provide and "preserve the tribes of animals and vegetables that dwell on its surface," according to Hutton.

Our question was addressed to the earth. The answer from strict uniformitarian principles is—nowhere.

A Challenge

We can challenge the circular rock cycle already presented on *two* grounds. Every geologic process we can describe involves the dissipation and continuous *loss of energy* by the earth. To speak of the earth as a perpetual motion machine is, then, nonsense. Machines consume and dissipate energy. We can only assume that over a sufficiently long period of time, the earth has progressed from an early state with a large supply of internal available energy to an eventual state where its internal energy will be zero. Clearly, we live somewhere in the middle of that scenario. But there is now no doubt that the earth's past was more energetic than its present and its present is more energetic than its future. The earth within is slowly running down.

In the scheme of volcanic events that we previously examined, we suggested that the source of most basaltic lava is many miles (kilometers) beneath the levels where even metamorphism is taking place and even further beneath the surface levels of weathering, erosion, and deposition of sediments. Rock melts therefore come mostly from *below* the crust—from below the part of the earth in which a typical rock cycle is assumed to operate—and from those *deeper* levels our earth draws material to its surface. Once on the surface, the rocks that are formed do become a part of the rock cycle.

Notice, however, that material brought from beneath the crust is usually basaltic, while magma originating through the melting of sediments is more granitic in composition. Igneous rocks that result from the *recycling* of other rocks are quite different from material introduced onto the surface *for the first time*.

Seen in this larger sense, there is a steady transfer of basaltic material from within the earth to the earth's crust. Once material becomes a part of the outer continental crust, it is apparently endlessly recycled from melt to mud to metamorphic to melt again. Continental crust, once formed, never returns to the deeper regions from which it came.

In contrast, there is much evidence that basaltic oceanic crust is constantly formed and then returned to the deeper levels of the earth. This concept is explained more fully in Chapter Seven.

For now, we can best say that the concept of the rock cycle is a significant aid to understanding the relation between each of the major rock-forming processes. But it *cannot* be a *closed* system going *nowhere;* the large-scale transfer of material within the earth to the surface has given us the granitic continents on which we live.

Perhaps the best answer to the question put to the earth was furnished by Heraclitus, a Greek philosopher of the sixth century B.C., who suggested that the earth was always in a process of change or, more simply, the earth was always in process. He suggested that we can never step in the same stream twice, that change simply is the order of the day. Perhaps that is all we should say just now—that the earth, like us, is always in the act of "becoming."

SUMMARY   Sedimentary rocks form as weathered materials—both insoluble fragments and soluble chemicals—are carried downhill to sites where collection, cementation, organic activity, and crystallization act in varied ways to form layered rocks. The textures formed by the clastic particles, the fossils that are preserved within the sediments, and the structures that form the larger-scale features of these plentiful rocks allow detailed reconstruction of the past environments in which they formed.

The activities of six scientists over 300 years were responsible for yielding the keys to the interpretation of history that were encoded in sedimentary layers. The principles of continuity, horizontality, superposition, uniformity, and faunal assemblage form the basis of deciphering the past from sedimentary rock assemblages.

Most metamorphic rocks form in a pressure-temperature environment intermediate between deposition and consolidation of sediments and melting of rocky material. Other types of metamorphism (which *literally* means "change in form") include cold shearing, baking, and recrystallization under abnormally high pressures. The textures of metamorphic rocks depend on the asymmetry of grains being formed, the orientation of the layering in the parent rock, and the orientation and type of stress that forces solid rock to yield, in time, as Silly Putty does. Both nonfoliated and foliated textures may be produced; foliated textures include slaty cleavage and schistosity. Metamorphic rocks illustrate that the strength of any apparently solid material is entirely a function of how long it must endure stress before it flows. Given enough time, everything flows.

The products of weathering and metamorphism are always opposite in character; each product expresses the totally different environment in which it was formed.

The rock cycle seeks to express the relation among rocks recycled within the outer part of the earth, but it also seems that still larger-scale processes affect the crust of the earth. The rock cycle may well be an open cycle, which suggests that the character of the inner earth and its outer crust are slowly changing through time. The change is unidirectional; internal energy sources are slowly running down.

EXERCISES

1. Devise a classification scheme for sedimentary rocks based solely on their ease of excavation. Who would use such a classification?

2. In some metamorphic rocks, schistosity having one orientation over a large area is consistently cut by schistosity having a different orientation. How can that observation be explained?

3. How do you explain the observation, offered early in this chapter, that the older a rock is, the more likely it is to be igneous or metamorphic? (*Note.* There are *at least two distinctively* different explanations for this observation.)

4. Suppose the earth's internal energy is running down, as suggested. If we work that inference backward, that means the ancient earth had more internal energy than the earth does now. Is that consistent with either of your answers to the previous question?

5. Others have argued that the rate of magma generation has remained constant with time. Is that consistent with either of your answers to question 3?

6. If granite were weathered in a cold climate and the same granite were weathered in a tropical climate, how would the sediments that resulted be different? How would the sedimentary rocks reflect past climate?

7. In light of our observation that nothing is solid, why is our earth spherical? (Other planets, too!)
8. Sand and gravel furnish a sizable business enterprise at the cornerstone of the construction industry. If you were to construct a graph of number of sand and gravel pits in use versus the elevation [in feet (meters) above sea level] of the pits, what would such a graph look like? Why?
9. If the earth's internal energy dropped to zero, but the sun still shone, what kind of rocks would cover the earth after many more millions of years? Would there still be continents?

SUGGESTED READINGS

Croneis, Carey, and Krumbein, William C., 1936, *Down to Earth,* Chicago, University of Chicago Press, 501 pp.
  Nearly 50 years old and more fun to read than ever. Try Chapters 14 and 23; just try to keep from smiling!
Harker, Alfred, 1930, *Metamorphism,* London, Methuen, 214 pp. (Reprinted in 1976, Halsted Press, New York.)
  Also half a century old and still the clearest description of metamorphic processes and rocks.
LaPorte, Leo F., 1968, *Ancient Environments,* Englewood Cliffs, N.J., Prentice-Hall, 127 pp.
  Brief, well-done review of the use of sedimentary rocks in interpretation of past environments.
Porter, Roy, 1977, *The Making of Geology,* Cambridge, Cambridge University Press, 288 pp.
  Brief review of the history of British geology during its formative years, including the history of uniformitarian thought.
Reineck, H. E., and Singh, I. B., 1973, *Depositional Sedimentary Environments,* New York, Springer-Verlag, 535 pp.
  Modern and ancient environments and their association with sedimentary rocks. Elegantly illustrated.

KEY CONCEPTS

Sedimentary Rocks
  Essentially deposited in water, rare exceptions; contain fossils; contain relict components from source rock, source climate, erosional agency, and depositional environment; textures, structures, and fossils

aid in interpretation; continuity, superposition, horizontality, uniformity, faunal assemblage.

Metamorphic rocks

Solids, mutual growth of crystals while solid; fluids, either while wet or while hot. Product is rock cleavage (commonly parallel mineral cleavage) intermediate between sedimentary and igneous environment.

All rocks

Product reflects agent(s) of formation; cyclic change as environment changes; additions from beneath the crust; sedimentary rocks *caused* by external energy; igneous and metamorphic rocks *formed* by internal energy, but *exposed to view* by external energy or by volcanism.

This photograph suggests the power of the 1906 earthquake that devastated northern California. The train and cars were thrown off the track by ground motion near Point Reyes, California. The two people in the photograph seem nonchalant; only the dog senses that something is wrong. (Photograph by G. K. Gilbert, U.S. Geological Survey.)

Chapter Six
DEEPER REFLECTIONS
earthquakes

''Nature, to be commanded, must be obeyed.''
Francis Bacon

Our earth is seldom quiet. Thousands of earthquakes disturb the sensitive, quivering pens of delicate recording instruments every single day. Every day, somewhere on earth, humans feel the earth shake. The tremor may be momentary and gentle—only a reminder of the forces beneath our feet. More rarely, buildings lurch and sway in tune with the wandering rock beneath. And, even more rarely, the earth shudders in violent waves, and people die among the cascading remnants of structures that once protected them.

Earthquakes have taken the lives of millions of people and are one of our most ancient scourges. Prayers for deliverance from earthquakes are among the oldest written records, because civilization in the Mediterranean area had to contend with both volcanic violence and a trembling earth. The association of earthquakes with volcanoes was recognized in earliest times and led many people to conjecture that great fires within the earth were the cause of earthquakes. Indeed, Pompeii, buried by the ash of Vesuvius in A.D. 79, had been shaken badly by a great earthquake only 16 years before and then rebuilt to await the suffocating ash.

THE ANCIENT AFFLICTION

Earliest peoples could only have found earthquakes yet another indication that the earth was to be feared; anything was possible in an earth that was both malevolent and productive. Explanations for this centered about the whims of gods, and nothing could be known or foretold. Earliest Babylonian and Persian writings contain prayers for deliverance from earthquakes. Their unparalleled devastation is perhaps our oldest curse.

The earliest known speculation on the cause of earthquakes was that of Thales of Miletus, who suggested, in the fifth century B.C., that the earth floated on a great body of water, and storms caused waves that made the earth rock violently. Other Greek writers, in succession, alleged that great caverns within the earth were the sites of earthquakes. Water or wind driven into the caverns, collapse of the caverns, and fires within the caverns were all alleged to cause earthquakes. The belief in a subterranean world of ominous caverns, pulsing springs, and violent wind currents now seems quaint, even comical but, to people who lived in an area where caverns and caves were common, they seemed to furnish a logical explanation for the collapse of parts of the earth and for the common association of volcanoes with earthquakes. Recall that the catastrophic eruption of Thera in 1450 B.C. (described in Chapter Three), which ushered in the Ionian civilization, was accompanied by violent earthquakes and giant sea waves.

In the first century B.C. Titus Lucretius Carus echoed prevailing opinion when he stated:

. . . yet the impetuous air itself and the furious force of wind is distributed abroad through the many interstices of the earth like an ague, and thus transmits the trembling. . . .Therefore men shiver in their cities with a twofold terror; they fear the houses above, they dread the caverns below, lest the earth's nature loosen all asunder in a moment, or torn asunder open abroad her gaping jaws, and in confusion seek to gorge it with her own ruins.

6-1
This old woodcut describes the scene in Lisbon, Portugal, during their great earthquake. Ships founder, parts of the city collapse into the sea, steeples topple, and seawater roars into the helpless city. (Courtesy of the History of Science Collections, University of Oklahoma Libraries.)

For the *next 1900 years* there was little change in speculations on the origin of earthquakes. Thus Shakespeare could write, "oft the teeming earth is with a kind of colic pinch'd and vex'd by the imprisoning of unruly wind within her womb, which for enlargement striving, shakes the old bedlam earth and topples down steeples and moss grown towers." In 1755, a giant earthquake devastated Lisbon, Portugal, and took the lives of 50,000 people (Figure 6-1). From this tragic event a new school of philosophers developed who wondered that a kind Almighty would allow such affliction to befall innocent people; a renewed understanding of earthquakes was attained by those who studied them. It was soon recognized that whatever their cause (which was still believed to be great fires raging within the earth), the energy released by an earthquake traveled through the earth at a speed approximating that of sound.

It was also recognized that these waves traveled through the earth and disturbed it as though it were an **elastic body;** that is, the rocky earth beneath us responds to the energy by *distorting* and *then regaining* its shape. The earth vibrates under the impact of released energy, much as a bell does when it is struck. The energy released by a great earthquake may travel for many thousands of miles (kilometers), ringing the earth like a colossal spherical bell. The oscillations of the surging earth can be readily felt and, amplified by zones of poorly consolidated or waterlogged soil, they are the basic cause of the collapse of structures during an earthquake.

Another result of the Lisbon earthquake was the recognition that the interval between the occurrence of the earthquake and the arrival of energy waves at some point correlated with the distance to the source of energy (Figure 6-2). Early attempts at pinpointing the direction of energy arrival also suggested that cooperative recording of earthquake wave information might yield important information as to source. The long

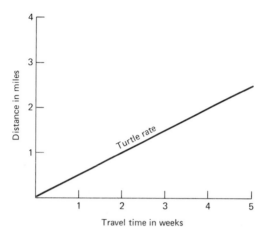

6-2
Suppose we have a turtle whose speed is known [½ mile (⅘ kilometer) per week], and we find it after a 4-week trip. How far away is its home? This whimsical example illustrates an important idea; given any two of the three variables (rate, distance, and travel time) in the graph, the third variable can be found. Such a simple curve works well as long as the rate is constant; if the rate constantly changes, a graph such as Figure 6-23 results.

road to understanding why earthquakes occur had begun. A great tragedy often marks a beginning, and the Lisbon earthquake may well mark the beginning of modern investigation into the mysteries of earthquake origin.

In the nineteenth century our understanding of how energy travels within the earth was greatly refined but there was little improvement in understanding the causes of earthquakes. People recognized that great smoldering fires in underground caverns or giant winds or waves were not causes of earthquakes, but the *cause* defied understanding until this century, even though the

effects were more and more skillfully measured.

Additionally, detailed measurements suggested that earthquakes released energy in several different waveforms and that passage of these varying types of waves through and around our earth illuminated the nature of the interior of the earth. Therefore, these rippling earth waves bring not only horror, but also knowledge that leads us to a totally new viewpoint on our earth and to an understanding that may allow prediction, and even prevention, of the ancient scourge.

THE CAUSES OF EARTHQUAKES

Twentieth-century analyses are based on the nature of earthquake vibrations and also on topographic data—accurately measured locations of many points on land and seafloor before and after an earthquake. From analysis of these data (especially from information available from the 1906 earthquake that devastated northern California), it is clear that earthquakes result from energy that is *stored* in rocks and *suddenly released*. The plane, or zone, along which separation of adjacent points eventually occurs is a **fault** (Figure 6-3).

For those who have participated in the sport of archery, the following analogy will help clarify things. The archer applies muscular energy to draw the bowstring back, arching the bow. The bow now has *energy stored in it,* energy that is released when the archer releases the bowstring and lets the arrow fly. For the earth, the source of applied energy is somewhat speculative, but rocks may curve and bend elastically under these forces. Movement continues until the solid rock can store no more energy; the

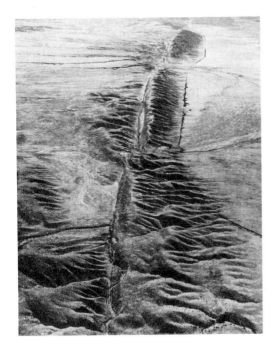

6-3

The narrow, linear valley cutting through the low hills in the center of the aerial photograph is the surface expression of a fault. The fault is the San Andreas Fault, perhaps the most dangerous one in North America. In this view, which looks south along the fault line, the block of rock occupying the right half of the photograph moves toward you a few inches (centimeters) per year. When such motion is blocked, enormous stresses may build up in the area adjacent to the fault zone, and the stage is set for disaster. (Photograph by R. E. Wallace, U.S. Geological Survey.)

breaking strength of the rock has been reached. Like an unlucky archer who bends a bow too far, causing it to break, the rock ruptures, and large blocks of earth shudder past one another at speeds of hundreds of miles (kilometers) per second. The energy, stored over many years, is suddenly released, and we feel the vibrations that are produced as the pent-up energy is released as an earthquake.

Laboratory studies of cylinders of rocks, placed under varying amounts of pressure, offer the best picture of what may happen miles within the earth as forces rise. When about one-half the force that will finally rupture the rock has developed, small cracks begin to form in the rock, *increasing its volume.* This phenomenon, known as **dilatancy,** can be measured on the surface of the earth as a swelling, or tilting, of the earth's surface. It can also be measured as an increase in the resistance of the rock to passage of an electric current (because of the electrical resistance of the air in the newly formed cracks) and as a dramatic change in the velocity of seismic waves from *other* earthquakes as they pass through the dilatant rock.

In the next stage of rock deformation, water diffuses into the shattered rock, raising the pressure across the now water-saturated cracks. The electrical resistivity of the rock falls, earthquake wave velocities change in a direction opposite to that previously described, and the rock is seriously weakened by the influx of groundwater. Catastrophic slippage occurs as the diminishing strength of the rocks falls to values that are less than the forces being applied; the energy released at failure is felt as rippling waves across the earth.

Now a **fault plane,** or **zone,** has been produced. The buildup of stored energy begins again; when the energy added is greater than the frictional resistance along the fault, the fault slips again, and *another* earthquake is felt. Thus faults identify zones where earthquakes may occur repetitively over some length of time. Not surprisingly, the longer the recurrence interval, the larger or more damaging the earthquake. It takes more time to build up the enormous amounts of stored energy released by very large earthquakes (Figure 6-4). Thus, in any year, there are a few very large quakes, many moderate quakes, and thousands of tremors, most of which are below the level of human perception.

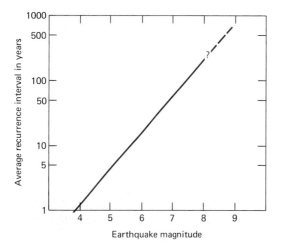

6-4
Since there is a relation between maximum displacement and magnitude (see Figure 6-10), if we assume a slip rate of 1 inch (2½ centimeters) per year, we can plot the curve shown for average recurrence interval. The longer the slip is forcibly held to zero, the greater the displacement and magnitude of the resulting earthquake. Recurrence interval and magnitude relations suggest that a magnitude 5 earthquake releases the energy stored for 5 years, while a magnitude 7 earthquake releases the energy stored for 70 years. Parts of the San Andreas Fault have not moved in more than 70 years. (After R. E. Wallace, U.S. Geological Survey.)

One puzzle in understanding earthquakes is the control over fault movement. It has long been recognized that earth movement along many faults is continuous; that is, objects on each side of the fault may glide past each other in small but steady increments. Measured rates may be 1 yard (approximately 1 meter) per century or so, and only *microearthquakes* gently disturb sensitive listening instruments nearby. This phenomenon, known as **seismic creep,** releases energy almost continuously. There is no buildup of devastating energy, and blocks of earth slide past one another, causing minor construction problems; however, little of this ruin is associated with faults that stick and then violently unstick. What causes one system of faults to glide in stately majesty and another to stick shut, only to snap at an unexpected moment and release waves of vibrating fury?

Perhaps some faults slide without sticking because they are well lubricated by natural fluids or because the forces across the faulted zone are low. Or perhaps because of some combination of the two they may be described as **aseismic faults,** faults that move continually by seismic creep.

Other faults do not fare so well; forces across them may be large, they may be dry and little lubricated, or they may stand their ground under the forces that assail them until, in several seconds, each block snaps away from its neighbor and shudders toward a new location.

Either of these models—the one caused by warping of rock or the one forming new planes of failure in a dilatant rock permeated with water—may apply to earthquakes that develop within the upper few tens of miles (kilometers) of earth. The storage of stress in warped rock has often been called the **elastic rebound theory,** which is a product of intense study of the mechanism of failure that caused the 1906 earthquake in the San Francisco area. The other model, often called the **dilatancy-diffusion** theory, is the result of experimentation within the last 20 years in laboratories, where attempts were made to simulate earthquakes by breaking rocks in giant, specialized hydraulic presses. Both mechanisms explain the early period of energy storage and the series of events preceding the release of stored energy. Both models suggest precursory events that should be recognizable in rocks before they fail, and the events predicted by both models have been recognized within the earth prior to natural earthquakes.

THE EFFECTS OF EARTHQUAKES

The point of failure along a fault is known as the **focus** of the earthquake; it is from the focus that energy radiates out in every direction. *Directly above the focus* on the earth's surface is the **epicenter,** an unenviable place in which to ride out an earthquake. Most earthquakes occur when the focus is within only a few tens of miles (kilometers) of the surface, but a few deep-focus earthquakes occur at depths as great as 400 miles (645 kilometers). It is difficult to imagine the elastic rebound or dilatancy-diffusion model explaining earthquakes at such great depths, but deep-focus earthquakes give us an important clue to events described in the next chapter.

Surface Faulting

Of all the hazards associated with earthquakes, perhaps the most obvious is the danger to structures when the ground breaks and moves beneath them. Such **surface faulting** (Figure 6-5) is one of the most perilous of earthquake-related events; it literally shifts the foundation under structures, causing major structural damage and building collapse. The amount of displacement that occurs during an earthquake is generally related to the length of the fault; longer faults yield greater displacements. The maximum displacement ever observed in a single earthquake is about 12 yards (11 meters); horizontal displacement during the 1906 San Francisco earthquake equaled about 6 yards (5½ meters). Not all surface faulting is associated with earthquakes; surface offset also

6-5
An example of surface faulting during a 1959 earthquake in western Montana. Try to imagine what would happen to a house built across the area of failure. (Photograph by I. J. Witkind, U.S. Geological Survey.)

may be produced by seismic creep, the steady movement between blocks in a faulted area. Creep is far less damaging to structures, although walls will be warped and slowly pulled away, windows will pop, and cracks will grow in foundations and walls. The damage produced by creep is subtle but cumulative and, eventually, will make structures both unpleasant and unsafe.

The history of surface faulting is probably the single most important tool available in evaluating the seismic hazard of an area. Many, but not all, earthquake hazards are associated with moderate- to shallow-focus earthquakes, which typically produce surface faulting. In a very general way, then, the risk from earthquakes is directly related to the distance to the nearest active fault.

Risk. The seismic risk is related to the potential ground motion, or the probable "acceleration" (rate of increase of speed), of the ground surface during an earthquake. The concept of risk has many components, but it always boils down to a value judgment: What is the worth of a human life? Even if probable ground motion in an area can be estimated and its recurrence interval specified, these are simply probability statements that are based on assessment of previous seismic history and local geologic conditions. The next step is to ask what it will cost to erect a structure that can ride out the expected maximum ground acceleration; construction costs rise logarithmically with expected ground motion. Eventually the cost of lives and property must be weighed against construction costs of various designs. As we continue to discuss the hazards of earthquakes, we should remember that no structure can be absolutely safe in every contingency. However, we do know enough

about the risks associated with living near active faults to be able to evaluate intelligently what can happen when they move and whether they will move disastrously.

Three types of risks and hazards can be identified: (1) risks to buildings built across the fault zone; (2) risks to buildings near the fault zone because of ground shaking; and (3) other risks caused by slope failure, seismic sea waves, dam collapse, and related phenomena. There is no satisfactory way to engineer any building to withstand the vertical or horizontal shifts of the ground several yards (meters) beneath its foundation. Such displacements characterize the effect of even moderately strong earthquakes. In human terms, *there is no known way that a building built across an active fault can be made safe*. Such buildings are simply disasters waiting to happen; they reflect a combination of ignorance, indifference, and greed among the city planning and zoning staff, developers, and real estate agents.

Evaluating the probability of damaging fault motion is among the geologist's most difficult tasks; seismic history is full of examples of apparently inconsequential faults that have moved with large displacement and little warning. A full-scale geologic evaluation would require detailed geologic field investigation and mapping, examination of boreholes in dangerous areas, measurement of the local magnetic and gravitational field, and evaluation of seismic records dating back many years. Assessment of the probable sense of movement, extent of movement, and ground motion should follow. Still more details on the nature of deformation must be collected and, ideally, instruments for monitoring creep should be installed. In the absence of this kind of effort (except in a few enlightened and strongly threatened communities, such effort is usually absent), it is more and more difficult to forecast which fault zones are potential problems.

Use. Since most of the information is available, intelligent planning advocates that geologists, engineers, and planners evaluate the consequences of faulting; where these effects might result in unacceptable levels of damage (note the value judgment when we say *unacceptable),* provisions should be required to insure that land use is compatible with the potential danger. Surprisingly, many forms of land use, including parks, cemeteries, and agricultural areas of all kinds, are perfectly compatible with expected surface faulting. Some cities have adopted a fault hazards easement that provides that no construction of any type may occur within a few tens of yards (meters) of the fault. Structures that may involve many people are required to be set back further from the anticipated zone of surface faulting than single-family dwellings. Once again we have defined the worth of a human life. At least we have a beginning—a recognition that it is witless to build sound structures on unsound ground. The moderate earthquakes experienced in 1971 in the San Fernando Valley provide another example of this. Freeways shattered, dams almost failed, hospitals collapsed, and hundreds of homes were made unfit for occupancy.

Considering the information available on seismic risk, the lack of detailed zoning against seismic hazard by many Western cities is scandalous. The failure to obtain the necessary information is at best a disgrace, but one that reflects normal human indifference to a hazard that is not obvious or immediate. There is no way to insure building safety when the building *straddles* a fault; hundreds of public buildings and thousands of homes straddle the dangerous faults of southwestern California, western Nevada, and central Utah. The hazards to the structures built across faults are *total.* At best, buildings will be shaken from their foundation and suffer intense structural damage; at worst, the building will collapse on those it once sheltered.

Ground Motion

What about the hazards that are not near the surface trace of an active fault zone? In a *very* general way, the greater the distance from a known, active fault, the safer the building, but this statement is full of exceptions. The basic hazard to any structure not built directly across the fault is **ground motion,** and ground motion is *not* directly related to distance from the fault.

The 1906 San Francisco earthquake illustrates the factors affecting earthquake damage; the study of damage along the more than 250 miles (400 kilometers) of the San Andreas Fault, where movement occurred, was extraordinarily thorough. Some of the residents living in homes atop San Francisco's famous hills were not even awakened by the tremor that threw other nearby buildings off their foundations (Figure 6-6) and caused many buildings to collapse. The great length [250 miles (400 kilometers)] of the fault zone involved led to large displacements [about 6 yards (5½ meters)]and to surface waves with amplitudes of up to 1 yard (almost 1 meter). The shaking lasted for 1 full minute; many buildings failed after enduring many tens of seconds of trembling violence.

The lesson was clear; homes built on solid rock foundations withstood the earthquake well; homes and structures built on landfills,

6-6

An example of ground failure under a house foundation during the 1906 California earthquake. Such failures will occur again, since nothing has changed. (Photograph by G. K. Gilbert, U.S. Geological Survey.)

reclaimed bay muds, and sands were literally shaken to pieces. Unsound ground and poorly compacted landfills amplify earthquake waves, much as a bowl of gelatin quivers under the slightest touch. Sixty miles (100 kilometers) away from the epicenter, San Jose was almost destroyed by vibrations whose intensity probably exceeded those felt immediately adjacent to the fault, because San Jose sits on a thick deposit of soft, valley-fill material.

Liquefaction

Recent Japanese earthquakes have demonstrated an even more catastrophic type of ground failure; soft, thick soils from reclaimed bays are often waterlogged, and continued shaking abruptly changes them from a solid to a foaming liquid, a process called **liquefaction.** The *liquefaction* of deep, waterlogged soils leads to total removal of support for overlying buildings, which may simply sink into the slimy material that once supported them or heel over (Figure 6-7) into rakish attitudes like sailboats in racing form. Ground settlement can be just as damaging to a building as separation along a straddling fault. Old riverbeds, deep valley fills, filled delta and marsh areas, filled and diked bay areas, ocean beach and cliff developments, and backfilled estuaries all represent very unstable ground.

Living or working in areas near known active faults is simply playing Russian roulette with all that you treasure. There are only two possible solutions: move away or reinforce home and office structures, buy earthquake and flood insurance, and hope for the best. A competent geologist can advise you on the hazards involved in any area, and a competent structural engineer can suggest relatively inexpensive ways of making your home or workplace more resistant to the rippling waves that will come some day (see Suggested Readings).

Other risks of living near active faults include the probability that earthquakes may touch off disastrous *landslides* and *rockslides* in the hills above you. Building on steep soils at the base of a cliff is triple folly. Not only may the soil fail beneath you, but the cliff magnifies the energy waves and creates still greater shaking. Rocks and soil above you may come crashing down, shaken from the steep slopes as nature tries to smooth out and flatten land slopes; this is a perfectly normal process, but one in which humans often lose, because we love to live

6-7
This aerial photograph, taken after the June 16, 1964 earthquake in Niigata, Japan, graphically displays the effects of liquefaction of "solid" ground by ground shaking. Apartment houses heeled over; residents of the central unit walked out of the windows and down the side of the outside walls to safety. (Photograph courtesy of NOAA/EDS.)

high up where we can see everything below us.

Seismic Sea Waves

Tsunamis, or seismic sea waves (see Chapter Three), are another hazard associated with earthquakes. Tsunamis are formed when faulting occurs *within* the seafloor or along the coast and there is a large energy release directly into the seawater. Since water, like almost any liquid, is essentially incompressible, the energy released is simply transmitted through the water. The waves produced are little higher than normal waves in the open sea, but they move across the ocean depths at velocities of many hundreds of miles (kilometers) per hour. When they approach a shoreline, the sudden velocity loss is translated into wave heights of more than 10 yards (9 meters). The Chilean earthquake of 1960 produced one of the larger tsunamis on record; Chile and Hawaii received the most of the damage. More than 8 hours later, the tsunami ravaged the coast

of Japan, 10,000 miles (16,000 kilometers) away. Thousands of Japanese lost their homes and their employment, and nearly 200 died. Property damage was about half a billion dollars from this one tsunami.

Again, coastal areas and low-lying areas are visibly hazardous places to live; nearby earthquakes will cause the mud beneath you to shake, and roaring tsunamis may later clear away anything left. One seismic sea wave in Japan 500 years ago destroyed a temple 10 miles (16 kilometers) inland.

Seiches

Seismic **seiches** are another example of earthquake-generated hazard; they are produced by the sloshing of water in lakes, reservoirs, rivers, or bays when the rock around them is shaken. Seiches may exceed 10 yards (9 meters) in height, but more usually are less than 1 yard (almost 1 meter) high. Waves in constricted bodies of water may also be produced by land sliding into the water. In 1958 in Lituya Bay, Alaska, an earthquake produced a rockfall into the bay that caused water to crash against the bay more than 600 yards (550 meters) above the former sea level. Another danger posed by earthquakes is the failure of dams; the near failure of the Van Norman Reservoir during the San Fernando quake is a chilling example of what might have been. More than 50,000 people lived below the dam; if it had failed under continued ground shaking, their lives and property might only be memories today.

EARTHQUAKE ENERGY

As suggested on p. 154, the energy released by earthquakes travels around and through the earth as various categories of elastic waves. There are two major types; one group of earthquake energy waves moves only along the outer surface of the earth, and another group moves through the interior of the earth. **Surface waves** move slowly around the skin of the earth, often vibrating its surface in very complex patterns of motion. **Body waves** move more rapidly than surface waves and provide the only means we have of investigating the physical properties of the earth's inaccessible interior.

Two types of body waves, *P-waves* and *S-waves,* are of particular interest. The **S-wave** is a **shear**, or distortional, wave; it causes particles in its path to vibrate at right angles to the direction of energy flow. The S-wave is of intermediate velocity and, like all shear waves, can travel only through a substance that is solid. The fastest wave is the **P-wave**, a **dilational wave** (*causing volume change*) that vibrates particles parallel to the path of energy flow. The P-wave travels through the earth much like a sound wave, traveling equally well through liquids, solids, and gases.

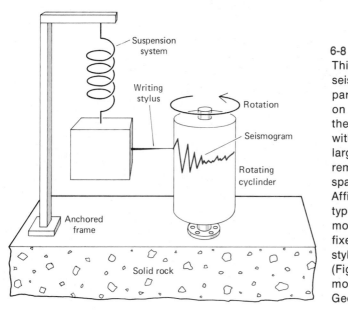

6-8
This sketch of a simplified seismograph shows its component parts. A rotating cylinder with paper on it is affixed firmly to solid rock. If the earth moves, the cylinder moves with it. Adjacent to the cylinder is a large mass, suspended so that it remains essentially stationary in space during earth movement. Affixed to the mass is one of many types of writing instruments. The motion of the drum relative to the fixed mass is recorded by the writing stylus as a line or *seismogram* (Figure 6-9), the record of earth motion. (Sketch modified from U.S. Geological Survey data.)

All earthquake waves are elastic waves; this means that material is only *temporarily* altered by their passage and springs back to its original shape as the energy moves on. The trembling that we feel as an earthquake occurs is very real, because the earth heaves and shudders as the energy passes by. Body waves passing through the entire earth cause it to vibrate like a giant drum; frequencies range from 1 to 3 cycles *per hour.* The earth may continue this quivering for several weeks after a large earthquake, producing music far too low pitched for human ears to hear and evidence that the earth itself is an elastic solid that is capable of resonating like any well-struck chime.

Instruments

The vibrations that shake the earth are *recorded by* a **seismograph,** literally an "earthquake writer," or an instrument that records ground shaking (Figure 6-8). The first seismograph was invented in A.D. 132 by Chang Heng and is another reflection of our curiosity about earthquakes. In the intervening 1800 years, seismographs have been greatly improved in sensitivity and precision, but the principle of their operation remains the same. One part of the instrument, usually a scribing or writing pen, is suspended in such a way that it is essentially independent of the earth (Figure 6-8) and remains fixed in position in space. The recording apparatus is firmly fixed to the earth and moves with it against the pen. The resulting **seismogram** is a written graph (Figure 6-9) of ground motion *in the plane parallel to the pen.* Three seismographs provide a complete seismic station as they individually record north-south, east-west, and vertical components of earth motion; the cumulative array defines ground motion in any direction.

Additional components of many seismic stations include *microseismic* apparatus, which are designed to record high-frequency motion from very small earthquakes (used primarily to study fault creep), and long- and especially long-period seismographs, which are used to study resonations of the entire earth. Still more instrumentation may include *strong motion seismographs* or *accelerographs,* which are comparatively *in*sensitive seismic writers used to describe the violent ground motion of very large earthquakes which may put more sensitive seismographs out of commission.

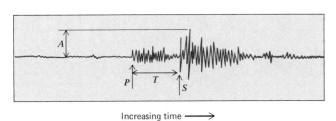

Increasing time ⟶

6-9
In this typical seismogram, the direction of travel of the paper strip was from right to left as time continued. The first wave to disturb the earth was the **P-wave,** known to be the fastest of the seismic waves. The second, slower, wave to arrive is the **S-wave.** The *amplitude (A)* of the wave is its vertical departure from the centerline; the amplitude shown is the maximum amplitude recorded, which is the information needed to determine earthquake **magnitude.** The interval *T* is the *time difference* between the arrival of the two waves and is a function of the distance to the earthquake source.

Seismographs have been recently used in the detection of underground nuclear explosions. Powerful underground explosions produce an energy release that is comparable to a small earthquake, and the energy waves travel through the earth in the same manner. There are, however, minor differences in the energy "signature" of underground detonations compared to earthquakes; seismograms can detect manufactured underground explosions and also separate them from natural events. **Seismologists,** geologists who specialize in the study of earthquakes, now routinely monitor the earth for artificial blasts, and have made an underground nuclear test-ban treaty a possibility, since on-site inspection is no longer necessary.

Measuring Earthquakes

Among the many efforts to record meaningful information from earthquakes, the oldest was an attempt to assess the *damage produced* over a geographic area. A scale (the Modified Mercalli) of damage intensity ranging from Roman numeral I (not felt) to XII (damage essentially total) provided the basic reference points; interviews from survivors and postcard data from a widespread region provided the raw data. Maps may be prepared from such data, which show the distribution of various levels of damage. Such maps have some use from the standpoint of engineering design, city planning, and the earthquake insurance business, but the damage to any one structure is dependent on too many independent variables to make the intensity scale particularly useful today.

A more modern method, useful in engineering design, is mapping, which relates the probable acceleration of structures in the area from the greatest probable earthquake. A map of *probable maximum acceleration* (how fast will the earth move?) is one of the most critical engineering design points, but efforts to predict earth acceleration are still in the early stages. Only experience will show how useful such estimates may be.

The scale most commonly used to record modern earthquakes is the **Richter magnitude** scale. This scale measures the amplitude (see Figure 6-9) of a particular type of seismic wave on a standardized seismographic record. The Richter magnitude is frequently given in newspaper accounts of earthquakes; it ranges, in practice, from 1 to 10. These magnitudes are based on a *logarithmic* scale, so that a change from 4 to 5 on the Richter scale corresponds to a change in *amplitude* of the recorded ground motion by a factor of 10. A change from 4 to 6 records an amplitude 100 times greater than 4. Remember that the Richter number records the *amplitude* or intensity of the most severe motion recorded. Sensitive seismographs can record ground motion corresponding to Richter magnitudes of much less than 1 (even negative magnitudes have been recorded), but humans rarely feel earthquakes until Richter numbers reach at least 3. The greatest earthquake ever recorded (in Chile in 1960) had a Richter magnitude of 9.5, meaning that its ground motion was more than 1 million times (10^6) greater than one that humans could barely feel.

The relation between Richter magnitude number, recurrence interval (averaged over a very long time), and energy released is fascinating. Richter magnitude is a measure of the amplitude of ground motion and does *not* directly measure the energy release, because ground motion depends on many variables, only one of which is the amount of energy released. In a general way, each increase in Richter magnitude by a value of one unit corresponds with approximately 32 times more energy released. Taking 30 as a conservative value, a Richter magnitude 6 earthquake releases 900 times as much energy as a Richter 4 earthquake and 27,000 times as much energy as a 3 quake (one barely felt by humans). The recurrence interval (averaged over 100 years or more) is an *inverse* function of energy released (Figure 6-4); weak earthquakes occur hundreds of times a day somewhere on earth, and very strong earthquakes (Richter nagnitude around 7) occur about once a month. Great earthquakes (Richter magnitudes in excess of 8) occur only once every few years. A few great earthquakes each year release far more stored seismic energy and cause greater offsets of the land surface (Figure 6-10) than all the thousands of weak earthquakes. One great earthquake releases energy (10^{25} ergs) equal to the cumulative energy released by all other earthquakes in an average year. The energy released in a great earthquake is the equivalent of the detonation of several thousand Hiroshima-size atomic bombs at once.

The energy released by great quakes must approximate the capacity of rocks to store energy. Great earthquakes tell us what the limits of rock strength are in dramatic terms.

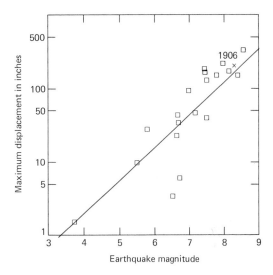

6-10
Relation between the maximum displacement and earthquake magnitude for historic faulting in western North America. The information for the 1906 California earthquake is shown with a cross and date. Using data from this graph, we can calculate that if 10 inches (25 centimeters) of elastic strain have accumulated, a magnitude 5.5 earthquake would release it. If the average slip rate is 1 inch (2½ centimeters) per year, a magnitude 5.5 earthquake should have a recurrence interval of about 10 years. (Data from M. G. Bonilla, U.S. Geological Survey.)

EARTHQUAKE PREDICTION

Among the many exciting developments within geology in the 1980s will be the attempt to predict earthquakes on scientific grounds. Earthquakes have remained unpredictable in the United States through 1973, when the first successful prediction was made. Prior to that time, the best that could be offered was an evaluation of seismic risk.

Evaluation of risk was and is an important geologic function; if reasonable statements of the probability of damaging ground acceleration in an area are available, city planners and engineers in an enlightened community can provide for building codes, seismic easements (areas where building is forbidden), and disaster preparedness, thereby reducing the hazard to life when the trembling begins. Evaluated seismic risk usually is displayed in the form of maps (Figure 6-11); these

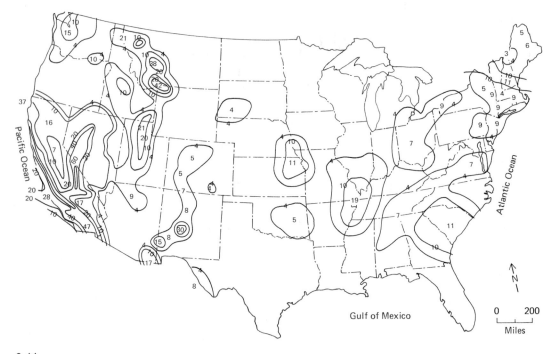

6-11

The map shows one way of estimating earthquake hazard in the United States. Levels of ground shaking, with 90 percent probability of not being exceeded in 50 years, are shown by *numbered contour lines.* These lines connect points whose probable acceleration is the same percentage of the force of gravity and thus define the hazard. As a rule of thumb, if horizontal acceleration is greater than 25 percent of the force of gravity, substantial damage to ordinary buildings results; at levels above 50 percent, damage is essentially total. At levels below 10 percent, damage is slight, but motion is felt by everyone. (Map from S. T. Algermissen and David M. Perkins, 1976, U.S. Geological Survey Open File Report 76-416.)

maps are based on an analysis of history. The principle of uniformity applies again; if there have been strong earthquakes in an area in the past, the odds are high that there will be more strong earthquakes in that same area.

But what is meant by the past? The recurrence intervals of giant earthquakes may be many centuries; in the United States, historical accounts stretch back only a few centu-

ries, and high-quality seismic information has been available for only about 70 years. Our sample interval may simply be too short for accurate evaluation of seismic risk. A comprehensive study of fault zones that were active within the last 1 million years might be more fruitful in evaluating seismic risk. A modest study would involve a major national effort and the expenditure of hundreds of millions of dollars. The result would be a better evaluation of the risk factors involved in living in any one location, but still no warning of when the trembling might start.

Approximately one-third of the population of the United States lives in the regions of highest risk (Figure 6-11). Seventy million people live, with significant risk to lives and property, in buildings not designed to withstand the earthquakes that were characteristic of the region within the last 100 years. How can we have gotten ourselves into this state of affairs? What of the future?

On a damage scale (Modified Mercalli) from I to XII, scale X and higher earthquakes record major, devastating earthquakes; the United States has only experienced quakes of this intensity 13 times in its history. One reason for our indifference to risk is that devastating quakes are rare, averaging only six per century. Thirteen hundred people have lost their lives and several billions of dollars in property damage have occurred, mostly as a result of the 1906 San Francisco, 1964 Alaskan, and 1971 San Fernando Valley earthquakes. As a nation, we have experienced few of the disasters typical of older, more heavily populated parts of the world, where an earthquake may end the lives of many thousands of people in a single event.

The future is far more ominous. We have become an urban country; millions of people live in cities, in zones of major earthquake risk. By recent government estimates, a magnitude 8.6 earthquake in Los Angeles or San Francisco—essentially a repeat of the 1906 event—would take as many as 15,000 lives and cause $25 billion in property damage. As a nation, we belittle the risk of earthquakes precisely because our experience with them is thinly scattered over 200 years and a large landmass but, as we crowd closer and closer together in zones of major earthquake risk, we will be more forcefully reminded that "civilization exists by geologic consent, subject to revocation at any moment."

Earthquake prediction, in contrast with evaluation of seismic risk, attempts to *pinpoint* the place, time, and magnitude of an earthquake hours, days, weeks, or months before it occurs. The prediction of earthquakes is a national goal and is currently in a stage of research and development in four countries: Japan, China, Russia, and the United States. Every attempt at prediction relies on early signs of changes in physical properties of rocks under stress, including surface tilting and bulging of rocks, changes in water that is circulating underground, changes in seismic wave velocities, changes in electrical and magnetic properties of the rocks involved; monitoring the behavior of domestic animals also is important to earthquake prediction.

These methods, used separately or collectively to enhance the confidence level of earthquake prediction, are based on recognizing well-documented observations on moderate- to shallow-focus earthquakes. Earthquakes result when energy is applied to an area, stored for some time, and suddenly released. The longer the period of storage and the larger the area of storage, the greater the eventual energy release. This is measured (rather indirectly) by scientists on the Richter magnitude scale and by everyone else in dollars, suffering, and loss.

Prediction, then, moves one step beyond evaluation of risk to try to alleviate the human losses and minimize the damage. Given time, we can evacuate and save lives. Given more time, we can strengthen buildings, demolish dangerous structures, and lay plans for appropriate actions during and after earthquakes. Interestingly, the larger the magnitude of the eventual earthquake, the longer the warning interval may be, stretching to several years for great earthquakes.

Earthquake prediction is a gift of the increasing understanding of the geologists who evaluate the mechanics of stress storage, elastic strain, and rupture mechanisms in rocks. **Stress** is the amount of force applied per unit of area; it is often measured in pounds per square inch (kilograms per square centimeter). Imagine a force of 1000 pounds (70 kilograms) applied over 1 square inch (5¼ square centimeters) (more conventionally expressed as 1000 psi). If the net result of applying this force on solid rock is to change its shape temporarily, much as a tennis ball is flattened by a racket at the moment of contact, the result is warped, or strained, rock. Either the *elastic rebound* or *dilatancy-diffusion* models, referred to earlier in this chapter, may now be used to narrow the search for prequake events; each

theory suggests a series of events that might occur before the final, catastrophic movement. Both ideas provide substantial clues to the behavior of stressed rocks within a few miles (kilometers) of the earth's surface.

Moderate- to deep-focus earthquakes cannot be predicted at this time, because their mechanism of failure is poorly understood. Fortunately, moderate- to deep-focus earthquakes spread their energy over such large areas of the surface that they represent less of a hazard than shallower quakes do.

Earthquake prediction research within the United States is also confined mostly to areas where surface faulting is observable and seismic activity is common. Essentially, earthquake prediction research is confined to the San Andreas Fault in California (Figure 6-12), because it currently stores and releases much of the seismic energy expended in the United States. Nowhere within the United States do more people live in greater

6-12
The San Andreas Fault is the largest of a network of faults that cut through the coastal region of California. The fault is a series of interconnected fracture zones that aggregate 600 miles (1000 kilometers) in length and extend vertically into the earth at least 20 miles (32 kilometers). Blocks on opposite sides of the San Andreas Fault move horizontally, the westerly block moving northwest with respect to the eastern block (see arrows). In some areas, as at Hollister, the fault moves rather steadily by seismic creep at the rate of 2 inches (5 centimeters) per year. In other areas (Fort Tejon, San Francisco) the fault is locked; stress is building up. See Figure 6-3 to translate lines on a map into reality.

risk than along the San Andreas Fault system, because southern and central California are, quite simply, earthquake country.

Methods

One of the older methods of detecting the coming of an earthquake is to measure, quite accurately, the changes in the length of a carefully surveyed line (Figure 6-13) through time. Such a survey describes the amount of

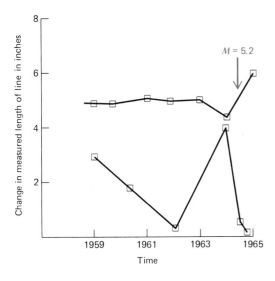

6-13

One method of earthquake prediction relies on knowledge that measurable changes in the length of several surveyed lines across a known fault often precede earthquakes. Shown in the graph is the change in the length of two surveyed lines near Corralitos, California; the time of the earthquake and its magnitude ($M = 5.2$) are shown with the colored arrow. (After Charles Hofmann, 1968, *Bull. of Dept. Wtr. Res.*, State of California, No. 116-6.)

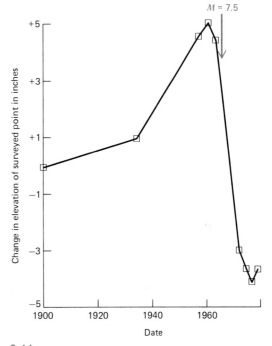

6-14

Anomalous uplift of the crust in the vicinity of Niigata, Japan, was observed for 20 years before a very large-magnitude earthquake in 1964 (see Figure 6-7). As with measurements of change in the surveyed length of lines, sudden reversals in the rate of change often seem to forecast the onset of an earthquake (colored arrow; M = magnitude). (Adapted from *Earthquake Prediction* by Tsuneji Rikitake, 1976, Elsevier Scientific Publishing Company, with permission of T. Rikitake and Elsevier.)

elastic strain or distortion that the rock has endured as well as the rate of strain. Such changes may be observed over several years or may precede an earthquake by only hours. Changes in elevation (Figure 6-14) can also be monitored; abrupt reversal in the direction of elevation change provides a pre-

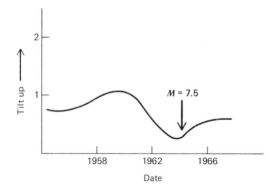

6-15
Data are from the same area as that shown in Figure 6-14. The tilt of the land surface reflected local strains several years before the 1964 earthquake (colored arrow). (Adapted from *Earthquake Prediction* by Tsuneji Rikitake, 1976, Elsevier Scientific Publishing Company, with permission of T. Rikitake and Elsevier.)

cursory warning. Tilting of the ground surface (Figure 6-15), with abrupt changes in *rate* of tilting, may also signal impending earthquakes. All of these methods share two common facets: (1) each method requires extremely precise location and elevation surveys of fixed points through extended periods of time, with repetition at sufficiently short intervals to detect anomalous changes while they still have predictive value, and (2) the larger the area over which anomalous changes are noted, the greater the magnitude of the forthcoming quake will be (Figure 6-16). The energy release is proportional not only to the length of storage time or recurrence interval, but also to the area of storage or the volume of strained rock.

A somewhat different system of predicting earthquakes relies on changes in the physical properties of the rocks themselves as they become severely strained prior to the earthquake. Strongly warped rocks can be recognized by the way they transmit seismic waves from other earthquakes, by changes in the local magnetic field, and by changes in resistance to the passage of an electric current through them. Still other symptoms of strain include anomalous behavior of water trapped underground in the rocks, and changes in the chemistry, color, temperature, and radioactivity of the natural water (see p. 173).

Changes in the velocity ratio between the P- and S-waves from *other* earthquakes identify some areas of strongly strained rock. The normal velocity ratio between these two waves is about 1.7; that is, the P-wave normally travels through the earth at a velocity approximately 1.7 times that of the S-wave. While normal rocks begin to store increasing amounts of stress as elastic strain

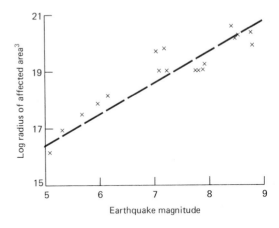

6-16
As this graph suggests, the larger the area of energy storage prior an earthquake, the greater the magnitude of the resulting earthquake. (Adapted from *Earthquake Prediction* by Tsuneji Rikitake, 1976, Elsevier Scientific Publishing Company, with permission of T. Rikitake and Elsevier.)

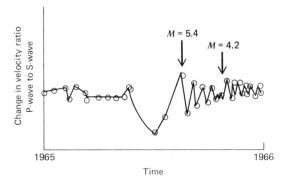

6-17

Changes in the ratio of compressional wave velocity to shear wave velocity were observed in southwestern Russia near the Caspian Sea before two moderate earthquakes. Similar abrupt changes in V_p/V_s ratios have been observed before other earthquakes (earthquake time and magnitude shown in color). (Adapted from *Earthquake Prediction* by Tsuneji Rikitake, 1976, Elsevier Scientific Publishing Company, with permission of T. Rikitake and Elsevier.)

energy, the elastic properties of the rock change, and the P-wave velocity from nearby earthquakes increases as the P-wave passes through the strongly strained area. Such changes (Figure 6-17) have been used for several years to forecast earthquakes. The ratio between P- and S-wave velocities falls and then rises, reaching its maximum *just* prior to the earthquake. The earthquake releases the stored energy, the rocks are no longer warped, and the ratio falls to normal after the earthquake. This method has some notable successes to its credit, but it requires continuous monitoring of seismic wave velocities in earthquake-prone areas in order to provide dependable forecasts.

Rising pressure within crustal rock also seems to influence the intensity of the *local* magnetic field. Pressure-induced change in magnetic properties has been demonstrated experimentally and also seems (Figure 6-18) to be an adequate predictor, if sufficient base data are available from an area before it began to strain. In some areas, variation in the strength of the magnetic field seems to signal the rise of magma from below, heating of the overlying rocks signals a change in pressure and also a rise in temperature, which diminishes the magnetic field. Continuous monitoring of seismic wave velocity and of magnetic field strength over large areas is fairly new; only time can tell what will come from this new area of research.

Another type of message from weakened rocks may signal the impending earthquake.

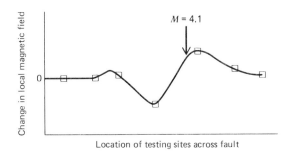

6-18

The data plotted are for simultaneous readings taken at different places along a fault. Each datum point records the *change* in the local magnetic field since some previous reading. This method of earthquake prediction relies on the observation that rocks placed under stress exhibit changes in their local, small magnetic field. The greatest changes through time occur immediately adjacent to the area of slip. (Data from Malcolm Johnston, U.S. Geological Survey.)

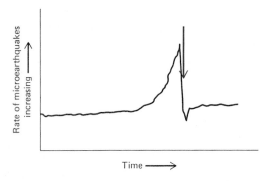

6-19

This chart of a hypothetical area displays the kind of information that has been received prior to several moderate earthquakes. At some time before the main earthquake (colored arrow), the intensity of microearthquakes in the area increases and then subsides as the strain is relieved by a larger earthquake event.

In areas of frequent microseismic activity, which are associated with creep along a fault, the rate of creep and the rate of microearthquakes may rise just prior to a small to moderate earthquake (Figure 6-19). Such abrupt changes in creep and microearthquakes apparently signal an accelerating rate of crack formation and culminates in fault slip. Stronger rocks react in exactly the opposite way, since microseismic activity in an area under stress is null. Stress now builds up without microseismic relief and signals that the fault is locked, held tightly shut by forces across the fault. Such periods of seismic quiet are ominous in an area under severe strain, because they forecast continuing storage of energy without release, and the future earthquake magnitude may be very high. Such locking and seismic quiet has been typical of both the Fort Tejon and the San Francisco areas of the San Andreas

Fault (Figure 6-12) for more than 60 years. Geologists estimate that the stress stored in the San Francisco region is already equal to that released in the 1906 earthquake that devastated northern California. If all this energy were released in one great earthquake, it would result in the greatest natural disaster in the history of North America.

Still another precursor involves deliberately passing an electric current into the ground in one area and measuring the remaining field several miles (kilometers) away. Such measurements yield data on the *resistivity* of the rocks—that is, how easily the rocks pass electric current. Resistivity seems to decrease for some rocks prior to an earthquake (Figure 6-20), perhaps because of the inrush of naturally circulating under-

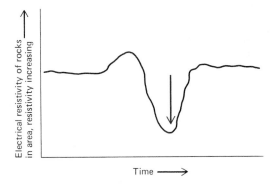

6-20

Substantial changes in the resistivity of the rocks to the passage of an electric current suggest that the rocks gain in resistance as cracking occurs in dry rock, creating air space and high resistance. As water then flows into the dilatant rock, resistivity falls, because the rock becomes a better conductor of electric current. Incoming water also lubricates the cracks, and earthquake slip follows.

ground water as the rocks experience intensified cracking. As the rocks become more highly saturated with water, their resistance to the passage of electric current falls, as does their resistance to the imposed stress. Rock failure follows when the saturated rocks can no longer withstand the load placed on them.

Monitoring the level, color, chemistry, and temperature of water in local wells may, in some areas, serve as a warning of impending earthquakes. The rise and fall of water in a well may be related to several variables, including rain, but may also reflect the change in the regime of underground water as it rushes in to fill the open space cracks in a dilatant, strongly strained rock. Again, the larger the area over which an anomaly is recognized, the greater the resulting earthquake will be if all other factors controlling the water level have been evaluated.

Unusual changes in the temperature or color of the water may also suggest imminent earthquake activity if the water in the well has an underground connection with the area undergoing strain. In one of the more successful methods of earthquake prediction, the content of a radioactive substance, *radon-222,* is continuously monitored. **Radon** is a product of the natural radioactive decay of elements that is going on within the earth at all times and is normally present in well water in minute amounts. The internal cracking that may precede earthquakes gives underground water sudden access to newly shattered rock and to a rich harvest of newly released radon. A rise in radon levels (Figure 6-21) may presage earthquakes *if* the well has access to a zone of cracking and dilation; if not, the radon level of the water should remain reasonably constant for many years.

All of the preceding phenomena *may* herald an earthquake if *adequate instrumentation to detect the phenomena for many years have been installed; the data must be continuously plotted and monitored to yield baseline data prior to a time of strain buildup.* Such systems of instrumentation, recorders, monitors, and evaluators are *expensive,* and earthquake prediction is still in its infancy. Even though early predictions will undoubt-

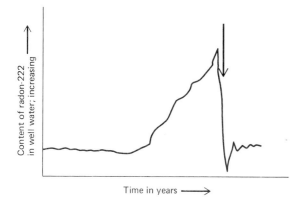

6-21

A chart of the hypothetical changes in the content of radon-222, a gaseous element formed by the decay of radium (see Appendix B). Radon is commonly present in minute quantities in well water as a result of the radioactive decay of elements in the rocks surrounding the water well. As the rocks near the well undergo more and more severe dilation and cracking, larger amounts of trapped radon are released into the well water. Radon content peaks at, or just before, earthquake. Such changes have been recognized before many earthquakes.

edly touch off some false alarms and be couched in probability statements, the benefit to cost ratio may be favorable. If a warning system costing half a billion dollars gave a sufficient warning so that 10,000 lives were saved in San Francisco by evacuation and billions of dollars in property were properly strengthened before the quake, thus minimizing the property damage, would the cost be worth the results?

One method of earthquake prediction does not require the outlay of seemingly endless dollars for instruments, technicians, computers, and evaluators, but it is the most controversial of all the methods we can mention. The Chinese have insisted for more than 10 years that careful observation of the behavior of domestic animals may well provide a premonition of earthquake activity; snakes are alleged to leave their holes, and dogs and cats scurry around in a frenzy. Chinese scientists tell skeptical Western scientists this is one of their important forecasting weapons. Before dismissing this as folklore, one should recall the well-documented tales of the fire horses of San Francisco attempting desperately to leave their stalls the night before the 1906 earthquake and the other stories of erratic animal behavior prior to the disaster.

Recent study of animal laboratory records in California has yielded an unexpected dividend. Tree-dwelling chimpanzees kept for experimental purposes have been observed to spend an *unusual* amount of time on the ground *just before* some low- to moderate-magnitude earthquakes in central California. Some scientists are now convinced that many animals may pick up subtle clues prior to earthquakes. No one knows what signs animals sense, but the case for animal observation as one more piece of evidence in earthquake prediction seems moderately strong.

Social Implications

Suppose the U.S. Geological Survey, based on the best scientific information available today, released the following news release: "Based on numerous precursory signs, there is an 80 percent chance that a magnitude 8.4 to 8.7 earthquake will strike San Francisco within the next 2 years. Further earthquake advisories will be issued as more definitive information is available." In such a scenario, what happens next?

We have little experience with major earthquakes; they are, fortunately, rare. False alarms are possible, and it may be *even more difficult* to declare an area earthquake safe. No one knows at this time how to say when danger ceases after a series of quakes or how to say that *any* area is *absolutely certain* to be free of earthquake activity. No doubt some earthquakes will occur without being predicted, particularly when instrumentation and baseline data in an area are sparse and poorly funded.

The social, legal, and economic consequences of earthquake prediction are staggering. Will all construction and repair work cease in an area that is soon to be devastated? Will all insurance be withdrawn after a prediction, or will premiums skyrocket? Who pays the cost of strengthening a building against an earthquake? Indeed, who pays the large costs involved in establishing the instrumentation and manpower for earthquake prediction? If a prediction turns out to be erroneous, who has the legal liability for the prediction? Does property astride a fault zone along which movement is imminent have *any* value at all and, if not, why pay taxes on it? Would the forecast of an earthquake create almost instant ghettos of property that have little or no value and are ripe for vandalism before the earthquake? Would massive fires result as property owners strove to collect the value of their property from fire insurance before it lost all its value in an uninsured holocaust? There will be no obvious signs of an imminent earthquake, no storm clouds whirling outside the window. Will people believe?

Why maintain a building that will soon be leveled? Would massive unemployment in the building and maintenance fields follow an earthquake prediction? How should the prediction of the soothsayers and itinerant prophets who will swarm like locusts to a site of future ruin be handled?

This last concern is already under study; people who desire to predict earthquakes, by whatever methods, are now encouraged to lodge their prediction with the U.S. Geological Survey prior to the event, so that the accuracy of their predictive method can be *objectively* established. The track record of private individuals to date has been abysmal.

Reputable scientists treat this time as a time of research and development that is rich with promise; adequate predictive services are perhaps several decades away. No one doubts that earthquake prediction will come, if we only have the will to support the effort to allay our oldest scourge before it strikes without warning.

The ability to predict earthquakes scientifically may arrive before we have the social and legal structures to handle predicted disasters, but prediction will become a fact of life in the heavily instrumented areas of the United States during the 1980s. The social,

economic, and legal aspects will probably be worked out *ad hoc,* although numerous study commissions involving the U.S. Geological Survey and political agencies are studying the ramifications of prediction.

The basic scenario should involve a long-term statement that a large area has an elevated level of seismic risk within the next few years or months. Such a generalized warning will most likely be followed by moving monitoring teams and portable equipment into the area of risk. As time goes on, estimates of magnitude, epicenter, and time of the earthquake should improve in precision as more data are accumulated. As time runs down to days or hours before the expected event, evacuation orders could be issued. Buildings would have been strengthened during the lead period, and particularly dangerous structures might well be demolished. *Much can be done* with several years or months of warning and with more and more accurate time, location, and magnitude statements that were made possible by constantly increasing amounts of portable monitoring equipment moved in to target the affected area.

Examples of this kind of growing specificity of prediction over a long lead time are not science fiction. They have been a fact of life in China in the 1970s, and there were reported successes in Russia and Japan as well. There also have been some false alarms, and some quakes have occurred without adequate prediction; both will continue to occur. Earthquake prediction relies not only on expensive, sophisticated equipment and the monitoring team to observe and evaluate data, but also on a state of scientific understanding of the mechanics of faulting that can now only be described as developing. In lightly instrumented areas, little or no predictive service will be available, and the devastation associated with earthquakes will continue to plague us. Again, the persistent value question arises. Equipment and monitoring teams are expensive; what is the value of a human life?

EARTHQUAKE PREVENTION—A PROSPECTUS

The possibility that earthquakes could be predicted and controlled comes from a combination of unhappy accident and shrewd observation. In the mid-1960s, the Army drilled a deep well just north of Denver and disposed of water contaminated with nerve gas by pumping it under high pressure into the rocks surrounding this deep well. At about the same time that the Army started pumping, Denver began experiencing its first earthquakes in decades. The Army kept pumping, and earthquakes continued, their cause unsuspected. Then Charles Evans, a geologist who was looking over pumping records, noticed that water injection was *coincident with* earthquakes. When the pump was shut down, earthquakes ceased. He surmised that the high-pressure water was being forced deep underground into an old, locked fault, which allowed the faulted rocks to move. Like Fleming's discovery of penicillin in an unwashed petri dish, linking pumping and earthquake activity together was a triumph of luck and shrewd intuition.

Later, geologists with the U.S. Geological Survey attempted to duplicate the Army's unknowing efforts at earthquake triggering in the Rangely Oil Field in western Colorado. There oil companies had been forcing high-pressure water underground to stimulate oil recovery; they had been producing minor earthquakes. The scientists arranged to "borrow" four wells for detailed tests. Raising the water pressure in wells astride old fault zones kicked off earthquakes; lowering the water pressure brought seismic quiet. For the first time, scientists had deliberately turned earthquakes on—and then turned them off.

Now let us speculate together. Drill several dozen wells along the San Andreas Fault, deep into the zone of locked, stressed rock. Pump high-pressure water into alternate wells, and pump water out of their neighbors. In the newly wet wells, the fault is lubricated and slips, passing the stress along to the next dry well, which remains locked. Now reverse the pumps, pumping high-pressure water into dry wells and water out of the alternate wet ones. The newly wet wells lubricate the fault zone again, and stress is passed on down the fault zone. By alternating wells, stress could be passed down the fault zone and out to sea, where it would presumably do less harm. What we have done is create a rippling effect; thousands of small earthquakes progressively pass the stress along to their neighbors at energy levels that are below the damage level.

Such speculation sounds like just that—speculation. No one has ever tried such an experiment in the highly stressed rocks of a major fault zone. No one has ever drilled *into* a major fault zone, but we do know that with lesser faults, altering water pressure controls quake frequency; the same results might reasonably be expected with larger faults. If we try, many tens of millions of dollars will be required for drilling and pumping time and equipment. If we fail, either nothing will happen or unmanageably large quakes will be produced with consequent liabilities. If we succeed, our ancient dream of controlling the destructive forces within the earth will have been realized. If we do not try at all, the stresses build up ominously every day, and we can only hope to predict adequately when the next savage trembling will shake our works into ruin once again.

A program to probe the San Andreas Fault with wells exists on paper at this time. The theory to support gradual release of stored stress from faults by water injection exists, and one field experiment suggests that the theory works.

No one should underestimate the uncertainties of such a project. No one has ever drilled into an area where stresses of such magnitude exist. New drilling technologies would be needed. The scale of such a project dwarfs the earlier Rangely Oil Field experiment, where much more was known. Extensive preliminary investigations would be needed. Such a project would be quite a gamble—equivalent in scale to an earlier commitment to place humans on the moon.

All that remains now is the financial commitment to attempt the project. The project may fail miserably, and the knowledge gained may be very expensive. The project may never be funded, and we will only wonder if it would have worked as we await the coming great earthquake. Or the project just might succeed, and we would have entered a new age. Our oldest affliction would have been brought under control.

A JOURNEY TO THE CENTER OF THE EARTH

Earthquakes yield more than violence. The passage of body waves through the earth offers insights into the nature of the inner earth, and the pattern of earthquake sources on the surface of the earth is one link in the evidence for a unified theory of the earth, presented in the next chapter. First consider earthquake energy passing through the earth's interior. Two fundamental questions must be answered before we continue. What *is* a seismic wave? *How* does earthquake energy move through the earth?

Some Basics

A seismic wave is difficult to visualize; it is only partially made visible by a seismograph. Attach one end of a long rope to a handy tree, pull it taut, and then shake the unattached end up and down. The result is familiar (Figure 6-22). A looping waveform is created and travels down the rope to its atached end. Notice that the curving *form* moves down the length of the rope, while the cord *itself* moves only up and down. The *speed of forward advance* of the looping wave *pattern* is the **wave velocity;** the rope is NOT moving up and down at the same speed. The wave velocity (the speed of forward motion of the waveform) remains constant. The speed of the up and down motion of the rope ranges from zero (at the point where the motion reverses) to some other constantly changing value. A **wave,** then, *is a pattern that propagates through a substance while the particles in the substance vibrate back and forth.* For the particles to vibrate, they must be *connected,* so that each particle affects its neighbor, and the vibrating substance must be *elastic,* so that displaced particles will return to their original position as the waveform travels on. The propagation (transmission) of a wave requires temporary displacement of particles; the substance is temporarily (elastically) deformed.

As a substance is deformed, two major

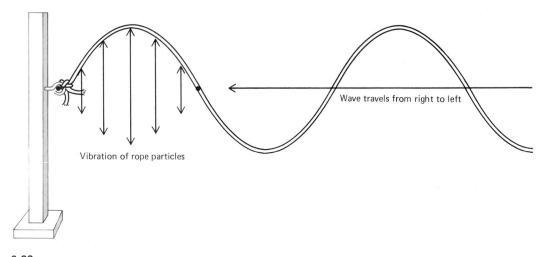

Wave travels from right to left

Vibration of rope particles

6-22
Take a limp piece of line, attach one end to a wall, and set the other end into vertical motion. The waveform travels from right to left. Any *point* on the rope vibrates up and down; the rope does not move horizontally at all. The velocity of the wave is constant; the velocity of vertical vibration of the rope changes constantly from point to point.

measurements of the extent of deformation are critical. The **bulk modulus** is a measure of any substance's resistance to a *change in volume* (its compressibility); the **shear modulus** is a measure of resistance to a *change in shape* (the rigidity of the material). The greater the bulk modulus, the more incompressible the material; the greater the shear modulus, the more *rigid* the material. Ordinary concrete has a high bulk modulus but a relatively low shear modulus. A concrete pillar may support a very large deadweight acting down its length but fail when smaller forces act normal to its length. The greater the value of the two moduli, the more strongly the particles are *connected* and the greater their resistance is to temporary displacement. The wave velocity, observed in thousands of experiments with many different materials, *rises* with rising bulk and

shear moduli; THE MORE INCOMPRESSIBLE AND RIGID A SUBSTANCE, THE FASTER THE WAVE PROPAGATES THROUGH IT.

One other factor that affects wave velocity is *density* (mass per unit of volume). The density of minerals was described in Chapter Two. It relates to the total mass of material in any particular volume. We *feel* density as the weight or "heft" of material under the influence of gravity. To a seismic wave, denser material contains larger amounts of particles per unit of volume; therefore *more* particles need to be disturbed as the wave passes. DENSER MATERIALS SLOW THE WAVE SPEED; LESS DENSE MATERIALS ALLOW MORE RAPID PROPAGATION OF THE WAVEFORM.

No other factors have been observed to affect wave velocity, so we can tentatively summarize our observations as follows.

$$\text{Wave vel. } \alpha \frac{\text{bulk mod. and shear mod.}}{\text{density}}$$

This generalized statement tells us that seismic energy travels through the earth as waveforms whose propagation speed depends on *three* measurable criteria. (The symbol "α" means "proportional to.")

The statement is also a fairly exact form of the relation observed when a P-wave travels through solid material. Liquids, on the other hand, exhibit a substantial bulk modulus, but *no* resistance to shear. By definition, a *liquid* has *no rigidity,* because a liquid flows instantaneously when one attempts to change its shape. It is impossible to talk about the shape of a liquid; a liquid adopts the shape of its container and offers no resistance to shearing forces. The wave velocity of a P-wave passing through a liquid (or a gas) is directly related to the bulk modulus alone, since the shear modulus is zero. Note that *P-waves should propagate more slowly through liquids than through solids,* because the accelerating effect of the shear modulus is now absent from our equation.

P-waves can pass through any material, although at diminished speed in liquids and gases. P-waves, as stated earlier, are waves that alternately compress and expand the particles they vibrate in a direction *parallel with* their line of propagation. Sound waves act in exactly the same way; P-waves are simply familiar sound waves generated by the vibrating earth, much as a vibrating guitar string generates music. The P-wave is the fastest of the waves, traveling through surface rock at speeds averaging 3 miles (5 kilometers) per second.

The S-wave travels or propagates by causing particles to oscillate in a direciton *perpendicular to* the line of travel, like the rope

in Figure 6-22. This method causes the substances affected by an S-wave to *change its shape, but not its volume.* S-waves affect materials unlike P-waves, which temporarily change *both* the *volume and shape of solids* and the *volume* of liquids and gases through which they pass. If we describe the effect of materials on S-waves, our statement is straightforward.

$$\text{Wave velocity (S-wave) } \alpha \frac{\text{shear modulus}}{\text{density}}$$

Notice that the bulk modulus is absent from this statement of relation, because no compression takes place as shear waves pass. This equation also gives us some more information that will soon become critical: *S-waves can only travel through rigid materials* (those having an appreciable shear modulus). S-waves cannot travel through fluids or gases, since they have no rigidity and cannot be sheared. S-waves travel more slowly than P-waves, averaging perhaps 60 percent of P-wave velocity.

Summarizing this background information will be useful, because the relation between seismic wave velocity, wave type, and the properties of the material through which the waves pass is critical as we attempt to view the interior of our earth. A summary of the interdependent properties of seismic waves and earth materials is given in Table 6-1.

We will now use velocity data to obtain information on the properties of the inner earth. But how are velocity data obtained? Because hundreds of thousands of earthquakes have occurred, the relation between travel time and distance to source has been well established (Figure 6-23). An analogy will help to clarify the assumption at work in the construction of this graph of travel time

6-1

Variation of Wave Velocity as a Function of Material Properties

Material and Wave Type	Effect of Variation in Material Properties on Wave Velocity			
	Increasing Density	Increasing Resistance to Compression	Increasing Rigidity (Resistance to Shear)	Increasing Fluidity
P-wave in a solid	Slows	Speeds	Speeds	Slows
P-wave in a fluid or a gas	Slows	Speeds	Rigidity absent	Slows
S-wave in a solid	Slows	No effect	Speeds	Slows or stops
S-wave in a fluid or a gas	Wave velocity is zero due to lack of rigidity; wave does not travel			

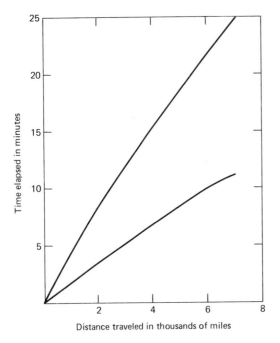

6-23

This is a sample of a time-travel chart for earthquake body waves. Can you figure out which line belongs to the P-wave and which belongs to S-wave? Compare to Figure 6-2.

versus distance. If friends leave their home 4 miles (7 kilometers) away and join you 16 minutes later, their average velocity was ¼ mile (⅖ kilometer) per minute.

As each earthquake occurs, seismic energy radiated into the earth follows many paths (Figure 6-24), but all the paths *curve,* because the *wave velocity increases at varying rates as depth increases.* The curving of the wave paths is known as **refraction** and is a consequence of the changing wave velocity. Other waves **reflect** from layering within the earth and eventually bounce back to the earth's surface (Figure 6-25).

The Layered Earth

Two pieces of information are immediately available: the wave velocities of body waves increase as they penetrate more deeply into the earth, and the earth's interior is *concentrically layered,* much like an onion. The skin of the layered earth is an outer crust, ranging in thickness from 3 miles (5 kilometers) to more than 35 miles (56 kilometers); it is divisible into thin, *basaltic oceanic* crust

180   Deeper Reflections Earthquakes

and thicker, *granitic continental* crust (Figure 6-26). P-waves passing through continental crust have average velocities of 3 miles (5 kilometers) per second, which is typical of granitic rock; similar waves traverse the ocean basins with velocity values near 4 miles (7 kilometers) per second, which is typical of basaltic rock. Deep drilling confirms these fundamental facts; *continents are mostly thick granitic masses* with a thin sedimentary veneer covering most of their surface; the *ocean basins* are *exclusively basaltic* and remarkably *thin*.

The crust is the *least dense* layer of the earth, with an average density three times that of water. It floats on the denser underlying mantle like a giant iceberg, the weight of the crust supported by the buoyancy of the mantle. But what madness is this to talk about floating and buoyancy in relation to a solid mantle? The mantle *must* be solid, because it transits both P-waves and S-waves and *fluids* will not allow S-waves to pass. The problem, again, is our concept of a solid (see Chapter Five); what is an elastic solid to the fleeting passage of seismic energy may be a fluid to loads that have been imposed for many thousands of years.

One of the more interesting examples of the long-term fluidity or rheidity (see Figure 5-22) of the mantle is the continuing slow rise in elevation of large areas of the north-central United States. This gentle, broad uplift reflects the rebound of this area from the load imposed by glacial ice, which last retreated from the area only about 10,000 years ago. The continental crust is like a great ship that has just been unloaded but floats deep in molasses; the continental "ship" is still sluggishly rising to a new equilibrium. Mantle material must slowly flow in under rising continental areas, much as a ship that is being unloaded continues to ride higher and higher in the water.

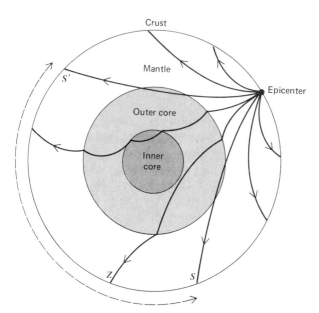

6-24
This sketch depicts the earth sliced through its center. A shallow-focus earthquake yields a multiple wave path. Only a few are shown and, for clarity, no reflected waves are shown (see Figure 6-25). In the zone *S-Z, no* direct wave energy is received, since *refraction* spreads the waves paths. In the much wider zone *S-S'*, no direct S-waves are received, since the outer core absorbs any S-waves; they are only received by recording stations situated so that the S-waves have traveled through crust and mantle. By recognizing and explaining the S-wave "shadow zone," the zone of no S-wave arrivals, and by computing the time-distance curves, a composite picture of the inner earth is created.

A Journey to the Center of the Earth **181**

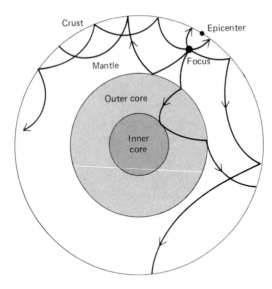

6-25
This sketch displays some of the *reflected* wave paths produced by seismic energy released in a deep-focus earthquake. Some of the waves bounce repetitively off of the crust, shown here in true scale as the thickness of the outer line in the circle. Other waves bounce off of the outer core discontinuity, while still others reflect from the inner core/outer core interface.

The concept of equilibrium between crust and mantle is simply a restatement of the Archimede's principle, which was discussed in Chapter Two, but it is now called the **principle of isostasy.** Briefly, the principle of isostasy suggests that crust and mantle are in almost buoyant equilibrium; higher elevations are attained where the crust is less dense and thicker, and lower elevations are common where the crust is both denser and thinner. High topography requires large buoyant forces to support it; lower topography requires less buoyancy to maintain its subdued level.

Beneath the crust is the **mantle,** about 1800 miles (2900 kilometers) thick. The mantle is about 80 percent of the volume of the earth. P-wave velocities within the mantle range from 5 miles (8 kilometers) per second near the crust-mantle contact to approximately 9 miles (14 kilometers) per second at the mantle-core contact. A distinct zone of low velocity occurs between 50 and 200 miles (80 and 300 kilometers) beneath the earth's surface. This low-velocity zone is anomalous (Figure 6-26) in a mantle where wave velocity *increases everywhere else,* and it has been named the **asthenosphere.**

The asthenosphere strongly muffles earthquake waves and causes a sharp reduction in the wave velocity of S-waves that pass through it. Both of these responses suggest that the asthenosphere is not wholly solid, but exists as a crystalline mush that has the structural properties of snowy slush on a warming sidewalk. Like *all* of the mantle, the asthenosphere seems to be composed of material that is chemically similar to olivine-rich basalt; only in the asthenospheric region does this material apparently undergo partial melting. Other evidence indicates that the asthenosphere may be partially fluid; it has been suggested that the asthenosphere *is the primary source* for basaltic lava erupted on the earth's surface, many miles (kilometers) above.

The asthenosphere separates the outer 200 miles (300 kilometers) of the earth into two separate zones of distinctly different properties. Above the asthenosphere is the **lithosphere,** a shell less than 60 miles (100 kilometers) thick, which transmits P-waves and S-waves efficiently at velocities higher than those characteristic of the asthenosphere. The lithosphere is a zone of solidity, rigidity, and strength; it encompasses both continental granitic and oceanic basaltic

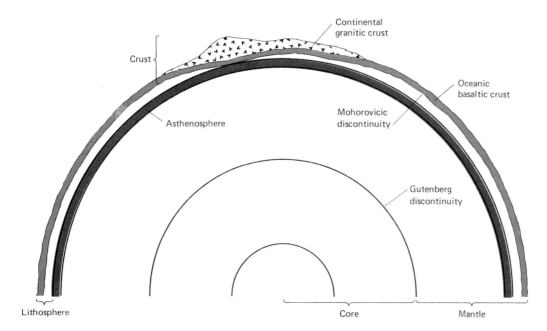

Continental
granitic crust

Crust

Oceanic
basaltic crust

Mohorovicic
discontinuity

Asthenosphere

Gutenberg
discontinuity

Lithosphere

Core

Mantle

6-26

Schematic view of the earth. Scale is approximate; if drawn to true scale, the crust would be a single thin line. In terms of CHEMISTRY, the important separation is between the granitic continents and the basaltic ocean basins, jointly underlain by the mantle. In terms of subdivisions revealed by SEISMIC WAVES, a low-velocity crust is sharply separated by the Mohorovicic discontinuity from a higher-velocity mantle beneath. The mantle, in turn, is set off from the core by the Gutenberg discontinuity, the boundary at which S-waves are absorbed. In terms of large-scale STRUCTURES, the earth has only two layers of importance: (1) the outer, solid, rigid *lithosphere,* which includes the crust and uppermost mantle; and (2) the *asthenosphere,* a zone of fluidity within the upper mantle that is both a magma source to the crust and a zone that allows isostatic compensation of the crust. The "plates" on the earth's surface extend through the lithosphere and rest on the asthenosphere.

crust in its upper part and also includes the uppermost mantle. Below the asthenosphere is the middle and lower mantle, which shows long-term fluidity.

The **Mohorovicic discontinuity** (Figure 6-26) is the boundary between crust and mantle *within the lithosphere;* it is named after its Yugoslavian discoverer. The Mohorovicic discontinuity (*Moho* for short) was recognized by Mohorovicic as the zone of abrupt velocity increase between crust and mantle, marking the area where wave velocities typical of the crust abruptly change to those characteristic of the uppermost mantle. The continental crust seems to be the end product of chemical differentiation of the mantle (see Chapter Three), and the oceanic crust seems to reflect much less change from its underlying parent mantle. *Although continental crust, oceanic crust, and uppermost mantle have some striking chemical dissimilarities, they form a structurally coherent, relatively rigid, solid layer as the outermost shell of the earth, the lithosphere.*

The outer 200 miles (300 kilometers) of the earth furnish one of the most exciting research frontiers in geology today. As the next chapter will suggest, recognition in the 1960s of the rigid nature of the lithosphere, the outer 60 miles (100 kilometers) of the earth, and the semifluid nature of the asthenosphere beneath the rigid lithosphere led to a totally new theory of the earth. A solid slab floating on a semifluid layer has possibilities beyond the imagination of geologists in the 1950s; we will soon discuss this topic.

Beneath the asthenosphere, numerous other zones can be recognized based on high quality data from modern seismographs. A *transition zone* beneath the asthenosphere is revealed by sharp increases in wave velocities as total solidity returns and abrupt changes in density occur under very high pressures. The details of the fine structure of the middle and lower mantle need not concern us here, although these same details raise interesting questions about possible vertical motion in the mantle in the next chapter. Density and velocity increase gradually as waves penetrate ever more deeply into the mantle; both properties reflect pressures that now rise to values of several million times atmospheric pressure on the earth's surface, with consequent increases in the incompressibility and rigidity of the mantle's rocky material.

The contact of the mantle with the outer **core** is marked by the **Gutenberg discontinuity,** which is named for its discoverer. The Gutenberg discontinuity marks a *second* major break in the normal pattern of constantly increasing velocity downward. As seismic waves strike the outer core, three things occur simultaneously: (1) S-wave velocity falls to zero, suggesting that the outer core is liquid, (2) many P-waves bounce off the core-mantle interface, so that less compressional energy enters the core; and (3) the velocity of P-waves that enter the outer core falls abruptly to values more typical of the uppermost mantle (Figure 6-27) and the exiting waves are strongly refracted by this abrupt velocity change (Figure 6-24). Collectively, these three changes offer impressive evidence that the *outer core is fluid,* even under unimaginable pressures. One observable effect of the outer core is the **shadow zone,** where no direct earthquake energy is received from *any* earthquake (Figure 6-24) because of wave refraction and reflection from the outer core.

An abrupt increase in density separates the core from the mantle and provides much of the reason for the precipitous drop in P-wave velocity within the core (Figure 6-26). The mantle has a density ranging from 4 to 6, which is typical of its assumed olivine-rich basaltic composition when placed under increasing pressure. The density of the outer core ranges between 10 and 12 times that of water and must correspond to a totally new composition. Since the core is about *one-third* of the *mass* of the earth, it must be composed of fairly abundant material. Few substances are both sufficiently abundant and sufficiently dense, but iron, with small admixtures of silicon and nickel, will produce a core whose estimated physical properties under extreme pressure coincide with those observed.

There is still another reason for proposing that the outer core is composed mostly of molten iron. The earth generates its own

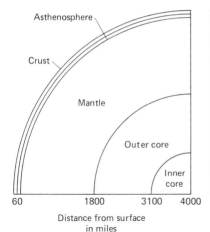

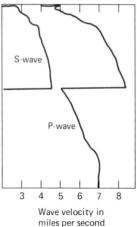

Asthenosphere

Crust

Mantle

Outer core

Inner core

S-wave

P-wave

60	1800	3100	4000

Distance from surface in miles

3 4 5 6 7 8

Wave velocity in miles per second

6-27
This diagram relates body wave velocity to the concentric shells within the earth. Both S-wave and P-wave velocity increase abruptly at the crust-mantle boundary (the Moho) and then increase steadily through the mantle. At the core-mantle boundary (the Gutenberg discontinuity), S-wave velocity drops to zero, and P-wave velocity is greatly retarded. On through the core, P-wave velocity gradually increases into the center of the earth.

magnetic field; its source was a mystery until geologists proposed a liquid, metallic outer core. Physicists were quick to point out that a rotating body of molten iron the size of the outer core would generate a magnetic field identical to the one that was actually observed. The reason our magnetic compasses work is now tied to a vast ball of spinning molten iron alloy, 1800 miles (2900 kilometers) and more beneath our feet.

An inner core whose density approximates 13 can be recognized. P-waves are speeded up once again, and the inner core responds as if it were a solid going all the way into the center of the earth. Its probable composition continues to be an iron alloy at pressures near 4 million times atmospheric pressure and at temperatures similar to those of the surface of the sun.

EARTHQUAKE ZONES—WHY?

After briefly investigating the earth's interior, a return to the surface concludes our journey toward greater understanding of

earthquakes. One question remains unasked. Do earthquake epicenters occur randomly over the earth or in distinct patterns? An answer to this question is crucial; if earthquakes occur randomly in time and space, their origin must be sought in random processes.

Our first task in attacking this question is to see how the location of the epicenter is obtained. In early investigations, the earthquake source area (focus) was assumed to be beneath the area where damage was greatest but, as we have seen, the nature of building foundation material is the major variable affecting damage. Epicentral location is, instead, obtained by cooperation among at least three seismographic recording stations at widely varying distances and directions from the epicenter.

Epicenter Determination

The principle is simple. If two racing cars cross the finish line exactly a minute apart, with car A averaging 5 miles (8 kilometers)

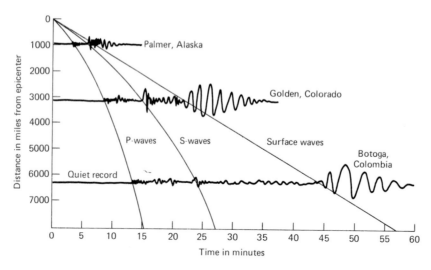

6-28

The colored lines in the sketch are seismograms of the same earthquake recorded by three progressively distant seismographs. The sweeping diagonal lines connect all points on the seismograms at which P-, S-, and surface-waves *first* arrive at the station. Each diagonal line defines a time-distance curve; each line is a travel-time curve. Notice that the *difference* in arrival time of the waves at *any one recording station* is a direct function of the distance to epicenter. If several seismographic observatories plot the distance to epicenter as a radius, the intersecting arcs define the epicenter (see Figure 6-29). (Courtesy of the U.S. Geological Survey.)

a minute and car B averaging 4 miles (7 kilometers) a minute, how far away was their starting point? A bit of sixth-grade arithmetic (for most people the most difficult kind!) will quickly convince you that their starting point was 20 miles (32 kilometers) distant— the *only* point that could produce the observed *difference in their arrival times* at the average speeds given. Similarly, when the seismograph picks up the rumblings of the faster P-wave and, later, the slower S-wave, the time difference (see Figure 6-9) between them (their speed is well known) is a direct function of distance (Figure 6-28). Now *one* station knows the distance to the epicenter;

if three or more stations cooperatively plot their epicentral distances as radii of circles (Figure 6-29), the unique location for the epicenter is established. The location of the focus requires a bit more detailed calculation, as does the determination of the first slip direction along the fault, which is important to understanding the stresses that produce the motion.

In an average year, perhaps 1 million earthquakes affect sensitive seismographs— an average of approximately two earthquakes per minute. Before the advent of high-speed computers, the calculation and plotting of epicentral and focal information

186   Deeper Reflections Earthquakes

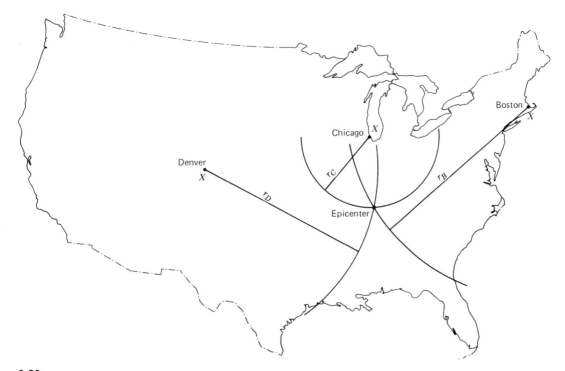

6-29
The simplest method of locating the epicenter is to find the time interval between the P-wave and S-wave arrivals at several seismographic stations. The distance from each station (r_D, r_C, and r_B) is then determined using travel-time curves (Figure 6-28) and plotted as a radius. The arcs intersect at a common point—the *epicenter*. In this example, seismographic observatories at Boston, Chicago, and Denver have located an earthquake in southeasternmost Missouri; a prolonged series of earthquakes between 1811 and 1812 in this same region were probably the most powerful earthquakes experienced in the United States in historical time.

was a time-consuming, laborious task. Within the last 20 years, computers have revolutionized **seismology,** the branch of geology that deals specifically with earthquake activity. High-quality seismographic stations, linked worldwide by telecommunication networks, compute and plot epicentral location data and focal position for thousands of earthquakes each year. The results were largely unexpected and have revolutionized our view of our not-so-solid earth.

An Unexpected Order

A cumulative plot of many years worth of focal information reveals unexpected, three-dimensional patterns of energy release. *Three narrow zones* on a world map (Figure 6-30) release more than *95 percent of the world's seismic energy.* Again, there is order; product reveals process. The outer 400 miles (650 kilometers) of the earth is divided by earthquake zones bounding irregu-

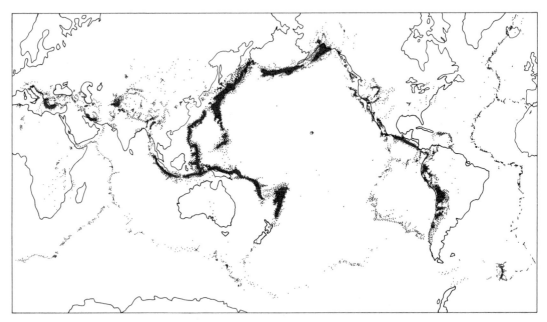

6-30
Plot of worldwide epicenter locations. One band of epicentral plots is within the world's ocean. A second band, with more numerous concentrations of points runs east-west through the Mediterranean-Alpine region. The most numerous earthquakes affect the Pacific rim. Epicenters plotted are for 1961–1969. (NOAA/EDS, U.S. Department of Commerce.)

larly shaped earth blocks, or "plates," that are mostly free of earthquakes. Within the seismic zones, further order is revealed. Earthquakes not only originate most often at plate boundaries, but they also form patterns dipping into the outer mantle in some areas (see p. 191).

The longest continuous seismic belt stretches nearly 50,000 miles (80,000 kilometers) around the world. It splits the Atlantic Ocean in half, swings around south and east of the African continent (mimicking its shape), with offshoots forming the Red Sea and splitting the eastern one-third of Africa; it then heads east across the southern Pacific, finally turns northeast, splits again off

South America, and runs inland under the Gulf of California (Figure 6-30). This belt yields about *5 percent* of the world's seismic energy in *shallow-focus earthquakes* (those occurring within the lithosphere). Along with shallow-focus earthquake activity, this zone also is a zone of modern *volcanism*, much of it submarine.

Studies of first motion or slip direction along this rifted zone reveal a movement pattern consistent only with *tension;* this zone represents areas of the earth where forces tend to *pull* the lithosphere *apart*, much as you would pull on a string to break it. Pulling in opposite directions on the lithosphere causes **rifts**, or **grabens**, faulted

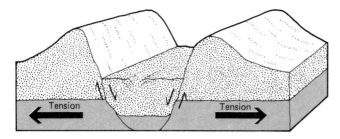

6-31

If a part of the earth's crust is being pulled apart by tensional forces within the crust, an area may collapse and move vertically downward with respect to its neighboring area. Such a depressed area is known as a *rift valley* or *graben*. Death Valley is a graben in the western United States; the Dead Sea of Jordan is another. Similar rift valleys are common in areas where the ocean floor has high seismic activity and basaltic volcanism.

areas where the central block (Figure 6-31) has sagged down to fill the space left when neighboring blocks are moved away from one another. The worldwide rift zone suggests that forces within the earth act to pull the lithosphere apart along nearly 50,000 miles (80,000 kilometers) of plate boundary, causing earthquakes *and* volcanic activity within the lithosphere. These rift zones are mostly, although not exclusively, oceanic; it seems that the Gulf of California, the Red Sea, and the rift zone of eastern Africa are also being spread apart by the same mysterious forces. Whatever the origin of the forces, (we will discuss this in the next chapter), logic demands another question. *If* the lithosphere is being torn apart in some areas, it must be compressed together in others *or,* is the lithosphere growing in volume? Keep that question in mind as we explore a little more.

A second seismic zone stretches in a series of curves eastward across the Mediterranean, the Caspian Sea, and the Himalayas and then south into the Bay of Bengal (Figure 6-30). This zone produces about *15 percent* of the world's seismic energy in shallow- and intermediate-focus earthquakes. Intermediate-focus earthquakes occur mostly *within* the asthenosphere; they are uncommon, since most earthquakes are of the shallow-focus type. Studies of the slip direction associated with the faults along this easterly trending seismic zone suggest that this is a zone of *compression,* because Eurasia and Africa, the Arabian Peninsula, and India are moving toward one another. Numerous high, young mountain chains, including the Alps and Himalayas, document what happens when continent crushes continent. This Alpine Himalayan zone seems to form much like a fold in a throw rug on a slick floor. The continental mass acts like the rug, and the asthenosphere provides the slick "floor"; both intermediate- and shallow-focus earthquakes are the result of the forces moving these continental landmasses together.

The third seismic zone encircles the Pacific Ocean Basin in a series of arcs that split into smaller arcs, bifurcating and rejoining as they split the Pacific world (Figure 6-32) into numerous smaller segments or plates. This zone yields fully *75* percent of the world's seismic energy and, with a rare exception or two, is the only place where *deep-focus* earthquakes occur. Deep-focus earthquakes stretch from the bottom of the

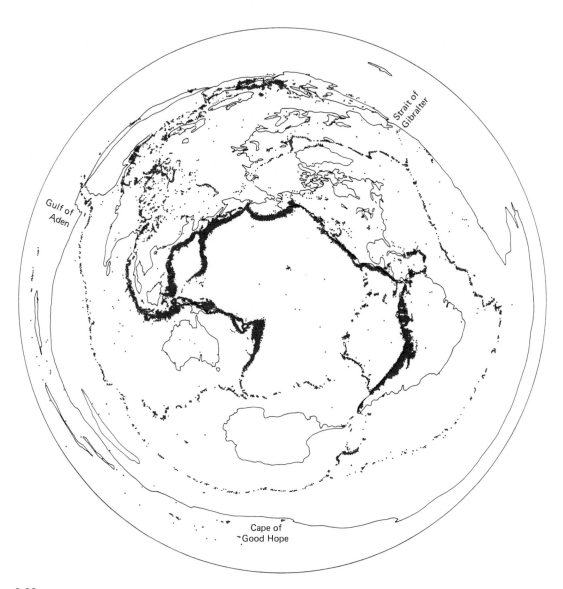

6-32
Epicenters for 10 years (1963 to 1973) plotted on an azimuthal equidistant projection centered on the Pacific Ocean. This plot reveals the concentration of earthquake foci around the Pacific especially clearly. (Plot by NOAA/EDS, U.S. Department of Commerce.)

asthenosphere down to 400 miles (700 kilometers), the deepest earthquakes ever recorded. Deep-focus events are rare, comprising about 3 percent of all earthquakes, and cannot originate by the same elastic or dilational processes that seem to trigger shallow-focus slippage. Both deep- and intermediate-focus earthquakes must involve processes other than simple shearing, which seems to be impossible at the high pressures that are typical of depths greater than 60 miles (96 kilometers). Laboratory experiments as well as the waveforms produced by intermediate- and deep-focus earthquakes suggest that they may originate because of dramatic volume loss as rocky material loses chemically bound water and shifts its atomic packing to a denser form.

Shallow-, intermediate-, and deep-focus events are all part of the Pacific rim. Volcanoes are commonly associated with both intermediate- and deep-focus areas and with slip directions that suggest that the Pacific Basin margin is *largely a zone of compression* whose forces are directed perpendicular to the earthquake zones. Even more intriguing, when viewed in three dimensions, the earthquake foci are progressively deeper the further into the continents their epicenters plot (Figure 6-33). Such a pattern suggests that compression may be accommodated by movement on great faults that dip under the continents, as if the Pacific Ocean Basin was being stuffed *under* the granitic and andesitic rocks that rim it.

In still other areas, slip along faults suggests that the segments or plates are grinding past one another and that their motion is primarily horizontal. Now the plates act like cars that sideswipe one another as they head in opposite directions; one such zone of sliding contact is the San Andreas Fault of southwestern California. It is typical of the many sliding fault zones around the Pacific Basin; seismic activity is all shallow focus and occasionally devastating; large energy buildups along locked fault zones are one apparent cause. Volcanic activity may be almost absent, as in California, or abundant, as in New Zealand.

The association of volcanism with the compressive margins of the Pacific Basin has

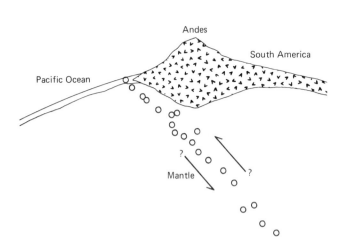

6-33
Earthquake foci beneath the western edge of South America establish a continent-ocean margin that seems to be a steeply inclined zone of contact and sliding. Such margins are typical of much of the Pacific rim and suggest strong compression forcing continents up and over the Pacific Ocean Basin. Sketch is not to scale; earthquake foci go down to 400 miles (650 kilometers) under the Andes, which reach not quite 5 miles (8 kilometers) above sea level.

earned it the name Pacific Ring of Fire (Chapter Three). The volcanoes occur in great arcuate patterns across the Pacific map; associated with them are deep oceanic trenches that *parallel* their seaward margin. These oceanic trenches, or **foredeeps,** seem to be linear downfolds of the ocean floor that dive to depths in excess of 6 miles (10 kilometers). The foredeeps are the site of shallow-focus earthquakes, with deeper-focus earthquakes progressively landward from them. Thus, the associated volcanoes and islands are situated over landward-dipping earthquake zones and mark the edge of what *geologists would call the continent,* even though the marginal part may often still be under shallow inland seas or form a part of the continental shelf.

The Pacific rim is the most complex of the three major seismic zones; it combines both compressional and sliding margins, shallow-, intermediate-, and deep-focus earthquakes, great arcs of volcanic islands, and associated arcuate foredeeps into patterns of ordered destruction. In spite of the complexity just described, the patterns are there, and they can be understood in terms of segments of the earth, reaching occasionally down to 400 miles (645 kilometers) in depth, jostling one another in head-on collisions or grinding sideswipes. Such a revolutionary view of the earth comes from sensitive seismographs, massive computers and, central to all, patient humans asking questions of the earth. The questions developed because a new order was discovered within the shuddering earth; the answers are more fully developed in the next chapter.

SUMMARY

Our knowledge of the causes of earthquakes comes through twentieth-century research; before this time people could only appeal to fancied sources to explain the trembling earth that occasionally overwhelmed them. Now we know that shallow earthquakes originate either by the formation of a new fault, as stressed rocks yield by accelerating crack growth with the assistance of water, or by the storage of energy in rocks adjacent to an old fault, until that stored energy exceeds the frictional resistance along the fault.

The hazards along an old fault zone can be identified and an evaluation of risk made, which should lead to more intelligent city planning and construction codes. The longer the period of energy storage, the higher the risk. Approximately one-third the population of the United States live in zones of high seismic risk.

Earthquake prediction relies on increasing knowledge of the changes in rocks that precede earthquakes, changes that are detectable by monitoring instruments placed across zones of high seismicity. Earthquake prediction is in an early stage of research and development, but it may become a fact of daily life in the 1980s along heavily instrumented areas; extension of such a system to other parts of the United States awaits the demonstration of reasonable levels of precision and the infusion of very large amounts of money. The social and legal impacts of earthquake prediction remain to be worked out, while scientists ponder the possibility of earthquake prevention by forcing high-pressure water into locked fault zones, passing the stored strain safely down the fault zone into areas where it will do less harm.

The body waves generated by an earthquake produce a view of the inner earth divided into a rigid lithosphere, into which both granitic continents and basaltic ocean basins are embedded in buoyant equilibrium with their density and elevation, underlain by a more plastic layer, the asthenosphere. Both the asthenosphere and the lower part of the lithosphere are included in the mantle, a thick layer that has the composition of olivine-rich basalt. Beneath the mantle is the metallic core, which is divided into an outer liquid shell whose rotation with the earth generates our magnetic field and an inner core, which acts as a solid.

The pattern produced by plotted earthquake foci is one of the outer earth divided into numerous segments, or plates; each plate is relatively earthquake free in its interior but is bounded by zones of abundant seismic activity. Four kinds of boundaries exist: (1) tensional or rift boundaries where plates pull away from one another; (2) compressional or collision boundaries where continental crust collides with continental crust, and mountains are formed in the vise; (3) compressional boundaries where continents override ocean basins along deep, planar, landward-dipping earthquake zones; and (4) sliding boundaries, where plates grind against one another in a steady release of seismic energy or lock and then unstick, releasing stored energy.

Most earthquakes originate at plate margins, releasing the energy produced or stored as plates pull away, collide, dive under, or grind past one another. The source of energy that seems to cause plate motion is unknown but, in the next chapter, we will speculate on some possibilities. The source of energy for intermediate- and deep-focus earthquakes must in some way be related to plate motion, since they only occur along plate margins. Most models provide for abrupt volume changes, perhaps associated with water loss, as the triggering mechanism under very high pressures. The origin of earthquakes *within* the plates remains speculative and not yet well accounted for in the developing models of the earth.

EXERCISES   1. Earthquake *intensity* is a measure of damage, commonly related to the degree of surface shaking; earthquake *magnitude* describes the amplitude of maximum ground motion observed during an earthquake. Perhaps surprisingly, the relation between these two factors is only moderate and is quite variable from one earthquake to another. Can you suggest reasons why?

2. What is the seismic risk in the area where you live? If you do not know, how would you find out?

3. Where is the nearest fault that has the potential for moderate to strong earthquake activity? If you do not know, perhaps you should find out.

4. Of an earthquake area's total energy, recent estimates suggest that less than a one-tenth of 1 percent of the total energy is radiated as seismic energy. Much of the remainder is released as heat. In view of this, how would you explain the occasional photographically verified reports of strongly lighted night skies during earthquakes?

5. One recent hypothesis is that animals are sensitive to changes in the electrostatic charging of particles in the air at some time prior the earthquake. Is that hypothesis consistent with the information in Exercise 4? Could such a hypothesis be tested? How?

6. A new measure of earthquakes is termed *seismic moment;* it is the product of the shear modulus, amount of offset, and area of rupture. Why should many scientists feel that seismic moment is a more realistic describer of seismic energy than magnitude?

7. If one averages the slip observed along portions of the San Andreas Fault, an average rate of motion is about 10 feet (3 meters) per century. Estimated total offset of some geologic units cut and offset by the fault is 350 miles (565 kilometers). How long has the San Andreas Fault been a zone of movement (assuming the rate is unchanged)? Assuming the same rate, how long before San Francisco and Los Angeles [currently about 350 miles (565 kilometers) apart] will be a single metropolis?

8. If the earth's outer core became solid, what effects would that have on the earth?

9. If there had never been any chemical differentiation of lava material coming from the mantle, would the continents still stand much higher than the ocean basins? Explain.

10. What four components are necessary to qualify any statement as an earthquake prediction? Which of the four would be most difficult to make in a seismically active region? In a seismically inactive region?

11. On p. 189, a difficult question was asked. If the world's longest continuous earthquake zone suggests that the lithosphere is under tension, either (1) the crust is under precisely equal amounts of compression somewhere else, or (2) the lithosphere is growing in volume. Was the question ever answered? How could we test the hypothesis that the world is growing in volume? That the lithosphere is expanding?

SUGGESTED
READINGS

Bolt, Bruce A., 1978, *Earthquakes—A Primer,* San Francisco, W. H. Freeman, 241 pp.
> *Thorough, authoritative, modern, and inexpensive, this little book covers it all.*

Bolt, B. A., Horn, W. L., Macdonald, G. A., and Scott, R. F., 1975, *Geological Hazards,* New York, N.Y., Springer-Verlag, 328 pp.
> *As the title implies, this book covers the field of geologic hazards, including earthquake damage.*

National Academy of Sciences, 1976, *Predicting Earthquakes,* Washington, D. C., National Academy of Sciences, 62 pp.
> *The scientific and technical aspects, in language for any interested person.*

National Academy of Sciences, 1975, *Earthquake Prediction and Public Policy,* Washington, D.C., National Academy of Sciences, 142 pp.
> *A sobering paperback. Read this one to assess what an earthquake prediction would mean to people.*

Rikitake, Tsuneji, 1976, *Earthquake Prediction,* New York, N.Y., Elsevier Scientific, 357 pp.
> *Somewhat technical summary of the state of the art. Thorough review and excellent references.*

Yanev, Peter, 1974, *Peace of Mind in Earthquake Country: How to Save Your Home and Life,* San Francisco, CA., Chronicle Books, 304 pp.
> *How to evaluate earthquake hazards, how to make your own home more earthquake resistant, and much more. As the subtitle suggests, this book could save your home—and your life. Strongly oriented to the western United States.*

KEY
CONCEPTS

Causes

Elastic rebound-dilatancy for shallow focus; poorly understood for deeper focus, although related to plate margin interaction. Friction? Partial melting? Catastrophic water loss?

Effects

Surface faulting, ground motion, liquefaction, landslides, tsunamis, seiches.

Energy

Released as heat, light (?), electric disturbances of the atmosphere, and surface and body waves, waves transmitted by elastic distortion of rock; wave velocity affected by density, rigidity, incompressibility.

patterns of body wave travel reveal crust, mantle, asthenosphere, lithosphere, inner and outer cores, isostasy.

Prediction

Depends on recognition of altered rock state prior to earthquake which, in turn, depends on increasing knowledge of how rocks fail; some animals are sensitive to precursors? social implication of prediction poorly known.

Patterns

Earthquakes strongly confined to a few zones, which are zones of crustal tension, crustal compression, and sliding; earth's surface broken into a mosaic of relatively earthquake-free plates, whose margins release more than 99 percent of the world's seismic energy.

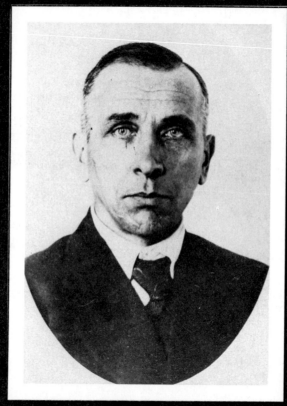

This photo of Alfred Wegener, taken sometime in the 1920s, captures the spirit of a scientist who looked for the forces that move mountains and continents. His ideas regarding continental displacement were the fertile ground from which the theories of plate tectonics emerged. (Photograph courtesy of United Press International.)

Chapter Seven

LARGER REFLECTIONS
Plate Tectonics

"To see things, it is necessary to believe them possible."
M. Bertrand (1891)

The ideas presented in this chapter have revolutionized our view of the earth as surely as Copernicus transformed our view of the earth's place in space. But ideas do not grow in ivory towers. They come from people and are judged by other people. If the ideas are revolutionary, they must overcome the emotional security of long-held ideas and the intellectual fashions of the day.

New ideas are the irritants of science, because scientific understanding is a human endeavor, and new concepts challenge current orthodoxy. Progress in understanding can only come from challenging the prevailing model, since understanding proceeds in uneven steps through time.

Mental models of the way things are may last a long time; Copernicus and Galileo stunned the world with the concept of a heliocentric (sun-centered) universe 2000 years after Ptolemy's earth-centered universe theory and thereby upset both the intellectual and religious worlds. Hutton and Lyell insisted that the world was a quiet battleground of cyclic, uniform, geologic processes; the catastrophic and Neptunian schools of thought resisted bitterly. Smith and Cuvier recognized that each form of fossil was unique to a particular layer of rock, and an orderly evolution of life was revealed; 50 years later Wallace and Darwin astonished the scientific community with their work in evolution.

There is a time for every idea, and a model advanced before its time is quickly negated by contrary prevailing opinion. Scientific understanding grows as new mental models replace older ones. Each model explains a series of known facts more acceptably than the model preceding it did and forecasts other not yet discovered or understood phenomena.

This chapter is concerned with two models. The first, *continental drift,* was developed by Wegener, a German meteorologist; its successor is *plate tectonics*. Although this chapter may seem, at first, to deal with models, it is really a study of scientific ideas—how they gain acceptance, where they come from, and the intensely human story of some of the scientists who spawned the ideas and others who spurned them.

CONTINENTAL DRIFT—A PERSPECTIVE

Briefly, the idea of **continental drift** suggests that all continents originated by the breakup, a few hundred million years ago, of a supercontinent whose pieces plowed through the ocean basins and the mantle to their current locations like giant ships drifting through warm tar. The notion is immediately an irritant, because it is obvious to us that the continents are permanent features of the earth's surface, just as it is obvious (on a clear night) that we are at the center of the universe. However, both of these "commonsense" perceptions are currently considered wrong; examination of the history of the idea of continental drift will help explain why.

From earliest times, humans regarded the continents on which they lived as permanent, and yet the evidence of change could be found in the rocks around them. Five centuries before Christ, Greek writers recognized fossils in sedimentary rocks as evidence that there was once marine life where there now was land. About A.D. 1200, a Chinese observer wrote: "In the high mountains I have seen shells. They are sometimes embedded in rocks. The rocks must have been earthy materials in days of old, and the shells must have lived in water. The low places are now elevated high, and the soft material turned into hard stone." One could not ask for a better observation or more lucid reasoning nearly 800 years later. Leonardo de Vinci made similar observations in Europe in the sixteenth century. Clearly, land and sea did not remain fixed; some way had to be found for land and sea to exchange places from time to time.

By the beginning of the twentieth century, still another puzzling aspect of continents needed to be explained. Fossil life from many continents was remarkably alike; how could such constancy among animal and plant species now separated by many thousands of miles of ocean be explained?

The Contraction Model

The answer to these and other questions seemed to be furnished by the *contraction theory,* which was the orthodox model for geology through the latter part of the nineteenth and the early part of the twentieth centuries. The contraction theory stated that the earth had originally been molten and was slowly cooling and contracting, or losing volume. Mountains originated on the earth's skin much as wrinkles did on the skin of an old, dried-out apple. Continents and ocean basins were regarded as essentially *alike;* the ocean basins merely represented the parts of the earth's crust that sank along gigantic fault zones while other areas (the continents) rose. If the ocean basins sank more deeply, water drained off the continents; as sediment filled in the ocean basins, the water level rose again.

As the ocean level fell, higher parts of the ocean basins became land bridges, and animals would wander back and forth among the continents at will, maintaining similar life forms on the continents. Then the sea rose,

and the land bridges were conveniently out of sight for a time. The contracting earth model was successful for its time; the ocean basins of the world were essentially unexplored, and the story of the lost continent of Atlantis furnished a happy analogy for the land bridges that appeared and disappeared.

In this model, *stability ruled.* The seas might oscillate gently up and down, ocean floors might subside, and continents might rise slightly, but all else was serene on a cooling earth. One could readily observe that the earth was losing heat in several ways, most obviously through volcanism. The earth was cooling and, therefore, shrinking.

Kelvin had used an *assumed* initial temperature and a reasonable cooling rate to figure the age of an originally molten earth— an age so young that uniformitarian geologists strongly protested. Kelvin, one of the most prestigious physicists of the day, replied, "If you cannot measure, your knowledge is meagre and unsatisfactory!" Reputation and great strings of numbers sustained Kelvin until another English physicist, Lord Rayleigh, the discoverer or argon, recognized that uranium, present in many rocks within the earth, provided the earth's own *source* of heat. Kelvin's model of a juvenile, steadily cooling earth was destroyed, because his strings of numbers were measurements based on an erroneous premise. The contraction model collapsed.

Continental Drift Before Wegener

At about the same time (1910), a 30-year-old German scientist, Alfred Wegener, recognized the remarkable similarity in the coastline shapes on each side of the Atlantic Ocean and wondered if the continents might represent pieces of some ancient jigsaw puzzle, separated, then strewn across the surface of the earth by unknown forces. Wegener was not the first to speculate in this direction; in 1620 Sir Francis Bacon had noted the congruent coastlines on a reasonably accurate map of the world without, however, suggesting how they might have originated.

The first person to have suggested a breakup of the Americas from Europe and Africa was Antonio Snider-Pelligrini, in 1858; he based his conjecture on the coastal fit of the Americas against the Old World. Snider-Pelligrini believed the breakup of the continental landmass to be the result of instability produced when all the continents were amassed together on one side of a rotating earth. Since the crust occupies about four-one-hundredths of 1 percent of the earth's mass, this source of the driving energy was quickly seen as unlikely. The concept died quickly; it was developed at a time when catastrophism was under severe attack by Lyell, and the rending of continents in two was most certainly a catastrophic idea.

In 1910, Frank B. Taylor, an American geologist, suggested that the young mountain ranges of the world are the result of the northern continents moving or drifting south against the ocean basins, India, and Africa from a point near Greenland. Read his description of the rift zone developed between Greenland (then believed to be a fragment of a still older continent, Atlantis) and Labrador.

We seem to have here a great irregular rift line along which North America has been torn away from Greenland. . . . Perhaps no one of these measurements . . . taken by itself is of much value, but the assembled group makes a strong case for the pulling away of North America from Greenland. . . . It is quite surprising to find the opposite walls of a rift 450 miles long pulled 560 miles apart, and still remaining so strikingly parallel . . . the [width of the] rift of the Labrador sea may therefore be taken tentatively as an approximate measure of the horizontal crustal movement of North America. . . .

Here was continental motion on a grand scale, its drive presumed to be tidal and gravitational forces. The breakup of the northern cluster of continents, *Atlantis,* and the southern cluster of continents, *Gondwanaland,* was believed to have taken place within the last few tens of millions of years. Thereafter, there was "a general crustal creep from high toward low latitudes in the northern hemisphere . . . [and] a rifting and pulling away of the earth's crust on all sides of Greenland. . . ."

Taylor's "general crustal creep" was continental drift, following the breakup of supercontinents Atlantis and Gondwanaland. His ideas of continental motion directed toward the equator were later restated, probably independently, by Wegener, but Taylor seems to have been the first to present some convincing evidence for continental drift. He felt that three lines of evidence were compelling: (1) the position of young arcs of mountains around the world, with associated rift zones, made sense in the context of continental breakup and drift equatorward; (2) evidence from the Mid-Atlantic Ridge (Figure 7-18); and (3) evidence of similar geologic histories between Africa and South America (Figure 7-1).

Taylor's discussion of the Mid-Atlantic Ridge is arresting reading that anticipated current thinking by 50 years. Others have suggested that revolutionary ideas, finally accepted, have usually long before been laid out in some detail, but ignored. Read what

Taylor said about the Mid-Atlantic Ridge *in 1910.*

One of the most remarkable and suggestive objects on the globe is the mid-Atlantic ridge. . . . The persistence with which this feature maintains a medial position in the ocean bed for nearly 9,000 miles (following its great curves) is very striking, and the position which it takes in passing between South America and Africa is still more remarkable. . . . It is apparently a horst ridge—a residual ridge along a line of parting or rifting—the earth-crust having moved away from it on both sides. . . . The great westward bulge of Africa north of the equator appears to fit very closely into the westward bend of the mid-Atlantic ridge, suggesting that Africa has drifted eastward from that position. . . . It is probably much nearer the truth to suppose that the mid-Atlantic ridge has remained unmoved, while the two continents on opposite sides of it have crept away in nearly parallel and opposite directions. The Cordillera [mountains] of South America show that that continent moved a considerable distance toward the west and northwest. . . . There are many bonds of union which show that Africa and South America were formerly united. . . . The release of strain [between Africa and South America] was found by a great diagonal fracture along which the crust divided in two parts that crept away in opposite directions. The mid-Atlantic ridge remained unmoved and marks the original place of that great fracture.

Taylor was greatly influenced by the writing of Eduard Suess, an Austrian geologist whose attempt to synthesize worldwide geology made him one of the giants of geology at the turn of the century. In 1893 Suess had published a brief suggestion as to the forces responsible for continental drift: "One is inclined to suspect that the formation of the curved chains in Asia, open to the north, stands in some connection or other with the outflow of superfluous earthmass from the pole—that is, with a flattening of the same." *There was the mechanism.* Taylor put it this way.

The same force [due to polar flattening, and held by Suess to be responsible for the rise and fall of the sea from the continents] must have been exerted at the same time and with the same power upon the land—that is, on the lithosphere or solid globe. And if it were, what would be the nature of the stresses set up and what movements might be expected when those stresses were relieved? . . . the earth being solid from its surface to its center, and more rigid than the hardest steel [a common assumption in 1910, and a critically important one as we'll soon see] . . . the forces would be . . . tangential forces radiating from the pole and affecting only a relatively thin crust. These forces would tend to cause the crust to creep away on lines of dispersion from the pole. An imaginary plane . . . gently sloping toward lower latitudes and situated beneath the earth's crust just within the zone of rock flowage, would seem to afford a basal slope down which the crustal sheets might move, and the tangential thrust forces exerted in the crust toward lower latitudes would tend to give the crust the requisite impulse to move.

The seed of continental motion is found in Taylor's massive exposition in 1910 on the "origin of the earth's plan." But the actual idea came from other germinal centers: Suess, whose thoughts published in German in 1898 may have been an important contribution to Wegener's later ideas, and Bailey Willis, a distinguished British geologist who proposed in 1907 that the mountains of Asia (including the Himalayas) were produced when the Pacific and Indian ocean basins underwent "northward spreading or underthrusting of the deep-seated mass beneath Asia."

How forward looking these ideas were! They anticipated current thinking by 50 to 70 years. A masterful compilation of ideas was now needed; first, however, one more critical link in these radical ideas, more evidence, had to be found.

DEVELOPMENT OF THE IDEA

Wegener, a German meteorologist, unencumbered by the geological prejudices of the day, was to spend the last 20 years of his short life marshaling the evidence and offering the idea of continental drift for others to attack savagely, at first, and eventually support. Starting in 1912, Wegener published his ideas in journals and four successive editions of his famous book, *The Origin of Continents and Oceans;* the last edition was published in 1929 prior to his untimely death in 1930. Wegener's major ability as a scientist was the breadth of his view and his willingness to test his own ideas; unlike many geological specialists who scorned all knowledge other than their own, Wegener searched for evidence throughout many diverse geologic fields and brought that evidence together.

Wegener assumed that all the landmasses of the world once must have been grouped together as a single supercontinent, **Pangaea**, meaning "all land." Pangaea broke apart perhaps 30 million years ago (Wegener's estimate in 1929), and the continents drifted to their current locations in the intervening time. For a man who spent most of his life in research on glaciers in Greenland, Wegener's own description is particularly apt.

South America must have lain alongside Africa and formed a unified block which was split in two ... the two parts must then have become increasingly separated over a period of millions of years like pieces of a cracked ice floe in water. The edges of these two blocks are even today strikingly congruent ... In the same way, North America at one time lay alongside Europe and formed a coherent block with it and Greenland ... Antarctica, Australia and India ... lay alongside southern Africa and formed together with it and South America a single large continent, partially covered by shallow water.

Figure 7-1 shows the reconstruction according to Wegener and is taken from the 1929 edition of his book.

Wegener pointed to five main lines of evidence supporting continental drift: (1) detection by repeated surveys of modern continental separation; (2) the congruence of the opposing Atlantic shorelines and the geologic correspondence in predrift rocks in continents now separated by the Atlantic Ocean; (3) fossil correspondence in predrift rocks in now separated continents; (4) distribution of ancient climates as revealed by the predrift rocks; and (5) isostatic equilibrium of the continents and oceans, yielding evidence on viscosity and the newly recognized substantial differences between continent and ocean floor.

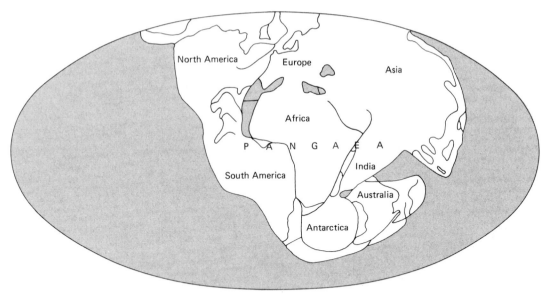

7-1
The ancient supercontinent of Pangaea incorporated all the world's
landmass, including the continental shelves. Wegener's reconstruction,
slightly modified here from that shown in the 1929 edition of his book, differs
only in detail from modern reconstructions made 50 years later. (Courtesy of
Dover Publications, Inc.)

Modern Continental Separation

Wegener believed that the most compelling
evidence he offered was repeated surveys
through time of the exact longitude and latitude of the same spot. If the latitude and
longitude of a given place systematically
changed through time, continental motion in
the modern day could not be doubted, and it
would be reasonable to assume that continental motion also operated in the past. Wegener's data *did* demonstrate drift or separation of known points from one another
through time, but critics attacked the accuracy of the measurements and then ignored
them. In fairness, long-distance surveying
was still a primitive art at the turn of the

century, and Wegener's critics were probably correct to challenge the accuracy of the
data. The data from *very* accurate latitude
and longitude measurements of two points
over a period of many years are potentially
a powerful argument for or against continental drift. Such data are being gathered by
satellites at this time.

Congruent Shorelines and Geologic History

On similar grounds, critics attacked Wegener's jigsaw puzzle fit of the opposing Atlantic shorelines as inaccurate and improbable—without, of course, giving their own

version of the incredible coincidence of the continental boundaries. Modern examples of shoreline matching at the edge of the continental shelf (the submerged continental border) avoid the uncertainties that plagued Wegener's attempts; computer estimates of the probability that such congruent shapes originated by accident run 1 billion to one and form a strong link in the evidence that Europe, Africa, and the Americas "separated . . . like pieces of a cracked ice floe in water."

Distinctive geologic trends that seemed to cross continental boundaries provide a clear-cut test of the continental drift theory, a criterion that Wegener immediately recognized. Patient geologic mapping in Europe, western Africa, and the Atlantic coasts of the Americas revealed startling similarities and culminated in the 1927 publication of *A Geological Comparison of South America with South Africa* by du Toit, a South African geologist. This book details many instances of parallelism between the geologic history and geologic features near the coastlines of the two continents facing the South Atlantic Ocean. du Toit stated: "Indeed, viewed even at short range, I have great difficulty in realizing that this was another continent and not some portion of one of the southern districts in the Cape [southern Africa].. . .''

Similar congruities exist among Europe, Greenland, and North America; restored to predrift positions, our Appalachian Mountains align perfectly with the Caledonian ranges of western Europe and Greenland and record a similar predrift history in detail. In Wegener's words, "This evidence for the correctness of our synthesis is very remarkable, and one is reminded of the torn visiting card [which when fitted back together is] used as a means of recognition."

Documented support met only with more criticism: the similarities were not as great as alleged; the patterns were far more complex and, even if they were similar, the patterns need not imply that the continents were once joined—and on and on. Orthodoxy dies slowly, and Wegener was challenging fundamental beliefs in the permanence of continents.

Distribution of Fossils

The distribution of animals and plants on the Atlantic continents was also studied by Wegener. Before the breakup of Pangaea, now known to have occurred about 200 million years ago, the faunas of the continents were remarkably alike, as if the animals had free access from one continent to another. Since then, the faunas of each continent became more divergent with time in accordance with evolutionary principles.

These facts were well known to Wegener's predecessors, but many biologists and *paleontologists* (geologists who specialize in the study of fossil life) had explained that the alternate raising up and sinking of land bridges connecting the continents as the oceans or the world rose and fell allowed the animals and plants multicontinent access. *Implicit* in these assumptions was the firmly established notion that ocean floors were simply continental material, faulted along continental margins, and dropped down. Wegener (and others) had shown that this fundamental assumption was false; it violated the *principle of isostasy* (see Chapter Six), which requires that ocean floors are dense and thin, while continents are thicker, lighter segments of the crust.

Wegener argued vociferously; one could not sink land bridges into the seafloor, because the seafloor was denser than the alleged land bridge! He took biologists to task for not keeping up with progress in the other sciences, (a problem that is familiar to all scientists today). Wegener fumed that:

... a large proportion of today's biologists believe it is immaterial whether one assumes sunken continental bridges or drift of continents—a perfectly preposterous attitude. ... It is only by keeping in touch with associated sciences that the study of earlier and present-day distribution of organisms over the globe can throw the full weight of its rich factual resources into the task of discovering the truth.

Wegener's formal university training was in astronomy, his lifelong profession was meteorology, and his lasting contribution was made in geology; his plea for scientists to listen to one another came from an impeccable source. The paleontologists did not listen, however, because geophysics and isostasy did not mix with paleontology. Wegener quoted one paleontologist who was short and to the point: "It is not my job to worry about geophysical processes." Land bridges maintained their place in paleontological literature several decades longer, and Wegener's faunal evidence was shrugged off as inconclusive.

Distribution of Ancient Climates Revealed in the Rocks

In 1913, Wegener married Else Köppen, the daughter of Emil Köppen, this century's most famous climatologist; he quite naturally blended his interest in meteorology with a developing interest in climates, past and present. Wegener quickly saw that if the continents had formerly been in far different positions than they are now, the *climate,* faithfully recorded in the character and fossils of the rocks from that period, *should have been far different.* Areas that were equatorial might have been in polar latitudes in the past; modern polar areas might once have been near the equator. The rocks would tell their own story.

Modern climates are essentially a function of latitude; equatorial climates are usually tropical, midlatitudinal climates are both arid and temperate, and high-latitudinal climates are characterized by intense cold. There is no reason to suppose that the distribution of climates was very different in the past, so abundant, thick coal deposits suggest that the area was tropical at the time of coal deposition and, therefore, *was near the equator.* Gypsum, rock salt, sandstones, cross-bedded, frosted grains—all these indicate aridity and suggest the area was in the subtropics, about 30 degrees north or south of the equator. Glacial deposits, stretched out on the grooved and striated rock beneath, suggest the area was in the higher latitudes at the time, under ice.

Animals and plants provide similar criteria. Lack of tree rings implies an unvarying tropical climate; prominent tree rings suggest a temperate domain. Large, cold-blooded animals such as reptiles can only live in warm areas; animals covered with heavy fur usually live in cold climates. Monkeys live in forests; horses live on plains.

Wegener's study of the climates of the southern continents yielded a great deal of information. Working with rocks that we now know are between 200 and 400 million years old, and hence *predating Pangaean breakup,* provides another major piece of evidence for continental drift. Scattered across India, Australia, Antarctica, southern Africa, the Arabian Peninsula, and most of South America were a series of rock units called the **Gondwana strata** (Figure 7-2); they record *similar geologic histories for a*

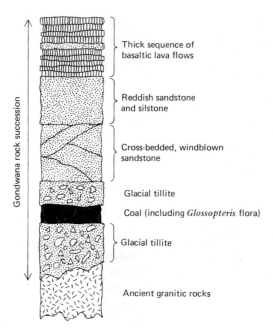

Thick sequence of basaltic lava flows

Reddish sandstone and silstone

Cross-bedded, windblown sandstone

Glacial tillite

Coal (including *Glossopteris* flora)

Glacial tillite

Ancient granitic rocks

Gondwana rock succession

7-2

A schematic composite columnar section of Gondwana rocks. This distinctive vertical sequence of rocks, with glacial tillites on the bottom (resting on much older rocks of many kinds) that are topped with sequences of unusual basaltic rocks, is now found on the widely scattered continents of Antarctica, South America, southern Africa, India, and Australia. That such a nearly identical sequence of rocks should form during the interval from roughly 100 to 300 million years ago on five widely separated continents is a puzzle—UNLESS the continents were once together as Gondwanaland. The coals between the tillites record interglacial periods. (Composite column from numerous sources.)

period of about 200 million years. They contain thick glacial deposits. These deposits, known as *tillites,* rest on severely striated rock whose grooves and polish furnish the evidence of ancient glacial flow about 300 million years ago. What are glacial deposits doing in these areas near the modern equator? To Wegener, the answer was simple; rotated back to their predrift positions (Figure 7-3), the continents clustered about the *South Pole.*

Interspersed within the glacial deposits are coals that attest to warmer times between glacial advances, much like the period of time in which we currently live. Within these coals and other nonmarine sediments is another clue to the truth of continental drift—the *Glossopteris* flora. This sequence of fossil plants is unique to the (formerly) southern continents. The seeds of *Glossopteris,* a seed fern (Figure 7-4) found in India, are like those found in the Antarctic. How could a whole group of land plants be spread across six continents and subcontinents that are now separated by many thousands of miles (kilometers) of ocean? The seeds are quite large; windblown dispersal seems out of the question. To Wegener, this was another piece in the puzzle of continental drift; the southern continents, plus the Indian Peninsula, were *joined* 200 million years ago.

The breakup of the southern continental group (**Gondwanaland**) is likewise well recorded by climatic records in their rocks. Evidence throughout these landmasses documents gradual warming of the overall climate—the result of their northerly drifting away from the luckless Antarctic continent, which moved toward the modern south polar region.

How could great trees and ferns have survived 6 months of polar darkness? *Glossopteris* plant fossils have recently been found within a few hundred miles (kilometers) of

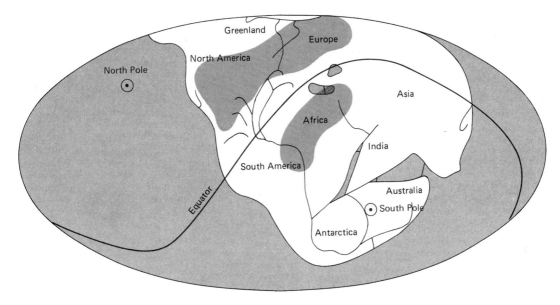

7-3

In rocks whose age of deposition was about 200 million years ago, Wegener could read ancient climate from the rock types. In the colored areas, the common rocks are desert sandstones, rock salt, and rock gypsum—all indicators that the area was arid. In the modern earth, deserts are commonly subtropical (see Chapter Eight) and are about 25 degrees north and south of the equator. The same situation must have been true in the past, since the earth's wind patterns remain much the same, regardless of continental positions. Nearer the presumed location of the equator, coals were common. Near the only pole that intercepted landmasses, evidence of glaciation in the southern continental group is widespread. (Courtesy of Dover Publications, Inc.)

the South Pole—along with skeletal remains of cold-blooded animals. The inference is clear. Antarctica has not always been shrouded in ice; it was located in more temperate regions in the past.

Still another independent test is available and was recognized by Wegener. If the southern continents enjoyed a polar climate 200 million years ago, northern continents should have been temperate and equatorial during the same time (Figure 7-3). Checking the rocks from this time provided the critical answer, because western Europe and the northeastern United States were covered by huge, tropical swamps whose eventual products were the industrial coals of western Europe and Appalachia. The fossil trees within these swamps lack tree rings, because the climate was equatorial. The final proof is that as the southern continents moved north toward warmer climates, northern continents also moved north toward more temperate climates that are typical of today; this climatic shift is exactly the opposite of that experienced by the southern continents. Such great shifts in climatic belts implied great shifts in the relative position of the poles and equator, a concept called *polar*

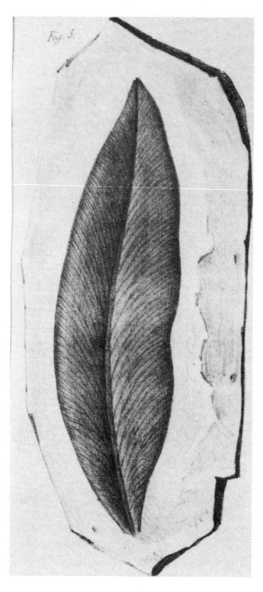

7-4
This leaf fossil, from the seed fern *Glossopteris,* is one bit of evidence for the former existence of Gondwanaland, on whose landmass it was a common plant. (From Alexandre Brogniart, 1857, courtesy of the History of Science Collections, University of Oklahoma Libraries.)

wandering by Wegener. Wegener, working with his famous father-in-law, Köppen, located the North Pole in the northern Pacific Ocean (Figure 7-3), placed the equator through the northern tropical coal belts of North America and western Europe, and fitted the midlatitude deserts into the reconstruction. *Surely* there could be no argument with ancient glacial deposits on continents that were now near the equator.

Most critics were less than kind. The land area covered by the southern glacier was exceedingly large, and many *glaciologists* (geologists who study modern and ancient glaciation) scoffed at the idea of such an enormous glacier so distant from the ocean, which is the source of necessary moisture. The matching of small glacial features as proposed by Wegener after more than 200 million years of erosion was ridiculed by America's most distinguished glaciologist, T. C. Chamberlain, who suggested that "Wegener's hypothesis in general is of the footloose type . . . and is less bound by restrictions or tied down by awkward, ugly facts than most of its rival theories."

Isostatic Equilibrium

One triumphal bit of information remained and, to Wegener, it was decisive. Wegener noted that the frequency distribution of elevations above and below sea level had two very distinct peaks (Figure 7-5), one approximately 300 feet (92 meters) above sea level, the other about 15,000 feet (4600 meters) beneath sea level. Other elevations on the earth are *far* less common; Wegener said: "For uplift and subsidence just as for fold elevations, we know only one law: the greater, the rarer."

As Wegener pointed out, the assumption, held by most geologists at the time, that the

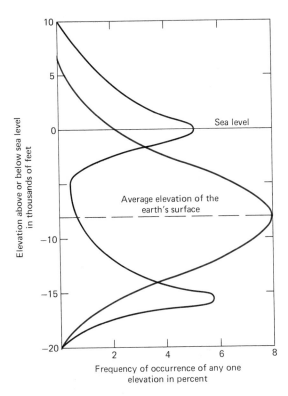

Elevation above or below sea level in thousands of feet

Sea level

Average elevation of the earth's surface

Frequency of occurrence of any one elevation in percent

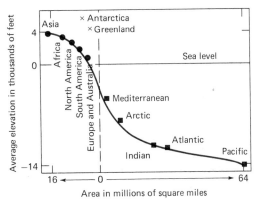

Average elevation in thousands of feet

× Antarctica
× Greenland

Asia

Sea level

Africa

North America

South America

Europe and Australia

Mediterranean

Arctic

Atlantic

Indian

Pacific

Area in millions of square miles

7-5a

If the topographical features of the earth's surface were formed by uplift and submersion of *identical* continental and oceanic crust, a random distribution of elevations centered about an average would be expected (the colored line), and continents would be both smaller and lower than they are. In fact, two levels *predominate*: the continental platforms just above sea level and the ocean floor, 16,000 feet (5000 meters) below sea level. (Adapted from Alfred Wegener, 1929, courtesy of Dover Publications, Inc.)

7-5b

Here is another way of looking at Wegener's old information. This chart compares average elevation of each continent with its surface area, which increases *both* directions from zero on the horizontal axis. The greater the area of continents, the greater their average elevation. Likewise, largest ocean basins occupy lowest elevations. Only Greenland and Antarctica are unusual; their abnormal elevations are due to the enormous mass of glacial ice on them. If the ice were to be removed, their elevations would be appropriate for their area. (Adapted with permission from *The Science Teacher,* September 1963, with the courtesy of Dr. Ned Ostenso.)

earth's crust was a relatively uniform layer, moved up to make continents and down to make oceans, was totally inconsistent with this well-known information! If uniform crust was moved randomly up and down

from a common primitive level, the elevations would form the curve shown as a *dashed* line in Figure 7-5a; this distribution is known as a *Gaussian*, or *normal*, distribution. To Wegener, the distribution of two peaks of elevation frequency could only mean that CONTINENTS WERE FUNDAMENTALLY DIFFERENT THAN OCEANS; continents accounted for the higher elevation peak, and ocean floors accounted for the peak well below sea level. In Wegener's words: "To put it in rather picturesque terms, the two layers behave like open water [analogous to the ocean floor] and large ice floes [analagous to the continental level]."

Wegener, along with a growing number of contemporaries, had recognized that continents were generally granitic and less dense than their more abundant basaltic ocean basin counterparts and therefore stood, on the average, 3 miles (5 kilometers) above the ocean floor. Furthermore, the prevailing concepts of isostasy, which dated back to the mid-nineteenth century, explained all this very nicely.

In the case of mountain ranges, we have to do basically with thickening of the light continental crust . . . but when we consider the transition from continental block to ocean floor, it is a matter of difference in type of material . . . the ocean floor consists of a denser heavier material than that of the continental blocks.

THE ARGUMENT

Now Wegener is ready to offer his final argument.

The theory of isostasy does, however, provide a direct criterion for deciding the question as to whether the continents can drift horizontally . . . the uplift of Scandinavia, still continuing today, at the rate of about 1 m per century . . . can be regarded as an aftereffect of removal of the inland icecap, which completely melted more than 10,000 years ago, especially since the greatest present-day uplift is to be observed where the ice disappeared most recently. Vertical movement of such a large portion of the crust obviously sets up flow in the substrate. . . . At all events,

the whole isostasy theory depends on the idea that the crustal underlayer has a certain degree of fluidity.

Now he presents the final logic in support of his argument

. . . if this is so and the continental blocks really do float on a fluid, even though a very viscous one, there is clearly no reason why their movement should only occur vertically and *not also horizontally, provided* [emphasis added] only that there are forces in existence which tend to displace continents, and that these forces last for geological epochs. That such forces do actually exist is proved by the orogenic compressions [mountain forming forces].

At last, logic had built the argument, step by step. There was no doubt that segments of continents could move up and down, supported by the viscous fluid beneath them. It was unmistakable that the earth was capable of acting as a fluid under long-endured stress; as Wegener pointed out, the distortion of the spherical earth, with its equatorial bulge and polar flattening, was *exactly* that expected from a very viscous fluid, rotating with the earth's known speed. If continents could move up and down, they could *undeniably also move sideways*. The existence of a force to make them move was obvious; major mountain chains reflected large amounts of horizontal force.

The Mechanisms

But from where did the force for drift come? Wegener doggedly speculated; as Darwin had said earlier, "without speculation there is no good and original observation.'' Wegener recognized only two possible forces: (1) ''pole-flight'' forces, and (2) westerly continental drift caused by tidal friction. Pole-flight forces, produced by complex gravitational phenomena, were alleged to move continents equatorward. Wegener recognized that these hypothetical forces were quite small, but ''the pole-flight force acts in the same direction and with the same strength for millenium after millenium. It is this which enables it to overcome the earth's viscosity, similar to that of steel, in the course of geologic time.'' The westerly drift of the continents was believed to be the result of gravitational forces from the sun and moon that slowed the earth's spin, mostly affecting the crust. If the crust slows at a greater rate than the fluid beneath it, the relative motion between the crust and the interior is such that the continents will move generally westward. The slowing of the earth by tidal friction is an observable fact today and necessitates the keeping of extraordinarily precise time (see Chapter Eleven), because each year grows tiny fractions of a second longer than the one before. Whether the earth's crust really slips to the west on its interior is a question that still engages the attention of some geologists today.

Wegener recognized that the mechanisms to drive continents were poorly worked out and left a great deal still to be done.

It is probable, at any rate, that the complete solution of the problem of driving forces will be a long time coming, for it means the unravelling of a whole tangle of interdependent phenomena, where it is often hard to distinguish what is cause and what is effect. . . . We may, however, assume one thing as certain: *The forces which displace continents are the same as those which produce great fold-mountain ranges* [emphasis added]. Continental drift, faults and compressions, earthquakes, volcanicity, transgression cycles and polar wandering are undoubtedly connected causally on a grand scale.

After making this broad statement, Wegener concluded his argument on continental drift. The next year he lost his life while doing research in Greenland. Wegener is an excellent example of a scientist who found current views of the earth seriously lacking, proposed bold, new comprehensive theories, tested them rigorously, and defended them lucidly. He died with his ideas unproven and under attack by the world's scientific community. There is a lesson here in how science works. Let us next examine Wegener's greatest adversary, Sir Harold Jeffreys, who almost single-handedly destroyed Wegener's theories.

The Counterattack

Sir Harold Jeffreys, an English mathematician and geophysicist, attacked Wegener's ideas precisely where they were weakest: the mechanisms for drift. Jeffreys had believed for many years that the earth was far too rigid and strong to be deformed as proposed by Wegener. Scornfully, Jeffreys showed that the westward drift of continents at the speeds Wegener suggested would result in tidal forces that would stop the earth's rotation within a year. He further argued that the notion that rigid materials behaved as fluids did over long periods of time was nonsense and that the earth was in far less perfect isostatic equilibrium than Wegener was willing to admit. Polar wandering was dismissed as being physically absurd, and the biologic evidence was rejected out of hand as being imprecise and open to numerous other interpretations. The geological evidence was set aside as biased and imprecise, and polar-flight forces were preposterously small to move continents through Jeffreys' rigid earth. In short, although certain kinds of paleoclimatic, topographic, geologic, paleontologic, and isostatic models might possibly suggest continental drift, it was mechanically impossible to push the rigid continents through the still more rigid material beneath them with the forces available. What was geologically faintly probable was physically impossible. That was that.

So great was Jeffreys' prestige that few asked the next obvious question. Many phenomena, including gravity, electricity, and magnetism, were accepted and used long before the mechanism behind them was understood. Even if the mechanisms tentatively proposed by Wegener were not right, how *could* the data reported by Wegener be explained?

For many decades, there was no answer.

Wegener in Retrospect

The lesson to be learned from Wegener is that any revolutionary idea is first seen as outrageous and is instinctively rejected. The world of science is full of outrageous ideas, including the following: the earth is a ball rotating in space, supported by nothing; the earth revolves around the sun, which is at the center of our solar system; and, if I am placed at one point between the sun and moon, I will weigh nothing. Yet we accept these ideas as a part of daily life more easily than we accept death and taxes. Wegener had to overcome a ponderous amount of scientific inertia. He was also an outsider; he

was not formally trained as a geologist and subconsciously, we seldom accept criticism well from those outside our field.

In Wegener's last edition he asked: " . . . where does the truth lie? The earth at any one time can only have had one configuration . . . the earth supplies no direct information. . . . We are like a judge confronted by a defendent who declines to answer, and we must determine the truth from circumstantial evidence. . . . How would we assess a judge who based his decision on part of the available data only?" And, finally, he stated that: "Scientists still do not appear to understand sufficiently that all earth sciences must contribute evidence towards unveiling the state of our planet in earlier times, and that the truth of the matter can only be reached by combining all this evidence."

THE SEARCH FOR A MECHANISM

Before his death, Wegener saw a few responsible geologists around the world beginning to accept the idea of continental drift mainly because it seemed *to work,* which was the ultimate test of any idea. Continental drift explained many puzzling aspects of geology much more satisfactorily than the cumbersome collapsing land bridges, disappearing continents, and rhythmically rising and falling ocean floors. Much more widespread recognition of the distinctive nature of the ocean basins validated Wegener's remark that "the whole idea of drift theory starts out from the supposition that deep-sea floors and continents consist of different materials and are, as it were, different layers of the earth's structure." However, a fundamental concern still existed. What *mechanism* could drive the continents through the mantle?

Among Wegener's best-known adherents,

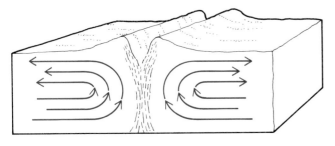

7-6
Colored lines represent the flow of heat as it rises from the hotter mantle beneath an oceanic ridge-rift system (compare with Figure 6-31). As hot material rises and flows away, the heat flow from the inner earth to the surface is increased, and the surface is placed under tension. The patterns of heat flow by convection are similar in a pan of water being heated on a stove.

Arthur Holmes, a twentieth-century British geologist, provided a new theory for the forces that might drive continents. Holmes had long worked with radioactive elements in rocks and had established a geologic time scale from their decay rates (see Chapter Eleven). Holmes was deeply interested in the heat produced within the earth by radioactive decay. It had long been known that fluids heated by any source transmitted their heat to colder fluids by a process known as **convection** (Figure 7-6). Physicists such as Rayleigh, whose discovery of widespread radium in rocks terminated Kelvin's insistence on a cooling earth, and others had worked out the physics of heat transfer by convection long before. Holmes' proposal was simple; if the mantle is being heated by radioactive decay of its elemental constituents, that heat could be spread by rising and falling currents of fluid, creating a *convection cell.*

The convective circulation, once begun, will rise and spread beneath the thick, continental block and will turn downward again in a series of irregularly shaped cells or polygons (Figure 7-6). Colder, denser material sinks; it is reheated and rises, expanding in the process. The same process is at work as water is boiled in a saucepan and can also be seen in a cup of cooling coffee as faint, polygonal patterns on the surface of the liquid. Furthermore, the *viscosity,* or resistance to flow, of a fluid declines as the cube of temperature; double the temperature, and viscosity decreases by a factor of eight.

Holmes recognized that slowly increasing temperatures in the earth would cause the strength of the subcrustal material to be far less than the "rigid steel" endorsed by Jeffreys. Heat is produced by radioactive decay, the driving force for convection cells, which drag the continents with them as they spread; heat also provides the necessary mantle fluidity to allow them to move. It seemed that Holmes had undone Jeffreys' theories and that Holmes' ideas could be readily tested.

The radioactive elements that produce heat as a consequence of their spontaneous decay are richly concentrated in granitic rocks and are much less common in basaltic rocks. The thicker granitic continents, which serve as a heat source, would have large amounts of heat radiated out into space; the thinner basaltic oceans would radiate far less. The *heat flow* (conduction of heat from warmer rocks beneath us) from continents and oceans could be measured; if it varied as predicted, convection currents within the mantle could be readily described, and the mechanism would be found at last.

The necessary measurements were taken worldwide. The heat flow data were unequivocal; heat loss was essentially *uniform* over the surface of the earth. What was the next step?

Was oceanic mantle somehow different from continental mantle? Long ridges across the ocean floor did seem to be sites of abnormally high heat loss; these mysterious ridges were mostly volcanic and areas of many shallow-focus earthquakes. What did this mean? What were the oceans all about? The time was right for a scientific revolution.

A NEW LOOK AT THE OCEANS

One of the triumphs of the idea of continental drift is that it explained continental geology relatively satisfactorily on an earth where 70 percent of the surface was hidden from view by seawater. The crust *between* the continents in the 1950s was much less well known than the surface of the moon; ironically, the investigation of the ocean basins unlocked the mysteries that still surrounded continental geology and vindicated Wegener's old ideas, which were seen in an entirely new light. Three separate lines of evidence coalesced in the 1960s to give us the earth model that geologists work with today; those newly gathered facts include (1) magnetic phenomena, (2) structural and geometric considerations, and (3) information on the ages of the ocean basins.

Magnetic Field

The earth's magnetic field develops from rotation of the earth's outer metallic core; this produces a dipolar magnetic field (Figure 7-7). The axis of the field approximately parallels the axis of rotation of the earth; throughout time the rotational pole (our north and south geographic poles) and the magnetic pole must coincide closely. Imagine that you are a flake of magnetite, a moderately common magnetic mineral, floating in the middle of a stream of cooling lava. As the lava cools, you (more correctly, magnetic domains within the mineral) swing around and point toward the magnetic pole, just as the magnetized needle on a compass does today. Magnetic minerals in certain reddish sandstones behave similarly; their magnetic fields parallel the earth's magnetic field at the time the rocky sediment was still accumulating. Measuring the inclination of the magnetic domains within the grain yields the latitude (Figure 7-7) at which the grain was fixed in position by cooling or cementation; other measurements yield field orientation and polar position, as discussed in the following paragraphs.

The science of paleomagnetism attempts to understand variations in the *history* of the earth's magnetic field by using the orientation of magnetic grains fixed in place in older rocks. Such magnetic mineral orientation is effectively a fossil compass and dip needle which, after appropriate laboratory analysis, yield latitudinal and polar locations *at the time the rock consolidated*. Not surprisingly, if rock samples only a few millions or tens of millions years old are tested, their magnetic minerals point to the *modern* position for the magnetic and rotational poles; this is additional evidence that suggests that magnetic and rotational poles of this earth have changed little with the passage of several tens of millions of years.

Polar Wandering. Rock samples more than 70 to 80 million years old, tell a differ-

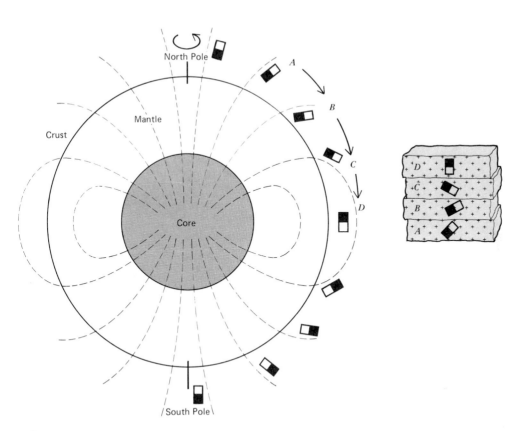

7-7a

A cross section of the earth reveals the core, whose rotation with the earth is believed to be the source of the earth's magnetic field; the lines of force are shown as dashed lines. Over any length of time, the magnetic pole is coincident with the rotational pole, so both poles are shown here as coincident. Shown arrayed around the earth are crystals of magnetite, with their "north," or "plus," magnetic end-colored. As each crystalline domain orients itself with the magnetic field, its orientation is a function entirely of latitude. Those crystals in southern latitudes point *upward;* their upward dip diminishes to zero at the equator. North from the equator, the crystals dip progressively *downward,* finally pointing straight down at the magnetic north pole.

7-7b

Imagine an area of the earth, subject to occasional lava flows, that moves through time from point *A* to point *D* (Figure 7-7a) on the earth. In the stack of lava flows shown in this sketch, the magnetite grains in each layer faithfully record the latitude they occupied WHEN THEY WERE FORMED. The record of *diminishing inclination downward* shown by the *vertical sequence* of lava flows is a record of the *change in position* of the area through time from point *A* to point *D.*

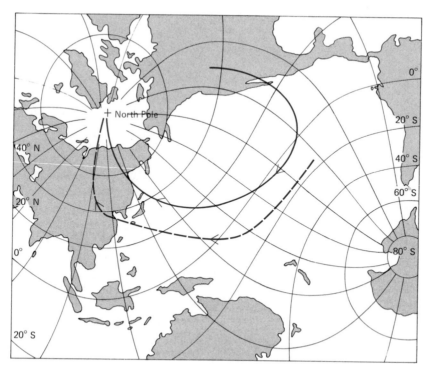

7-8

In this map, centered on the Hawaiian Islands, the apparent pole positions for the last 2000 million years for the European continent (solid line) and the North American continent (dashed line) are plotted. A curve like this from a *single* continent can be explained by wandering of the magnetic (and rotational) poles through time across the earth. When *two* now separate continents yield pole positions that follow parallel paths through time but are separated by about 30 degrees until the last 100 million years, such divergent apparent polar wandering paths are better explained as the drift of North America away from Europe after being rifted after the formation of the Atlantic Ocean Basin. (Adapted with permission from *Continental Drift,* 1962, Academic Press, and with courtesy of S. K. Runcorn.)

ent story, because magnetic poles plotted from successively older rocks (Figure 7-8) *seem* to "move" *progressively* away from the North Pole. Here is a dramatic documentation of the ideas of Wegener, whose proposal of apparent polar wandering had been ridiculed by many only 20 years before.

Like Wegener, few modern geologists believe the rotational and magnetic poles of the earth have *truly* wandered; changes in the earth's rotational axis appear inconceivable for a celestial body as massive and rapidly rotating as our earth. Instead, geologists speak of *apparent polar wandering;* the rotational (and hence magnetic) motion of the poles have remained *fixed* in space, while the *apparent* motion of the poles occurs because parts of the outer shell of the earth, with their magnetic minerals *already* frozen in place, drift over the interior.

The results are analogous to sitting in a train and watching an adjacent train pull away; to observers in *both* trains, the *other* train seems to move. The tiny prisms of magnetite have pointed to the same pole wherever and whenever they formed, but large segments of the lithosphere that enclose them moved over the face of the earth throughout earth history; the results *seem* to show the *poles* in motion.

As if to support Wegener further, the polar wandering paths produced from information taken from rocks of a single continent are roughly consistent internally, but they vary somewhat systematically with data taken from rocks of a different continent. Taking Europe and North America as an example, their apparent polar wandering curves (Figure 7-8) were parallel but separated by 30 degrees—until relatively modern rocks are sampled; then the apparent pole positions coincide. As scientists considered these data in the early 1960s, the conclusions were obvious. The apparent separation would disappear if North America were joined to Europe until perhaps 100 million years ago and then separated as each continent moved away from its former neighbor, opening up the present Atlantic Ocean.

Fifty years after Taylor, geologic thinking had come full circle; it was Taylor who, in 1910, had proposed the eastward drift of Africa and Europe and the westward drift of the Americas, while "the mid-Atlantic ridge remained unmoved and marks the original place of that great fracture." Now data taken from hundreds of tiny prisms of mag-

netite in the laboratories of the world seemed to tell the same story. But how could oceans form while continents moved away? Rounded, water-worn consolidated pebbles are among our most ancient rocks; the earth has had oceans from near its beginnings. Are oceans created and destroyed? Are they as transitory as the continents were now seen to be?

Field Reversal. The answers to these questions came quickly, because the science of paleomagnetism had found *another* anomaly in the magnetic record of the earth. Working with geologically young rocks, scientists discovered that many magnetic minerals recorded latitudinal positions identical with the latitude at which they were found, but they pointed toward the *opposite* pole. We are all familiar with the modern compass—one end of the needle points north, the other to the south. Imagine the confusion if the needle of your compass disobediently pointed due south! Yet this is what the magnetic domains within minerals in rocks have done many times in the recent past, suggesting that the polarity (direction of the positive pole) of the earth's magnetic field has flip-flopped many times.

Approximately every 500,000 years (the schedule is *quite* erratic), the magnetic field of the earth declines and reverses in sign or polarity; a few hundred thousand years from now, the compass needle may point south and, later, point north again. If we could imagine an area undergoing almost continuous volcanism, the stack of lava that would ensue (Figure 7-9) would faithfully record the reversal of the magnetic field; each layer of lava would store the magnetic field direction affecting it as it cooled.

The reasons behind the field reversal are still obscure, although some physicists argue

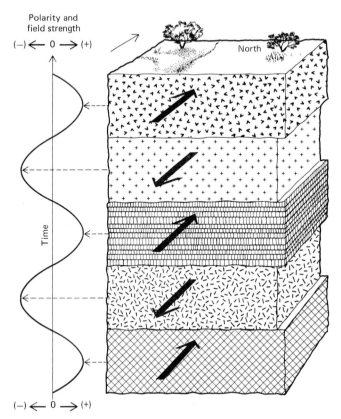

Polarity and
field strength

$(-) \leftarrow 0 \rightarrow (+)$

North

Time

$(-) \leftarrow 0 \rightarrow (+)$

7-9
Suppose that we carefully examine a pile of lava flows, all deposited and cooled within the last few million years. The magnetite grain domains in the uppermost modern flow will point to the north (downward in northern latitudes). In every other layer beneath the top one, however, the magnetic orientation of the magnetite is reversed. Such magnetic reversals are fairly common and are recognized in magnetic materials from around th world; they record the changes in polarity and field strength of the earth's dipolar magnetic field (see vertical graph).

that rapid field reversals in an erratic pattern through time are just what should be expected from phenomena produced in a molten, rotating core. Whatever the cause of the reversal and whatever the speculative effects it may have had on past life, the effect of the reversals, measured in the rocks of the ocean floors, overturned our earlier view of the permanency of the ocean basins.

SEAFLOOR SPREADING

The ocean basins can be divided into three divisions, each of roughly equal area: (1) basin margins, including the continental shelves, island arcs, and foredeeps; (2) abyssal floor, seismically quiet; and (3) oceanic ridges, seismically and volcanologically active. Scientists measuring the field strength and polarity from oceanic rocks *across the ridge systems* found that stripes of rocks parallel to the ridge yield normal field direction adjacent to other bands of rocks that yield reversed field direction (Figure 7-10). The linear bands of normally and reversely polarized rock *precisely paralleled the ridge for hundreds of miles (kilometers), and the linear bands of magnetized rock on one side of the ridge were the mirror image of those on the other side* (Figure 7-10).

In the early 1960s the intellectual atmo-

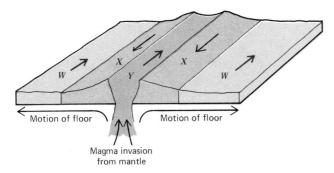

7-10
In this isometric sketch of a part of an ocean ridge, modern extrusion of lava (*Y*) splits *X*, a slightly older flow, and shoves it aside. *X*, in turn, once split the still older *W* flow, which once occupied the rift zone. Layers *W* and *Y* record epochs when the polarity of the earth's field is normal (to the north), and *X* was intruded while the field was reversed. Note that each successive strip of rock further from the ridge is older, colder, and thinner because of volume loss on cooling. Compare with Figures 7-6 and 7-19.

sphere in the geologic community was in ferment. What could these strange patterns mean?

One answer came quickly. If the ocean ridge system is a place where the earth's outer shell is being pulled apart, the crack produced would continually widen if it was not filled in with material from below (Figure 7-10). The hot rock entering from the mantle is, of course, basaltic; as it cools, its magnetic minerals record the direction of the then current earth's magnetic field. (Presently the field is north and downward in the Northern Hemisphere and south and upward in the Southern Hemisphere, as shown in Figure 7-7). As the ocean floor continues to crack, spreading of the ocean basin continues (Figure 7-10), and a strip of magnetized rock is *produced* that parallels the ridge (strip *X* in Figure 7-10). If, over the course of a few thousand years, the field reverses, the next strip of reversely magnetized rock (strip *Y* in Figure 7-10) *separates* the split halves of the earlier strip. The rate of formation of new rock in the central rift valley of the oceanic ridge is the *sum* of the spreading rates on the two sides of the ridge.

A completely new idea had been born. The concept, called **seafloor spreading**, implies that ocean basins are formed by nearly continuous volcanism along the ridge systems, which are often called **spreading centers**, and lateral migration of the resulting basaltic rocks away from the spreading center. Each strip of magnetized rock, in turn, records the *magnetic field orientation at the time it occupied the central rift* within the spreading center (when it was liquid).

There are a number of ways to check this seemingly incredible idea. If the idea is valid, there must be: (1) a mechanism, (2) modern examples, (3) consistent age relations among the rocks on the seafloor, and (4) either expansion of the earth as new seafloor is added *or,* assuming an earth of constant volume, the new material added must be consumed at the same rate it formed. Let us examine each test.

The Seafloor Transformed—The Mechanism

As further detailed mapping of oceanic ridge systems continued, usually by echo-sound-ing apparatus from oceanographic research vessels, it became clear that the ridges or spreading centers were not one *continuous* ridge; instead, the submarine rift and mountain system that we call the oceanic ridge is frequently offset along major fracture zones, which are mostly perpendicular to the linear trend of the ridge (Figure 7-11). J. Tuzo Wilson, a well-known Canadian geologist, suggested that such offsets formed a new class of faults, unique to spreading centers, called **transform faults**. Transform faults connect the axes of spreading centers and thus *transform* the *spreading* motion of the two ridge segments into a *sliding* motion between two segments of crust bounded by the transform fault. Only where the segments slide past one another in *opposite* directions between spreading centers (area *T* in Figure 7-11) do shallow-focus earthquakes occur; elsewhere along the fault, where motion of both segments is in the same direction, the fault, now

"extinct," produces no earthquakes, only a cliff or abrupt slope.

The existence of transform faults had been theoretically predicted by Euler 200 years before. Since surface area is neither created nor destroyed in slip along a transform fault, the relation motion of the two segments on a spherical earth must be a rotation around some pole, called the *pole of spreading*. The transform faults must parallel circles of latitude with respect to the pole of spreading, while the *rate* of motion is a function of the *distance from the axis* of spreading to the point of motion. Thus geometric necessity suggests that the slip planes between segments moving at different rates along the surface of a sphere, described as theory in the eighteenth century by Euler, are the realities of part of the mechanism of seafloor spreading discovered in the twentieth century.

The driving forces for seafloor spreading

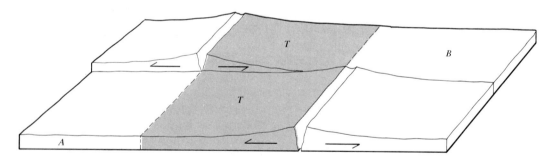

7-11

Shown here in perspective sketch are two blocks of the seafloor, affected by a spreading center and cut by a transform fault. As the seafloor is spread away from the two central rift zones, *only* in areas *T* (shaded in color) are the two areas of ocean floor sliding in OPPOSITE directions. Along such areas, shallow-focus earthquakes may be common, because rock on each side of the fault alternately sticks and lets go, releasing stored energy. In the unshaded areas of the diagram, both pieces of the seafloor are sliding in the SAME direction at essentially the same rate. Such areas of a passive fault are free of earthquakes. Prove this to yourself by adding arrows to points *A* and *B*: compare the movement directions obtained with those of the adjacent plate.

remain somewhat speculative, although they are better understood than they were in Wegener's time. Convection cells within the mantle, or the upper mantle at least, are a favored mechanism, but the search for a more detailed understanding of the processes continues. It is clear to most geologists that the forces driving the ocean floors away from their ridge systems must, in some way, be the surface result of the earth's vast reservoir of heat, both conducted and convected from deeper sources.

Modern Examples

If the seafloor spread in the past, it would certainly be satisfying to find one or more places on the earth where motion of the seafloor away from a spreading center could be demonstrated today. Three brief examples suggest the diversity of types of modern geology explained by seafloor spreading: (1) the Red Sea-Gulf of Aden area; (2) the African rift zone; and (3) the San Andreas Fault zone of southwestern California.

The Red Sea and the Gulf of Aden (Figure 7-12) mark the rift zone between the Arabian Peninsula and the continent of Africa. Even a casual inspection of Figure 7-12 will suggest that the sides of this rift can be pushed back together with the same matching exhibited by the coasts of South America and western Africa. Furthermore, the rift area is part of the geographic extension of the Indian Ocean Ridge (Figure 7-12). The pro-

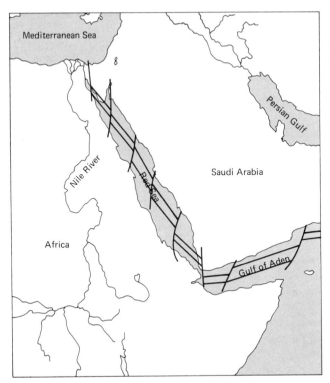

7-12
In this map of the Red Sea area, double lines represent spreading centers of the Red Sea rift zone and the Indian Ocean Ridge, which trends through the Gulf of Aden. The single lines are diagrammatic transform faults that offset the spreading ceters. The Red Sea is where Saudi Arabia is being pulled apart from Africa; it is a zone of abnormally high heat flow, abnormally hot, saline, metal-rich water in the deepest zones, and abundant basaltic volcanism and rifting. In the Afar Triangle (the large *A* on the map) rifting, recent submarine volcanism, and similar features are well displayed. The Red Sea, like the Gulf of California, is underlain by quite new oceanic crust; they are ocean basins caught in the process of formation.

cesses that produce continental separation are mostly hidden in the ocean, but *here* we can watch separation taking place on dry land. One area, the Afar Triangle in eastern Ethiopia (Figure 7-12), has only very recently become dry land. The area abounds in long *graben faults* (see Figure 6-31) that are parallel to the length of the Red Sea and in eruptions of recent basalt of a type found in ocean basins. Deposits of gypsum and salt are common and reflect the recent evaporation of seawater.

The spreading center in the Red Sea floor is a zone of shallow-focus earthquake activity that is accompanied by abnormally hot and saline seawater. Water temperature approaches one-half of its boiling point, and its salinity is nearly the highest ever recorded. The heavy metal content of the water is abnormally high, and sediments in the area contain very rich deposits of metals, including iron, zinc, gold, silver, and copper, that are worth several billion dollars. Here the earth displays a modern hydrothermal system (see Chapter Two) that is related to a rift; by analogy, similar processes may have been responsible for older ore deposits elsewhere. Beneath all this, 6000 yards (5500 meters) of rock salt testify to frequent periods of total evaporation of the Red Sea in the recent geologic past—a history shared with the Mediterranean Sea to the north.

The Red Sea is part of an oceanic ridge system, the Indian Ocean Ridge (or Carlsberg Ridge). The hot brines, the rich metal content, the pattern of young, striped, magnetized rock, the extensive salt deposits, and the many shallow-focus earthquakes all are the symptoms of the processes that have occurred as Africa and Arabia spread apart. The Red Sea represents an early stage in the growth of an ocean basin, when an oceanic ridge system splits apart a continent and

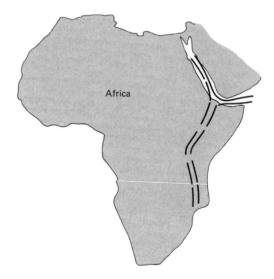

Africa

7-13
The east African rift zone is a zone of tension that has fragmented the eastern quarter of Africa and joins the Red Sea-Gulf of Aden rifts to the north in a characteristic triangular pattern. The east African rift zone is a zone of abnormally high heat flow, recent volcanism (including Mount Kilimanjaro), elevated terrain, and long, linear lakes in depressions bounded by faults (such as Lakes Nyasa and Tanganyika).

sends each continental fragment on its own separate way.

The east African rift zone (Figure 7-13) has been known for more than 100 years, but only recently has this linear zone of towering volcanoes, lakes, boiling springs, and frequent earthquakes made geologic sense. This zone seems to record an even older stage in continental breakup than the Red Sea. But the evidence is still there; east Africa once separated slightly from the rest of Africa, apparently as an older spreading center beneath Africa split the continent. A cross section across the African rift zone

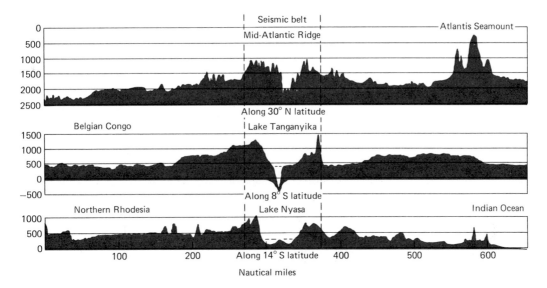

7-14
Two profiles of the African rift valleys compared with a profile across the Mid-Atantic Ridge. The lower two profiles are taken from topographic maps of Africa; the top profile came from profiles made from ships crossing the Atlantic Ocean. The scale on all profiles is the same. Notice the great similarity in form of the rift valleys in these three profiles; similarity in form implies, but does not prove, similarity in origin. (From *Continental Drift*, 1962, with permission of Academic Press and S. K. Runcorn.)

and the Mid-Atlantic Ridge (Figure 7-14) suggests how much alike these two zones of spreading really are; one has been oceanic for perhaps 200 million years, and the other reflects an aborted stage of continental breakup.

A somewhat more controversial example of geology affected by spreading centers is the San Andreas Fault of western California (Figure 7-15). Horizontal movement along this fault was well documented in 1906, when northwestward movement of the western block up to 7 yards (64 centimeters) relative to the eastern block produced one of the most devastating earthquakes in North American history. Many geologists now believe that the San Andreas Fault is nothing

more than a transform fault between the Juan de Fuca and East Pacific ocean ridges (Figure 7-15). Perhaps the only thing unique about this particular transform fault is that it happens to cut across a sliver of the American continent and is sending western California toward an eventual collision with the Aleutian Islands to the north. Not all geologists are convinced that the San Andreas Fault is a transform fault, but it does satisfy most of the geometric requirements, connecting, as it does, the displaced ends of the East Pacific spreading center. The power of the idea of seafloor spreading is well established by the diversity of crustal features it can explain, such as the Red Sea, with its potential mineral wealth and hot brines, the

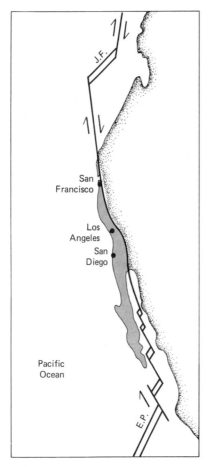

7-15
Double lines are spreading centers, including the East Pacific (E.P.) and the Juan de Fuca (J.F.) ridges. Single lines are transform faults that connect spreading centers. In this interpretation (compare with Figure 6-12), the San Andreas Fault is a long transform fault connecting two spreading centers. Part of the San Francisco Bay region and all of Los Angeles and San Diego are part of the Pacific plate; the rest of the United States is part of the American plate.

African rift zone, with its boiling volcanoes and lakes, and the San Andreas Fault, bounding a sliver of California.

Age Relations on the Seafloor

Among the most powerful tests of the theory of seafloor spreading is establishment of the age of the rocky floors of the ocean basins. *If* oceanic floor is created at ridge centers and moves horizontally away from ridges as strips of newer lava occupy the ridge center, the age of rocks *should* increase in roughly linear fashion with increasing distance from the ridge. There are two fundamental ways of finding out the age of the ocean floor: (1) chemical analysis of the ocean floor basalts, which yields radioactive age dates (see Chapter Eleven) for the time of rock cooling; and (2) obtaining the age of sediment overlying the basalt by analysis of tiny marine fossils trapped in the sediment.

Both methods have been employed, and each serves as a check on the other. The instrument used to gather the data was an oceanographic research vessel, the *Glomar Challenger*. This floating laboratory is capable of drilling into the ocean floor and recovering long cores of rock. Scientists the world over are still participating in a major effort to characterize the ocean floors that began in the 1960s. Thousands of cores of ocean floor sediment and underlying basalt were obtained that contained within them the history of the earth's ocean basins.

After laboratory study of the specimens, the results confirmed the theory of seafloor spreading beyond expectations and created an instant puzzle of gigantic proportions. FIRST, the age of the ocean floor varied directly with distance from the ridge crests around the world (Figure 7-16). That 70 percent of the earth's land surface could be explained by a model as simple as seafloor spreading is one of the astonishing results of the study of thousands of cores of recovered oceanic rock by the patient scientists who probed their secrets. SECOND, the sediment

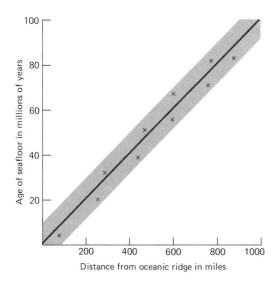

7-16

In this hypothetical chart, taken from real data, the data points are best interpreted as a linear relation between distance from ridge center and age. What is the spreading rate in this area? Was this graph prepared using Atlantic or Pacific data?

on or near the ridges was either absent or thin and geologically very young, while sediment *thickness* and *age* increased in a similar linear fashion with distance from the ridge. THIRD, the theory of reversal of magnetic polarity was brilliantly confirmed, as basaltic oceanic rocks of the same age from around the world yielded similar patterns of polarity reversal stretching back about 100 million years.

Isochrons, lines connecting points of *equal age* on maps, stretch parallel to the ridge system of the world's oceans like grooves left by a garden rake (Figure 7-17). Parallel to the Mid-Atlantic Ridge, the isochrons are closely spaced, those parallel to the Indian Ocean Ridge are somewhat less so, and those that parallel the East Pacific

Ridge are widely spaced. We have just discovered how to *measure the spreading rate;* the *width* of ocean basin between isochrons 10 million years different in age reflects the *rate of magma generation* during that 10 million-year interval. The spreading rate varies from approximately 1 inch (2½ centimeters) per year along the Mid-Atlantic Ridge to about 5 inches (13 centimeters) per year along the East Pacific Ridge (Figure 7-17).

Simplicity. The regularity of the magnetic pattern and the associated isochrons suggests that the ocean floors move away from the ridge systems as remarkably rigid plates whose area includes many thousands of square miles (kilometers), offset only by transform faults that connect ridge systems. The whole ridge pattern (Figure 7-17) across a map reminded one geologist of "the stitching on a baseball."

The apparent simplicity of the ocean basins, born from their own ridge and rift zones, complicated only by transform faults perpendicular to the ridges, and carried away at spreading rates of a few inches (centimeters) per year, is astounding. The two paradoxes created by this simple model were to be the final key to a model of the world's plan that seems to unify and revolutionize the geologic view of our earth.

Paradox. One paradox can be stated as follows. The world's ocean basins are no older than 180 million years, and much of their area is less than one-half that age, and yet oceans were among the *first* features to form on a solid earth, well over 3 billion years ago. How can an ancient earth, whose sedimentary rocks testify to oceanic origins several billions of years ago, have ocean ba-

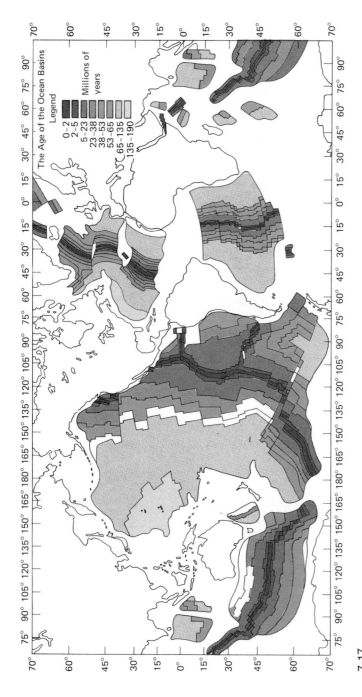

7-17
Age patterns of the ocean floor. The youngest portion of the floor coincides with the location of oceanic spreading centers (see Figure 7-18), and stripes of rock of equal age are symmetrical about spreading centers. Notice that stripes of rock of equal age tend to be wider in the Pacific, suggesting that the *rate* of floor formation in the Pacific is *higher* than anywhere else. Also notice that in the Pacific, the Americas have consumed large parts of the ocean floor, while in the Atlantic the symmetry of ages about the Mid-Atlantic Ridge is nearly perfect. [Printed by permission from the Geological Society of America, Inc. Copyright © 1974 and with the permission of Walter C. Pitman III, 1974, *Age of the Ocean Basins* (map).]

sins that record only the last 5 percent of the earth's history? Rephrased, how can the sedimentary rocks of the continents be so very old and the sedimentary rocks of the ocean basins be so extraordinarily young?

The second paradox was mentioned before as a test to the theory of seafloor spreading (see p. 221). If new material is constantly being *added* the seafloor through the ridges from the mantle, where does it all go?

PLATE TECTONICS—A REVOLUTIONARY VIEW

The attempt to resolve a paradox is *not* an incidental activity in science; IT OCCUPIES THE CENTER OF SCIENTIFIC EFFORT. Discovery frequently begins with the recognition of paradoxes—when something will not fit neatly into current theory.

Prevailing theory permits us all to decide what can be and what cannot be. *If* the mantle is as rigid as steel, continental drift *cannot be*. Jeffreys thought he had buried Wegener's concept of continental drift almost single-handedly by showing that the mechanisms Wegener proposed were not allowed by the current theory of his day.

From our viewpoint 50 years later, we can see that even incorrect theories—such as Jeffreys' assumptions of a highly rigid mantle—provide valuable insight, because incorrect assumptions may focus ideas as easily as correct ones. As geologic evidence mounted that continetal displacement was probable, Jeffreys' theory forced examination of the characteristics of the supposedly rigid mantle that seemingly made it all possible; the new view of the mantle (and its asthenosphere) that resulted was a giant step forward.

Scientific understanding is characterized by long periods of theoretical agreement, when scientists in a particular field see the world in terms of a theory which they all basically agree—a theory that causes them to view the world through the constraints imposed by that theory. Thus, *new bits of evidence may be warped, unconsciously, to fit the old theory*. Jeffreys saw the world as stable and permanent, the continents and ocean basins oscillating gently up and down, and the mantle beneath rigid as steel. Therefore, horizontal displacement was impossible.

Periods of theoretical agreement may be lengthy, but they are eventually broken by rapid shifts in outlook. In the past, such shifts often were the product of one or two scientific giants—Aristotle, Ptolemy, Newton, Franklin, Galileo, Darwin, Copernicus, Lavoisier, Hutton, Lyell, and Einstein come quickly to mind. In many cases, a new point of view stemmed from a new way *to* view; where would Galileo have been without the new telescope?

For the revolution in geology we have been discussing, the synthesis was the product of many different scientists whose work in the 1960s was the culmination of three major developments: (1) the capacity to plot rapidly earthquake foci worldwide, made possible by high-speed computers; (2) recognition of apparent polar wandering and magnetic field reversals; and (3) recognition of answers to the paradoxes posed by the theory of seafloor spreading.

The **plate tectonics theory** states that the earth's surface is broken into an uneven mosaic of perhaps a dozen plates (Figure 7-18); each plate is almost 60 miles (100 kilometers) thick and contains either oceanic or oceanic and continental crust embedded within it. The word *tectonics* comes from a Greek word meaning "builder," or "archi-

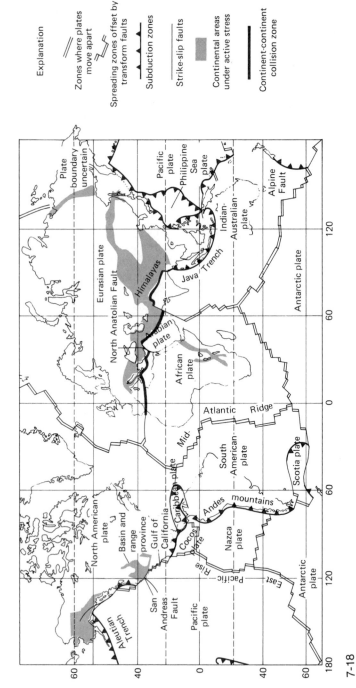

Explanation

Zones where plates move apart

Spreading zones offset by transform faults

Subduction zones

Strike-slip faults

Continental areas under active stress

Continent-continent collision zone

7-18

Plates and plate boundaries of the earth's lithosphere. Data for this map were compiled and adapted from numerous sources and much simplified in complex areas. (Modified from Warren Hamilton, U.S. Geological Survey.)

tect''; we are now talking about processes that build the earth and provide its fundamental architecture.

The lowermost boundary of each plate is within the asthenosphere (see Figure 6-26) and is heated to perhaps 1200 degrees Celsius. The plates are usually rigid and move independently across the asthenosphere at rates of a few inches (centimeters) per year. Where plates separate, collide, or slide by one another, a wide variety of distinctive geologic phenomena occur. The plates may be driven by convection currents within the mantle, although there is far from widespread agreement on the mechanism that causes plate motions.

If we consider the world from the viewpoint of plate tectonics theory, our world suggests a remarkable sense of pattern and order, but both the pattern and the order are overwhelmingly new. The plates themselves are not entirely new; we speculated on their existence at the end of Chapter Five and recognized that worldwide patterns of earthquakes outlined distinctive plate or surface segments bounded by earthquake zones. These same plates exist now, but they have much larger powers of explanation. We begin our discussion of plate tectonic theory with an analysis of the kinds of junctions plates can make with one another.

Plate Margins

If we consider ships at sea as a crude example of plates in motion, the following may occur. The ships may (1) separate, (2) sideswipe, or (3) collide head-on. The equivalent plate margins are (1) divergent boundaries, (2) sliding boundaries; and (3) collision boundaries.

Divergent Boundaries. Separation of plates creates oceanic ridge zones—places where the earth's lithosphere is being torn apart by tension (Figure 6-31). These zones are called **divergent plate margins**, or *spreading centers;* they are characterized by prodigious basaltic volcanism, high heat flow, and shallow seismic activity (see Figure 6-30). The central part of the oceanic ridges is commonly the site of rifting as the plates are forced apart and move horizontally away over the asthenosphere. Transform faults allow the spreading motion between offset ridge axes to be converted into sliding motion parallel to latitudes of rotation, which define a pole of rotation; transform faults permit conservation of surface area and are commonly approximately perpendicular to a ridge or spreading axis.

Note that the displacement between any two plates on a spherical earth can *always* be described *only* as a movement about an axis of rotation. Since transform faults define circles of rotation, the *only* allowable movement along them is sliding motion. Relative motion *not* parallel with transforms will inevitably involve either divergence (separation) or convergence (collision) of plates.

Plate boundaries parallel to circles of rotation will slide past one another. Plate boundaries at some angle to circles of rotation will diverge or converge. Once again, theory describes what can and cannot be.

Divergent boundaries, then, typically form perpendicular to transform faults; the rate of spreading increases with distance away from the assumed pole of rotation. Rates of spreading may vary from essentially zero at the pole of rotation to rates measured in the Pacific of nearly 8 inches (20 centimeters) per year; such a rate would carry a plate all the way around the world within the last 5 percent of earth history, if that rate were to be maintained.

Divergent plate boundaries, spreading centers, oceanic ridges, rift zones—by whatever name we call them—are an extremely common type of plate boundary. The oceanic ridge system, for example, stretches more than 35,000 miles (56,000 kilometers) across our globe and has been a zone of basaltic volcanism for more than 200 million years. Seventy percent of the surface area of the earth was formed by the oceanic ridge system during that time. We know little about the volcanic output of this zone, because the eruptions are mostly submarine, but the total volume of volcanic rock produced exceeds that on the continents many times over.

One of the interesting consequences of this outpouring of basaltic lavas from oceanic ridge systems is that the depth of the seafloor generally increases with increasing age (Figure 7-19). On the average, the oceanic ridges stand about 2 miles (3 kilometers) above the seafloor, since the newest rock is hotter and less dense than its older counterparts, which slowly contract and subside as they move away from the ridge where they were formed. That depth and age should be dependent variables is one of the other remarkable simplicities of the ocean floor and contrasts sharply with the usual complexities of continental geology. Or it may be that the apparent simplicity of the world's ocean basins is a function of the sampling level and data-gathering techniques; rock samples presently average four to six recoveries per 1 million square miles ($2\frac{3}{5}$ million square kilometers).

We have previously mentioned several areas of divergence, including the east African rift zone, which is perhaps an incipient spreading center, and the Red Sea, which is

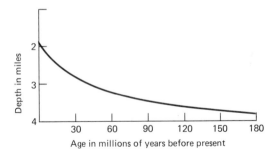

Depth in miles

Age in millions of years before present

7-19

As the seafloor cools and contracts, it is also moved away from the ridge, where if formed as a liquid. The result is that older seafloor is at a progressively lower elevation with respect to the ridge. The curve shown corresponds to the predicted curve for a cooling plate 75 miles (120 kilometers) thick whose base is at 1200 degrees Celsius temperature. (After D. P. McKenzie and Frank Richter, "Convection Currents in the Earth's Mantle." Copyright © 1976 by Scientific American, Inc. All rights reserved.)

an example of continental fragmentation that is under way. Now we will examine Iceland, an emergent piece of ocean floor and home to nearly 250,000 people. Cut by glaciers, strewn with huge areas of barren lava, and warmed by ocean currents, Iceland is a remarkably scenic island, famous for its fish and the world's oldest parliament, the *Althing*. What is less well known to the public is that Iceland is directly astride the Mid-Atlantic Ridge and is formed by the violent volcanic outbursts that heal this part of the plate boundary between the American and European plates (Figure 7-18).

Iceland was settled in the ninth century by Norsemen fleeing a dictatorial king; since then it has been racked by volcanic outbursts many times, occasionally in inhabited areas. Volcanism is common, since the *whole* of Iceland was formed within the last 1 percent of earth history. Bubbling hot springs are everywhere, and their heat is tapped to heat homes and greenhouses; the fires that feed the enlarging Atlantic Ocean are used to grow orchids on the Arctic Circle! One bubbling, erupting spring named *Geysir* has given its name worldwide to this phenomenon (Figure 7-20).

The eastern part of Iceland moves eastward, while the western fragment moves westward. The rift between them is a series of grabens that have been filled by basaltic fissure eruptions over the past 16 million

7-20
America's most famous geyser, "Old Faithful" in Yellowstone National Park, in eruption. Yellowstone, like Iceland, is an area where magma is close to the earth's surface and provides very high heat flow. (Photograph by J. R. Stacy, U.S. Geological Survey.)

years. So Iceland grows in size, an emergent product of the processes that make seafloor beneath the oceans elsewhere.

Between 1973 and 1974, scientists in a joint exploration project entitled Project FA-MOUS (French-American Mid-Ocean Undersea Study) engaged in submarine observation and sampling across a section of the Mid-Atlantic Ridge just south of the Azores. The thousands of photographs and cross sections returned from this venture describe a bizarre landscape, cut by fractures and graben structures, complete with spectacular cliffs, and bulbous, pillowlike submarine lava flows. Not surprisingly, the most intense volcanic and structural activity was basically confined to the inner rift valley; open fissures and faults that are parallel to the length of the ridge are the dominant topographic feature. Interestingly, modern mineral deposits much like those found in the Red Sea were located along a few of these structures.

Sliding Boundaries. The second type of plate boundary is the sliding boundary; this is typically a transform fault along which relative plate motion is usually horizontal at rates of a few inches (centimeters) per year. Three examples of this type of plate margin include the Alpine Fault of New Zealand, the North Anatolian Fault of Turkey, and the San Andreas Fault of California. All of these fault zones are characterized by fairly large horizontal displacements between adjoining plates that are accompanied by shallow-focus earthquakes, occasionally of high magnitude, and the absence of volcanoes.

The North Anatolian Fault (Figure 7-18) has been the site of very large earthquakes for the past 40 years. These earthquakes have brought misery and death to the residents of northern Turkey; horizontal displacements up to 13 feet (4 meters) have accompanied some of the quakes. This fault is approximately 800 miles (1300 kilometers) long and forms a small part of the boundary of the Eurasian plate; the northerly segment has been moving east at the rate of 1 inch (2½ centimeters) a year for at least the last 15 million years. The total displacement along the plate boundary is several tens of miles (kilometers).

A small part of the boundary between the giant Pacific plate and the North American plate causes much concern to Californians, since the San Andreas Fault marks the sliding boundary between these two plates. The San Andreas Fault is the dominant fault among the many faults that lace southern and central California (Figure 7-15). The San Andreas Fault may have originated 100 million years ago, although most geologists suggest its age as somewhat less than that. Like the North Anatolian Fault, if you were to stand on the ground on one side of the fault and look across it, the rock on the opposite side would always seem to have moved to your right. The cumulative displacement over the many tens of millions of years of its existence may be as great as 300 miles (500 kilometers). Although this seems to be an incredibly large displacement, geologists are able to match up geologic features now offset by the fault rather convincingly. Current rates of relative movement along the fault average 1 to 3 inches (2½ to 7½ centimeters) a year; extended over a possible 100 million year life span, displacements of 300 miles (480 kilometers) are not unreasonable.

If the motion should continue in the same direction at the same rate, Los Angeles will be a western suburb of the San Francisco Bay area in about 20 million years. Southwestern California will crash into the Aleu-

tian Islands several tens of millions of years later after a lengthy existence as a long, narrow island proceeding majestically northwest across the Pacific Ocean Basin at the amazing speed of a few inches (centimeters) a year. What will happen then?

Collision Boundaries. When plates collide, *two* very different kinds of plate boundaries may be formed. One is best illustrated by the problem just posed. What happens when the western sliver of California eventually runs into the Aleutian Islands? Here we have a confrontation. Oceanic plates (with a fragment of California rafted along with it) runs into continental plate. The oceanic plate (in this case the Pacific plate) is thin, rigid, and dense; the continental plate (in this case the northwestward corner of the North American plate) is thick, rigid, less dense, and more buoyant. The results are utterly predictable; the resulting collision reminds one of a Volkswagen "bug" colliding with a Greyhound bus; the ocean floor is forced beneath the continental plate, which obligingly overrides it.

The result (Figure 7-21) encircles the margin of much of the Pacific plate; the ocean floor is buckled downward, forming the deep *trenches* or *foredeeps* previously described. These deep infolds of the ocean floor are not the only result; bands of everdeepening earthquake foci stretching under the continent from these oceanic deeps define a zone dipping down into the mantle away from the trench. These zones of *inclined earthquake foci, unique to areas of ocean-continent collision,* were named **Benioff zones** after Hugo Benioff, the geologist who first adequately defined their geometry. These sloping zones record earthquake foci down to 400 miles (700 kilometers), the deepest earthquakes

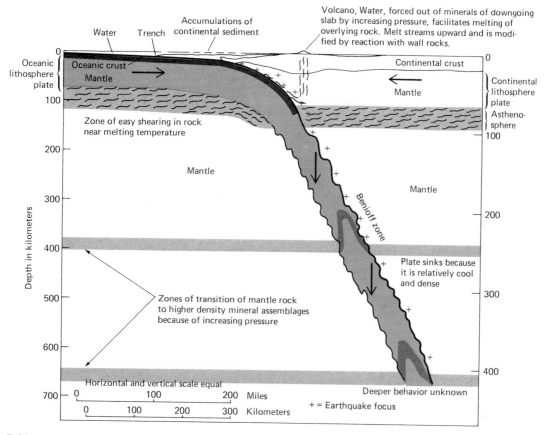

7-21

Cross section through a subduction or Benioff zone, where oceanic lithosphere is forced beneath a continental plate. In this sketch, horizontal and vertical scales are equal, so there is no vertical exaggeration. The Benioff zone is created by the zone of steeply dipping earthquake foci that outline the contact between the subducted plate and the crust and the mantle. Details and dimensions are those for western Java and the Java Trench system, but other continental systems are similar. (Modified from Warren Hamilton, U.S. Geological Survey)

known on earth; such *deep earthquake foci are essentially unique to Benioff zones.*

If oceanic crust is carried down 400 miles (700 kilometers) along Benioff zones, oceanic material is carried down well below that lowest part (Figure 7-21) of what we regard as the asthenosphere into what geol-

ogists regard as the transition zone within the upper mantle. At the temperatures and pressures prevailing in this area, no slab of oceanic rock can maintain its identity. Partial melting and diffusion of its components must result.

We have answered both paradoxes posed

by *seafloor spreading at once*. As new material is added to the earth at spreading centers, it goes to the oceanic trenches, to be remelted. An ancient earth can have young oceans because the ocean basin material is *formed* at spreading centers and, at some distance from the ridge, the ocean floor material is *consumed* again. Ocean floors, in an ironic analogy, are like people; they are born and they record and participate in the events of the day; eventually, they are buried. But oceans leave evidence of their existence in sedimentary rocks, which are faithful records of the ocean basins of the ancient past. Likewise, the oceanic rocks entombed beneath a Benioff zone have a future; volcanism (Figure 7-21) brings their less dense (lower melting point) components to the surface again, where they make new additions to the continental crust.

Zones of plate consumption rim all but the southeastern margin of the Pacific Ocean Basin (Figure 7-18); this obviously indicates that the Pacific plate, relative to all of the adjacent plates, is traveling generally northwestward across the surface of the earth. As with all plate motions, we can only talk about *relative motion among plates;* our earth (almost a synonym for solidity) yields no fixed reference point about which to record the actions of the earth's plates. Other, much smaller, zones of plate consumption include two small arcuate areas in the Caribbean and South Atlantic (Figure 7-18).

Geologists call these zones of plate consumption, marked by great arcuate ocean trenches, **subduction zones**. The verb *subduct* comes from the Latin verb *subducere,* which means to lead away, to withdraw, or to lead under. Our nearest familiar word is the verb *subdue*. Geologists have chosen the word subduction to convey a precise image; many geologists believe that newly formed

crust is *pushed* away from the ridges while it is hot, and *pulled* down into the subduction zones while it is dense and cold. Such a view of an oceanic plate, *pushed* out of its fiery nest and *pulled* down into its own grave, may seem the ultimate in imagination, but it provides one of the more satisfactory models for plate motion just now.

What about southern California? Its future seems assured—entombment under the Aleutian Islands millions of years from now, its remnants of civilization remelted to appear in some far-off day in some distant volcano.

Interestingly, one of the serious suggestions for the disposal of our solid waste is to dump it into subduction zones. The human population of the earth generates 500,000,000 tons (450,000,000 metric tons) of waste a year, a small fraction of the rock material drawn into the subduction zones of the world each year. Radioactive wastes and other products have even been suggested as grist for the subduction mill. The image of a future volcano ejecting recycled twentieth-century garbage is overwhelming, but this image is one of the minor by-products of our developing understanding of our earth.

We may also have just begun to answer the questions originally asked near the end of Chapter Five. What is the future of the earth? Where do cycles go?

Notice that continental crust has an inherent physical advantage; it is relatively more buoyant and less dense than the ocean floor. It seems that continental crust not only originates as the lightest surficial part of an evolving basaltic mantle (see Chapter Twelve), but that collision of older, oceanic, basaltic crust always results in volcanism landward from the subduction zone, with lighter fractions (having a lower melting point) of the basalt added to the continental crust. Once added, the lighter material *never* entirely leaves the continental areas, because it is now too buoyant to be moved back down into the mantle or even the basaltic ocean floor. Continental plates *cannot* be entirely consumed; therefore they record essentially *all* of solid earth's history. Ocean floors, which are constantly renewed, record only the last 5 percent of earth history.

Is it the fate of continents to grow ever thicker and larger, and therefore higher, as time continues? Incredibly, Wegener thought so in 1929, and our model *is* suggestive of this. The evidence for such a model would have to be looked for among the more ancient rocks on earth, because the earliest continents would have been thin, subjected to intense heating, and barely above sea level—*if* our evolutionary model is correct. Early continents would hardly have been rigid, either, because they would have been too thin and too hot to be rigid. *If* our interpretation of the earth is based on a uniformitarian model, plate tectonics and seafloor spreading have always been in process; *if* the earth is heading somewhere—moving toward some specific end—plate tectonics must have *started* sometime in the past.

Such speculations are at the core of geology's most interesting philosphic discussion. What is the future course of earth changes? To date we have covered only the physical aspects of part of the earth's total story, so speculation at this point is based on small fragments of the total evidence. Chapter Twelve will provide far more of the picture and also a surprising conclusion, but we can take one more look at continent-making processes by looking at one specific zone of ocean-continent collision—the collision of the Nazca and South American plates and the origin of the Andes.

The Andes form the western spine of South America and are paralleled, offshore, by the Peru-Chile Trench—a typical oceanic trench of foredeep (Figure 7-22). Nine miles (15 kilometers) of elevation separate the rocks at the top of the Andes from those at the bottom of the adjacent trench. The Andes form an exceptional example of mountain making as spreading ocean floor is subducted beneath a continental plate. The ocean floor basalts are being forced under the western margin of South America at a rate of 2 inches (5 centimeters) per year, a process that may have begun nearly 200 million years ago. The broad outline of the formation of the Andes will suggest how seafloor spreading may form lofty mountains.

As the basaltic ocean floor was stuffed beneath South America, it reached the melting point of its lowest-melting components, and the lighter, more siliceous magma rose toward the surface. The volcanic rock that resulted is called *andesite* (see Chapter Three); the abundance of this rock type in the Andes gave the rock its name. As more and more basaltic crust passed beneath the continent and melted, more andesite continued to be added to the west coast of South America. The lighter continental crust was thickened and began to *rise*.

Perhaps somewhat less than a 150 million years ago, South America broke away from Africa and headed west, accelerating the rate of subduction of Pacific Ocean crust. Continued thickening of the crust and the crushing compressive forces from the overriding of South America along the downward-thrusting Benioff or subduction zone shattered the great thicknesses of sediments deposited along the continental shelf of western South America; they, too (Figure 7-21), metamorphosed in part and became a part of the Andes.

Now our study of ocean-continent colli-

7-22
The Andes are the result of the consumption and partial melting of the Nazca plate as South America moves west. The trench and mountains are mirror images of one another. Compare with Figure 7-18.

sions is complete. If an oceanic plate should collide with thin continental material, **island arc** *and* **foredeep systems**, which are typical of the western Pacific, are formed. Volcanism caused by partial melting of the descending oceanic slab or lithosphere will produce arcuate island chains of generally andesitic composition; *these mark the edge of the geologic continent.*

If an oceanic plate should collide with thicker continental material, the result of long-continued sedimentation and/or island arc volcanic activity, mountains are formed, their growing low-density root is the major *cause* of uplift; horizontally directed forces from the collision crumple the former offshore sedimentary wedge at the same time. These crumpled, shallow-water sedimentary rocks become a major ornament of the range; their intricate folds and faults are a delight to the eye and a challenge to geologists who try to unravel their detailed history.

The older offshore sedimentary wedge just alluded to might well have been called a **geosyncline**. The term *geosyncline* describes an older model for the origin of mountains composed of folded, abnormally thickened sediments and was proposed by an American geologist, James Hall, in the latter part of the nineteenth century. This model stated that a geosyncline was an elongated, subsiding trough that filled with sediments as it subsided and was a necessary predecessor to later mountain belts formed by the crushing and uplifting of the former geosyncline. The forces that crushed and uplifted the geosyncline always remained somewhat enigmatic, and no satisfactory way could ever be found to cause a trough full of loose sediment of very low density to sink into the far denser mantle beneath it. Now we can see

that the horizontal spreading of the ocean floor provides a strong, crushing force, that the continental shelves and slopes provide the necessary place of accumulation for the sedimentary deposits, and that buoyant uplift of a thickened crust provides the uplifting mechanism.

It is one of the many triumphs of the theory of plate tectonics that phenomena as apparently diverse as volcanism, earthquakes, oceanic trenches, island arcs, and major folded mountain chains can all be explained by a single, encompassing idea. We should have expected this, however; Wegener told us 50 years ago that a theory of the earth would integrate all these seemingly unrelated features of the earth.

One type of plate collision must still be described. What happens when continent rams continent? Modern examples include the Alps, formed when Italy rammed into Europe a few tens of millions of years ago, and the lofty Himalayas, produced when the subcontinent of India, having broken away from Gondwanaland 75 million years ago, traveled northeast for about 35 million years, unimpeded, and then rammed into the continental shelf, or geosyncline, that bordered Asia's southern margin. The result of this mighty collision of continent with continent was the trapping of the central wedge of marine sediments into the vise between the colliding continents and the uplift of the Himalayas.

Such continent-continent crush zones complete our review of convergent plate margins. Continental collision is a collision between equals. Neither plate can dive beneath the other, since both are buoyant; the zone of collision is marked by shallow- and intermediate-focus earthquakes over a wide, diffuse zone and lofty mountain ranges that were formed from intensely compressed, deformed, thrusted, and uplifted geosynclinal sediments. Such a zone stretches easterly from the Alps and Pyrenees to the Himalayas along the contact between the Eurasian and African plates (Figure 7-18).

Plate Tectonics in Review

It has been said that any worthwhile theory not only explains the currently known, but also interprets the past and predicts the future. What can the theory of plate tectonics do for our view of the earth—past, present, and future?

With regard to the past, plate tectonics became a logical successor to the concept of continental drift. Egocentric humans had envisioned their continents as great ships plowing through oceanic crust; now we know that continents are merely passive lumps on lithospheric plates that glide along on the asthenosphere. Continental margins facing the Atlantic and Indian oceans do, indeed, coincide and share similar geologic histories; *those oceans are rift oceans,* formed by spreading centers that mimic the shape of the continental margins.

It is fortunate for us that the ocean floors and Atlantic continents have remained so rigid and passive; the jigsaw fit of their Atlantic margins, which caused many geologists to assume that they had separated eventually, led to the recognition that the *Pacific margins were totally different from the Atlantic and Indian margins.* The continental margins fronting on the Pacific Ocean are sites of great plate activity (the famous Ring of Fire) and form the great arcuate zones where oceanic plate is consumed as rapidly as it is formed many miles (kilometers) distant at the ridges.

Now we know that plate margins rarely coincide with the edges of continents but, when they do, as in much of the Pacific, they are marked by earthquakes, volcanoes, transform faults, and subduction. It is quiet along the Atlantic and Indian coastlines, because these coastlines are mostly former rift zones; they are now only *passive* continental margins, where sediments pile up along the continental shelves.

An Expanding Earth? The rifted edges of the Atlantic and the more complexly rifted fragments of continents that border the Indian Ocean yield another intellectual dividend. One alternate answer to the problem of the mechanism for seafloor spreading is that a diminishing gravitational ''force'' causes the earth to swell in volume constantly; *that, too, would allow for seafloor spreading.* Suppose that after the breakup of the Atlantic continents between 100 and 200 million years ago the earth continued to gain volume. The Atlantic continents have undergone very little deformation along their passive Atlantic edges since their separation, an impossible situation if the earth had continued to expand, because the continents would have fragmented as surely as dried mud stuck on the surface of an inflating balloon. The earth is a mute witness, but the evidence is there.

A New View. What about the future of those quiet, passive Atlantic coastlines? Can plate tectonics take us ahead of our modern times or back to what once was with understanding? The answer to both questions is a resounding affirmative. Consider the past first.

Stretched along the eastern and south-central part of the United States is a single, although discontinuously exposed, mountain chain known as the Appalachians in the east, the Ouachitas in Oklahoma and Arkansas, and the Marathons in Texas. Many geologists believe this long, linear arcuate chain resulted from an older collision of the European, African, and American continents that was later followed by their separation across the newly formed Atlantic Ocean. The reason that the Appalachian chain shares so many similarities with the mountains of westernmost Europe (and eastern Greenland) is, indeed, because they were once crushed together, just as India and Asia are today. The Urals , a mountain range of folded marine sediments midway between Europe and Asia and many miles (kilometers) from the sea, may record a similar ancient collision of Europe and Asia. Plate tectonics can reach into the past; this forms one of two central themes that are developed in Chapter Twelve as we search the past.

The future of those quiet, passive Atlantic coastlines is equally predictable, because the ancient rocks in the interior of our continents are the remnants of rocks formed deep beneath mountain ranges whose surface rocks must have once formed in the sea. At some future time, the westward drift of the Americas and the eastward drift of Eurasia and Africa may halt, and the Pacific Ocean Basin will no longer lose surface area to the overriding, triumphant continents. The Americas may then begin to move to the east, only to meet Eurasia and Africa heading west, perhaps overrunning the Mid-Atlantic Ridge and opening up inland seas like the modern Gulf of California. As the Atlantic continents collide once again, the sediments accumulating in the intervening but shrinking ocean will once more be thrust toward the sky, and a new mountain range will be born east of the modern Appalachians.

Meanwhile, the west coast of the Americas, which then will be the trailing (passive) edge of a plate being pushed eastward from the Pacific ridge systems, will be quiet, and great thicknesses of sediments will slowly accumulate at the foot of the Andes and North American coastal ranges. The side-swiping, rifting, subduction, and collision of the earth's plates will continue. On the Pacific shores the piles of sediment on the continental shelves will grow, waiting their turn in the sky once again.

SUMMARY   Challenges to current scientific models provide the only means for change; if the challenge is substantial, the model must change to incorporate it. The challenge of continental drift to the stable world of uniform oscillation of identical continents and seafloor on a contracting earth was *total*. If continental drift was correct, everything that scientists of many disciplines "knew" about the earth would have to be discarded.

Many scientists reacted negatively to Wegener's model of continental rifting and displacement. Wegener's model had many predecessors, but only Wegener meticulously searched for and challenged his own evidence. He confronted his antagonists through four editions of the book that outlined the new model and the more and more detailed evidence in its support.

In the end, most geologists in the Northern Hemisphere rejected Wegener's model outright; although they perhaps recognized it as geologically plausible, continents plowing through ocean basins and mantle had been shown by Jeffreys to be mechanically impossible. Geologists in the Southern Hemisphere tended to ignore the obvious defects in the mechanism proposed by Wegener and insisted that many different types of geologic information only made sense when the southern continents were brought together in one continental landmass some time prior to 200 million years ago.

Holmes suggested convection within the mantle as one driving mechanism, but too little was known about the upper mantle to be reasonably certain that this model worked; the source of horizontal driving forces remains unsolved today and is the subject of lively speculation. In 1960, Harry Hess, a professor at Princeton, suggested the idea of seafloor spreading in an article he called "an essay in geopoetry."

Proof of seafloor spreading was demonstrated first by recognition of the stripes of reversely and normally magnetized rocks parallel to the ridges, each faithfully recording the earth's magnetic polarity. As these stripes formed, they documented the fact of spreading and the *rate* of spreading. Further confirmation was soon provided; age dates of both basaltic rocks and their overlying sediments on the ocean floor offered dramatic confirmation of the reality of seafloor spreading.

The step from seafloor spreading to plate tectonics is a brief but critical one. If the seafloor spreads, an earth with ancient continents and juvenile ocean basins is the wrong model (if continents *plow through* ocean basins), as Wegener had suggested. Nearly simultaneous recognition of the partial fluidity of a thin layer of the upper mantle, called the asthenosphere, and of the pattern of earthquake foci, breaking the earth into distinct segments, formed the basis for plate tectonic theory.

Plate tectonic theory states that the earth's outer lithosphere, perhaps 60 miles (100 kilometers) thick, is driven across the asthenosphere by enigmatic forces within the earth. The continents ride as passive bumps on plates whose boundaries may or may not coincide with continental margins. At plate margins a wide variety of earthquake, mountain-building, and volcanic phenomena testify to active geologic processes in zones of:

1. Divergence and seafloor spreading.
2. Shearing and sliding of plate margins.
3. Convergence of oceanic and continental plates, with subduction zones extending downward from oceanic trenches and continental margins thickened by various combinations of volcanic accretion in both island arcs and major mountain ranges.

4. Convergence of two continental plates, with the formation of intensely crumpled geosynclinal sediments into high mountain ranges, marking the zone of collision.

The theory of plate tectonics seems to suggest that continents grow with time; once added to the continent from the mantle, lightweight material can never be returned. Equally important, since subduction zones seem to extend down to 400 miles (700 kilometers) beneath the earth, whatever the processes that drive the plates, they must include the upper 400 miles (700 kilometers) of the earth in the transfer of mass from one area to another.

It also seems that plate motion may extend back several billion years into the earth's history; however, models that deal with increasingly ancient events become more and more speculative, because much of the necessary evidence is destroyed in the incessant collision, separation, shearing, and subduction of plates.

Each continent is made up of fragments from other continents. It is perhaps one final ironic twist to our sense of territoriality that the ground beneath our feet may once have been part of another continent and will most surely be a future part of a world whose geography would make no sense to us if we were to return in a few hundred million years.

EXERCISES

1. The following table contains some information on real rocks that are now separated by the San Andreas Fault, with part of the rock on each side of the fault.

Rock Formation	Age (Million Years)	Amount of Offset [Miles (Kilometers)]
A	25	200 (320)
B	20	175 (280)
C	17	130 (210)
D	13	78 (126)
E	3	19 (30)

(a) Plot a graph of relation between offset and rock age.
(b) What is the *average* rate of movement of the San Andreas Fault?
(c) Is the rate of fault motion constant?
(d) What factors might control the rate of motion?

2. Some geologists today believe that the primary driving force for the movement of oceanic and continental plates is the westward tidal lag

of all plates with respect to the middle mantle. This westward drift of the earth's "skin" was an idea discussed by both Taylor and Wegener. What kind of evidence would you search for to support or deny such a hypothesis?

3. If plates are pulled down into Benioff zones by their own density, or are driven westward by tidal lag, is lava filling the oceanic rifts the *cause* or the *effect* of spreading?

4. What can you make of the observation that the majority of spreading centers on the earth are aligned north-south, and the majority of the transform faults are subparallel to the equator?

5. At this time, the only motion we can describe for any plate is its relative motion with respect to an adjacent plate. Can you think of a method to obtain the *actual* motion of a plate? (There is a way!)

6. It has been said that the truly creative mind is one that looks for unexpected relationships. Do you agree?

7. It has been observed that there is a systematic decrease in heat flow with increasing age and depth of the seafloor. How might these relations be explained? [Heat flow is the measured conduction of heat upward from the earth's hotter interior (Figure 3-4).]

8. If we *increase* the spreading rate (greater volumes of lava are spilled out per unit of time), what would this do to the volume of the ocean basins? What effect would this volume change have on the continents? Could we *see* the results of changes in past spreading rates in the extent of sedimentary rocks on the continent? (*Hint.* We *do*.)

9. Granted that older rocks on the ocean floor display less heat flow, would the same thing be true for continental rocks? Should older rocks also be thinner? How could one test these ideas?

10. Does Figure 7-5*b* say *anything* about isostasy? Does it say anything about the relative age among continents or among ocean basins?

11. If the lithosphere continues to thicken with time what, if anything, will that do to rates of plate motion? Is plate tectonics a phase in the earth's evolution?

12. Do other planets exhibit plate tectonics? If not, how are their surfaces different from the earth's surface?

SUGGESTED READINGS

Press, F. (compiler), 1974, *Planet Earth,* San Francisco, W. H. Freeman, 303 pp.
  The whole is worth reading, but see especially Part III.
Hallam, A., 1973, *A Revolution in the Earth Sciences,* London, Oxford University Press, 127 pp.
  Perceptive review of the history of ideas.

Phillips, O. M., 1968, *The Heart of the Earth,* San Francisco, Freeman, Cooper & Co., 236 pp.

Takeuchi, T., et al., 1970, *Debate about the Earth,* San Francisco, W. H. Freeman, 217 pp.

Uyeda, Seiya, 1978, *The New View of the Earth,* San Francisco, W. H. Freeman, 217 pp.

> *The preceding three titles lay out the scientific background of plate tectonics.*

Wegener, Alfred, 1929 (translated, 1966), *The Origin of Continents and Oceans,* New York, Dover Publications, 246 pp.

> *The original.*

Wylie, Peter J., 1976, *The Way the Earth Works,* New York, Wiley, 296 pp.

> *Authoritative, thorough, witty, and occasionally irreverent, this is* must *reading!*

KEY
CONCEPTS

Continental drift

Evidence for.

Congruent shorelines and matching geologic history; modern continental separation; distribution of fossils; distribution of past climates made sense if continents reassembled; isostatic equilibrium proved continents could move vertically—why not horizontally?

Evidence against.

Mechanisms proposed too weak; mantle thought to be far too rigid to allow continental displacement.

Seafloor spreading

Apparent polar wandering; magnetic reversals on the ocean floor basalts; age relations of ocean floor; transform faulting; floor produced at ridges, consumed in trenches

Plate tectonics

Plates include lithosphere, glide across asthenosphere; margins may *conserve* surface area (sliding), *destroy* surface area (subduction), *produce* surface area (oceanic ridges), or *diminish* surface area by folding, faulting, and uplift (continent-continent collision); passive margins collect sediment from continent in geosynclines; active margins may crush and uplift or bury, metamorphose, and melt sedimentary accumulations; mechanisms for plate motion are speculative, but include convection currents and westward tidal lag of the plates over the asthenosphere.

A meandering stream, cut into recently uplifted land, leaves behind great looping landforms on a restless earth. (Photograph by Michael Collier.)

Chapter Eight
LANDSCAPES

"Standing here in the deep brooding silence all the wilderness seems motionless, as if the work of creation were done. But in the midst of this outer steadfastness we know there is incessant motion and change."
John Muir

Landscapes form a stage for humans and, for us, seem changeless. Rocks may fall, floods may churn, stinging winds may shift the sands, and thundering waves may attack the shores, but the land seemingly endures. Yet the changeless land testifies to change; each scene offers its past for examination.

Where there is now glacial ice, Antarctic rocks tell of past tropical swamps. Seas often invaded the American midwest where there are now only fields of corn. The *distant* past can be read from the rocky framework of the land. Landscapes, in contrast, tell a story of modern change, because they record only perhaps the last one-twentieth of the earth's history.

Each landscape records a delicate interplay among the life, the rocks, and the soil, that compose the landscape and the unending forces that are acting to change it. The diversity of human experience with the land is great, but it can be comprehended by considering only two basic variables: gravity, the universal property of mass, and water, earth's most precious gift from within its own substance.

EROSION—MASTER SCULPTOR OF THE LAND

A geologist once suggested that understanding the earth hinged on one "disgracefully simple" idea: "First it goes up, and then it comes down." In that statement is a basic key to understanding the landscapes around us. Landscapes record the interplay between energy and the solid stuff of the earth as the earth's surface is alternately built up and then torn down, only to be built up again.

Two centuries ago James Hutton recognized that the land's surface was always in a state of reconstruction. "There is a certain order . . . for the circulation of matter upon the surface of the globe. . . . This earth, like the body of an animal, is wasted at the same time that it is repaired." The analogy between the earth and the body of an animal is interesting; Hutton's formal training was in medicine, and the wasting away and repair of the human body were more than just words to him.

Today, the wasting away of the earth is more than words to us, because we are daily witnesses to the process. Bits of loose soil slump down, houses settle and crack as the earth beneath them moves downward and, from time to time, tons (metric tons) of rock and soil roar down hillsides, engulfing everything in its path. All of these phenomena have a single driving force, the incessant pull of gravity, which draws everything closer to the center of the earth.

Eventually, if nothing else interfered, gravity alone would level the earth's surface to a flat plane, like the top of the sea. Fluids possess no strength, so a cup of soup and the Pacific Ocean yield the same response; their surfaces are leveled by the same force that pulls rocks down from the mountains. The movement of earth material down to lower places is accomplished in many different ways; downward movement *driven by gravity alone* is called **mass wasting.**

As Hutton saw (Chapter Five), the wasting away of the earth's mass is the most *visible* one-half of the life history of the earth, since we are rarely conscious of the forces that move the land up again. Uplift may be continuous and gentle, little noticed except by precise surveys, or uplift may be erratic, accompanied by damaging earthquakes. Whether it is felt or not, uplift goes on, at a worldwide average of 1 yard (approximately 1 meter) per 1000 years or so; it is driven by the twin forces of heating and expansion within the earth and by the isostatic rebound of the mass of the crust. Indeed, the laws of an isostatic earth *are* beautifully simple: *mass deficiency beneath the earth's surface* REQUIRES *mass excess* above it. Replace denser mantle rock with less dense crustal rock, and the area will rise until the mass excess above sea level compensates for the mass deficiency beneath it.

Remove the material of mountains to another place, and the area of the eroded mountains will rise; the mass that was removed is compensated for by mantle material replacing crustal material in the mountain's diminishing "root" (Figure 8-1). In this simple earth, wasting away the earth causes uplift, and uplift causes wasting away. We have again encountered Archimede's principle (Chapter Two). The wasting away of the earth is *balanced by uplift;* the earth's continents, on the average, lose about 1 yard (1 meter) of material every 1000 years to the lower ocean basins that surround them. If this were not true, we would all be fish, because the continents would have worn away into the level of the oceans many millions of years ago; if the forces of uplift were to cease today, the continents would be at sea level in only a few tens of millions of years.

Rocks, unlike fluids, possess some strength and, for a time, resist being pulled down toward the earth's center. But rocks resist only for a time, because the destiny of any matter on the earth is to be moved always downward, until it can move downward no more or until restoring forces lift it back up again. Perhaps, as we have already suggested, rocks are really only very stiff fluids; given time, they also tumble, always downward, seeking their lowest level just as the water in the ocean does.

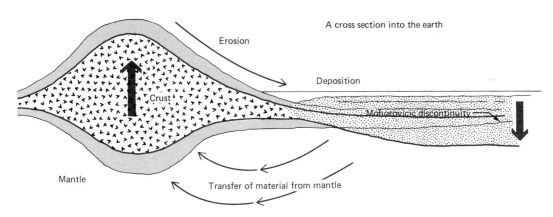

8-1
The scene prior to erosion is shown in black, that after erosion, in color. Erosion of material from the mountain top is partly compensated for by the rise of the crust as the weight is removed. As the crust rises, materials from the mantle move in to take the place of less dense crust, and the depth to the Mohorovicic discontinuity diminishes. Because of the difference in density, 5000 feet (1500 meters) of erosion would be compensated by about 4000 feet (1200 meters) of uplift. In the area of deposition, if 5000 feet (1500 meters) of sediment were added, they would sink about 3000 feet (900 meters) into the mantle.

FORCES OF EROSION

The pull of gravity is the basic driving force for the many processes that erode the earth, sculpting its surface and giving it form. *Erosion,* a concept first developed in Chapter Five, is the term that embraces all the agents that gnaw away at the earth's surface, such as mass wasting, erosion of rock material by gravity alone, and the effects of several other erosive agents that are driven primarily by gravity.

Glaciers, which are sluggish rivers of ice, excavate and fill the land; running water gullies and tears away the land in what one impish geologist called the world's greatest "terrain robbery"; wind moves sand and silt in arid areas; and pounding waves cut and straighten coastlines. Even beneath the sea, erosion continues; powerful currents, caused by density differences, cut and scour the ocean floor, moving material downward. Each erosional force has its own prime arena; glaciers are confined to high elevations and high latitudes today, and wind is the most obvious agent in deserts (although not the most important one); running water is the chief erosional force wherever it is found.

The erosion of the earth's surface results from the interplay of two powerful sources of energy: the gravitational energy of all matter, and the heat energy within the earth and from the sun. The heat within the earth provides the energy to lift up its surface; the heat from the sun adds water (and snow) from the sea and disturbs the atmosphere by causing uneven heating, winds, and waves. Finally, gravity acts to pull every particle toward the earth's center; loose rocks and soil, flowing rivers, and frozen glaciers all cascade downward under the grip of gravity, wasting the earth's solid substance. Every-

thing is brought down with time; "the oceans are the graveyards of the land."

GRAVITY—THE PATIENT GIANT

Any elevated object has the potential to move downward, and the measure of the work it could do in moving from a high to a low place is its *gravitational* **potential energy.** The amount of energy available depends on only two factors: the mass of the object and the distance it can move downward. A very large rock perched high above a valley floor possesses a potential for substantial work; if the rock should begin to move, its potential energy is converted to kinetic energy (energy resulting from motion). Because the rock has moved from a high valley wall to a valley floor, work (the transfer of energy) has been done; the rock has come to a rest (its kinetic energy is now zero), and its potential energy has been lowered (Figure 8-2). Only when a rock reaches the lowest point on earth can its potential energy be regarded as zero; place it anywhere else, and it has the capacity to do work as it falls further down.

The same analysis can be made for a raindrop. If it falls in the ocean, little work can be done but, if it falls on Mount Everest, it possesses substantial potential energy, perched about 30,000 feet (8 kilometers) above sea level! As before, only two factors describe the available energy: the mass or volume of the water and the vertical distance down which it can flow.

Slopes are nature's highways. They provide a surface that is steep enough to allow the products of weathering to be transported away by gravity alone or by running water and glacial ice that are driven by gravity. Since the eventual resting place for all the

8-2
Cross section of a hilly area. Before, in black. After, in color. The potential
energy of the boulder is the product of its mass (*M*) and its height (*h*). If the
boulder begins to move, potential energy is converted into kinetic energy,
which is used to flatten the illegal still. *Moral.* Potential energy is still-
dangerous.

material of the continents is the sea, most
slopes are inclined toward valleys which, in
turn, drain toward the sea. Slopes and canyons are little more than elaborate funnels,
or highways, toward the sea.

Decrease the slope and the weathered material will build up on it until the angle becomes sufficiently steep to start downslope
movement again. Increasing the slope
speeds the rate of downslope movement
sometimes with disastrous consequences for
humans. If the oversteepened surface should
fall, rapid changes in profile may occur;
when movement ceases, the final profile will
be less steep than the original slope, and
equilibrium will have been restored.

What factors control slopes and what factors control slope failure? These are hardly
entirely academic questions, since failure of

rock and soil account for property damage
and loss of life every year.

Forces

Any sloping surface is being acted on by two
opposite forces: gravity and cohesion. Gravity acts to drive the material down the slope;
cohesive forces tend to hold the material in
place. The *force* of gravity does not change,
although we can increase its *effect* by steep-
ening the slope. Slope failure, then, must result from either or both of two basic causes:
(1) oversteepening a slope, which increases
the effect of gravity by decreasing the support for the rock or soil; or (2) diminishing
the cohesive forces that hold the material
together.

The cohesive forces for solid rock are similar to those for coarse, angular soil, but much different from those that constrain clayey soils. This paradox results from the very different kinds of cohesive forces acting to keep each of these three classes of material together. Gravity tugs at all particles equally, but fine-grained materials (clay and fine silt) resist the tug of gravity because of small *electrical forces* that attract the clay particles to one another. Coarser materials (coarse silt, sand, and gravel) lack these electrical forces, but they resist failure because of the *friction* between angular grains of varying size. Sand dunes, which are piles of loose, dry sand, are one example of the ability of loose material to form a stable slope; cinder cones are another. Perhaps the most spectacular example of cohesion is furnished by **loess,** a wind-deposited angular silt of glacial origin, which may make stable *vertical* slopes (Figure 8-3). With loess, both the electrical attractive forces and the great angularity of the silt grains act to form an unconsolidated material of substantial cohesion. The inclination of the steepest stable slope is the *angle of repose;* for most natural materials it ranges between 20 and 40 degrees. The angle of repose for loess is 90

degrees, a spectacular exception to the general rule that natural slopes on unconsolidated material rarely exceed 40 degrees.

Partly water-saturated soils may also yield temporary high cohesive forces, because both air and water occupy the pore spaces between grains. Forces created at the boundary between air, water, and the grains produce *surface tension,* a familiar force that causes the contact between water and a drinking glass to be curved. Surface tension causes the sand grains to be pulled tightly together; this force is familiar to anyone who has built castles out of damp sand at the shore. Cohesive forces produced by surface tension are temporary; if the water dries out of the sand, the castle will collapse. If more water is added and the air is driven out of the pores, the sand castle will liquefy and flow away. Sand that has water filling *all* the space between the grains is called **quicksand;** its cohesion is zero.

Solid rock is held together either as a result of interlocking crystals (in some chemical sedimentary rocks and most metamorphic and igneous rocks) or by particles cemented together by natural cement (most sedimentary rocks and some fragmental volcanic rocks). Most rock is quite strong and

8-3
This photograph, taken in 1928, is of a road cut in vertical banks of loess near Jersyville, Illinois. (Photograph by W. W. Rubey, U.S. Geological Survey.)

is capable of supporting many vertical miles (kilometers) of its own mass without failure, *unless there are natural planes of weakness inclined down a slope,* such as bedding in sedimentary rocks, foliation in metamorphic rocks, flow banding in some igneous rocks, and natural fractures and joints in every type of rock. If these natural planes of failure are steeply inclined down a slope, the potential for failure by slippage along these planes is very high.

To review, clay-sized particles are held together mostly by natural electrical forces among the grains; coarser, loose sediment is held together by frictional forces between grains. The addition of *small* amounts of water may enhance cohesion among grains by creating forces through surface tension; larger amounts of water provide a buoyant effect, destroying cohesion. Solid rock is only as cohesive as its weakest plane; natural planar surfaces within rock that inclines steeply downward are potentially disastrous. Let us look at one example of a recent disaster; notice how many factors combined to lessen the cohesion of both rock and soil.

An Example

The Vaiont River in the Italian Alps cuts a narrow valley deep into clay-rich limestones; many clay-rich bedding planes dip down toward the valley bottom. Glaciation a few thousand years ago further polished the valley walls, and rebound after the ice melted away left many zones of natural fractures roughly parallel to the valley walls. These fractures were enlarged by the river and were the gliding plane for one visible, prehistoric landslide. In 1959, this dangerous valley was blocked by the highest thin-arch dam in the world, which backed water up-

stream for 4 miles (6 kilometers). In 1960, a large mass of soil and rock slid into one side of the filling reservoir, causing additional fracturing of material left on the slope. As the reservoir contined to fill, lake water that was under the pressure of many tons of overlying water was forced into the clay-rich, fractured layering in the lowermost valley walls. In September 1963, earth movements at rates greater than 16 inches (40 centimeters) a day were being recorded in the valley walls. One month later, nearly 300 million cubic yards (230 million cubic meters) of rock and soil roared down the canyon wall.

Displaced water stormed over the dam in waves more than a 100 yards (90 meters) above dam level; it was accompanied by blasts of explosively compressed air that flattened every living thing. Downstream, several thousand people died, and property damage was in the many millions of dollars. The dam, incredibly, survived the onslaught—an engineering triumph and an unfortunate monument to geologic ignorance. The dam is still in use, but at a much lower, less efficient, but safer water level.

Everything worked together to produce disaster. The soil was clay-rich and loose, abundant fractures were inclined down the valley and rich with clay, and water from the lake plus rain lubricated the fracture planes, destroying the forces that held them together. Gravity did the rest.

Mass Wasting Methods

Although landslides are the most spectacular, perhaps, of the many varieties of mass wasting, other examples of mass movement caused by gravity affect our landscape in many ways. Figure 8-4 suggests the many

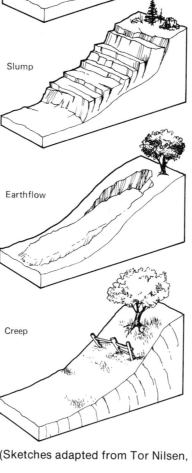

Rockfall

Loosened rock and debris fall from a cliff through air, bounce down a slope, and come to rest as a talus pile.

Debris slide

Loosened rock and debris move downslope by sliding on a surface that underlies the deposit. Instability is increased by fluid pressure along planes of potential failure and by vibration.

Slump

Coherent masses of soil or poorly consolidated rock move downslope by rotational slip on surfaces that both underlie and penetrate the soil.

Earthflow

Soil and poorly consolidated rock move downslope in a manner similar to a viscous liquid, forming lobate ridges on the valley floor.

Creep

Soil and poorly consolidated rock move extremely slowly downslope, causing flexing of vertical layers and bending of fences, tree trunks, etc.

8-4

Common types of mass movement. (Sketches adapted from Tor Nilsen, U.S. Geological Survey.)

8-5

Glacial scenery high in the Uinta Mountains of Utah is augmented by massive talus at the base of the cliff. (Photograph by W. R. Hansen, U.S. Geological Survey.)

possible varieties. Material may journey downward in one of five modes: it may *fall, slide, slump, flow,* or *creep* downslope.

Falls. Cliffs and steep slopes are the normal sites for *rockfalls,* where rock particles occasionally fall from cliffs for many tens of yards (meters), bounce off the slopes below, and come to rest. The key ingredient for such behavior is aridity. Humid areas are weathered so intensely that steep slopes and cliffs can rarely form. The material that has fallen collects at the base of cliffs as great piles of angular rock debris called **talus.** Talus piles are locked together by the frictional resistance of their angular, large rock

fragments and remain as stable landforms (Figure 8-5) at the base of many cliffs.

Slides. *Landslides* (also called *debris slides*) involve rapid downslope movement of various mixtures of rock and soil wherever frictional forces cannot hold oversteepened slopes in place. Downslope movement is initiated along natural planar surfaces that dip toward the valley floor, as in the Vaiont River dam disaster. The addition of water to potential planes of failure may further weaken cohesive forces, and a disaster is ready to happen. The final key ingredient is often a light vibration—a minor earthquake, an explosion or sonic boom, or even a passing truck.

Once the suspended landslide mass breaks along the failure planes beneath it, its motion downslope often becomes chaotic and turbulent. Air trapped beneath the moving mass becomes strongly compressed, and the mass moves along a carpet of compressed air; the contact becomes essentially frictionless. Downslope speeds in excess of 60 miles (96 kilometers) an hour have been estimated. Air pressure forces the rock and soil particles apart, and the mass is carried downslope as a great turbulent cloud of compressed air, rock, and soil—not unlike the *nuée ardente* volcanic eruptions described in Chapter Three.

Even entire huge slabs of rock may slide down oversteepened slopes, riding on a turbulent aerial carpet much as a Hovercraft rides along. One example from an area just east of the Grand Canyon in Arizona is shown in Figure 8-6 as an unusual variant of the common landslide. Geologists call such a structure a *slip sheet;* it is one example of the many types of gravity-driven structures.

Landslides are one of the many hazards associated with earthquakes, which may

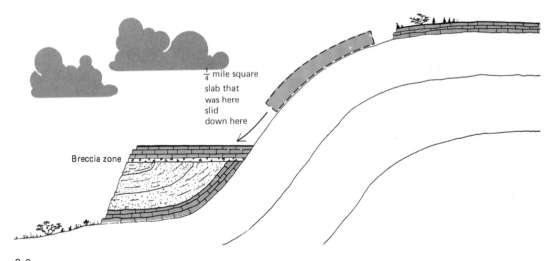

$\frac{1}{4}$ mile square
slab that
was here
slid
down here

Breccia zone

8-6
Cross section of an area of strongly folded rocks about 60 miles (96 kilometers) southeast of the Grand Canyon. A slab of steeply dipping limestone, whose former position is shown with dashed lines, broke loose, and slid about 1000 feet (305 meters) vertically, coming to rest on top of strongly folded rocks, including a vertical layer of the same limestone.

rock the ground so severely that unstable rock is set free for its downward tumble. The Good Friday earthquake near Anchorage, Alaska, in 1964 is one sad example. The Tunagain Heights area of Anchorage was an area of high-priced homes on a promontory overlooking the Bering Strait. The potential for disaster was there, because Tunagain Heights was an unlifted area of soft, marine clays, tipped steeply seaward by the forces that lifted it above sea level. Geologists had warned in the 1940s that the area was dangerous; the combination of steeply dipping, young, soft, poorly consolidated clays is a classic example of a disaster waiting to happen in an area where earthquakes may be both large and common.

Figure 8-7 shows what happened next. Homes were constructed on Turnagain Heights, the earthquake occurred, and the area collapsed into the sea, carrying millions of dollars of homes and many dreams into oblivion. Once again, some combination of greed, indifference, and ignorance had allowed homes to be built where danger should have been expected, and those who trusted public officials found their trust misplaced. There is no excuse for allowing construction in areas where ground failure has been predicted or when unstable rock and soil hover menacingly over our homes, waiting for a chance combination of rain and vibration to flatten the slope and everything below it.

Slump. *Slump* involves the failure of soil or of soft, poorly consolidated rock wherever the slopes are oversteepened by the work of people or nature. Slump occurs most commonly along a stream valley (Figure 8-8), where streams may cut into soft

8-7
Aerial view of the west part of the Turnagain Heights area of Anchorage, Alaska, after the 1964 earthquake. Snow covers the ground, accentuating the pattern produced by the debris slide on soft clay layers beneath this area. The area slid toward and into the Pacific Ocean. (Photograph by A. Grantz, U.S. Geological Survey.)

soil and rock. Failure occurs along a curving slope, cutting a crescent-shaped scar in the slope as the material rotates backward and downward as a semicoherent unit. Near the base of the slump block, moisture may collect, and the slumped material may begin to flow. Slumps produced where highway road-cuts oversteepen a slope are more dangerous than most slumps along streams. The slump that results may well quarry away huge volumes of loose material as well as the highway itself.

Flow. Flowage phenomena include a wide range of individual types of mass wasting phenomena that are connected by a single thread: solid material turned to soupy muck by the addition of water that then flows downhill. Many flowage phenomena occur in conjunction with slump, since the two processes are remarkably similar. One type of flow was described in Chapter Three; heavy rains on fresh volcanic ash saturated the ash, which flowed down the slopes of Vesuvius and buried Herculaneum 19 centuries ago. Similar volcanic mudflows have occurred within the last few thousand years on Mount Rainier and continue to be one of the major geologic hazards affecting cities such as Tacoma, Washington.

The material in a mudflow may be as stiff as fresh concrete or as thin as a very muddy stream. The only necessary ingredients are loose soil material, a source of water, and a slope. Many mudflows start as muddy streams and pick up more and more material as they move downslope. Density increases as more solids are incorporated; ultimately, the mudflow may be able to pick up huge blocks of rock, homes, railroad engines— anything in its path. The damaging mudflows in the Los Angeles area are particularly hazardous, because fires burn off the scrubby chaparral vegetation and heavy rains later attack the unprotected slopes. The result is churning masses of mud streaking down steep canyons where people live.

The result of a mudflow is a deposit of randomly mixed mud, rock, and other debris

8-8

This aerial view is of a slump of the riverbank into Bad River, South Dakota. Notice the arcuate pattern of the scar left by downslope movement. (Photograph by D. R. Crandell, U.S. Geological Survey.)

on the valley floor. The deposit forms a mass whose volume may be enormous. One mudflow near Tacoma, Washington, has a volume estimated at 1 billion cubic yards (760 million cubic meters).

A variety of slow mudflow that is unique to arctic regions is called **solifluction.** Solifluction (literally meaning "soil flow") occurs when permanently frozen soil (*permafrost*) is warmed in the spring, when the upper 1 or 2 yards (1 or 2 meters) thaws. The water produced has nowhere to go, because the soil beneath is still frozen hard. The upper soil layer turns to soup and, even on a gentle slope, gravity does its work. Solifluction causes a major construction prob-

lem in arctic areas. Any structure must have its foundation below the zone of thawing; otherwise foundation and structure alike will slowly flow downslope during the next thaw.

Creep. All of the mass wasting processes considered so far have been those whose movement is readily seen. Unseen, a continuous process of downslope movement called **creep** probably moves more material downslope then all of the faster, more obvious processes together. Creep involves downslope movement of loose material at rates of a few inches (centimeters) per year, which is at the opposite velocity spectrum from landslides, rockfalls, slumps, and catastrophic mudflows.

Creep is a complex process involving many agents that produce downslope movement. Animals trampling the surface, the drag of snow creeping down a slope, root and animal burrows filled from upslope, alternate wetting and drying of the clays, and frost wedging produced by the freezing of water all contribute to imperceptible movement of material downslope. The results can be seen when fences, telephone poles, gravestones, and trees all lean gently downslope in response to the shifting soil. A somewhat more obvious example is the bending of vertical layering in rock exposed on a steep slope (Figure 8-9); even solid rock is bent downslope under the incessant pull of gravity.

RUNNING WATER

A little over 200 years ago, Benjamin Franklin made what could be described as an incisive geologic statement: "Rivers are ungovernable things, especially in Hilly

8-9

This photograph of a railroad cut in Schuylkill Valley, Pennsylvania, illustrates the flexing of formerly vertical layering in rocks under the incessant pull of gravity downslope. (Photograph by E. B. Hardin, U.S. Geological Survey.)

Countries.'' American rivers seem to be more thoroughly governed now; they are choked by dams that are strewn across their width and length, often with less than full appreciation of their consequences.

Approximately one-third of the water falling on the United States runs directly back into the sea; the remaining two-thirds is taken up in life processes and evaporated back into the atmosphere. An even smaller fraction, often less than 5 percent of the water that falls, soaks down deep beneath the soil and flows toward the sea at incredibly slow rates. Such stored water is called **groundwater;** its use and problems are the subject of Chapter Ten.

The average elevation of the United States is approximately $\frac{1}{2}$ mile ($\frac{8}{10}$ kilometer); the average yearly rainfall about 30 inches (75 centimeters). Water falling on high places acquires gravitational potential energy, just as an elevated rock, mentioned previously, does. As water moves downslope, its potential energy (the energy of position or elevation) is converted to kinetic energy; this is analogous to a high boulder beginning its roll downhill. Water, like the boulder, always seeks its lowest level and travels downslope until it reaches the sea. The level of the sea is the elevation below which water cannot do effective work on the rocks of the continents; sea level is thus called the **ultimate baselevel,** or elevation below which runing water cannot erode continental rocks.

The energy expended on the land surface by running water is that of a 30-inch (75-centimeter) column of water dropping $\frac{1}{2}$ mile ($\frac{8}{10}$ kilometer) in elevation. The numbers involved, which are only averages, may seem quite small, but estimates of the amount of land removed quickly reach gigantic numbers. About 4 billion pounds (not quite 2 billion kilograms) of sand and silt move by New Orleans on the Mississippi River *each day;* the total mass removed from the continents of the world by running water approximates 40 trillion pounds (18 trillion kilograms) *each year.*

Stream Mechanics

The energy expended by running water is obviously prodigal, and its effect is clear in all climatic zones except the arctic areas, where glaciers perform the same function as running water but move at more ponderous rates, which befit their great thickness and

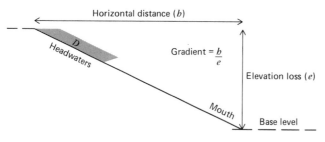

8-10
Concepts relating to stream energy. Compare this sketch with Figure 8-2. A stream's energy, or capacity to do work, involves the mass (volume) of water [the stream's *discharge (D)*], moving from its headwaters to its mouth down a slope (the stream's *gradient*) until it reaches its mouth, at *baselevel*. Like the boulder in Figure 8-2, the energy available in a stream is the product of mass times elevation loss; the greater the volume of water and the greater the elevation loss that it incurs, the greater the energy that is available.

stiffness. The energy available to a stream is a direct function (Figure 8-10) of only two quantities: the *volume* (or mass) per unit of time and the *slope* (or elevation difference). The volume of water moving past a point per unit of time is the stream's **discharge,** usually expressed in cubic feet (meters) per second. The stream's slope is the stream's **gradient,** or elevation loss per unit of horizontal distance; gradient (Figure 8-10) is expressed as feet per mile (meters per kilometer).

All other quantities necessary to describe stream energy are derived from those just presented. The stream's rate of flow is its **velocity,** expressed as miles per hour (meters per second). The velocity of a stream is mostly a function of the stream's gradient; streams with high gradients yield high velocity of flow. The velocity, in turn, controls the stream's **competency,** which is defined as the *largest* particle the stream can move. *Competency is roughly proportional to the square of velocity;* tripling the stream's velocity increases its competency approximately ninefold. Streams in a high-velocity flood stage are capable of moving rocks of extraordinary size as well as houses and almost anything else in their path. The total soluble and insoluble material in the stream, expressed in tons (metric tons), is the

stream's **load;** *load is proportional to the square of discharge.* Double the stream's discharge and its load can quadruple *if* the sediment is available.

Stream's carry their load in one of three ways: (1) coarser material is rolled and bounced along the bottom as *bed load;* (2) finer material is carried in suspension in the turbulent, flowing water as *suspended load;* and (3) the products of chemical weathering are carried as *dissolved load* in solution in the water. Only precipitation or evaporation can remove the dissolved chemical load, but collecting the water in a jar, which thereafter remains still, allows the suspended load to settle to the bottom of the jar. The bed load has been felt by anyone who has in a creek barefoot waded; the water moves bed load materials over one's foot as easily as over any other impediment. The stream's load is simply bed load plus suspended load plus dissolved load.

In arid areas, few streams run year around, and chemical weathering is unimportant. Stream loads, produced during infrequent, often torrential rains, are usually bed and suspended loads. Humid areas release relatively little insoluble rock and soil to the stream, because abundant vegetation holds the soil firmly in place; streams in humid areas usually carry a dissolved load. In areas of 10 to 16 inches (25 to 40 centimeters) a year precipitation, both chemical and insoluble loads are maximized. Such semiarid areas endure the maximum erosion and lose the products of both chemical and mechanical weathering in large amounts.

Of all the questions that could be asked about streams as agents of landform change, three questions are important to people who live around streams and their valleys.

1. What causes river valleys?
2. What causes a stream to form bends, or *meanders?*
3. What can be done to control, even predict, floods?

We will now discuss each of these questions; the answers to them may surprise you.

What Causes River Valleys?

To sixteenth-century people, there was little question as to the origin of streams or their valleys. Streams (and springs) were supplied with water from gigantic caverns (Figure 8-11) within the earth; the valleys within which streams flowed were formed by catastrophic cracking of the earth's crust during earthquakes. Four centuries later, these ordinary conceptions of the earth are ludicrous, but we have depended on rivers much longer than we have understood them.

In 1580, Bernard Palissy first recognized that water circulating underground was the source of springs—and that this water came only from rain: " . . . these waters, falling on the mountains, through the ground . . . always descend and do not stop until . . . having found some channel or other opening, they flow out as fountains or brooks or rivers." Fellow scientists remained skeptical. Scientists all the way back to Aristotle

firmly believed that there was too little rain to serve as the source for springs and rivers; rain could only augment the flow from the oceans of water *within* the earth.

Almost 100 years later, Pierre Perrault studied the rainfall in the area surrounding the Seine River in France and also recorded the amount of water leaving the area in the Seine River. He found that six times as much rain fell as left in the river! There was far *more* rain than was needed, and an idea that dated back more than 1900 years finally died, the victim of patient measurement and curiosity.

Aristotle had also recognized that streams eroded their own channels deep into the earth; this idea was also advanced by Agricola in the sixteenth century. Again, the ordinary people were skeptical; the earth was only a few thousand years old; it was created perfectly and was little changed by anything other than occasional catastrophic events. Any fool could see that earthquakes created canyons, and the rivers simply took advantage of ready-made canyons!

It remained for eighteenth-century scientists to establish that streams carved their own valleys—a concept that *required* the earth to be unimaginably old. In 1746, Jean-Etienne Guettard described in great detail the erosive results of running water; 50 years later John Playfair, Hutton's friend and fellow scientist, recognized a number of observable facts about stream valleys that were irreconcilable with streams occupying preexisting, earthquake-formed chasms. Playfair's arguments include:

1. Tributary streams join main streams at a common elevation, an unlikely occurrence if the main stream flowed in a canyon that was created by catastrophe.

8-11

In this seventeenth-century engraving, water is sucked up from the sea, causing whirlpools, and is taken up to the hills by a series of underground siphons to waterfalls within the hills. From there, the water flows out of springs into surface streams and back to the sea. (From *Mundus subterraneus,* 1665, courtesy of the History of Science Collections, University of Oklahoma Libraries.)

2. Stream valleys are rarely straight in a map view for any great distance, which is also unlikely if streams followed ready-made fractures in the earth.

3. Valley width was generally proportional to the amount of water flowing in the stream; this is improbable if the valley was created by earthquakes.

4. Valleys became smaller as the elevation of the valley floor increased, never the other way around.

Although we assume that valleys are cut by the streams that occupy them, this view has been generally accepted only for the last couple of centuries, and it suggests an earth old enough for the slow processes of stream erosion to make valleys over 1 mile (1$\frac{6}{10}$ kilometers) deep in some places.

Even today, to say that a stream cuts its own valley is only partly correct. Consider (Figure 8-12) what a valley would look like in cross section if that were literally true. If streams cut their canyons, nearly all stream valleys would be narrow canyons, just as wide as the stream, and stream-cut valleys would resemble nothing more than saw cuts partway through a board. Figure 8-12 suggests a more realistic model; the stream cuts down, and the unsupported stream walls collapse into the stream by various mass wasting processes. Seen in this way, streams have a new identity; they do not entirely carve their valleys. Instead, they function as conveyor belts at the bottom of the valley and attempt to carry away the material *fed to them* by gravity. Streams are great transporters, but they are relatively weak excavators of solid rock. Downcutting in solid rock takes an immense length of time, time in which the valley walls slowly collapse into the stream to give the stream valley its characteristic notched or V-shaped cross section.

The *headwaters* of a stream is up high where the stream is just beginning. Valley walls tend to be steep, stream gradients high, and sediment particle size coarse. V-shaped valleys in cross section are the rule (Figure 8-13). Moving partway downvalley, the stream valley widens as tributaries add to stream discharge, and valley slopes flat-

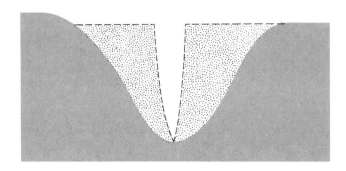

8-12
Cross section across a stream valley near its headwaters. If a stream *only* cut its canyon, the profile shown in color would result. Instead, once a stream begins to notch the land surface, mass wasting processes flatten the resulting slope continuously. As a result, all of the rock shown in the colored stipple pattern falls, slides, slumps, flows, or creeps into the stream canyon, to be removed later by the energy of running water. The result is a V-shaped wide canyon, as shown in black.

8-13

This old photograph is of a typical V-shaped stream cross section formed in a recently uplifted area. Notice the coarse boulders on the valley floor; they have been brought down steep slopes by mass wasting and rounded by stream energy. (Photograph by J. K. Hillers, U.S. Geological Survey.)

ten as the V-shaped valley widens. Still further downstream, the valley continues to widen as stream discharge still increases *along with velocity* as more and more water is brought to the main stream by its tributary streams. The stream gradient has now diminished, valley walls have flattened considerably, and the valley is much wider (Figure 8-13).

Mass wasting is now a distant process for the main stream, which feeds materials into only its tributaries near their headwaters. The tributaries, in turn, feed only finer material into the main stream. Here, down near the *mouth* of the stream, the stream normally enters some other body of water—a lake, another still larger stream, or the ocean. This area is near the base level of the main stream, and little potential energy is left. The elevation of each main stream establishes an elevation *below which its tributaries cannot* cut. Such a limiting elevation is called the **temporary baselevel;** it is temporary because each stream eventually erodes until it finally reaches the *ultimate baselevel,* which is the level of the world's oceans. No continental stream can cut below sea level.

Stream elevations are therefore *controlled by the streams into which they flow;* the level of each stream limits the erosive energy and baselevel of all the streams above it. It is as if each stream were an engine, whose throttle is controlled by the larger engine beneath it. The master control for the thousands of engines of different size, all linked together, is sea level. Lower sea level (or raise the elevation of the continents), and all the engines race a little harder. Raise sea level (or lower the continents) and each engine throttles back. The analogy of streams with engines is an apt one, for streams toil incessantly at removing the products of weathering, fed to them by gravity, and carrying the whole to the oceans, "the graveyards of the land." With some exceptions, all valley walls face toward a stream, and all streams flow toward the sea; this is an intricate network whose slopes are just sufficient to get the work of stripping the continents of their debris done.

What Causes Meanders?

An airplane flight over the land is always a special treat for a geologist, since many landforms are especially visible from above.

8-14
The Milk River, in northernmost Montana, displays the typical meandering pattern and wide floodplain of a stream some distance from its headwaters. The outer part of meander curves are areas of erosion; the inner parts are areas of deposition and consequent tree growth. (Photograph by W. G. Pierce, U.S. Geological Survey.)

Seen from the air (or on a map), streams are generally fairly straight *near their headwaters* but, downstream, they usually begin to meander; the river course is a series of gentle loops confined by valley walls or sprawling in intricate bends (Figure 8-14) across a wide valley floor that is composed of stream deposits. A valley floor, built up out of stream deposits, is called a **floodplain.** This is a highly descriptive word; the stream in flood leaves its meandering channel, which is cut *in* the floodplain, and covers the entire floodplain, renewing its cover of river-deposited gravel, sand, silt, and mud.

An orderly progression of stream patterns downvalley again implies that the process that causes meanders can be understood, because the pattern produced repeats itself in most of the world's stream systems. A repetitive downvalley pattern in cross-stream profiles has already been suggested. The pattern is one of narrow valleys with steep valley walls near the headwaters; it gradually changes to broad, open valleys and then to gentle valley slopes far distant from the main stream (Figures 8-13 and 8-14). Since there is an observable change in the pattern of the stream itself downvalley, there must also be interdependent changes in downvalley profiles as the stream gathers more water, more speed, and more load near its mouth.

Any stream is an open physical system; rock material and energy both enter and leave any stream. The physical limits of the system are defined by the **drainage basin,** the area of the earth whose debris is collected by a stream and its tributaries (Figure 8-15) and fed to a main stream that drains the area. In a map view, most drainage basins are roughly pear shaped (Figure 8-15) and are bounded by **drainage divides,** areas of highest elevation that separate one drainage basin from another.

The open physical system that we call a stream obeys one simple, fundamental law: *changes in the stream valley that tend toward equilibrium persist, while other changes are transient.* Stream equilibrium can be recognized by observing six factors:

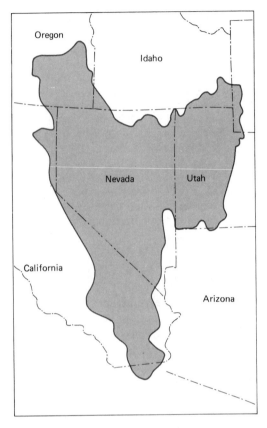

8-15

The Great Basin, shown here in color, is an example of a very large drainage basin. About 210,000 square miles (550,000 square kilometers) in area, it is a region of interior drainage. The colored line bounding this area defines the drainage divide, the ridge of land that separates water flowing in one direction from water flowing in the opposite direction. As an example, water falling in southeasternmost Idaho flows south into the interior basin, while water falling only a short distance to the north flows into the Snake River of Idaho and eventually reaches the sea. (Map modified from G. K. Gilbert, 1890, U.S. Geological Survey Monography I, Pl. II.)

velocity, gradient, width, depth, load, and size of sediment being carried.

Watch a stream at equilibrium handle an increase in discharge produced by heavy rains, and the concept of a stream as a dynamic open system becomes obvious. An increase in discharge requires *either* an increase in load or an increase in size of material in transport in order to utilize the available excess energy. If the stream is not furnished with either more load or larger particles, it starts cutting away at its own banks, thereby increasing the stream's area and reducing its velocity while giving the swollen stream a temporary source of coarser sediment and greater load. As discharge declines, the stream has more load than it can carry, so it drops part of its load, diminishing the area of the stream while increasing its velocity. Thus the stream maintains its equilibrium, responding to changes by changing to a new equilibrium state. This is another expression of Le Chatelier's Principle, discussed in Chapter Three. The equilibrium is dynamic instead of being in a steady state. The plan of the stream is always changing, because velocity, gradient, width, depth, load, and size of sediment constantly vary, but the changes are always toward minimizing the effect of changes; that is, the stream always *tends toward* equilibrium.

Why, then, should a stream meander? If we examine the flow of water in a natural stream, the pattern of flow is rarely simple. Downstream flow mixes with complex flow patterns that cause water to eddy in flow patterns directed across and even up the stream. Rocks, sandbars, trees, and other debris further complicate the flow pattern. As a result, streams will tend to undercut their banks in areas of higher-velocity eddies while depositing the same material just downstream where average veloctiy is lower. The water takes an approximately helical or spiral flow, sweeping material from the concave bank of a stream (Figure 8-14) at the same time that it deposits material on the convex bank. Even along straight stretches of a stream the same turbulent, helical flow can be observed; this flow results in riffles and pools. At low discharge, the riffles may well be above the water level, and the flow can be seen to move from pool to pool on *opposite sides of the stream;* even in a straight stretch of stream valley, the flow swings from side to side, similar to meandering. Whatever the cause of meandering, meandering flow is extremely common; straight channels are simply not the fashion in the natural world.

Initially straight channels, which are carved into a bed of uniformly sized sand in a laboratory and fed by uniform discharge, are changed slowly by local erosion of the channel sides. The load provided is deposited downstream, and so a series of meander bends is created, even in the ideal, unvarying regime of a laboratory table of uniform slope, uniform composition, and uniform flow. Increase the discharge or gradient, and the radii of the meander bends increase. Use finer material, and the channels produced are deeper and the gradients are lower; coarser materials produces higher gradients and wide, shallow channels. The laboratory artificial stream, like its natural counterpart, increases its gradient to handle coarse loads and diminishes its gradient to handle finer loads.

Once the intitial meander is formed, the curving pattern *propagates downstream;* each meander generates another meander below itself. Every meander causes the stream to *increase* its total length and *diminish* its average gradient. It is therefore not surprising that meanders are best developed down near the mouth of the stream, where the stream is flowing across relatively uniform-size, fine-grained material. The stream's discharge is in excess of the load furnished to it; the equilibrium that results is a product of load deficiency. Given a deficiency of load, the stream responds by *lengthening itself* and diminishing its gradient until it is just sufficient to carry the available load. *The landform that most effectively diminishes the gradient is the meander.*

The meander pattern probably results from a variety of processes, including helical flow and local erosion, that initiate a meandering pattern that is propagated downstream. Whatever the causes that produce meandering, this common stream form must be an expression of the river's capacity to minimize change and minimize concentrations of energy at any one point along the stream.

Any irregularity along the course of a stream—waterfalls, which yield extremely high gradients, and lakes, which yield abnormally low gradients—are transient, since they represent radical departures from equilibrium. The stream will cut down the waterfall until it is the merest ripple; it will fill in the lake and later cut a river channel across the lake sediment.

The river heals itself and regulates itself through wide-swinging meander loops that are spread across a floodplain, which is one of the river's principal weapons. But what are floodplains, if not also an expression of equilibrium? How are floods related to floodplains? Can floods be predicted? Can they be controlled?

Floods and Floodplains

A floodplain is *the part of a river valley that is subject to sporadic flooding* and is covered with material deposited by past floods. Floodplains are also attractive places to live. Transport of goods along nearby navigable streams is cheap, floodplain soil is often rich and easily available for domestic and agricultural use, and water sports of all kinds can be readily enjoyed.

Approximately 16 percent of the nation's urban areas already are located on floodplains; the rate of urban expansion onto floodplains averages 2 percent per year—a growth rate that suggests that nearly one-third of our urban areas will be on floodplains within the next 40 years. Increased development on flood-prone areas both benefits and costs. The benefits have already been presented; now consider the costs.

The first national policy for flood control was enacted in 1936; it was preceded by 100 years of gradually evolving federal interest in aiding navigation and minimizing damage along the lower Mississippi valley. After almost 50 years of federal involvement and the expenditure of many billions of dollars in engineering works ranging from massive dams to local engineering studies, annual flood losses approximate $2 billion. Other hidden costs include disaster relief, emergency low-interest loans, maintenance of engineering structures, and new national flood insurance programs.

Flooding is probably no more frequent now than in the past, but increased construction of "permanent" structures on known floodplains dramatically increases the risks and costs. The very word "floodplain" suggests that this inviting, level land is the product of flooding streams, so why should we continue to make ourselves more and more vulnerable to a danger that can be so easily predicted? Ironically, the very engineering features that may effectively reduce flood frequency or severity encourage further encroachment into flood-prone areas, and relatively few city building codes adequately forbid development of permanent structures in these areas. The same combination of ignorance, indifference, and greed that leads to homes built across known active fault zones also leads to homes and factories built on flatlands that are subject to periodic flooding.

Floods cannot be predicted, but it is possible to assess the *risk* of flooding. The discharge of most of America's streams has been recorded for many years by the U.S. Geological Survey. Each level of discharge is plotted against its recurrence interval (Figure 8-16), and the history of flooding along any stream is displayed. Given such information, the *probability* of a particular discharge is easily computed. For a particularly high discharge that would cause severe flooding, it might well be possible to say that the odds are 1:100; that is, such a flood will probably occur *on the average* of once every 100 years. It is NOT possible to say when it will occur, only that over many centuries, such a discharge will occur every 100 years or so.

Such a discharge, equaled or exceeded only once a century, is called the **100-year flood.** For most engineering purposes, the 100-year flood is the design standard; if engineering works can protect an area against a discharge expected only once every 100 years the engineering works are deemed adequate. Protection of an area against still greater floods would simply cost too much money for the benefits expected. The value

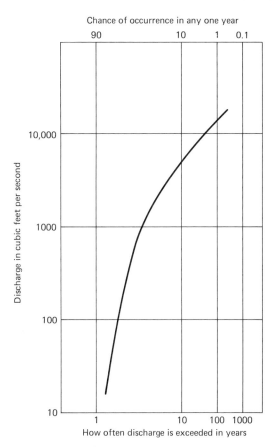

Chance of occurrence in any one year

8-16

Graph of discharge versus recurrence interval for Orestimba Creek, near Newman, California. Based on 42 years of recorded data, it seems that a discharge of 10,000 cubic feet per second (285 cubic meters per second) is probable every 50 years (has a 2 percent chance of occurring in any 1 year). The *100-year flood* should be about 11,000 cubic feet per second (310 cubic meters per second), and there is a 1 percent chance of it occurring in any 1 year. (Graph modified from *Guidelines for Determining Flood Flow Frequency,* U.S. Water Resources Council, 1976.)

of human life and property has once again been defined.

If only the probability of recurrence can be spelled out, how can the damage resulting from floods be reduced? Until recently, the only answer was increasing federal money poured into: (1) dams and allied engineering works, (2) after-flood relief and rehabilitation, and (3) other costs of flood damage.

The increasing futility of dams, levee systems, channel straightening, and other forms of channel modification should have been predicted before such structures were initiated. Building levees along a river bank will control flooding but increase the risk of severe downstream erosion because of the high velocities *artificially* produced when rivers in flood are retained within the channel walls. Straightening a stream course—removing some of its meanders—causes an *increase* in stream gradient and in downstream erosion. Dams reduce high-discharge periods but increase the duration of low-discharge periods. Upstream from the dam, the resultant lake fills with sediment that once would have gone on its way downstream. Downstream, the sediment-free water may severly erode the banks, while tributary streams may now furnish the main stream with coarse sediment that it can no longer carry; this armors the streambed and causes navigational problems.

Few people would argue with the beneficial aspects of impounding floodwater behind a dam to regulate discharge, but the costs of such regulation are high; as more and more people encroach onto floodplains, the costs of flood damage grow each year. More recently, attempts to reduce flood damage have centered about five areas of public policy: (1) support for research on flooding and flood hazards; (2) additional federal support for communities in delineating the 100-year floodplain; (3) provision of a national, heavily subsidized flood insurance program; (4) tough new floodplain building codes that are linked with flood insurance; and (5) acquisition of floodplains by government agencies for recreational or agricultural purposes. Several uses of floodplain areas are perfectly compatible with the peril they pose; these uses include many forms of agriculture, parks and playgrounds, sand and gravel quarrying, and other nonintensive uses of the land that do not require permanent structures.

Some of our problems with floods and floodplains are similar to our problems with earthquakes. We need to recognize the zones of peril. Then, if we choose to live within these zones, prudent engineering design of any structures should be required. Even better, zones of danger, which predictably will be in chaos someday, should be used for other than residential purposes.

Urban sprawl onto previously undeveloped floodplains is a national menace that is heightened by the urban sprawl itself. As more and more streets, roofs, parking lots, and concrete bedeck the land, larger and larger volumes of the rain and snow that fall will become runoff, because less and less land surface is available to absorb the water that falls. We contribute to our own peril in our desire to live near a beautiful, peaceful stream, because we forget its potential to destroy.

ARID LANDS

Deserts offer a uniquely fascinating scene—one made familiar to us by generations of Westerns, filmed among the beauty of our southwestern deserts. Stark scenery, bare rock, savage sandstorms, rippling sand dunes, and alkali lakes—the words conjure up visions of desolation and a hostile land. Yet deserts also offer warm, sunny living, clear air, stunning scenery and, with the advent of central air conditioning, an escape from the stinging cold and the gray, snowy skies of winter elsewhere. The population shift to America's Sun Belt suggests that arid land and semiarid lands will be home to increasing numbers of Americans.

Trying to define a desert yields a variety of answers. Many geographers describe deserts as areas that receive an average annual rainfall of less than 10 inches (25 centimeters). Others would raise the upper limit to perhaps 16 inches (40 centimeters). No matter what limit is chosen, a desert is an area that receives relatively little rain; evaporation usually exceeds precipitation in the world's deserts.

Geologists would prefer a slightly different definition of a desert, one based on geologic process. Most geologists would agree that a desert is an area where the runoff does not leave the area; stream courses are short, stream flow is intermittent, and drainage is into local basins. More simply, *deserts are areas where there is no external drainage*.

Like all definitions, this one suffers from exceptions. In the southwestern United States, the Colorado River system consists of about 50 individual streams that drain one-twelfth of the United States and a small area of Mexico. Snow, which falls among the highest peaks in western Colorado, eventually flows through barren, parched desert land. Nearly 2000 miles (3200 kilometers) of permanent stream slash across the heart of America's southwestern deserts; the Nile likewise bisects the eastern Sahara in Africa.

No matter whose definition we choose,

deserts are areas where rainfall is sparse, evaporation is high, and drainage is mostly internal. Defined in this way, approximately 20 to 30 percent of the world's land surface is desert, and one out of six people lives in a desert.

For those who live in deserts, their existence from birth to death is a battle for water. Such a statement may seem extreme to southwestern city dwellers, who turn on their faucets to enjoy all the water they want, whose backyards may contain large, private swimming pools, and whose refrigerators are stuffed with fruits and vegetables from nearby irrigated fields. However, the statement is not really that exaggerated. Many citizens of southwestern America are simply living on borrowed time; the water they use so freely is a rapidly diminishing, ancient resource—a resource discussed more fully in Chapter Ten. Time and water will run out for many dwellers in southwestern deserts in this century, and there will be enormous political and social consequences.

Currently the earth's deserts are growing in size, swallowing up more productive lands on their fringes and causing the starvation of millions. As estimated 400,000 square miles (1 million square kilometers) of land has been lost to the desert, partly as the result of climatic changes, but mostly because of population pressures and consequent overuse of the desert's fragile agricultural resource. Such overuse is hardly confined to the widely publicized Sahel region of Africa; excess demand on desert resources is a worldwide phenomenon as people contribute to the growth of deserts.

For every desert area, there is a maximum population that the land can support; if this level is exceeded, the agricultural plan that once sustained life fails, and more desert is created. Scrub brush takes the place of life-giving plants; precious water supplies are now used to grow scrub, and more land is given over to the desert. Humans move on in search of more fertile land or starve.

What Causes Deserts?

The hot deserts of the world are a *midlatitude phenomenon*. One group of the great deserts of the world coincides with a belt centered on latitude 25° N and S (Figure 8-17). The deserts of western Australia, the Kalahari and Sahara of Africa, the deserts of northern Mexico, the Arabian Desert, and the Thar region of Pakistan all coincide with areas of stable, high, atmospheric pressure. These areas are characterized by air currents descending toward the earth. As air descends, it is compressed (hence the high pressure) and, as it is compressed, it is warmed. As the air is warmed, its capacity to hold moisture is increased, and so these deserts (shown in a stipple pattern on Figure 8-17) are areas of hot, drying air. Evaporation exceeds precipitation; in many of these deserts less than 2 inches (5 centimeters) of rain falls in an average year.

Another group of deserts form a band centered on latitude 40° N and S of the equator. The southwestern deserts of America, the Patagonian desert of Argentina and the great Gobi desert of central Asia, comprise this group. The mountain ranges stretching down the west coast of the Americas provide an effective moisture barrier. As moist air rising from the Pacific Ocean moves east and rises over these ranges, it cools. Cool air holds less moisture than warm air—a phenomenon familiar to anyone who has breathed on a cold mirror—and so rain and snow fall out of the rising air on the western slope. As the air rises across the ranges and

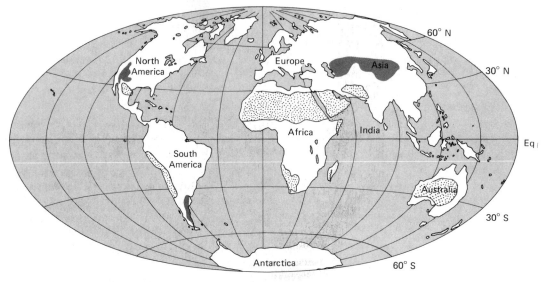

8-17
Midlatitude deserts are shown with a stipple pattern in color, while rain shadow and continental deserts are shown in solid color. Polar deserts include essentially the area poleward from the Arctic and Antarctic circles. The deserts of the world aggregate one-third of the world's land area. (Data from numerous sources.)

descends to the other side, it is compressed and heated (Figure 8-18). Thus, the descending air is hot and dry in **rain shadow deserts,** which are deserts in the lee of a major mountain mass. The Gobi and other deserts of central Asia owe their existence partly to the rain shadow of the Himalayan ranges to the south; they are also intensified by their great distance from the ocean—the only source of moisture—because they are situated in the center of a vast continent. The Gobi and associated deserts are *continental deserts* that formed because they were isolated from a distant source of moisture.

The world's hot, arid areas have three major origins: (1) intense evaporation and heating in areas of stable, descending, warm air; (2) rain shadow areas, where mountain masses upwind wring the moisture out and leave only drying, descending, warm air; and (3) areas in the center of vast continental masses that are remote from any reservoir of moisture.

Other minor sources of aridity include cold ocean currents that release little or no moisture to the air mass as it moves inland (the Atacama Desert of Peru is one example) and areas where the average temperature is below freezing, producing *polar deserts*. The Antarctic continent is an example of a polar desert; precipitation falls, but always in solid form. The result (all water is in solid form) is among the most arid deserts on earth.

Just as hot deserts are a midlatitude phenomenon today, they presumably have always been in the past. The distribution of worldwide air currents is little affected by

272   *Landscapes*

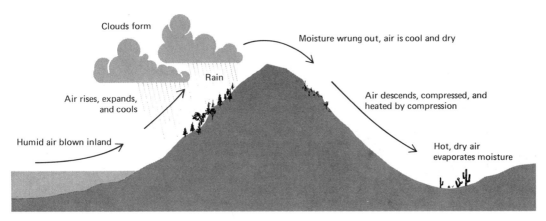

Clouds form

Moisture wrung out, air is cool and dry

Rain

Air rises, expands, and cools

Air descends, compressed, and heated by compression

Humid air blown inland

Hot, dry air evaporates moisture

8-18
Formation of rain shadow deserts is explained in this sketch. The windward side of the mountain mass forces the humid air up, causing it to cool, expand, and lose its water. The leeward (downward) side of the mountain mass receives air that is dried out and heated by compression as it descends. The area is a rain shadow desert; move the intervening mountain, and the desert would disappear. An example of a rain shadow desert in the western United States is the Death Valley region, east of the Sierra Nevada near the California coast.

the presence or absence of land. Areas on the western side of continents at latitudes of 25° N and S have probably always been areas of extensive deserts. The principle of uniformity again suggests that understanding the present is the key to understanding the past.

If we could recognize ancient rocks that must have originated under desert conditions, we would have a good key to their probable location on earth at the time the rocks were forming. Such thinking led Wegener, more than 50 years ago, to a bold reconstruction (see Figure 7-3) of continental positions in the past that was based partly on interpreting the latitude occupied by a continent in the past from the climatic record written into those rocks. If we are to understand what kinds of rocks deserts are making today, we must ask some familiar

questions. What products result from desert geologic processes? What is happening in the arid world?

Desert Processes

The desert is a place of fascinating deception. Craggy, splintered mountains split the crystal-clear sky only to end abruptly at the margin of huge, gently sloping plains (Figure 8-19). Because the desert world appears to be geologically quiet, space and time seem endless, as if change were frozen. Few plants hide the geologic scene, slopes are stark and rugged, and sunlight is intense. Soils are poorly formed, thin, and gravelly— enriched in soluble alkalies that would be washed away in a more humid land. Weathering, in the near absence of water, is pain-

8-19
This view, taken from the top of the House Range, in Utah, is typical. The mountain range is adjacent to a wide, flat basin; the contact between the basin and the range is a long, gentle slope. (Photograph by W. D. Johnson, U.S. Geological Survey.)

fully slow. Mechanical weathering provides occasional fresh rock fragments, while evaporation, after the infrequent rains, brings various soluble metals to the surface. This produces thin crusts of whitish alkali salts and dark crusts of clay, with minor iron and manganese oxides called *desert varnish* (Figure 4-9).

Mass wasting processes are dominated by two processes—rockfalls and mudflows. Rocks fall vertically from steep cliffs; they collect as talus slopes at the base of the cliff and may stay in place for centuries. Mudflows are one of the hazards of deserts; their loose, sparsely vegetated soils are easy prey for the occasional thundering rains. Rainfall in desert areas is rare; when it occurs, it is often torrential. Runoff is rapid; valleys that have been dry for many years may experience flash flooding. Sediment load is high, erosion is intense, and valley walls are steep.

Perhaps the greatest surprise in desert scenery is the pervasive influence of running water in a land of little water. Precisely because the occasional stream flows are powerful, desert scenery is dominated by long periods of little landscape change and brief periods of catastrophic restyling. Desert dwellers know the folly of camping in dry streambeds; the occasional storm-filled dry streams have been a source of tragedy for many years.

A look at most arid and semiarid lands reveals a series of new landforms, all created by familiar geologic processes. The same stream that cuts a deep, steep-walled canyon in the mountains spills out on the adjacent plain—its temporary baselevel—and immediately drops its load, forming an *alluvial fan*. An alluvial fan is a cone of rocks, sand, silt, and mud radiating from the mouth of a stream valley on the floor of a desert basin (Figure 8-20).

8-20
An alluvial fan near Salt Lake City, Utah. The original engraving was drawn by
W. H. Holmes; the human figures suggest scale. (From G. K. Gilbert, 1890,
U.S. Geological Survey Monograph 1, Pl. XLIV.)

The fan's surface is crisscrossed by dry stream channels, remnants of mudflows, and occasional plant debris. The fan slopes more steeply near the mountain and more gently near the plain; each slope is neatly adjusted to the approximate size of the particles that comprise it. Again, the reach for dynamic equilibrium is apparent; steep slopes are necessary to carry the coarse debris deposited near the mountain, while finer debris is swept out closer to the basin floor. Finally, as baselevel is approached, gradients become too low to carry anything, and even the finest material is deposited. Still further out on the basin floor, the material carried in solution is deposited by evaporation; the whitish alkali lakebeds are a common part of the center of most desert basins (Figure 8-21). The total profile from the top of the alluvial fan, near the mountains, to the shimmering dry lake is a profile of equilibrium. Each slope is just enough to do the work imposed on it by the load reaching the slope. Nature is conservative with energy; slopes steeper than necessary are soon flattened by erosion, while gentle slopes are steepened by deposition.

Streams in deserts are widely spaced, since rainfall is rare. There is still another difference. Streams lose their water by evaporation or soaking into the porous, gravelly desert soil; they rarely flow across the desert

8-21
A playa lake in Death Valley, California. The peaks in the background, with clouds over them, wring the moisture out before it gets to Death Valley. The polygonal lines in the dry lakebed are large mud cracks, formed when the playa lakebed dried out a few days after an infrequent rain. (Photograph by J. R. Stacy, U.S. Geological Survey.)

for more than a few miles (kilometers). Streams empty into desert basins, which are commonly blocked by other mountains, landslide debris, lava flows, and alluvial fans. The lakes that form in the center of basins are ephemeral; they are perhaps 1 yard (1 meter) deep but several miles (kilometers) wide. A few days after a rain, the lake is dry and the dissolved material has evaporated. Such alkali lakes are fascinating to mineral collectors, because sparkling crystals of highly soluble minerals may be found here. The lake deposits may also have

economic value as natural concentrating pools of certain minerals. Borax is the best known of the minerals collected from alkali lakes; the borax deposits of the Death Valley area are the only known economic source of this valuable substance.

Desert Landforms

Many desert landforms have already become familiar; talus piles, deeply eroded canyons, alluvial fans, and alkali lakes, for example, have become a part of our comprehension of deserts. Other landforms remain to be discussed; among them is a mystery called the **pediment.** Pediments are among the most characteristic landforms of an arid region (Figure 8-22), but their origin is still a controversy after 100 years of patient investigation. Pediments are long, gently sloping aprons of hard rock; they are covered with a thin veneer of loose sediment that grades imperceptibly into large alluvial fans near the valley floor. The longitudinal profile of the pediment (Figure 8-23) is generally concave upward, much like the profile of many modern streams. For these and other reasons, pediments are usually regarded as the result of sheet flow of water during storms, combined with sidecutting by the streams.

Few landforms have, however, created more controversy, since pedimentlike landforms are also found in humid regions. Pediments, however, seem to form in deserts as the result of streams eating their way *back* into hard rock. In more humid climates, streams eat their way *down* into bare rock.

If desert slopes retreat back, gentler slopes replace steeper ones and the land gradually becomes buried under its own debris, because rock fragments become stable

8-22
A pediment surface from the Growler Mountains, in southeastern Arizona. The pediment surface is covered with a few feet (several meters) of loose rock and soil, with desert scrub vegetation on top of it all. (Photograph by James Gilluly, U.S. Geological Survey.)

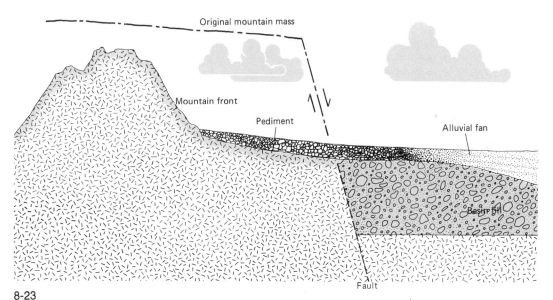

Original mountain mass

Mountain front

Pediment

Alluvial fan

Basin fill

Fault

8-23
The pediment advances or grows in size by eating its way back into the mountain front, while alluvial fans catch the debris transported across the pediment surface. The mountain mass was originally twice (dot-dash line) the size that shows at the surface; the edge of the uplifted mass is now marked by a buried fault (dashed line) that separates the mountain range from the adjacent basin, which is filled with debris shed from the mountains that surround it. This cross section would be typical of many areas in the desert west.

on slopes too gentle to allow them to move. The story of desert scenery is, then, the story of mountainous areas being carved into long, sloping pediments, awash with their own debris. The remnants of the mountain mass now form isolated knobs, centered in radiating sheets of debris that rest on pediment surfaces. Such a landscape is stable and little changing. Slopes are too low to allow movement of materials across them; the rate of change becomes very low until this condition of landscape equilibrium is changed.

Wind and Sand

The mention of deserts causes us to think of sand dunes, yet sand dunes occupy only a small fraction of the areas of the world's deserts. In many desert areas, strong winds have blown the sand away until the gravelly material that was originally mixed in with the sand is all that is left behind. This coarser material that has lagged behind is called **lag gravel** (Figure 8-24); the surface of the desert is now effectively armored against further **deflation,** or *wind erosion.* The power of wind to move sand and silt high into the air is rarely appreciated unless you have lived through a desert sandstorm; then the violence of roaring wind and rasping sand will never be forgotten. Parts of the Hawaiian Islands, thousands of miles (kilometers) from the nearest source of quartz, are mantled by soils that contain silt-sized fragments of quartz that could only have come from the distant continents.

The movement of air is much like that of running water, since air is only a fluid of extremely low viscosity and density. Like water, wind can carry a load in turbulent suspension above the ground surface and

8-24
Lag gravel on the surface of Death Valley. The hammer is about 1 foot (30 centimeters) long. Notice how the rocks fit together, almost like a mosaic, to protect the surface. (Photograph by J. R. Stacy, U.S. Geological Survey.)

can roll and bounce a coarser bed load along the land surface; wind, of course, carries no dissolved load.

All that is necessary for sand dunes to form is a plentiful source of loose sand and strong winds. Riverbanks and ocean and lake beaches also fulfill the requirement, because sand dunes are not restricted to deserts. The sandy material may be of any composition. The White Sands of central New Mexico are sand dunes of gypsum deflated from a nearby alkali lake; some dunes near beaches in Hawaii are composed mostly of olivine; ancient dunes in the Bahamas are composed largely of fossil shell fragments; and snowdrifts are a type of temporary "sand" dune. However, most dunes are largely composed of sand-sized grains of quartz, since only quartz is sufficiently abundant to form a major source for the sand dunes of the world.

Sand dunes form whenever flowing air meets an obstruction and there is a consequent loss in velocity and deposition of the load being carried. Blowing sand grains, deflected by an obstacle, may fall into a wind shadow area. Sand begins to pile up, and soon the sand itself becomes an obstacle, piling up more sand in its own wind shadow. As the dune grows in size, the whole dune begins moving downwind (Figure 8-25); the sand is blown upslope on the windward side and avalanches down the leeward side. Any dune facing the wind rapidly develops a streamlined form that often consists of a gently sloping windward side and a steeply sloping leeward side. The leeward side is a steep angle of repose slope; the angle is determined by the cohesion of the grains of loose sand, which is a frictional effect.

One of the more intriguing examples of the power of wind results from recent investigations of boulders resting on the surface of dry desert lakebeds in California and Nevada. Cobbles and boulders, ranging from a few ounces (a few tens of grams) to a few hundred pounds (kilograms) in weight, rest at the end of tracks up to 200 yards (180 meters) long. Speculations as to why boulders move across dry lakebeds have been endless; they were recently ended by careful observation.

By weighing and measuring a number of sample boulders and carefully observing the nature of the track, geologists concluded that the boulders were skidded across the wetted surface of the lakebed by wind during a violent storm. A thin layer of water overlying a firm clay base provides the prerequisite—a near frictionless surface—and high-velocity wind does the rest. Gusts of wind start the boulders skidding, and they sail on at speeds estimated at up to 1 yard (1 meter) per second. Perhaps the most famous area of deflation-induced boulder sailing is Racetrack Playa in Death Valley National Monument in California. There, tourists have been

8-25
Sand dunes in the San Luis Valley, Colorado. The steep face is in shadow, while the gentler windward slope dips to the right. The prevailing wind in this area must blow from right to left; the dunes themselves must also migrate downwind. (Photograph by C. Siebenthal, 1903, U.S. Geological Survey.)

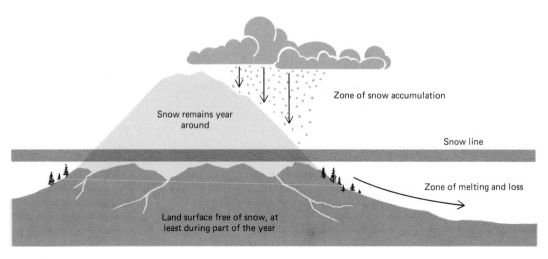

8-26
In this cross section of a mountainous area, the elevation of the snow line is essentially the *equilibrium* point. Above the snow line, snow accumulates year around and may move downslope as glaciers. Below the snow line, the end of the glacier is constantly melting, producing streams of running water. If the climate warms, the snow line rises, and the glaciers retreat upslope, undergoing a loss in total volume.

treated to the enigmatic wandering boulders for many years; now the mystery is apparently solved.

Even though deserts seem to be alien places to many people, they are just another variant on a theme. Areas of ample water display gentle sloping landforms, all graded toward the sea. Areas of much less water display stark, rugged slopes, graded toward central basins in our southwestern deserts. In still higher latitudes, another erosive agent, glacial ice, quarries the land. The touch of ice has affected *every* continent at some time. What causes glaciers? Will they come again?

THE TOUCH OF ICE

Glaciers are hardly everyday reality for most people, because most of the world's population lives at lower elevations in the temperate climatic zone. But glaciers are powerful erosional agents today in high-latitude areas, while many modern landscapes indicate that glaciers have extended into lower elevations in midlatitude areas in the recent past. A glacier forms wherever snowfall stays year around and collects to some depth; each delicate snowflake is transformed into a coarse ice crystal by the weight of overlying snow. If thousands of square miles (kilometers) of land were to be covered, the ice would begin to flow slowly across the land surface under its own weight, much as freshly poured concrete flattens its own surface. Such a glacier, several miles (kilometers) thick, covers the Antarctic and Greenland continents and is called a **continental glacier.**

In lower latitudes and at high elevations, snow collects in stream valleys and flows down the valleys as stiff, viscous rivers of ice. **Valley glaciers** are relatively small and are confined by valley walls high in the mountains. Their ponderous downvalley descent may be measured in yards (meters) per year. As the mass of ice continues downvalley, the ice passes below an elevation where snow will stay year around. During the warm season of the year, the lowest part of the glacier melts and becomes running water, while the upper part of the same glacier may continue to receive snow. The area of the glacier is in equilibrium with the prevailing climate.

The elevation (Figure 8-26) above which snow stays year around is the **snow line.** Above the snow line, the snowcap is perennial; below it, snow melts away at least part of the year. The elevation of the snow line is, not surprisingly, a function of latitude; it reaches nearly 20,000 feet (6000 meters) near the equator (Figure 8-27), averages 10,000 feet (3000 meters) in the midlatitudes, and drops to sea level at both the Antarctic and Arctic circles. In a very generalized way, the snow line rises approximately 3000 feet (920 meters) for every 15 degrees of latitude equatorward from the poles. The availability of moisture also affects the snow line, which rises in elevation with increasing distance downwind from the oceans and falls in equatorial regions of heavy precipitation.

The snow line is another measure of climate; snow line elevation rises as average temperatures rise and falls with declining warmth. Nearly everyone knows that the earth has recently experienced several epochs of intense glaciation, but few realize how widespread glaciation has been within the last few tens of thousands of years. Twenty thousand years ago, the worldwide snow line had dropped well over 3000 feet (920 meters), glaciers had pushed about 20 degrees of latitude toward the equator (as

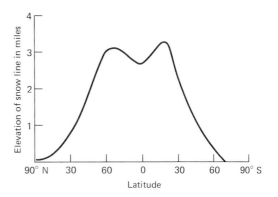

8-27
The relation between average snow line elevation and latitude on earth. Can you explain why the snow line is highest at about 20 degrees north and south of the equator? (Data from numerous sources.)

compared to modern glaciers), average temperatures were lower by 5 degrees Celsius, and almost one-third of the world's land area was under glacial ice.

The story of the recognition of repeated, recent periods of glaciation is another story of one man's insistence, in the face of opposition from essentially the entire scientific community, that recent, worldwide glaciation was a reality based on evidence from the rocks themselves. The principle applied was uniformitarianism: the present is the key to the past. The man's name was Jean Louis Rodolphe Agassiz. His profession was zoology, and the locale was the Swiss Alps.

Agassiz and Ice

Louis Agassiz (Figure 8-28) was born in 1807, a time of scientific, social, and political revolution. To most people of the time, the earth was, at most, a few thousand years old and had changed little since the recent Noachian flood. First, in the late 1700s, Hut-

8-28
Louis Agassiz is remembered both for his contributions as a zoologist and as the scientist who established proof of recent glacial advances in midlatitude areas.

ton had insisted that granite, basalt, and kindred rocks had once been molten and poured out onto the soils of Europe and Great Britain in the *distant* past. Hutton had maintained that the earth was incredibly old, constantly changing and, therefore, always new—wasting away, yet growing. Next Cuvier insisted that giant elephants and other monsters had roamed the Paris area several thousand years earlier.

In 1837, after studying in the Swiss Alps, Agassiz, a Swiss zoologist, startled Europeans by announcing that much of Europe had only recently been submerged under vast sheets of glacial ice. It was all too much!

The Swiss Alps were an ideal place to study glaciation; modern alpine valley gla-

ciers streamed from the high mountain valleys into the rivers and lakes that made Switzerland the mountain jewel of Europe. The erosive power of mountain glaciers had long been understood by those who lived near them; Swiss mountaineers recognized that: (1) valley glaciers move downvalley at incredibly slow rates; (2) the moving glaciers gouge and scratch the rocky valley floors over which they flow; and (3) the moving glaciers carry quantities of boulders with them, leaving piles of boulders behind as they melt back and carrying many miles (kilometers) isolated boulders from their place of origin.

The first geologist to recognize the role of glaciers in modifying mountain valleys was John Playfair. Playfair, a professor of mathematics and physics at the University of Edinburgh, was a lifelong friend of James Hutton; after Hutton's death in 1797, Playfair became his greatest exponent and commentator. In 1802 he published a commentary on Hutton's theory entitled *Illustrations of the Huttonian Theory of the Earth.* It is through Playfair's lucid exposition of Hutton's theory that Hutton's ideas on uniformitarianism gradually won acceptance. Hutton's own writing was ponderous, disorganized, and difficult to read; Playfair's *Illustrations* is enjoyable reading and contains a fine summary and amplification of Hutton's ideas. It includes the earliest known reference (1802) to the erosive power of glaciers and the nature of evidence for glaciation

For the moving of large masses of rock, the most powerful engines without doubt which nature employs are the glaciers, those lakes or rivers of ice which are formed in the highest valleys of the Alps, and other mountains of the first order. These great masses are in perpetual motion ... impelled down the declivities [slopes] on which they rest by their own enormous weight, together with the innumerable fragments of rock with which they are loaded. These fragments they gradually transport to their utmost boundaries, where a formidable wall [of fragments] ... attests the force ... of the great engine by which it was erected. ... In this manner, before the valleys were cut out in the form they now are, and *when the mountains were still more elevated* [emphasis added], huge fragments of rock may have been carried to a great distance. ...

Here was a vivid testimony to the power of glaciers to transport rocks "to a great distance." Many people had suggested a limited glacial concept long before Agassiz, but only he developed the evidence fully and forced the grudging acceptance of yet another controversial idea.

Among the early scientists to study the extent of glaciers was Ignace Venetz, a civil engineer in southern Switzerland who, as a result of contact with local mountaineers, recognized that past glaciers had extended some distance beyond their present confines. His friend, Jean de Charpentier, a mining engineer and director of the salt mines at Bex, was soon converted to Venetz's theory and, in 1834, presented a scientific paper in which he proposed that the glaciers in the Alps had formerly, in a much colder climate, extended far beyond their current position. Among the many in the audience who received these ideas with disbelief was Agassiz, then a researcher on fossil fish. Agassiz knew de Charpentier from high school days

and was convinced that his friend was sorely mistaken.

Two years later, Agassiz spent his summer vacation in Bex with de Charpentier in order to dissuade him from his errors. After visiting with both Venetz and de Charpentier among the glaciers of southern Switzerland and along the great Rhone River valley, it was Agassiz whose mind was indelibly changed; evidence of past, extensive glaciation was everywhere. De Charpentier had patiently collected the evidence, sifted it, and refined it; he offered it all to Agassiz during several months of field study among the glaciers of the Swiss Alps.

Agassiz was to Venetz and de Charpentier what Playfair was to Hutton; he took their ideas, clarified them, expanded them, and devoted 10 years or more of his life to the forceful exposition of an extension of their theory, an extension so enormous in scope that Agassiz is remembered 100 years later not only as a distinguished zoologist, but also as the man who proposed the theory of worldwide glaciation in the recent past. Read his description of his theory.

In my opinion, the only way to account for all these facts and relate them to known geological phenomena is to assume that at the end of the [recent] geologic epoch ... the earth was covered by a huge ice sheet. ... This ice sheet filled all the irregularities of the surface of Europe ... the Baltic Sea, all the lakes of Northern Germany and Switzerland. It ... even covered completely North America and Asiatic Russia. ...

Agassiz had greatly extended the ideas of others before him, who had suggested that ice traveling down Alpine valleys might well have transported debris several tens of miles (kilometers) from their current position. Agassiz had ice covering all of northern Europe, Scandinavia, Russia, and North America! He had proposed no less than a recent **Ice Age,** a period of time when the climate was so cold that glaciers covered much of the northern world.

Agassiz presented his ideas in 1840 in a book entitled *Studies on Glaciers.* The first chapter was a very fair review of the work of others who had preceded him, including de Charpentier, who taught him the core of glacial geology. The remaining chapters described the glaciers of the Alps and Jura mountains and included many ideas on biological control of glaciation and the physics of glacial motion that are now known to be erroneous. In the final chapter Agassiz extended his glacial ideas to propose a recent Ice Age in which glaciers covered much of the northern world. Adam Sedgwick, an English geologist, summed up the reaction to Agassiz's ideas succinctly: "I have read his Ice-book. It is excellent, but in the last chapter he loses his balance, and runs away with the bit in his mouth."

How did Agassiz so vastly extend the glacial ideas of others which were limited to cautious extensions of glaciation some distance down Alpine valleys to his idea that glaciation covered one-third of the world? He had recognized three kinds of evidence produced by modern glaciers: (1) grooved, scratched, and polished rock (Figure 8-29), produced as glaciers grind rock over rock; (2) **glacial erratics,** enormous boulders (Figure 8-30) of rock carried many tens or hundreds of miles (kilometers) from their point of origin by the flowing ice; and (3) **moraines,** sinuous ridges of rock fragments (Figure 8-31) left behind as the glacier melted back from its position of maximum advance. Quite simply, Agassiz saw these same awesome reminders of the power of glaciers wherever he traveled over northern Europe, North America, and Brazil. To him,

8-29
Polished and grooved rocks from the Alps. (Louis Agassiz, 1840, Pl. 17, *Etudes sur Les Glaciers,* courtesy of the History of Science Collections, University of Oklahoma Libraries.)

8-30

The original caption for this photograph, which was taken in 1908, is "Perched geologist on perched boulder, both erratics." Photograph on Moraine Dome, Yosemite National Park. (Photograph by G. K. Gilbert, U.S. Geological Survey.)

the signs of massive glaciation were everywhere, and they unmistakably pointed to recent, widespread glaciation.

To others, the grooved and polished rocks, giant boulders far from their source, and the sinuous ridges of rounded rock all indicated a *different* agent—the Noachian flood, or perhaps subsequent floods. Even Lyell had believed the grooves and polish in British rocks to be the work of water or of

ice rafts in seawater, because there seemed to be no other natural process that could account for them. Agassiz recognized that if the present is the key to the past, the evidence left by modern glaciers would be like that left by still larger glaciers of the past.

The battle was on, and it raged for several decades. To those comfortable with an earth a few thousand years old, recently deluged by the flood of Noah, Agassiz's ideas were a frontal attack; the erratics (boulders transported long distances from their source), the moraines, and the grooved and polished rocks had all been taken to be signs of the biblical flood, not of some fanciful vast ice sheet covering most of Europe. Staggered by Hutton's insistence on a world without beginning and Cuvier's Parisian monsters, Agassiz's world of ice was yet another uncomfortable intrusion into a comfortable, static world.

The war between the *diluvialists,* who insisted that geological features supported the flood of Noah, and those who found the work of streams and glaciers sufficient to account for modern landscapes is one of the interesting sidelights of glacial history from which stories such as that of Dr. William Buckland, geologist and clergyman, developed.

Buckland, who was a confirmed diluvialist in the 1820s, published numerous articles asserting that geologic features supported a recent flood or deluge. Twenty years later, Buckland went to Switzerland, intending to attack Agassiz's glacial theories at their source; instead, he came away a confirmed believer in a recent period of extensive glaciation. He spent his remaining years a vigorous proponent of glacial theory and accompanied Agassiz on several expeditions in England and Scotland, where glacial fea-

8-31
The lower end of La Perouse Glacier, Alaska. The debris pushed ahead of the glacier is the moraine. The glacier was overruning the forest on the far left when this photograph was taken in 1889. (Photograph by G. K. Gilbert, U.S. Geological Survey.)

tures abound. Figure 8-32 presents carica-ture of Buckland that was drawn by a friend and student.

In time, Agassiz's meticulous accumula-tion of evidence won the acceptance of the world's scientific community, and he is re-membered as the father of the theory of the Ice Ages. During a triumphant tour of the United States, he again recognized wide-spread evidence of glaciation. His concepts were accepted only slowly and after much debate, but now time was on his side. Agas-siz's dual interests in glaciers and fish were the pinnacles of a brilliant scientific career— a career whose late stages in the study of zoology took place at Harvard. The erratic boulder that marks his grave came from the glacier of Aar in Switzerland, where his studies started.

Origins of the Ice Ages

Critics of Agassiz's insistence on a recent Ice Age attacked the idea at its weakest link.

What had *caused* such a remarkable change in climate? Agassiz, of course, did not know and could only speculate by analogy with the biologic realm he knew so well. He be-lieved the earth had been through multiple cycles of glaciation. Following a glacial ''death,'' the earth warmed and life re-turned, only to be followed later by another period of cold. Such an idea offended the sensibilities of many of Agassiz's friends as well as his enemies, and many made light of what was obviously a poorly developed scheme for climatic change. Climatology was in its infancy in the early 1800s; little was known about the forces affecting the earth's climate, so the question of the origin of glacial ages remained unanswered.

To twentieth-century geologists, the ulti-mate cause of glaciation is still a subject of speculation. It is well known that large-scale volcanism churns out millions of pounds (kilograms) of ash, many geologists have wondered if periods of intensive volcanism might not produce glaciation, since sus-

8-32
This caricature of Buckland by one of his students proves that university humor was alive and well 100 years ago. Buckland, attired for study of modern glaciers, did present a ponderous image. (From Elizabeth Gordon, 1894, *The Life and Correspondence of Wm. Buckland,* p. 145, courtesy of the History of Science Collections, University of Oklahoma Libraries.)

pended ash partially absorbs heat radiated from the sun.

Some astronomers have suggested that galactic hydrogen clouds are the cause; others have declared that the sun's output of energy is variable and that glaciation is the inevitable result of slight declines in the sun's energy. Indeed, a mounting body of evidence suggests that our sun is anything but a static star, because its energy output seems to vary over a wide range of time intervals.

Among recent theories about glaciation is a slightly revised version of a 100-year old idea. One idea offered to Agassiz as an explanation for glacial cooling was changes in solar radiation caused by variations in the earth's orbit around the sun. Recently, three geologists were able to obtain an essentially continuous climatic record from deep oceanic sediment cores and associated fossils deposited within the last 500,000 years. Matching those observed past climatic changes to predicted variations in the earth's orbit around the sun reveals correlations so strong that the theory seems reasonably conclusive, although variations in solar energy output may also be a major factor leading to the onset and retreat of glaciers.

Three kinds of orbital changes are involved. The earth and sun are currently closest to one another in January; in 10,000 years they will be closest in July. Times of coldness are associated with summer earth-sun distances that are greater than normal in a cycle lasting about 23,000 years. The second orbital cycle includes a change in the tilt of the earth's rotational axis with respect to the sun; this cycle lasts about 42,000 years. The third and dominant cycle lasts about 100,000 years and results from changes in the earth's orbital path around the sun. This longer change in the earth's orbital path modifies the effect of the other two cycles. When each of these three cycles superimposes optimum conditions for glaciation on the earth, glaciation ensues. It seems, therefore, that changes in the earth's path around the sun, the tilt of its axis, the change in timing of close solar approach, and variations in solar output are the basis causes of the ice ages of the past.

Interestingly, using this model, the long-term trend of variations in the earth's orbit suggests that the next several thousand years should see a gradual cooling and renewed extensive glaciation. Such a cooling, although gradual, may begin to have important agricultural, social, and political effects for a growing population whose food supply is more and more tied to highly adapted plants and sophisticated, massive agriculture.

How much of a change is required? A change in the worldwide *average* temperature of approximately 5 degrees Celsius would be all that is required to bring glaciers as far south as Kansas City once again. The balance of temperature that holds off glaciation is delicate, indeed.

Glacial Landscapes

The movement of ice takes place as gravity acts on the mass of collected snow. Within the lower part of a glacier, ice flows like slowly moving water as ice crystals are readily deformed by the weight of ice above

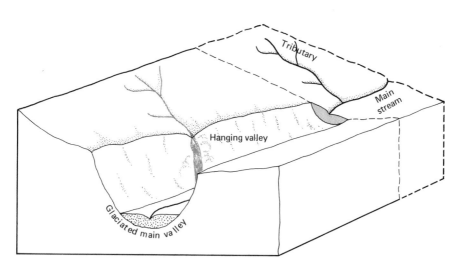

8-33

A "before and after" sketch of a hanging valley. Before glacial erosion (the back block with dashed lines), a stream enters the main stream as a tributary from the side. After glacial erosion of the main stream channel (the front block of the diagram), the main channel is deepened and changed to a U-shaped channel. The former tributary valley was not glaciated and is now well above the main channel, poised in the air as a hanging valley. Its stream flow into the main channel is now a waterfall.

them. Like a river, the velocity of flow generally increases upward away from the frictional zone at the glacier's base and, if the glacier is confined by valley walls, flow rates also increase away from its contact with the rocky walls of the valley. The upper, more brittle surface of the glacier is carried along by flow beneath it and is commonly broken into cracks called *crevasses.*

Ice is a prodigous erosional agent, able to carry material of almost *any* size that was furnished to it from above by mass wasting; ice can also wedge away large amounts of material from its base by frost wedging (see Chapter Four). The base of a glacier may be more rock than ice, so that the base acts as a rasp, scouring and grooving the rocks over which the glacier glides. Additionally, every square yard (meter) of ice on the sides and bottom of a glacier has a nearly equal ability to erode actively; the erosive power of a glacier is proportional to the *area* of ice-rock contact.

For glaciers confined to a valley, the control of ice movement by older stream valleys results in a map pattern like that of the original stream drainage. Wide, deep, master stream valleys accumulate large snowfields whose massive glaciers deeply erode the main valley, while smaller tributary valleys are much less affected. The result is that main valley glaciers cut far more deeply than their tributary ice streams. After the glaciers melt back in a warming climate, stream junctions are no longer at a common elevation; the juncture of the tributary valley with the main valley is now a **hanging valley** (Figure 8-33). If water should once again flow from the tributary to the main stream, the hanging valley is the site of a *waterfall;* the extent of the fall is a measure of the differential glacial erosion between the tributary and the master stream.

8-34

Deadman Canyon, Tulare County, California, is a typical U-shaped valley. (Photograph by F. E. Mathes, U.S. Geological Survey.)

Another consequence of active glacial erosion proportional to ice-rock contact area is a change in the shape of the original V-shaped mountain stream valley. The cross-valley profile is altered from a deeply cut notch to a *catenary curve* (Figure 8-34) which is a broadly open shape similar to the downward curve of a power line between two poles. The downvalley profile is often marked by numerous steplike basins and the valley begins up high in a large natural amphitheatre (Figure 8-35), called a **cirque,** which is formed by intense erosion and rotational slip of the ice in the area where the snowfield formed and fed the glacier.

The original stream divide is roughened and honed by glaciers that eroded away valley walls to form grooved, polished, and striated surfaces. The knife-edged stream divide is now an *arête* (Figure 8-36), and coalescing cirques leave **horns,** of which the Matterhorn in the Swiss Alps is an example.

At the lowest terminus of the valley gla-

8-35
A small glacier occupies the *cirque* near the top of Cloud Peak, Big Horn Mountains, Wyoming, in 1901. (Photograph by N. H. Darton, U.S. Geological Survey.)

8-36
This photograph, taken in 1936 near Mount Whitney, California, illustrates the sharpened former stream divides now known as *arêtes*. (Photograph by F. E. Mathes, U.S. Geological Survey.)

8-37
This rolling topography, near Prairie du Sac, Wisconsin, is typical morainal topography. The regolith is drift; the soils are apt to be deep, sandy, and rocky. (Photograph by W. C. Alden, U.S. Geological Survey.)

8-38

This hill is a drumlin, streamlined and formed by the passage of a continental glacier over land that is now near Newark, New Jersey. (Photograph by G. K. Gilbert, U.S. Geological Survey.)

8-39

"The Windrow," an esker near East Hartland, Connecticut, is a sinuous ridge of stratified sand and gravel, winding across the countryside. (Photograph by H. S. Palmer, U.S. Geological Survey.)

cier, stream processes dominate as meltwater from the glacier carries away quantities of the finer material. The limit of ice advance is marked by a hilly area of jumbled rock that ranges in size from huge blocks to very fine *rock flour*, which is produced by intense grinding of rock against rock. These low, rolling hills of unsorted rock debris are *terminal moraines* (Figure 8-31); they mark the limit of glacial advance much as a pile of debris may mark where a bulldozer operator quit for the day. Most of the rock fragments

8-40

This photograph, taken in 1900, is of an area near Orando, Montana, where kettles in the ground moraine are full of water. Such kettle lakes form roughly circular ponds and lakes in many glaciated regions. (Photograph by Charles D. Walcott, U.S. Geological Survey.)

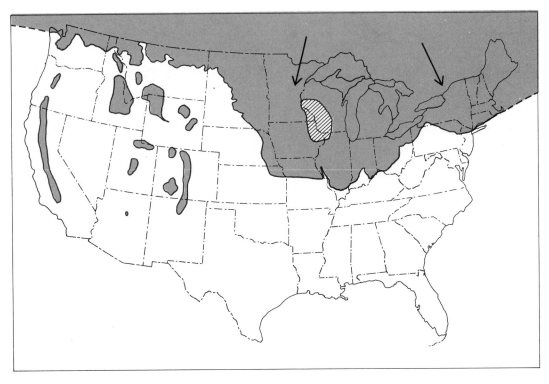

8-41
This map shows the maximum extent and direction of advance of glaciation
(arrows) during the various ice ages that have affected the conterminous
United States in the last few million years. South of the margin of the
continental glacier, on the high mountains of the west, valley glaciation was
common during the ice ages. In the area of diagonal stripes, evidence of
glaciation is sparse, although not totally lacking. This area of western
Wisconsin, northeastern Iowa, and southeastern Minnesota is often called the
"driftless area." (Modified after Dorothy H. Radbruch-Hall and others, 1976,
U.S. Geological Survey Map MF-771).

in a moraine are faceted, polished, grooved, and scratched, and some of the fragments may be unique kinds of rocks whose source can be found only many miles (kilometers) upvalley from their current resting place. Such large boulders that are distant from their source are *erratics* (Figure 8-30); this simply means that they are foreign or unusual. Erratic boulders were among the ear-

liest evidence for glaciation; Playfair recognized their glacial origin in 1802.

The general term for glacially deposited sediment is **drift,** a term dating from the time when such deposits were assumed to have "drifted" into place during the flood of Noah. Moraines are composed of drift and, together with widespread deposits of drift, produce a gently rolling surface that is underlain by ground moraine (Figure 8-37). Large parts of the midwestern United States are veneered with *ground moraine,* morainal hills on their surface that mark the limit of the last glacial advance. Other depositional landforms of continental glaciation include **drumlins** (Figure 8-38), low, streamlined hills produced as glaciers plastered drift over obstructions to their flow; **eskers** (Figure 8-39), sinuous, narrow ridges of stratified drift produced by meltwater streams flowing *under* a glacier; and **kettles,** roughly circular (Figure 8-40) depressions in drift produced when chunks of stagnant, buried ice melted underneath sheets of drift. Kettles often hold small ponds.

North America and the Ice Ages

Continental glaciers spread out radially from zones of heavy snowfall. The Ice Age glaciers that affected the northern part of the United States came from central Canada (Figure 8-41). The rich, fertile soils of America's central "breadbasket" are largely a gift from the glaciers of central Canada, which eroded soil and rock to a depth of a few tens of yards (meters), and carried the load to the south. As the glaciers advanced, the earth's crust sank under the load; as the glaciers melted back about 10,000 years ago, the crust began slowly bounding back up a few hundred yards (meters) still another sign that the earth's mantle, beneath the crust, responds over the long term as a fluid.

Much of the glacial drift is little weathered, an indication that glaciation has indeed been recent. Radioactive dates on wood fragments entombed by the last ice advance suggest that ice last left North America only about 10,000 years ago. Other exposures of drift display unweathered drift overlying

strongly weathered drift; this signifies that the most recent glaciation was preceded by an earlier one whose drift was weathered into soil before the youngest glacier arrived. Exposures in some areas of the midwestern United States document at least *four* major periods of ice advance and retreat, beginning nearly 3 million years ago. Detailed study of

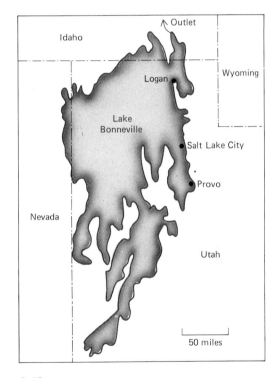

8-42

Extent of Lake Bonnevile, an Ice Age pluvial lake that at one time covered much of Utah and spilled north into the Snake River of southern Idaho. Evidence for the past existence of the lake includes abandoned shorelines, wave terraces, and river deltas near the lake margin. The cities of Provo, Salt Lake City, and Logan are built on various levels of lake sediments. (Modified after G. K. Gilbert, 1890, U.S. Geological Survey Monograph I, Pl XIII.)

glacial evidence in local areas suggests innumerable periods of minor advance and retreat—a phenomenon documented in modern climatic records. In the highest part of the Alps, farms and villages were overwhelmed by glacial ice a little over 200 years ago during a period of minor glacial advance.

Among other glacial changes produced in North America were **pluvial lakes,** which developed when the climate was much cooler and rainier in lowland areas that were not overcome by glacial ice. In a cool and rainy climate, continental lakes may become extensive, such as the world's largest lake, an ancestor to the Caspian Sea, and a smaller ancestor to the Dead Sea. Three glacial lakes in the United States were particularly large. Lake Bonneville (Figure 8-42) covered most of northwestern Utah and drained northward into the Snake River; the Great Salt Lake is its tiny survivor. Lake Agassiz, named for Louis Agassiz, covered large parts of Manitoba and North and South Dakota. Lake Missoula covered parts of Washington state, northern Idaho, and much of Montana and was held in place by a natural ice dam.

About 18,000 years ago, Lake Missoula contained half as much water as modern Lake Michigan. Then, one day, the ice dam broke, releasing more than 500 cubic miles (2000 cubic kilometers) of water in one instant.

The flood boiled across Spokane valley with a discharge estimated at 400 million cubic feet (11 million cubic meters) per second—about 10 times the *combined* flow of the world's rivers. The raging water tore across eastern Washington, sweeping everything before it and creating a catastrophic landscape still termed the "*channeled scablands.*" Near the Oregon border, the torrent roared west of the present city of Walla Walla into the Columbia River and finally built a massive delta where the Columbia River enters the Pacific Ocean. After perhaps a month of torrential flow, streams returned to normal, leaving the region with landforms that still bear the scars of a catastrophe beyond our comprehension.

SUMMARY   Landscapes are the expression of three independent variables: (1) rock resistance, (2) climate, and (3) gravity. Additionally, landscapes are not simply developed on passive, unresisting material with no previous history; most landscapes contain traces of earlier climatic conditions quite different from the modern scene. It is difficult to understand modern landscapes completely without some knowledge of the changes in climate within the last few million years.

Gravity, acting alone, is resisted by the cohesive forces among loose particles and by the strength of solid rock. Whenever the cohesion is diminished or the strength impaired—often by the addition of water in large quantities—the slope will flatten of its own accord at rates that range from imperceptible to disastrous.

Slopes are the fundamental unit of a landscape. Steep slopes suggest resistant rock, arid climate, and a landscape dominated by mass movement. Gentler slopes suggest softer rock, a more humid climate, and processes dominated by running water. Intense erosion is favored by increasing elevation and decreasing vegetation; semiarid zones at high elevation lose the most sediment per unit of area. In very arid areas, however, less material is lost, because little water is available to move material. In more humid areas, more abundant vegetation makes erosion more difficult.

In midlatitude areas that are far from a moisture source, in the rain shadow of a major mountain range, or in zones of continually descending heated air, deserts provide unique landscapes. Wind piles up streamlined hills of sand and produces minor erosional forms on softer rocks, but running water dominates the scene. During the infrequent rains, water carries away the accumulated products of weathering and mass wasting, but never very far away. Low areas receive the debris from high areas in a timeless land where drainage is sparse and internal. In time, the land is buried under smooth aprons of its own debris.

In high-latitude areas, erosional processes are dominated by glaciation. Continental glaciation tends to plane off high places and fill in low places, which lowers the relief of the preglacial landscape. Valley glaciers tend to roughen the surfaces over which they flow, quarrying valley walls and floors with equal ease while sharpening ridgelines by intense frost wedging. The snow line elevation, which is an indicator of climate, limits the extent of glaciation and varies as a function of latitude and moisture availability.

In mid- and low-latitude areas running water is the dominant erosive agent. In such areas, three laws of fluvial erosion were recognized 100 years ago by G. K. Gilbert, an American geologist. *Steepness of slope bears an inverse relation to the quantity of water, a direct relation to the resistance of the rock, and a direct relation to distance to the stream divide—the highest area between streams.* Erosion is most rapid where slope is steepest; deposition is most probable where slope is least steep.

Variation in stream flow causes large changes in the quantity and size of material carried by streams; streams do most of their work while they are in flood. However, variation in glacial flow causes no change in the quantity or size of material carried by ice, whose carrying power is independent of velocity. In contrast, large variations in wind velocity cause relatively large changes in the wind's capacity to carry objects in suspension, because the transport agent is now a fluid of extremely low density and viscosity. Particles coarser than sand are always left behind.

Wind deposits are thus well sorted; all the fragments in a sand dune are of similar size. Water-laid deposits are less well sorted by size; each layer reflects changes in the velocity and discharge of the fluid from which particles were deposited. Drift, which is deposited directly from ice, is nonsorted; boulder lies alongside minute silt grain.

The erosive capacity of a stream depends on two factors: gradient and discharge. For air, the analogous factors are pressure gradient and air mass; for glaciers their erosive capacity depends on ice-rock contact area and velocity. Each of these three erosional agents is influenced by gravity, while the resultant landforms are largely an expression of the viscosity of stiffness of each of the three quite different fluids acting on rocks of varying resistance.

EXERCISES

1. The speed of the water during the Spokane flood that created the channel scablands has been estimated at 45 miles (72 kilometers) per hour. What kind of *evidence* would one need to estimate past stream velocity?

2. One fairly common landform is a stream that has the map pattern of a meandering stream (that is, it has wide, flat valley floors); however, the valley width is narrow and the wall is solid rock. Such landforms are called *entrenched meanders;* how could they form?

3. In parts of North Dakota, geologists recognize former river valleys that are several miles (kilometers) wide, yet the stream flowing in them today is only a little creek. Why should a small stream be flowing in an extremely wide valley?

4. Since sand dunes tend to move downwind, if you were foolish enough to own a house just downwind of a large dune, how would you attempt to stabilize the dune?

5. It has been said that urbanization *causes* flooding. Explain.

6. In parts of Scotland, fields of rich, deep soil are surrounded by fences made of huge boulders laboriously dragged out of the soil. Where did the boulders come from and how could they have gotten into large areas of sandy soil?

7. Along the Mississippi River, the depth of loess diminishes away from the river, yet it is known that loess is deposited by wind, not water. Explain the apparent contradiction.

8. According to Mark Twain, if we straightened out the Mississippi River, its mouth would be over 1000 miles (1600 kilometers) out into the Gulf of Mexico. What was he talking about?

9. In some mountainous areas, the valleys up high in the mountains are U-shaped in cross section, while the same valleys at lower elevations are V-shaped in cross section. Explain.

10. In general, the lakes of northern Minnesota are elongate in map view while those in southern Minnesota are round. There are exceptions, but how could this generalization be explained?

SUGGESTED
READINGS

Agassiz, Louis, 1840 (translated and edited by A. V. Carozzi, 1967), *Studies on Glaciers,* New York, Harper & Row, 244 pp.
Beautifully illustrated; a readable masterpiece.

Butzer, Karl W., 1976, *Geomorphology from the Earth,* New York, Harper & Row, 306 pp.
Comprehensive review of landscapes in a human context.

Morisawa, Marie, 1968, *Streams: Their Dynamics and Morphology,* New York, McGraw Hill, 126 pp.
Brief and lucid, this is the book about streams.

Zaruba, Quido, and Vojtech, Mencl, 1969, *Landslides and their Control,* Amsterdam, Elsevier, 341 pp.
Comprehensive discussion of mass movement.

KEY
CONCEPTS

Landscapes, the result of interaction of
Isostatic uplift and gravity-driven erosive forces; earth materials and time; climate and process.

Gravity
Mass wasting; rivers and potential energy; glaciers and potential energy.

Solar energy
Brings water to the land; causes wind.

Running water
Forms slopes that funnel weathering products to the sea; energy product of weight (discharge) and slope (gradient); most effective agent except in glacial areas.

Wind
Minor agent, with some effect where vegetation nearly absent.

Ice
Major agent at high latitudes and high elevations; has been major agent in shaping high mountains and midlatitudes within the United States in recent past.

Products
Sorting, size, and stratification identify process.

This image, taken by the DMSP Air Force weather satellite, is of the eastern half of the United States at midnight; it graphically portrays the relation between energy use and population. (USAF photograph distributed by NOAA.)

Chapter Nine
ENERGY

"In the physical world, one cannot increase the size or quantity of anything without changing its quality. Similar figures exist only in pure geometry."
Paul Valery

The technology that sustains us also isolates us. Dinner comes from the supermarket, and heat comes from the furnace. A wise gardener knows that dinner comes from the farm, but that is still one step from reality. Food and furnace heat are both forms of energy, and they both come, ultimately, from the sun. In our isolation, we have used energy extravagantly while failing to understand what energy is and where it comes from.

Energy is defined as the *capacity* to do work; it appears in many forms, and each form maybe converted to another form—at a price. The energy of a boulder perched high on a hillslope (Figure 8-2) or the energy of water trapped behind a dam is *potential energy*, which can be instantly converted into *kinetic energy*, the energy of motion. The energy of motion is expressed in many forms: electricity is the flow of electrons, while atomic radiation is the flow of subatomic particles. Heat is the movement of molecules.

Energy is the child of the sun. Green chlorophyll in plants uses the sun's energy to make carbohydrates and thereby provides energy for all living things. After the death of a living thing, the carbohydrates may be stored as coal, oil, or gas, which are forms of concentrated solar energy that await our bidding.

Above all, energy is life. Our bodies are efficient machines that convert food into useful work by oxidation (the recombination of carbon and hydrogen from food with oxygen). The flow of energy from cell to cell distinguishes the living from the dead.

Energy is also independence. Dictatorial societies of past and present are based on the many serving the idle few. Since we have harnessed energy sources other than human muscle, life has become less toilsome

and more enjoyable for all. The dream of the world is enough energy for everyone, because living standards are tied closely to energy consumption.

ENERGY DEMAND

The United States, with one-sixteenth of the world's population, consumes one-third of the world's energy. Energy consumption has, historically, doubled every 20 years. We consume more energy per capita than any nation on the face of the earth—more than twice that of Sweden or West Germany. Americans also produce more goods and services per capita than any nation—again, nearly twice of our nearest competitor.

The energy demand (Figure 9-1) comes primarily from five markets: (1) generation of electricity; (2) commercial or business use; (3) residential consumption in space heating, air conditioning, water heating, and food preparation; (4) industrial needs; and (5) transportation.

Transportation demands one-third of our energy and is dominated by automobiles; the average driver has increased the annual distances driven every year for the last 20 years. We are a highly mobile society, in love with the automobile and endless miles (kilometers) of superhighways.

Industrial and agricultural demand, another one-third of our energy demand, includes the basic energy needs necessary to manufacture everything from toothpicks to steel. Also included is a large and growing component of petrochemical demand. Petroleum and natural gas are chemical resources for a vast range of material, from plastics to synthetic fabrics, and a broad range of agricultural pesticides and fertilizers. The de-

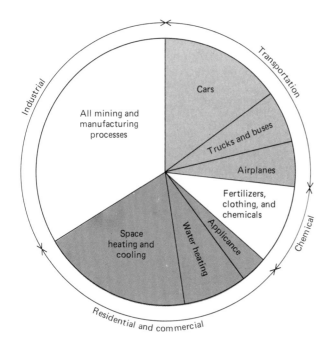

9-1
Components of the U.S. energy
demand. (Data taken from numerous
sources.)

mand for petroleum by chemical industries is a rapidly growing component of our total energy need.

Both residential and commercial enterprises use energy for the same purposes—space heating and cooling, lighting, food preparation, and water heating—and constitute the remaining one-third of our energy demand. The American plan of hermetically sealed buildings and shopping malls enclosed in artificial climates squanders energy prodigiously. More attention to weatherproofing, insulation, and double windows may soon make our structures more energy-efficient.

Electrical generation has had a growth rate of 8 percent per year—the highest growth rate among all the components of energy demand. Electricity is convenient and clean to use. All electricity is generated by converting some *other* energy source to electricity, which may then be transmitted long distances. Electricity is our most wasteful energy source; there are always costs in converting one form of energy to another, and those for conversion to electricity are huge.

Energy Measurement

The standard unit of measurement for energy is the **British thermal unit** (abbreviated as **Btu**). A *Btu* is the amount of heat required to raise the temperature of 1 pound (450 grams) of water 1 degree Fahrenheit (approximately ⁵⁄₉ degree Celsius) and is the approximate output of one wooden match. Other equivalent units of energy include the calorie which is the heat required to raise 1 gram (³⁄₁₀ ounce) of water 1 degree Celsius; 252 calories equal 1 Btu. The **kilowatt-hour** (abbreviated kWh) is the standard unit of measurement for electricity; 1 kilowatt-hour equals 3413 Btu. A barrel of crude oil yields nearly 6 million Btu, while 1 ton (⁹/₁₀ metric ton) of coal yields about 25 million Btu.

Another way to measure energy is to look at cost-to-benefit ratios for familiar fuels. A 5-gallon (19-liter) can of gasoline equals the work of 1 person-year (that is, the hard labor of one individual for a full year), and it currently costs us less than the value of 1 hour of our own labor to buy it. One kilowatt-hour equals 1 week of heavy labor; we pay for it with ½ minute of effort. Energy has been cheap and, therefore, valued lightly and wasted. Americans used 74 quintillion Btu of energy in 1976; a large component of that enormous demand is waste.

Energy Waste

Four centuries ago Johannes Kepler, a German physicist, reminded us that "nature uses as little as possible of anything." We Americans, vastly enriched by seemingly inexhaustible supplies of everything, including energy, have seemed bent on using as *much* as possible of everything. Now, while both our population and our aspirations swell, we are discovering the harsh truth in another old adage: "There is no such thing as a free lunch." As energy costs continue to rise, energy waste is one item that we *can* do something about. Let us examine the primary causes of energy waste.

The transportation industry is peculiarly dependent on oil and gasoline. While other sectors of demand *can* use alternative energy sources, diesel oil, jet fuel, and gasoline provide the wherewithal to move people and things in America. Automobiles account for over 90 percent of all personal travel in the nation. We own so many cars that every

American could be placed in a car and never have to use the back seat. As one sector of energy demand dependent on scarcer and scarcer petroleum-based energy, transportation is perhaps the prime target for the elimination of waste.

Figure 9-2 suggests a useful way to compare transportation efficiency. How much energy is consumed in moving one person 1 mile (1⁶/₁₀ kilometers)? The figures are sobering; note that it takes *four* times as much energy to get a person from home to work in a standard automobile as it does in a bus. The shift from standard to subcompact cars for one-half of our driving would save more fuel than the Alaska pipeline delivers. A ton of freight shipped by truck takes nearly six times the energy as one shipped by rail. The supersonic jet transport, the ultra-high-speed train, and the bloated, standard American car are dinosaurs in a world where the ratio of resources to people grows leaner each day. Thrusting its way across the heavens, an average American commercial jet aircraft once flew with one-half of its seats empty; reducing this to only 20 percent empty seats by consolidating airline flights and lowering fares has saved 500,000 barrels a day of jet fuel. There is no single area where waste is more amenable than the cost of moving people from place to place.

In our homes, closing the drapes can cut heat loss by one-half, while one-quarter of the heat energy used currently escapes through poorly insulated roofs. An electric light bulb produces 95 percent waste heat and 5 percent light (see chapter opening photograph), and the pilot light on a gas range consumes one-third of all the fuel the appliance uses. Ten percent of the natural gas consumed in the United States is used to keep pilot lights burning, although pilotless ignition systems have long been available. The potential savings from much better in-

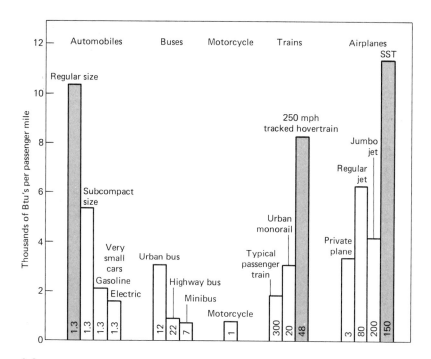

9-2

The energy consumed in moving people from place to place can best be compared by looking at energy consumption per passenger mile. For the transportation systems shown such costs are, of course, quite sensitive to the number of people being carried (the figures within each bar on the graph). High-speed planes and trains, and the standard U.S. automobile, are remarkably inefficient. (Reproduced from Shell Oil Company's booklet *The National Energy Problem: Potential Energy Savings.* Source is Richard A. Rice, 1973, "Energy Efficiencies of the Transport Systems, SAE Congress Paper 730066. Used with permission of Shell Oil Company, the Society of Automotive Engineers, and Richard Rice.)

sulation, increasingly energy-efficient appliances, pilotless ignition systems, and moderating our heating and cooling demands exceeds the equivalent of 1 million barrels of oil a day.

In the industrial market, greater efficiency in the recovery of waste heat from various processes and increased efficiency in heating, cooling, and lighting promise energy savings that exceed another 1 million barrels

of oil a day. Still greater savings may be possible in the electric demand area; electricity is currently our most wasteful fuel.

Electricity is *derived* energy—energy transmitted over power lines after being generated from some other form of energy. The conversion of one form of energy to electricity may involve substantial loss; the conversion of coal, oil, or natural gas to electricity wastes 67 percent of the energy in the fuels *at the power plant.* Another 14 percent is lost in transmitting the electricity in power lines; therefore only about *one-quarter* of the total energy available in the original coal, oil, or natural gas is *actually delivered* to our homes, factories, and offices. The conversion of older generating plants to currently available high-efficiency steam plants, combined with technology to recover some portion of the waste heat, could save the equivalent of another 1 million barrels per day of fuel oil by 1990.

If we add up the energy savings obtained by plugging up the largest of our wasteful energy uses, we might save between 5 and 7 million barrels a day of petroleum fuels. Assuming a total energy demand in the United States in 1980 of approximately 30 to 40 million barrels a day equivalent, we can estimate that about *one-sixth of our current energy demand is from preventable waste.*

No nation on earth has ever squandered energy so recklessly; our energy demand in the next decade will equal that of all the world in all of recorded history. Our energy consumption is just equal to about 80 servants working for each one of us, and our appetite for energy doubles every 20 years. Perhaps, as the world's largest consumer of energy, we should look and see from where all that energy is coming; our eighty servants come from different places, and at different costs.

ENERGY SUPPLY

In the 1980s our energy supply will consist of two major sources: (1) fossil fuels, which will provide over 90 percent of all available energy, and (2) minor and developing sources. In the following pages, each fossil fuel is discussed in order of abundance; a review of the minor and developing energy resources is then presented.

The term **fossil fuel** describes three major energy resources: coal, oil, and natural gas. Each of these resources share several common factors, because fossil fuels are concentrated plant or animal life from the past. The carbohydrates that fossil fuels are composed of were formed as the plant or animal lived and were modified and concentrated after its death. Fossil fuels are essentially stored solar energy, converted by life in the past into organic compounds that we extract and burn for our energy needs millions of years later. Burn a cord of hardwood, and it releases about the same amount of energy as 1 ton ($9/_{10}$ metric ton) of coal. The heat energy obtained from the wood is simply solar energy that was stored as compounds of carbon, hydrogen, and oxygen in the living tree by photosynthesis. The stored sugars, resins, cellulose, and other materials of life become the substance of a cheery fire in the fireplace, and the stored energy of life is released as light, radiant heat, and waste heat: 90 percent of the heat produced in a fireplace goes right up the chimney! Burn coal instead and the stored, concentrated energy of *ancient* life works for us—hence the term *fossil* fuel. Wood and coal differ in three important ways: (1) coal is highly concentrated, compressed, and distilled plant matter; (2) coal is much older, stored for our use for hundreds of millions of years as "the stone that burns"; and (3) coal contains more heat per unit of weight.

Coal

Coal is a sedimentary rock that burns. It forms from the accumulation and partial decay of huge amounts of plant matter in swamps. After thousands of years of burial under a continuing rain of decaying trees, mosses, sedges, and other plant material, the material is called **peat;** the development of peat is a preliminary stage in the formation of coal. Garderners know one form of peat as peat moss, and peat is a common fuel in many parts of the world. The Irish have always heated their homes and factories with peat; about one-quarter of Ireland's electrical energy comes from the burning of peat. Scotch whiskey acquires its distinctive flavor from malt dried over peat fires. Peat is immature coal; prolonged, deep burial and loss of some water will change peat to a denser, darker rock called **lignite,** or brown coal.

Further weight, time, and dewatering will modify lignite into a still denser and thinner layer of **bituminous coal,** which is the standard industrial coal (Figure 9-3). If these layers are crumpled and slightly metamorphosed, the bituminous coal changes to **anthracite,** a hard, glossy coal sometimes used for home heating. Peat, lignite, bituminous, and anthracite are all names for increasingly high-quality grades of coal, which is America's major energy resource.

Coal makes up nearly 80 percent of our energy reserves, but it currently provides only one-quarter of our energy needs. Our coal resources can be measured, at current rates of consumption, in the centuries. Coal is to the United States what oil is to the Middle East—fantastically plentiful (see Figure 14-4) and a major worldwide energy resource. Why is such rich energy resource so little used in these times of energy scarcity?

To understand why coal is fairly unused, we must step back in time about 50 years. At that time, coal was *the* major energy resource; in 1910 coal provided nearly 80 percent (Figure 9-4) of our energy needs. Dur-

9-3
Here is coal in its normal habitat—interlayered with other sedimentary rocks. This particular layer is called the Big Dirty Coal Bed, in McCone County, Montana. (Photograph by C. E. Erdmann, U.S. Geological Survey.)

ing the 1930s, 1940s, and 1950s, the coal market progressively sagged under the convenience and efficiency of relatively cheap oil and natural gas.

Coal home heating gave way to fuel oil and natural gas, while coal-fired steam engines gave way to diesel locomotives. Petroleum products—cheaper, cleaner, easier to transport, and cleaner to burn—dominated the transportation and home markets, and

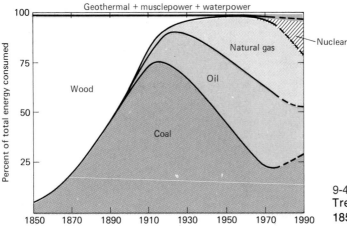

9-4
Trends in American energy use since 1850. (Data from Bureau of Census and Bureau of Mines.)

even many electric utilities turned to oil or natural gas. Now, as prices for oil and natural gas skyrocket, coal will undoubtedly recapture much of the utility market, leaving oil and natural gas to heat our homes and run our transportation system.

The reconversion to coal as a major energy source will be slowed by the same problems that caused many to abandon coal 50 years ago. The mining, transportation, and combustion of coal create problems, and the problems are not small.

Coal buried more than 100 yards (90 meters) underground must normally be mined by underground means, and underground coal mining is the most hazardous occupation in the United States. It is also expensive in dollar terms. A modern underground mine brings only one-eighth as much coal to the surface (per hour of human effort) as a surface strip mine.

Surface mining in both the eastern and western United States has, however, had catastrophic effects on the land surface. Therefore the safety and economy of strip mining are balanced against the costs of re-

storing the land, since the costs of land restoration are now also a part of the costs of recovering the coal.

Strip mining follows a basic mining process that involves six steps. First, bulldozers scrape off the topsoil and put it in special piles. Second, the rock overlying the coal is drilled and blasted. Third, enormous draglines or power shovels (Figure 9-5) remove the waste rock and stack it in spoil piles. Then the coal is drilled, blasted, and loaded onto trucks. Finally, the spoil piles are graded into place by bulldozers, which restore the land surface to its former contour; topsoil is added, and the surface is reseeded with native vegetation.

In the Appalachian region, strip mining has resulted in acid drainage, because rainwater has reacted with the sulfide minerals that are associated with the coal. Slope instability, massive erosion, and wholesale destruction of streams and valleys also resulted. The mined area was simply treated as a resource to be gained, and the land was sacrificed. Modern reclamation practices, which involve returning the surface to its

9-5

Draglines such as this make removal of coal from the surface a relatively inexpensive operation because of labor costs. The environmental costs of stripping remain an ambiguous issue. (Photograph by E. F. Patterson, U.S. Geological Survey.)

original contour and careful reseeding and reforestation, can return the land to productive use once more.

In the western United States, where approximately three-quarters of our coal reserves are located, strip mining is again a logical choice. Most of the coal is near the surface; it also has a lower sulfur content than eastern coals, making it a less polluting fuel. But much of the western coal region is in an area where water is scarce; planting the mined area and preserving it from erosion during flash floods have proved to be extraordinarily difficult. Mining may also lead to contamination of the surface and subsurface water flow in a region where water is a critical resource.

Since most western coal mines are relatively young and reclamation practices have

been attempted only within the last decade, no one can be certain as to the *total* costs of strip mining coal, although reclamation costs can be estimated at about 10¢ per ton (metric ton). Whether we are sacrificing larger and larger areas for a one-time cash crop of coal or merely interrupting a current land use prior to returning the land to equal productivity is a subject of continuing debate.

Burning coal provides another set of problems. Coal contains small amounts of sulfide minerals and incombustible material; once burned, the sulfide minerals react with the atmospheric moisture to produce strong acids, while some of the incombustible material goes out the stack as ash, which makes the air dirty. Treatment of the stack gases produced by coal combustion can remove almost all the fly ash (whose disposal is *another* problem), but at a substantial cost in *electrical* energy. The problems produced by sulfur in the stack gases and by the various oxides of nitrogen, which create smog, have been much less amenable to treatment. The problems are not new (Figure 9-6); in 1306 the king of England decreed death for anyone who burned coal in London while he was there.

One alternative to the problems of the direct combustion of coal—most commonly to generate electricity—is to transform coal into synthetic natural gas. Coal gasification is an old technology that can be improved. Before World War II, nearly every major eastern city had its own gasworks, where coal was converted into gas for lighting and cooking. This gas was eventually replaced by natural gas, which was cheaper and had twice the Btu value. Modern technology has now converted coal directly into synthetic natural gas, whose heat content equals that of ordinary natural gas.

Most gasification processes involve com-

9-6
As this seventeenth-century engraving makes clear, air pollution from burning coal is certainly nothing new. The process shown here is ore roasting or smelting. (From G. E. Loehneys, 1679, *Hof-Staats und Regier Kunst,* courtesy of the History of Science Collections, University of Oklahoma Libraries.)

bining the carbon from the coal with hydrogen to form methane, the primary component of natural gas. This conversion exacts a penalty; approximately one-third of the energy in the coal is lost in the gasification process. The conversion also offers several benefits. The gasification of coal to produce synthetic natural gas is nearly *twice* as efficient as the burning of coal to produce electric energy—essentially one-half as much coal is needed to provide equivalent amounts of energy. The emission of pollutants during gasification is significantly less than that from direct coal combustion, and the result—synthetic natural gas—is the cleanest burning of all fuels.

In summary, coal is our most plentiful fuel, but its use is limited by mining problems and by pollution problems that occur when coal is burned directly. The gasification of coal causes the loss of one-third of its energy, but this is still twice as efficient as the conversion of coal to electricity, and there is also a smaller cost in air pollution. Coal seems to be limited to use in industrial boiler and electrical generating facilities; it has never made a very satisfactory home heating fuel, and it cannot be used anywhere in our modern transportation system.

Coal is a tantalizing fuel; it is eminently available, yet difficult to use. Our technology for mining and combustion of coal stretches back to the last century; refinements in both are necessary before coal can better share in supplying America's burgeoning energy demand.

Oil and Natural Gas

The United States is using almost twice as much oil as it produces and nearly 10 times as much as it is finding (Figure 9-7). As this country enters the declining side of the consumption-discovery curve (Figure 9-7), it imports not quite one-half of its petroleum needs. Our country thus joins many other industrial nations whose energy appetite exceeds their supply, including all of western Europe, Great Britain, and Japan.

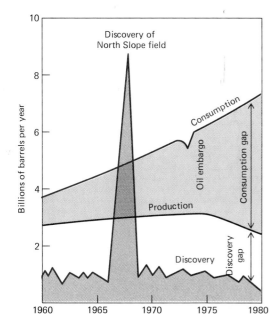

10

8

6

4

2

Billions of barrels per year

Discovery of
North Slope field

Consumption

Oil embargo

Consumption gap

Production

Discovery

Discovery gap

1960   1965   1970   1975   1980

9-7

Discovery rate, production, and consumption of oil in the United States. The gap between consumption and production is made up by *importing* ever larger amounts of oil. The gap between production and discovery is made up by *diminishing* our total domestic oil reserves. (Chart is generalized from data furnished by Exxon Company, U.S.A.)

Petroleum products, like coal, are **hydrocarbons**—mixtures of compounds that contain carbon, hydrogen, and oxygen in various proportions. Oil contains about twice as much hydrogen as coal, which makes it a potent fuel. Ten gallons (38 liters) of crude oil contain the energy equivalent of 1 ton ($\frac{9}{10}$ metric ton) of coal. Petroleum products include a variety of materials recovered from the earth, but we will concentrate on only two: crude oil and natural gas.

Crude oil has been a commercial item for nearly 5000 years; records of its recovery and sale as a fuel go back to 3000 B.C. and were reported by Confucius. The wells were "drilled" by driving hollow bamboo rods into the ground; they supplied natural gas as a fuel and heavier flammable materials for war. Oil was recovered from the distillation of oil-bearing shales in both Great Britain and the United States in the early 1800s, and coal was changed into a type of natural gas at about the same time.

The completion of the first modern oil well in 1859 marks the beginning of modern commercial oil development. The invention of the commercially successful internal combustion engine in the early 1900s brought with it a surging demand for petroleum products. Our energy mix changed from a heavy reliance on coal (Figure 9-4) to an accelerating reliance on oil and natural gas; petroleum currently accounts for three-quarters of our energy use.

Oil is thus the inverse of coal; oil is an increasingly scarce fuel on which we rely for the majority of our energy needs, while coal, our most abundant fuel, is relatively little used. Oil and natural gas dominated the market in the twentieth century because they were cheaper, cleaner, more powerful, and much easier to transport from the production area to the consumer. Petroleum fuels have everything going for them, and our society is based on their lavish use. As our domestic supplies skid, we might ask how such a valuable, versatile energy source was formed—and how it is recovered.

Nearly one-half of all geologists spend their professional careers in the search for oil and natural gas and for understanding how petroleum products form. Only recently has the origin of oil and natural gas been well understood. The basic requirement for oil and natural gas formation is abundant organic matter and rapid deposition or burial of this organic material in marine sediments. Shallow, sunlit ocean water teems with life and provides many times the protein per acre (or some other equivalent unit) of the most prolific farmland. Areas such as the margins of deltas, and reefs, lagoons, and other parts of the continental shelf provide an ideal environment for profuse life and quick burial of its remains.

After burial, changes in the organic matter depend on two factors: time and temperature. With plant matter buried in swamps, time and temperature both cause gradual in-creases in the rank of coal from peat to lig-nite to bituminous and to anthracite; each step is accompanied by an *increase* in car-bon content, *loss* of water, and *increase* in available heat energy. Marine organic matter reacts in much the same way (Figure 9-8), maturing from organic matter through var-ious stages into kerogens (waxy precursors to oil), crude oil, and natural gas.

Changes in organic matter occur over a wide temperature range, depending on the time factor. At temperatures near 80 degrees Celsius organic matter may be converted into a *kerogen*, a yellowish brown solid that

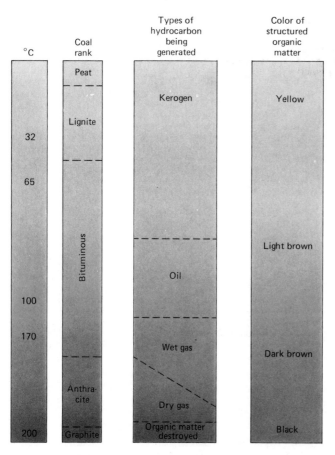

9-8
Comparison of temperature and maturation of coal and petroleum products. Temperature is not the only factor affecting maturity. In particular, greater length of burial may cause greater maturity at temperature levels less than that shown. Type of organic matter source and type of source rock are other factors. (Compiled from numerous sources. Concept largely after A. Hood *et al.*, 1975, with permission of the author and The American Association of Petroleum Geologists.)

is not oil but can be further distilled into oil. If temperatures during burial rise to about 100 degrees Celsius (the boiling point of water), the kerogen is converted into a dark, fluid oil. As temperatures rise, more and more of the oil is naturally distilled into natural gas, so that at temperatures of 160 degrees Celsius, all that is left is gas. At 200 degrees Celsius all organic matter is destroyed, and nothing of commercial value is left.

Petroleum products, then, represent a unique combination of circumstances: a great deal of organic matter (whose type determines the character of the eventual product), rapid burial, and "cooking" for just the right time and temperature to convert the organic material into a variety of hydrocarbons.

After the conversion to petroleum, the newly formed material must be expelled from the rocks in which it formed; it moves along other *permeable* rocks (those having interconnected open spaces within them) until the fluid is trapped by *impermeable* rocks that seal the petroleum off from the surface. Oil and gas may fill the pore spaces (Figure 9-9) of the rock in which they are trapped and wait for the probing drill to expose them once again. The location for drilling is directed by geologists and geophysicists.

We must not entirely forget that oil and natural gas are the end products of a long chain of events; each event is necessary if we are to enjoy the use of petroleum-based fuels and chemicals. Consider the geographic distribution of the world's major accumulations of oil. Petroleum is normally recovered from oil fields (Figure 9-10), areas where oil and natural gas wells recover material from one accumulation or a series of connected accumulations. *Two percent* of

the world's petroleum fields contain more than *three-quarters* of the world's known oil and gas reserves, and *none* of these giant accumulations are in the United States.

The vast majority of the world's known oil reserves are in the Middle East; *individual* fields contain more known reserves than the entire North American continent has ever produced. Other areas of enormous oil reserves are found in the Soviet Union and Mexico. These lucky geographic accidents give those countries unbelievable economic power in a world whose major energy resource is petroleum.

In the longer run, the future of petroleum seems assured. Among the fossil fuels, petroleum will continue to be the preferred fuel everywhere it is available and will make its Middle Eastern owners wealthy beyond comprehension. But even the gigantic Middle Eastern fields cannot support the rising energy needs of the entire world for long; petroleum products will be in a worldwide decline before the end of this century. Two other potential sources of petroleum products—oil shale and tar sands, or heavy oil—appear as more distant sources of oil.

Oil Shale. In 1967, an oil-hungry world started to consume more oil than geologists found, a situation that continues in the face of exponentially rising demand. It is not surprising that technologies addicted to petroleum began to seek out alternate sources for the same fuel; they investigated oil shales. Oil shale is simply shale that is usually deposited in ancient lakes whose organic content matured to, but not beyond, the kerogen stage.

The kerogen in the shale is in the solid form that can be converted into oil by distillation. This is an old process that was used over 100 years ago in both the United States and western Europe. Oil shale had been

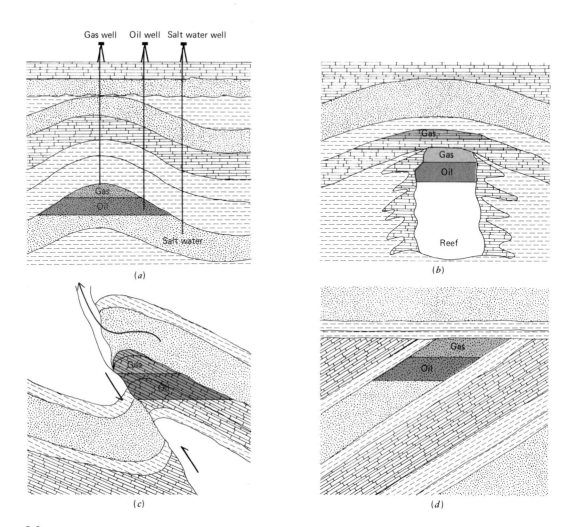

9-9

Gas, oil, and water may migrate upward together and may reach the earth's surface, forming oil seeps (as in part c), unless blocked by an impermeable layer. (a) The impermeable shale traps oil and gas in an upfold; a well too far off the structure will produce saltwater. (b) A buried reef limestone area provides a source. (c) A fault provides a seal for lower layers, but an avenue of escape for oil and natural gas traveling through higher layers. (d) An abrupt change in tilting of the layers is produced when upper layers are deposited across tilted lower layers prior to oil migration.

9-10
Here is an old (1915) oil field in Creek County, Oklahoma. The old wooden derricks are tightly spaced in the Cushing Oil Field. (Photograph by A. E. Fath, U.S. Geological Survey.)

mined and converted into oil in Utah and Pennsylvania before liquid oil was discovered in Pennsylvania in 1859, but the liquid oil boom that followed squelched the oil shale industry in its infancy.

Basically, three factors serve to limit severely what *could be* an impressive resource; the oil potentially available from the oil shales of Utah, Wyoming, and Colorado is greater than our nation's *original* fluid oil reserves (Figure 9-11). First, almost every oil shale recovery effort requires mining vast amounts of rock by strip mining, and the shale is located in regions where reclamation of the enormous mined areas required might be impossible. Second, mining and treatment of the shale would require gigantic amounts of water, and the shales are in the middle of regions that already have serious water shortages. Third, it now takes so much energy to mine, transport, and distill the oil that the result is expensive in today's competitive market.

As the price of oil continues to rise, shale oil has become economic once again, but its recovery may be an unmitigated environ-mental disaster. The very highest-quality shale might yield 1 barrel of oil [42 gallons (160 liters)] per ton (metric ton) of rock; because the United States uses about 18 million barrels of oil a day, the environmental and mining problems are of unprecedented magnitude.

Tar Sands and Heavy Oil. Tar sands and heavy oil deposits have many common features and will be discussed together. As the names suggest, there deposits are composed of porous rock bodies that are permeated with oil that is too thick or too heavy to flow unless it is heated. Two examples will describe the problems and potentials of these resources: the tar sands of Alberta, Canada, and the heavy oil in the Orinoco area of eastern Venezuela.

The Albertan tar sands include four major deposits of heavy oil and tar in northeastern Alberta. Collectively, these deposits contain approximately 900 billion barrels of crude tar and oil. Some of the tar sands are exposed at the surface, and others are buried under younger deposits at depths up to a few hundred yards (meters). The oil and tar are

9-11
Getting oil out of oil shale is still frustrating.
(Cartoon by Sidney Harris, *American Scientist,* September–October 1975. Reprinted by permission.)

We have known about the heavy oil belt in northern Venezuela for 50 years, but its oil has the consistency of cool molasses and is filled with sulfur and metallic elements. Extraction would require injection of steam or solvents, or even underground forced combustion to heat the oil so it could be pumped to the surface. Refining the sulfurous, stinking crude would require major modifications and additional expense. In short, the heavy oils of Venezuela seem to have little to recommend them—as long as lighter, easily obtained oil is available. At current consumption rates, Venezuela's lighter oil may last until 2000. What then?

Estimates of Venezuelan reserves range from 800 to 3000 billion barrels; the latter figure is much greater than the proved reserves of the entire world. Obviously, Venezuela has a huge stake in eventually learning to cope with heavy oil. The U.S. Bureau of Mines estimates that the United States has about 150 billion barrels of heavy oil reserves—an amount that could double our nation's proved petroleum reserves.

Current Status

In summary, petroleum products are produced where they are not used, and they are used where they are not produced. The United States uses one-third of the world's energy, produces only one-sixth of the world's supply, and imports the rest. Our economy, which uses enormous reserves of petroleum, cannot continue without an every-growing dependence on imports. The large oil fields of North America have already been discovered and are almost depleted; they were small to start with, by Middle Eastern and Soviet standards. Oil and natural gas accumulations are the end

not only thick, but they are also of rather low quality; they contain high sulfur and heavy metal contents, which makes refining difficult.

Removal and transport of the heavy oil and tar require either the injection of solvents or the heating of the deposits with steam. Both processes have been tried, but they were a commercial failure. As oil prices rise, the difficulty in extracting and processing these deposits has been partially overcome, and these vast deposits are beginning to be used. They potentially contain four times as much oil as the North American continent has used in the last century.

product of a long series of events; all of the many independent variables must combine perfectly to create a commercial oil field.

The industrialized world consumes energy at exponentially increasing rates, but petroleum is a finite resource. The industrialized nations which depend heavily on imported oil, must accept increasing control of their economies (and their destinies) by oil-exporting nations or develop alternate energy sources.

Coal cannot solve all our energy needs, and petroleum supplies are diminishing. What other energy sources are available for the next 25 years? The newer energy plan that America will be following in the next century is reviewed next.

ENERGY FOR THE FUTURE

Our nation, which recently has run mostly on oil, is running out of that resource. First, food, converted to muscle, was the only energy source; then fire (discovered by chance), electricity, the steam engine and, finally, radioactivity provided energy. The possibility of another energy mix in the future is inevitable. But trends are not destiny, and each energy mix brings with it its own scramble of potentials and pitfalls, just as our current energy mix does. *Energy sources are not neutral;* our choices should be conscious and based on information. Let us consider some alternatives.

Nuclear Energy

Many people have characterized the nuclear power bargain as Faustian (Faust was the mythical hero who sold his soul to the devil in exchange for power), holding out the promise of unlimited power at the peril of nuclear disaster.

The benefits of nuclear power are well known, because it currently provides about 10 percent of our electrical energy. A properly operating nuclear reactor produces electrical power with much less environmental damage than a coal-burning power plant does. Present experiences with nuclear power plants suggest that they are probably safe; we have had over 3000 reactor years of experience without a reactor accident that *killed* anyone outright. Indeed, taking the environmental consequences of strip mining, the manifest hazards of underground coal mining, and the lung disease brought on by both coal mining and the effluents from burning coal, nuclear power seems, at first glance, to be a lifesaver.

The hazards are equally clear. Disposal of radioactive waste is, as yet, an unresolved issue. Is there any place on our mobile earth that will be an absolutely safe repository for radioactive wastes for thousands of years? Who will guard nuclear reactors against sabotage? How will the intensely radioactive power plants ever be dismantled once they become too old? The horrendous ultimate accident (a *meltdown*) has yet to happen (although the Three Mile Island incident in 1979 came close), but is the terrible risk worth the benefit? Finally, it is clear that the United States is running out of uranium minerals—the raw material to feed nuclear reactors. At current consumption rates, our uranium supplies may be good for 20 to 30 years more. After that, we will again be dependent on imports—an international market in which there are already many buyers.

There seems to be only one solution, the development of the breeder reactor. The conventional reactor uses uranium inefficiently, which is a waste of an extremely scarce commodity. Breeder reactors, in principle, can use many more forms of radioactive elements and can produce more fuel than they consume; this would mean an everlasting supply of cheap, clean energy.

The problem is that plutonium would be produced as a by-product. Plutonium is one of the most deadly poisons on the earth; it is the raw material used in the manufacture of atomic weapons. The facilities necessary for breeder reactors offer unparalleled opportunities for sabotage, unparalleled risks in waste disposal, unparalled possiblities for holocaust, and unparalleled opportunities for cheap, clean energy in almost endless quantities.

Nuclear energy, with its boundless potential and peril, poses a fundamental question. To what risks am I exposed, and what benefits (if any) do I receive from that exposure? For nuclear power, the perceived risks are clear; incidents from minor radiation damage, with consequent mutations and cancer, to the awesome mushroom cloud are a part of the heritage of the atomic age. Thus a small risk, vividly portrayed, outweighs benefits, which are often stated in abstract, economic terms. As long as the public perception of nuclear power is that it is fundamentally hazardous, the benefits from its use will seem small. Rising construction and operating prices, declining uranium reserves, nagging questions about the economic and environmental costs of very long-term storage and reprocessing of radioactive wastes, the unknown costs of attempting to shut down and decontaminate an old nuclear plant, and other environmental demands all may cause the early demise of nuclear power.

Geothermal Energy

Hot water and steam are among our oldest uses of the earth's resources. Hot springs must have relaxed our ancestors much as a hot bath relaxes us today—but without the intervening gas or electric water heater. The first commercial use of geothermal energy was at the beginning of this century, when natural steam was used to produce small amounts of electricity in Italy. Since this early success, steam has been used to drive turbogenerators in New Zealand, Mexico, Japan, Iceland, and California. The total electrical capacity of these plants is about equal to the electrical demand of a city of 1 million people, or the output of one large, conventional power plant. Geothermal energy provides a fraction of 1 percent of our total energy needs, but what about future use of geothermal energy?

Until now, geothermal energy has been developed only in regions where hot water and steam were easy to find, where the system surfaced. In such areas, cooling magmas represent a large reservoir of the earth's internal energy and cause water seeping downward to be converted into hot water or steam. The steam fields are especially easy to find and utilize; one can hardly miss seeing geysers and massive steam vents (Figure 9-12). Unfortunately, such systems of natural steam production near the surface are rare, and most of the existing ones are fully developed. Shallow fields that produce hot water are somewhat more common, but they are difficult to utilize. The hot fluids—usually called **brines**—are corrosive and contain large amounts of heavy metals. The ability to use this hot water without massive damage to piping, turbines, and the environment is beyond modern technology.

9-12
Casa Diablo Hot Spring in Mono County, California, is near an area of geologically recent volcanism and is an example of the geothermal energy available from many western areas that have been recently volcanic. (Photograph by A. H. Blake, U.S. Geological Survey.)

Among the promising resources for the future are areas of elevated rock temperature at depths that are dry. In these regions, after drilling, water is pumped down to the dry, hot rock and is then recovered as steam or very hot water and used to generate electricity. Prospecting for these deeper sources of ''free'' heat is in its infancy.

Likely sites for geothermal exploration include any area that has undergone volcanic activity within the last few million years. In these areas, finding precise targets for drill-ing has been a vexing problem, as has been the technology of drilling itself. No technology now exists for drilling into zones of superheated water and steam; consequently, much of the exploration for geothermal energy awaits new developments in exploration and drilling technology.

Although geothermal energy seems to promise an endless supply of energy from within the earth, the realities are quite different. For the few hot, dry steam areas that are being utilized around the world, they do constitute an almost model, nonpolluting way of generating electricity. However, for many hot water systems, the water may be quite corrosive and laden with poisonous metals. The major air pollutant is hydrogen sulfide; this component dissolved in water renders the water highly corrosive. Scale forms rapidly and clogs pipes; the water produced may be both highly saline and the source of substantial chemical pollution.

The future of geothermal power seems to be limited to providing a fractional percent of electrical power needs, while lower-temperature warm water may be locally used for space heating and health spas. As problems in exploration, drilling, and handling of corrosive, metal-laden water are solved, geothermal energy may form a future source of large amounts of electrical energy.

Solar Energy

To an astronomer, our sun (Figure 9-13) is a variable star near the outer fringe of the Milky Way. As a whirling star, it is somewhere near middle age, and one of more than 10 billion similar stars in the galaxy. The sun is also a vast, raging furnace that burns hydrogen and produces helium and, as

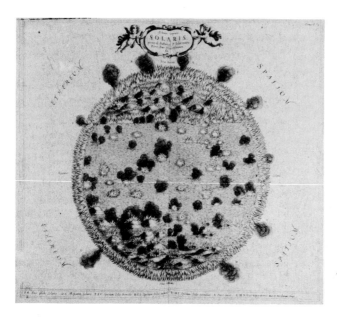

9-13

A view of the sun, drawn not long after the invention of the telescope, shows a fiery body, with hills (volcanoes?), flares, and sunspots. (From A. Kircheri, 1665, *Mundus subterraneus,* courtesy of the History of Science Collections, University of Oklahoma Libraries.)

a by-product, produces 70,000 horsepower per square yard (⁸/₁₀ square meter) of its surface.

The sun is our source of wind and weather, wood, coal, oil, gas—and life. Our earth, more than 90 million miles (150 million kilometers) from the sun, intercepts not more than two-billionths of 1 percent of the sun's radiant energy, and yet this energy is *hundreds of times the total energy we now use.* In only 3 days, the sun showers the earth with energy that is equivalent to *all* the earth's fossil fuel reserves. It is no wonder that in an energy-short world we look to the sun as an energy source.

For all its energy potential, the sun is also a difficult energy source to utilize. Its energy is diffused (spread over the entire earth) and difficult to collect and store. Sunlight is also variable; cloudy days follow sunny days, and night follows day. The energy from sunlight must, in some way, be stored and spread out over the rising and falling energy demands of an average day.

Attempts to use the sun's awesome energy are hardly new. Archimedes supposedly turned giant solar mirrors on an attacking Roman fleet at Syracuse in 214 B.C., and the ships, which were built of wood, cloth, and pitch, became instant funeral pyres.

Most of the basic components of modern solar devices—solar furnaces, food dryers, and steam plants—are well over 100 years old. Perhaps the largest solar demonstration of all was the steam-driven irrigation plant constructed in 1913 in a village not far from Cairo. The sun provided the energy to make the steam, which drove equipment pumping water at the rate of 6000 gallons (23,000 liters) an hour. The solar engine was no different from any other steam engine except for the source of heat that generated the steam. The sun's heat was focused with the aid of large, curved mirrors on a black pipe filled with water. The water flashed into steam, the engine turned, and irrigation water splashed forth. The mirrors were turned to follow the sun through the sky, and the equipment stopped at night.

As just described, the oldest method of using solar energy has always been to focus the sun's rays (Figure 9-14) to heat a fluid or the air. The sun's energy is then used to provide steam for an engine or turbine. More diffused sunlight may also heat air or water,

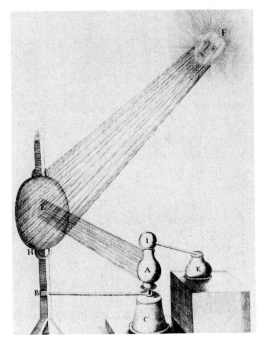

9-14
Here the sun is used, after reflection from a concave mirror, to heat a small distilling device, whose distillate was captured and carried into a small, squat jar. (From A. Kircheri, 1665, *Mundus subterraneus,* courtesy of the History of Science Collections, University of Oklahoma Libraries.)

which is then used for space heating or the production of hot water. Modifications of the oldest solar systems are beginning to make an impact on the American building market and, thereby, on our fuel bills. Space and water heating account for almost one-quarter of our nation's fuel bill, so the impact of solar heating may be very large indeed.

Many systems involve solar energy collectors located on the building roof; the resulting heated air or water is stored under the building in tanks or in large masses of rock. This stored energy is then recovered by convection or blower systems. Prolonged cold or cloudy spells call for backup conventional furnaces, which are little used in a well-insulated home. Since a conventional home loses 25 percent of its heat through the roof and up to 40 percent of its heat through its windows, the combination of adequate insulation and effective window treatment may make a solar-heated home a remarkably energy-efficient structure.

Sunlight may also be used to generate electric power in either of two ways. One method calls for sunlight to be focused on a boiler; the resulting steam is run through turbines to generate electricity. Such a system might find a particular application in hot areas, where air conditioners impose an enormous peak demand on our current electrical generating system. A solar system would provide surplus electricity just when demand was highest, (and the sun is at its hottest).

A second method uses devices called **photovoltaic cells** that produce electricity directly from sunlight. The radiant energy from the sun, which strikes photovoltaic cells that are made mostly of silicon, is converted directly into electricity with an efficiency of something less then 10 percent. Production of the high-purity materials needed for the photovoltaic cells is costly, which limits their application to space satellites and other remote outposts where conventional electricity is unavailable.

We have known about generating electricity from sunlight for over 100 years; the photographic exposure meter is a familiar example. The current efficiency is too low and the production costs are too high to suggest that photovoltaic cells may provide large amounts of electrical energy in the near future, although technological breakthroughs may occur.

Several plans that use photovoltaic cells might make a major, future impact on America's power needs. In one proposal, photovoltaic cells would be arrayed across desolate parts of our southwestern deserts. At an efficiency of 10 percent, a collecting area 2 miles (3 kilometers) square would provide 1000 megawatts of electricity—the output of a typical large, conventional power station. Such a power station could only be an auxiliary power unit, because it would only produce electricity when the sun was shining; during sunny days it would reduce the fuel demand from conventional generating stations. A much larger area (about 6000 square miles, 15,000 square kilometers) could theoretically power the entire country. An area the size of Connecticut or roughly 5 percent of Nevada's area would do the job.

Alternatively, solar power stations could generate electricity when the sun is shining and store it for later use. The electricity could be stored by separating hydrogen from oxygen in ordinary water with electricity and saving the hydrogen to be burned like ordinary natural gas or fed into fuel cells to regenerate electricity. Still another method of storage envisions using the electricity

generated to pump water up into a storage basin. The energy would be retrieved as needed by allowing the water to fall back through turbogenerators, which would produce electricity exactly as a modern hydroelectric project does today. Even though each of these storage systems is inherently inefficient, solar energy is free, photovoltaic cells do not wear out, and energy storage systems must be a part of any system that is furnished energy by intermittent sunlight.

Another scenario is fascinating, but it is frightening for those whose money is invested in electric utilities. Imagine a building with solar cells on its roof that provides electricity that is stored in batteries. Additionally, the roof would contain solar heat collectors that utilize the 90 percent of the sun's energy that the photovoltaic cells cannot convert into electricity to provide both space and water heating. Such a building would be nearly energy self-sufficient, and our need for massive power plants and distribution systems would be greatly diminished. Such a combined photovoltaic and solar heat collector system is not a reality today, since the prices of conventionally procured heating, cooling, and electrical energy are far lower than the system envisioned. As the price of fossil fuel continues to rise and the price of photovoltaic cells continues to fall, the sun may provide a growing amount of future energy independence.

Waterpower

A fractional amount of our total electric demand is presently provided by allowing water, backed up behind a dam, to fall through turbogenerators and generate electricity. There seems little reason to assume that hydroelectric power will be much further developed, since few spots of economic potential remain on America's rivers. Hydroelectric power also has its price; water backed up into lakes is wasted by evaporation and seepage, and the water that remains becomes more saline and less fit for use. The lakes behind the dams slowly fill with sediment, whose removal is usually an unforeseen cost of dam construction.

Although the cost-benefit arguments over dams continues, hydroelectric power is often a good bargain for America. However, it is a resource that is already fully developed. Its total contribution to America's power needs is fractional and will become a smaller and smaller percentage of a growing demand.

ENERGY—A PERSPECTIVE

The story of civilization is a story of increasing per capita use of energy. Industrial societies are based on **power**—the *rate* at which useful work is accomplished. The growth and decline of a society depend on the energy resources it can exploit and the efficiency with which energy is turned into useful products. People, too, are energy converters; we convert the sun to grass to beef to human flesh.

Earliest people had only the energy of the food they ate. Later, people discovered fire; still later, they added the muscle energy of domesticated animals to their store. Coal may have come next, along with the use of wind and water to grind and mill and alter the environment in many ways. The industrial revolution of the nineteenth century developed on the basis of the steam engine, which was coal fired. People became intoxicated with energy, which was a willing servant to do all our tasks. Then came the dynamo—and the generation of electricity was possible.

Americans now use nearly 20 trillion kilowatt-hours of energy.

We Americans inherited a generous land. The more energy we have used, the more we have made our cities and our lives dependent on growing energy use. That energy use has been funded entirely on fossil fuels, which are a finite resource. For the next few decades, we will continue to depend on fossil fuels. We can improve coal combustion technology, and we can sow grass on mountains of waste. But, as citizens of a generous land, our days of energy waste are over.

Waste, to some extent, is an inevitable part of the conversion of energy. Waste rock and acid water from coal mines, radioactive waste from power plants, air pollution from automobiles, furnaces, fireplaces, and power plants, and spilled offshore oil are by-products of the tremendous *flow* of energy through our society.

Electric power production is a particularly wasteful process; it converts less than one-third of the energy used to useful energy. The cooling water required by power plants already uses 10 percent of the total U.S. stream flow, and the *waste* heat from power plants is more than enough to *heat every home in the United States*. We are substituting electricity, which has a total efficiency of less than one-third, for direct fuel use with efficiencies of 60 to 90 percent. The fastest growing electrical service is air conditioning; our air conditioning demand doubles every 5 years.

The standard American car is another notoriously inefficient device. More than 80 percent of the energy poured into the gasoline tank is blown right back out the exhaust pipe, where it becomes a major air pollutant.

Electric cars are not the answer; they substitute the inefficiency of electricity (and the further inefficiency of the battery) for the inefficiency of the internal combustion engine. Air pollution is removed from the city, but it increases at the power plant.

The future calls for major changes in power technology, substantial reduction in pollution, better management of wastes, increases in efficiency, and the search for a source (or sources) of energy that is inexhaustible. Such a plan for the future quickly excludes all fossil fuels, because they are a rapidly diminishing, finite resource. The extravagant disaster potential of nuclear power and the finite mineral resource on which it is based seem to limit the nuclear potential. Geothermal energy is likewise a finite resource and capable of more pollution than is widely recognized.

We are left with the sun as an energy source. The challenge is to harness the sun's prodigious energy, diffused and intermittent though it may be, in order to provide a new generation of power for us all. Certainly that is sufficient challenge for any society, but there is a much more immediate challenge—the present.

CONSERVATION AND AFFLUENCE

As Americans concerned over our prodigal energy use, we should keep our perspective on what energy means. Energy is the capacity to do work. Although Americans consume one-third of the world's energy, we also produce more goods and services per capita than any other nation on earth (Figure 2-23). Other countries are also consuming increasing amounts of energy as they develop, so our fraction of the world's energy

demand will constantly lessen in the next few decades. As Figure 2-23 suggests, there is a rough correlation between per capita consumption of energy and the per capita output of goods and services, expressed as gross national product. The facts are straightforward; we use more energy and produce more with it per person than any other nation.

From that simple fact flows the overwhelming affluence that most Americans take for granted. The resources of America, converted to useful products through the application of energy, have made us the most productive nation of all time.

As our energy appetite runs up against the growing world demand for a finite resource, the first response may be to wonder about our future. Are we engaged in a long slide back down the line that arches through Figure 2-23? If energy and production *are* tied together, what happens to our living standards as energy resources fade?

The answer depends on our vision, not on our resources. If we continue on our wasteful way, driving the biggest cars we can afford, basking in refrigerated, frigid air in the summer, and luxuriating in tropical warmth in the winter—in short, wasting energy as if there were no tomorrow—our future decline is certain. We must stop wasting energy, and we must rapidly break free of our addiction to petroleum. We MUST use less energy, and we must use diverse energy sources.

Where will that leave us? Suppose we cut our per capita energy consumption almost in half—perhaps an unattainable goal. If we did that, our living standards would be those of Australia, Sweden, West Germany, or Great Britain—not a difficult life-style to accept. If we cut our energy consumption by one-third, we would still enjoy a greater affluence than almost any other country; we could terminate oil imports on that same day, because we would no longer be dependent on others for energy.

During the Arab oil embargo in the early 1970s, Americans *voluntarily* reduced their energy consumption by 15 percent. Further reductions can and must obviously be made, as is being proven by the gas shortages Americans experienced in 1979. We only need to insulate our buildings better, drive smaller cars and drive them less, turn down our thermostats in the winter and raise them in the summer, and constantly press for more efficient use of the priceless stores of fossil fuel that remain.

Our future must be less wasteful, or we will have no future. The challenge is individual; each one of us can conserve. As Will Rogers once said: "When we want wood, we chop down a forest. When we want oil, we drill a hole. When we run out, we'll find out how good we really are."

SUMMARY   Energy is the fundamental means of transferring raw materials from the earth into useful products; its flow determines the vitality of an industrialized society. That flow, by whatever means it is measured, has three components: (1) maintenance of current living standards; (2) improved living standards for more people; and (3) nonproductive energy use, or waste.

More than 90 percent of America's energy needs today are met by the use of fossil fuels, which are concentrated, stored solar energy. The reconversion of these fuels to heat is the fundamental energy drive for our nation; every reconversion has its own price, including air pollution, waste heat loss, rising carbon dioxide levels in the atmosphere, with possible consequent climatic changes, and increasing problems with disposal of recovered pollutants.

Fossil fuels are hydrocarbons in solid, liquid, or gaseous forms; with 5 percent of the world's petroleum and gas supply within U.S. borders, this finite resource once provided essentially *all* of our energy demand. Coal, whose production, transportation, and consumption are characterized by a variety of problems, constitutes an immense resource whose problems match its potential.

Other energy sources include waterpower and wind, which are derivatives of solar energy, and geothermal and nuclear energy. Waterpower seems to be fully developed and geothermal energy provides only a fractional percent of the U.S. energy demand; nuclear energy holds the promise of quiet, clean electric energy, which is based on rapidly diminishing resources of uranium ore. Decades after the dawn of the atomic age, there is still no safe way to store toxic radioactive wastes. Once the life of a nuclear power plant is over, it cannot be torn down, and it will remain toxic for thousands of years.

The search for the ideal energy source continues. One thing is certain;

our energy mix is changing away from petroleum-based fuels toward something else. More and more, Americans look to the sun as a source of energy; the sun sends more energy toward us every second than people have used in the course of human history. The search for a better technology with which to harness the sun, whose energy is the foundation for life, is perhaps the most exciting area in energy technology today.

We live in a transition period, a time of change in the way we do things. There are many decisions to be made about future energy options. The final certainty in all of this is that the only thing scarcer than oil is time.

EXERCISES

1. A 1-pound (about 450-gram) can of corn contains about 375 kilocalories of food energy, but requires 450 kilocalories of fossil energy to plant, cultivate, fertilize, and harvest, 1760 kilocalories to can, and 800 kilocalories more to bring it home in the car. Comment?

2. Ninety percent of the fossil fuel reserves in the United States are coal; one-half of that is located in the western states. Do you regard that as a problem or an opportunity? How can the two be separated?

3. Ralph Waldo Emerson said "Nature never gives anything away. Everything is sold at a price." What is the price for solar energy? Is the price different for on-site versus central solar energy?

4. A gallium arsenide photovoltaic cell converts 20 percent of the energy it receives into electricity and 70 percent into heat. Such a cell could provide both electricity and hot water or steam for a house by making use of nearly all incoming solar energy. What factors might limit the use of gallium arsenide photovoltaic cells?

5. Today you used the energy equivalent of 7 gallons (26 liters) of oil. Your parents, *at your age,* used about one-half as much. How was their life-style different than yours? (Incidentally, this statement is generally true, regardless of your age.)

6. It takes one-half of a glass of diesel fuel to put one glass of milk on your table. How was it used?

7. Over one-half of the land in many cities is devoted to streets, garages, service stations, and parking lots. How would our cities change if the 56 percent of all commuters who now drive to work alone used public transportation?

8. Estimates of the remaining petroleum reserves in the United States range from 60 to 120 billion barrels of oil. In 1975 we produced about 3 billion barrels of oil. How long will our domestic supply of oil last?

9. The United States *uses* almost double the oil that it *produces* from its own reserves. If we were forced onto its own reserves, how long would our domestic supply of oil last?

10. The release of carbon from fossil fuels into the atmosphere as carbon dioxide has been increasing at an exponential rate since the beginning of the industrial revolution about 100 years ago. The major effect of increased atmospheric carbon dioxide should be a warming; some scientists are convinced that the worldwide average temperature may rise by 2 to 3 degrees Celsius. How would this affect human life?

SUGGESTED READINGS

Bredehoeft, J. D., 1978, *Geologic Disposal of High-Level Wastes—Earth Science Perspectives,* U.S. Geological Survey Circular 779, 15 pp.
   A really sobering appraisal if you think nuclear is nifty.

Committee on Government Operations, 1978, *Nuclear Power Costs,* 95th Congress, 2nd session, House Report No. 95-1090, Union Calendar No. 555, 149 pp.
   *A **devastating** look at the **real** dollar cost of nuclear power.*

Cook, Earl, 1976, *Man, Energy, Society,* San Francisco, W. H. Freeman, 197 pp.
   Comprehensive review of the role of energy in society.

Department of Energy (1980), *Statistics and Trends of Energy Supply, Demand, and Prices,* Washington, D.C., Superintendant of Public Documents.
   An annual report to Congress; loaded with information.

Federal Energy Administration, 1976, *Comparison of Energy Consumption between West Germany and the United States,* Washington, D.C., F.E.A. Conservation Paper 33A, 104 pp.
   Eye opening, sobering, and a view of the future.

Hubbert, M. King, 1971, "*The Energy Resources of the Earth,*" *Scientific American,* September 1971, 14 pp.
   Classic statement of the sources and future of energy.

Office of Technology Assessment, 1978, *Applications of Solar Technology to Today's Energy Needs, Volume I,* Washington, D.C., U.S. Government Printing Office.
   The most exciting book I know of today; a clear view of the future, meticulously documented. READ IT!

Skinner, Brian J., 1976, *Earth Resources,* 2nd ed., Englewood Cliffs, N.J., Prentice-Hall, 152 pp.
   See Chapters 3 and 4 for brief summary; over all a fine book.

Energy demand

Electrical, commercial, residential, industrial, and transportation; includes a component of waste.

Energy supply

Currently, supply is essentially all from fossil fuels; fossil fuels are stored sunlight and a finite resource; future supply sources include nuclear and solar energy, with minor components of geothermal energy and waterpower.

Energy flow

Equivalent to national production or value of goods and services produced; energy waste is part of flow; economic necessity forces increasing conservation.

Rain clouds promise moisture to a lonely land, watched over by a windmill. Both are part of the cycle that brings life to the land. (Photograph by Michael Collier.)

Chapter Ten
WATER

"When the well's dry, we know the worth of water."
Benjamin Franklin

More than two-thirds of this earth is covered with it, yet many people do not have enough of it. More than one-half of everything alive is formed from it. Centuries ago, it was too often the bearer of death, corrupted by typhoid and other devastating plagues. Today, it is the bearer of life, yielding food from once-parched earth. For those who have known drought and the agony of unending thirst, its value is greater than that of diamonds. Our bodies are composed mostly of it, and a change of more than 2 percent in our delicate fluid balance causes death.

Napoleon called it "the greatest necessity of the soldier." Thoreau spoke of it as "the only drink for a wise man." Alas, Coleridge's Ancient Mariner saw his vast supply was useless.

Water is a gift from an ancient beginning (Chapter Twelve). Ninety-seven percent of the world's water is salty and fills the earth's ocean basins. Another 2 percent is locked up as fresh water in the ice caps of the Antarctic and Greenland. We are left with 1 percent of the total supply as fresh water with which to work. Most of that remaining 1 percent is stored temporarily underground, while a far smaller amount can be seen on the earth's surface.

Fresh water is a present to us from the sun's enormous, flaming energy, which distills the sea and flings its distillate onto the land. Small parts of this fresh water are

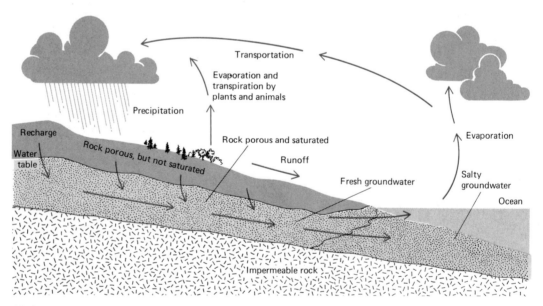

10-1
Components of the water cycle. Recharge (water intake) + evaporation + transpiration (loss through plants) + runoff (water that runs off the land surface) = precipitation. What factors control the recharge-to-runoff ratio? (After R. B. Feth, 1973, U.S. Geological Survey Circular 601-I.)

caught in lakes or flow directly to the sea in streams; a much greater store remains underground in permeable rock and soil. The movement of *all* fresh water is toward the sea; surface water moves swiftly, while water stored underground moves more slowly.

SURFACE WATER

Surface water is what we all think of when someone talks about a water supply. The water we see in lakes, ponds, reservoirs, and streams historically is the water that is used first, because it is easily available. Like all fresh water, surface water is simply recycled seawater, evaporated from the sea (Figure 10-1) by solar energy. And, like all fresh water everywhere, wherever it is found, surface water is on its way back to the sea.

Surprisingly, the majority of surface water is stored in lakes. The Great Lakes of North America store nearly one-quarter of the earth's surface water, with the large lakes of Asia and Africa each storing another one-quarter. What fills the hundreds of thousands of smaller lakes and all the rivers of the entire world is less than one-quarter of the earth's total fresh surface water.

Rough estimates suggest that the stream channels of the world carry approximately 300 cubic miles (1200 cubic kilometers) of water at any one time—an amount of water equal to the water used by the citizens of the world in 4 months. The world's river channels only contain enough water to *maintain* their flow, on the average, for about 2 weeks. How, then, do rivers continue to flow throughout the year, even during rain-free periods that last longer than 2 weeks?

GROUNDWATER

Groundwater is our *unseen* resource—fresh water stored beneath the earth's surface—and it comprises more than 90 percent of our available fresh water (see Chapter Eight). As fresh water falls on the earth, the majority is evaporated back into the atmosphere or used directly by plants and animals in their life processes. Perhaps one-third of the water that falls on the United States returns to the ocean as runoff (Figure 10-2) and is called *surface water.* Another very small fraction soaks into the permeable rock and soil of the earth's surface and is called *groundwater.*

Groundwater is fresh water stored within the outer portion of the earth's surface. This water also flows toward the sea, but its rate of flow is very slow, and it usually flows into rivers and creeks, which then flow into the sea. Valleys thus interrupt (Figure 10-3) the flow of groundwater toward the sea; now we know why many rivers flow year around. A part of the source of any river in a humid region is groundwater (Figure 10-4), trickling into the valley from large underground storage reserves; its flow is independent of minor changes in rainfall pattern. Any stream or lake thus contains two kinds of water—*runoff water,* which flows directly into it from rain or melting snow, and *groundwater,* which flows into it year around.

In a humid climate, the pattern is as just described. The water surface in a lake or stream is continuous with the *boundary between saturated and unsaturated loose rock and soil,* which is called the **water table.** The water table (Figure 10-3) is the boundary between soil and rock that are saturated with water below it and soil and rock that contain

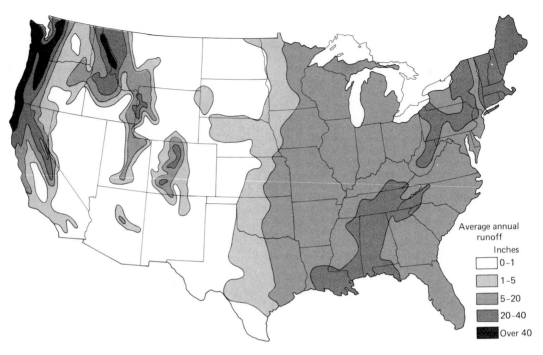

10-2
Average runoff in the conterminous United States. (From U.S. Water
Resources Council, 1968, *The Nation's Water Resources.*)

Average annual
runoff

Inches
0–1
1–5
5–20
20–40
Over 40

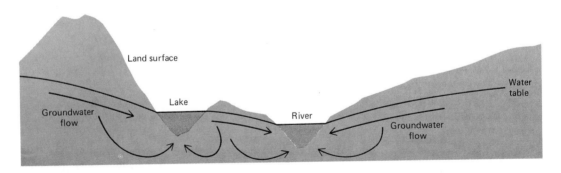

Land surface

Water
table

Groundwater
flow

Lake

River

Groundwater
flow

10-3
Groundwater table profile and flow of groundwater in a humid region.
Compare with Figure 10-6. Both stream and lake contain water year around;
they are *perennial.*

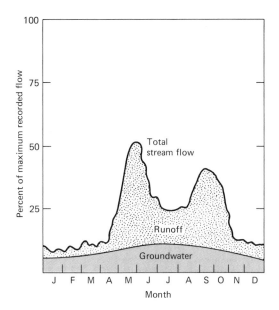

100

75

Percent of maximum recorded flow

50

Total
stream flow

25

Runoff

Groundwater

J F M A M J J A S O N D
Month

10-4

Hypothetical duration-flow curve for a stream
in a humid region. The groundwater
contribution to the total streamflow remains
fairly constant.

both pore spaces full of air and water above
it (Figure 10-5). If the elevation of the water
table coincides with the land surface, the
area is marshy or swampy. In a humid region, the elevation of the water table follows

the land surface (Figure 10-3), and the water
level in most lakes is continuous with the
elevation of the water table.

In an arid region, the situation is quite different. Notice that in Figure 10-2 there are
large areas of the western United States
where runoff is *absent*. Streams do not flow
year around; they flow only after an occasional rain. In arid regions, the depth to the
water table may be very great, and groundwater does not feed into streams. Instead,
streams, when they do flow, leak water (Figure 10-6) into underground water storage.
Such streams rarely reach the sea. As suggested in Chapter Eight, drainage in arid regions is internal; streams are a *source* for
water storage, not an *interruption* of storage, as they are in more humid areas.

Groundwater Movement

Anyone who has ever dug a hole in the soil
deep enough to intersect the water table has
watched the hole partially fill with water.
Thus, we know that water can move slowly
underground. But how does it move? Intuition suggests that water, or any fluid, including oil, can only move through earth materials that are **porous** (materials that have

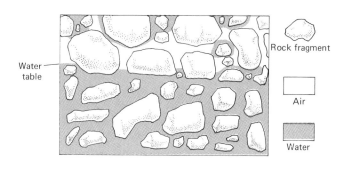

Water
table

Rock fragment

Air

Water

10-5

Enlarged view of the water table in a
permeable sediment. Above the
water table, water may coat the rock
fragments, but the space (pores)
among grains is filled mostly with air.
Below the water table, the sediment
is saturated with water.

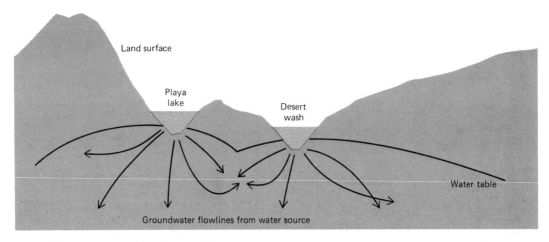

10-6
Groundwater table profile and flow of groundwater in an arid region, shown after a rainstorm. Both the playa lake and the desert wash contain water, but they are water *sources.* In a few days or weeks both will dry up; they are *ephemeral.* Compare with Figure 10-3.

space between the grains). In soil, the upper part of the soil normally has air filling most of the pores, and water adheres tightly to the surface of grains. Plant rootlets can pull the water away from grains until nearly all the water is gone. Water may move into the soil from *below,* from groundwater storage, and from *above,* as rain or melting snow, or from the water used when we water plants.

The movement of water, both horizontally and vertically through material, requires not only that it be porous, but also that each pore be at least partly connected with its neighbor, so that fluids can migrate through a system of interconnected open space. The *amount of interconnected pore space* in rock or soil is called the material's **permeability;** fluids can only flow through material that is permeable.

A good example of material that is porous but impermeable is the volcanic rock called pumice. Pumice is full of holes formed by gas bubbles trapped in a rapidly cooled lava, but none of these holes are connected. Pumice is so porous but, at the same time, so impermeable that it floats on water. Its high porosity makes it buoyant, but the lack of permeability will not allow water to enter; therefore pumice is the only rock that floats.

Water trapped within a permeable zone moves for the same reason a fluid anywhere else moves. It moves under pressure to areas of lower pressure, which usually means that water runs into streams, wells, and lakes. Groundwater flows toward the sea, interrupted in humid regions by lakes and stream valleys and uninterrupted in arid regions. The rates of flow are slow by human standards—perhaps a few yards (meters) a year—because flow is greatly retarded by friction along the tiny passages water must move through.

Springs

Sometimes the movement of groundwater is interrupted by an impermeable layer beneath the earth. The water trickling downward has nowhere to go, except to spread out and flow along the upper surface of the impervious layer. The water table is thus *perched* above the elevation of the normal water table.

Water then flows laterally until it either finds a way down to the normal level of water storage or runs into a valley wall, where the water leaks out as a **spring** (Figure 10-7). It is a common experience to find that springs occur right above an impermeable layer, because springs form wherever the water table is cut by the land surface.

WATER USE

As we have suggested, surface water and groundwater are connected; all precipitation is part of a single system. Pollute the surface water and, in time, the stored groundwater becomes polluted. Use more groundwater than precipitation provides, and both the streams and springs will eventually dry up; the level of the water table has fallen, and streams will no longer receive a perpetual inflow. Use poor grazing practices in a semi-

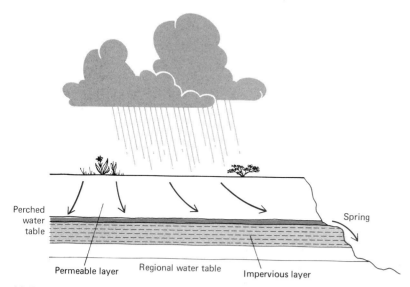

Perched
water
table

Spring

Permeable layer   Regional water table   Impervious layer

10-7
An example of one way in which a spring is formed. Water percolating downward through a permeable layer encounters an impermeable stratum causing a perched water table. The water travels laterally and exits at the nearest valley cut through the water table.

arid region, and brush will replace the grass. Brush needs more water than grass and draws it from deeper sources, so streams will soon cease flowing as the elevation of the groundwater table declines. Kill the brush and reduce grazing demands, and the streams and springs will flow once again.

Water, like petroleum products, has been abundant, cheap, and wasted. As populations continue to rise, we are discovering that fresh water—although a renewable resource—*can* be polluted and overused. Wise management practices are being learned through trial and error, with plenty of both commodities in evidence. As we increase our use of water, we might ask where we use it and how we waste it.

Measurement

Many different terms are applied to measurement of water. For simplicity, we will use only the familiar American units here; because worldwide metric standards have not yet had any impact on how we describe the volume or flow of water. For domestic and industrial use, the common volume unit is the gallon; the unit of flow is gallons per minute, gallons per hour, or gallons per day.

One gallon per minute seems unimpressive, but that equals 1440 gallons per day, enough for a family of five to use with a healthy allowance for waste. With careful conservation, several families could live on that amount.

Agricultural water use is expressed in multiples of a quantity known as the *acre-foot*—the amount of water that will cover 1 acre (about the size of a football field) to a depth of 1 foot. One acre-foot is about 300,-000 gallons.

Domestic Use

In our homes, an average usage is 50 to 100 gallons per person a day. The heaviest single use is lawn watering which, for an average-sized lawn, may require 30,000 to 200,000 gallons of water per year, depending on the climate.

Water use directly reflects the details of American life. Usage sharply peaks between 6 and 10 P.M., when we eat, water the lawn, and bathe. Another peak occurs between 6 and 9 A.M., when we have breakfast and bathe. In hot, arid areas, where water is used for evaporative air conditioning, water use peaks in the afternoon hours. Finally, in most American cities, there is an especially heavy peak usage on Saturday night; the Saturday night bath is apparently still a tradition.

Industrial Use

Ninety-four percent of the water used by industry is used for cooling, and much of this water can be reused. Repeated reuse of the same water calls for massive cooling towers to vent waste heat into the atmosphere or, preferably, for systems that reuse the waste heat for productive purposes. The greatest industrial use of water is by the electric power industry, which uses water for cooling fuel-powered generators. Petroleum, coal-processing, and chemical industries are the second largest users of water.

Water use by industry averages less than 100 gallons per employee per day, so total water use in most American cities is about 150 gallons per person per day, but the range is wide. The use of cooling water in some industries may require several tens of thousands of gallons of water per person per day; such extravagant use of water poses special demands for many water-short areas.

The demand for cooling water in electrical power generation has another component that has been difficult to reconcile with minimum damage to the environment. The problem of disposing of hundreds of thousands of gallons of warm water from power plants is unsolved. Cooling towers can vent much of the heat into the atmosphere but, eventually, the water is usually returned to streams and lakes. Streams and lakes are thereby warmed, changing the local environment. In some heavily industrialized areas, where the same stream water is used by several power plants in succession, water temperatures have been increased 20 or 30 degrees Celsius above normal, causing disastrous results to life in the stream.

Electrical power demand is forecast to double within the next 20 years; one wonders not only where the fuel is coming from to feed such an inefficient system, but also where the water is coming from to bleed away the vast amounts of heat wasted in electrical generation. Thermal pollution of water has become a major environmental concern, because it represents yet another problem in a tremendously wasteful energy system.

Agricultural Use

Irrigation is our greatest deliberate use of water. It is practiced precisely where rainfall is scanty and the sun shines all year; huge crops must therefore be grown on irrigated land. Since land typically is irrigated primarily in areas where there is little natural surface water, irrigation water must be obtained from large dam and irrigation canal projects or by pumping from underground water resources.

The transfer of surplus water from one area to another for irrigation is only possible with massive federal subsidies; the network of dams, canals, and pumps developed have made choice pork-barrel projects for over 100 years. Even now, farmers in west Texas are eyeing Mississippi River water, while southern California and Arizona are squabbling over plans to divert part of the Columbia River from the northwest to the southwest. Northwestern congressional representatives say hands off our river; southwestern senators darkly suggest that perhaps if they cannot have the excess northwestern water, perhaps southwestern oil and natural gas should be kept at home. Water politics has always been interesting, and the war is really just beginning.

Groundwater for irrigation in drier areas is a *major* resource; it is also a battleground. Farmers cheerfully reach into the next county or state for more supplies, while the mines and cities press the courts for the same water. Throughout most of the southwestern America, irrigated agriculture has been responsible for precipitous declines in the elevation of the groundwater table, because water is generally being consumed faster than nature replenishes it. For much of this area, the question is where to find still more water as more and more people, high-yield farms, and utilities flock to the driest part of the United States.

Consider one typical southwestern state—Arizona. In Arizona, 90 percent of the *total* water used in the state is used by irrigated agriculture. The total usage is about 7 million acre-feet of water per year. Remember that only 3 acre-feet equals 1 million gallons; this means that in Arizona there is an extraordinary amount of water in a state whose basically desert climate currently makes it the fastest growing state, in population, among the 50 states.

Of the 7 million acre-feet of water used for agriculture in Arizona, about one-third of this is *in excess* of the natural replenishment rate. A tank holding the water used for irrigation in *1 year* in Arizona that is in *excess* of naturally available water would be the size of a football field, and over 400 miles (640 kilometers) high.

Water is a renewable resource—*but only when it is used no faster than it is naturally resupplied*. Throughout much of the irrigated western United States, water use from groundwater resources is at a much higher level than natural replenishment. What nature has taken tens of thousands of years to store in a desert climate, irrigated agriculture will squander in less than 100 years. In this context Arizona, and most other areas of substantial irrigation, are using a *nonrenewable* resource.

Irrigation in many of the irrigated western states, which use 84 percent of U.S. water consumption, is by traditional methods of surface flow in rows or surface sprinkling from overhead pipes. The newest irrigation system is the center pivot system, which delivers water from overhead pipes that are moved in a circle that is centered on an irrigation well. In one study of the use of this system in Nebraska, nearly one-half of the total energy used in agriculture is used to pump water for irrigation. During a typical irrigation season, one center pivot system consumes enough water for a city of 1000 people for an entire year; it also uses around 8000 gallons of diesel fuel a year. Hundreds of such systems are in use, and more are being added every month.

Such surface irrigation systems not only consume huge amounts of energy and water,

but they are also notoriously wasteful of water. Spraying water into the arid air of the southwestern states leads to a *minimum* loss of one-half of the water by evaporation. Similar losses occur with row irrigation. In one area of Arizona, *six* times as much water is used to grow citrus as in Israel, where climate and soil are similar to those of Arizona. The only difference is that Israelis use *drip irrigation* systems, developed because Israelis appreciate the value of water, which is often obtained by the desalinization of seawater.

Drip irrigation systems deliver water to the base of a plant one drop at a time. The water moves directly to the root zone; loss by evaporation is minimized. The whole system of drip irrigation grew from a chance observation by a curious Israeli engineer. He noted in the mid-1930s that one tree in a row was much taller than the others. After a closer look, he realized that although all the trees were being irrigated, the tallest one was also being watered by a constant drip from a leaky connection.

Modern drip irrigation systems consist of a plastic pipe, with drip holes spaced at the base of each plant. Drip irrigation saves a great deal of water and improves crop quality by providing dependable water supplies where the plant most needs it. Also, in sandy soils somewhat brackish water can be used for irrigation; salt is concentrated at the outer edge of the wetted zone and is not carried down to the roots of the plant.

As more and more arid western land is being opened to irrigation, the pressing demand for fresh water grows. We will see many more attempts to cross state lines to obtain water in distant areas. One fascinating proposal has icebergs being *towed* to the Los Angeles area from the Antarctic. When saltwater freezes, the salt separates from the ice, so the icebergs would furnish ice-cold, pure water at costs currently estimated at $35 per acre-foot. Each iceberg might supply 1 million acre-feet of water at a cost nearly one-half that currently being paid for brackish Colorado River water. What started as a humorous proposal may become reality as water needs for irrigated agriculture increase.

WATER RECOVERY AND TREATMENT

A review of the conventional methods of water recovery is presented next. Water for domestic, industrial, and agricultural uses now comes from some combination of four sources: surface water, springs, conventional wells, and artesian wells. Each water source has its unique set of problems and rewards.

Surface Water

The greatest value of surface water is its easy availability and low initial cost. It is simply there, in lakes and streams, and only a pump and piping system is necessary to acquire it. For that reason, surface water is generally the first water used as a new area is opened for development.

There are also problems connected to the use of surface water. In all except the most pristine wilderness areas, surface water is contaminated by a variety of pollutants and requires substantial water treatment to make it safe for human consumption. For industrial use in cooling, no such standards apply; for agricultural use, water that is not contaminated by chemicals and that is not excessively brackish, will usually suffice. For human use, surface water requires at least three forms of treatment.

First, surface water may contain a large quantity of silt and clay that must be removed by a combination of chemical treatment and filtering. Second, surface water usually contains bacteria that make people sick; the standard American treatment is chlorination. Third, surface water may contain undesirable chemicals, dissolved organic matter, and material that makes the water smell or taste bad. Again, the standard practice consists of running the water through various combinations of activated charcoal to remove odor and of sophisticated chemical and biological treatment to remove other contaminants. The science of water treatment for human consumption is a complex science.

Spring Water

Depending on the distance traveled underground, spring water may be thought of as slightly modified surface water or slightly modified groundwater. If the water pouring out of a spring entered the earth not far away in both distance and time, it contains most of the pollutants associated with surface water and a few of the problems associated with groundwater.

Perhaps the most common problem associated with spring water is the incorporation of various chemical compounds and elements dissolved from minerals by the water as it slowly flowed through permeable, undergound rock. The incorporation of small amounts of certain elements (ions) can be regarded as medically beneficial; larger amounts of the same elements (ions) or smaller amounts of toxic elements (ions), or those (like iron) that cause stains or scale on pipes, may require treatment before the water can be used.

Conventional Wells

A typical groundwater well is simply an opening drilled into an underground accumulation of water below the water table (Figure 10-8). In order for water to flow laterally into the well, the material carrying the water must be permeable. Such an underground, permeable source of water is called an **aquifer**.

An aquifer may consist of a layer of unconsolidated gravel or an area of rock broken by numerous fractures; it may also consist of a layer of nearly solid, still slightly permeable rock so that water can slowly flow through. Regardless of description, an aquifer must contain water and must be sufficiently permeable to allow the water to move through it at an economic rate.

From a well drilled into an aquifer, both benefits and liabilities accrue. On the plus side, well water may have flowed slowly through many miles of rock, and the water is generally clear in color and devoid of silt and clay. Additionally, the long distance traveled underground has caused the oxidation of most, if not all, potentially harmful bacteria.

Thus the *majority* of well water may be free of both bacterial and foreign matter pollution; however, in most areas of highly contaminated surface water, well water is *far* more suspect. Surface water and groundwater are eventually parts of the same system of water flow toward the sea. As a routine practice, almost all well water is treated with chlorine on the premise that the water may yield some bacterial contamination; in all except the most isolated areas, this is simply good, safe practice.

Well water carries two liabilities. It may contain large amounts of dissolved ions, and it is more expensive than surface water to find, to drill for, and to pump (Figure 10-9). If the water contains large amounts of ions dissolved from minerals, we describe the

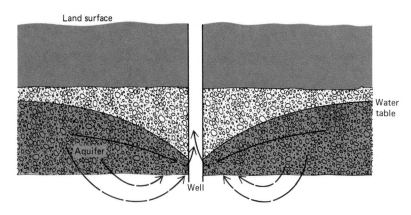

10-8
Cross section of a conventional well drilled below the water table. Notice that while the well is being pumped, the water table is locally depressed due to rapid water withdrawal. The well, therefore, must originally be drilled much deeper than the water table elevation with the pump turned off.

10-9

A 1903 photograph shows what it was like to drill a water well deep in the piney woods of Georgia. The process has not changed much in 80 years. (Photograph by M. L. Fuller, U.S. Geological Survey.)

water as **hard water.** Hard water causes scaling and corrosion problems in pipes and problems in trying to wash things clean. Stains, crusts, and discoloration also result from the use of hard water. Various types of treatment to rid the water of undesirable dissolved minerals are available, but costs of treating large volumes of water may be high.

Artesian Wells

Among the expenses associated with a conventional well is the continuing cost of pumping the water out of the ground—a cost avoided in some areas where the water in the aquifer is naturally pressurized and rises to the surface without pumping. A well that punctures such a pressurized aquifer is called an **artesian well,** and it may provide the benefits of well water without the cost of pumping.

In a typical artesian well area, the aquifer is tilted (Figure 10-10), and the water enters the sloping aquifer *above* the areas from which it is later recovered. If the aquifer is surrounded by impermeable layers, the aquifer becomes, in effect, a pipe to which water is added at the high end and recovered, under natural pressure, at the low end (Figure 10-10), since pressure increases with depth in a fluid.

Artesian systems provide a highly valuable water resource and have been an important part of America's water history. Like any resource that provides dependable water under natural pressure, it may be overused. If too many wells puncture the pressured aquifer, the water pressure (and the amount of available water) drops. In a well-managed artesian basin, regulations strictly govern how many wells can be drilled and how much water can be produced from each well. Other than an unusual value as a naturally pressured well water resource, water from artesian systems has the same liabilities and assets in its use as conventional well water.

WATER PROBLEMS

Our problems with water—once we have located a supply—fall into two broad categories: contamination and overuse. To some extent, these problems with the American water supply are interrelated; overuse of a resource leads to contamination, and the costs of returning the water to a usable state

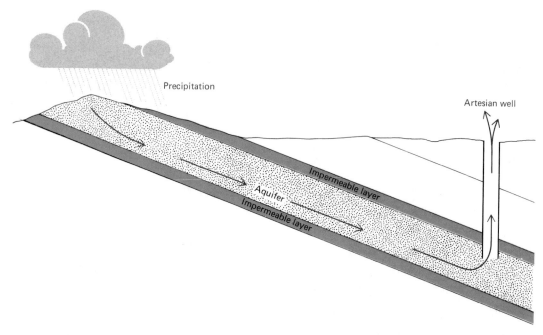

10-10
Components of an artesian well system. Water enters a permeable rock unit at a higher elevation and travels down the dipping aquifer, which is bounded by impermeable layers. The water rises in a well drilled into the aquifer; the difference in elevation between the area of recharge (precipitation) and the top of the well provides the necessary pressure to cause the water to flow to the top of the well.

may only be a part of the much larger costs of restoring the whole area to a usable resource. More simply, water consumption is dependent on two characteristics: water quality and water quantity.

Water Quality

Problems with water quality (the suitability of water for its intended use) appear in many guises: the increasing salinity of the lower Colorado River; New York City reaching more than 60 miles (96 kilometers) past the Hudson River for its water sources; and the sudden recognition that traditional water treatment practices may be increasing the risk of cancer in certain American cities.

The sources of pollutants are varied, ranging from outhouses to city garbage dumps and including massive industrial polluters and the runoff from fertilized farms. Perhaps if there is a key to understanding water quality troubles, it lies in recognizing that water is an *open* system, easily susceptible to subtle degradation or massive poisoning. Water quality problems arise in one of two basic instances: (1) injection of material into surface water, and (2) injection of material into groundwater.

Our most serious problem with water quality arises from the direct dumping of industrial wastes and poorly treated or untreated city sewage into open streams. The problem is an old one. In 1883, Major A.J. Hains of the U.S. Army reported that the stench from sewage sludge on the Potomac River "was inappropriate to the official residence of the first magistrate of the land." Since we began creating wastes, the rivers and seas of the world have seemed a handy place to get rid of them.

As typhoid and other diseases were traced to sewage-laden waters, the treatment of city waste began in earnest only about 30 to 40 years ago. Until then, many rivers in metropolitan areas were essentially devoid of dissolved oxygen; their waters were so polluted with organic wastes that decomposition of those wastes required all the dissolved oxygen, and more, that the river had to offer. The effects of loading rivers with untreated sewage effluents are not only to cycle human disease and parasites from upstream populations to downstream communities, but also to deprive the river of oxygen, with devastating effects to riverine life.

Within the last 20 years, the federal government has sponsored some water pollution control and clean water legislation. Recent legislation has proclaimed that waterways can no longer be used for the dumping of untreated waste of any type and that the cost of improving water quality should fall most directly on those who degrade it. With more and more active federal involvement, major industrial and domestic water pollution may slowly become a distant memory.

Progress in improving water quality will be slow; water quality costs money. Rivers and lakes are slowly improving, particularly around major industrial and municipal sources; however, nothing has been done to prevent the fertilizer and pesticide wastes that flow into both surface and groundwater supplies from a modern agribusiness, and small industrial or municipal sources may lack the money and technology to mend their ways.

Debasement of groundwater is a more subtle process and is more difficult to monitor or alter. Basically, all contamination fed into groundwater is inadvertent and is often unrecognized until substantial damage has accumulated. Sources as varied as outhouses, feedlots, and city garbage dumps (Figure 10-11) may yield fluids that slowly work their way downward into an aquifer. Once the damage is recognized—usually because of illness among the people using the groundwater resource—the damage is hard to clean up, because the contaminant may continue to seep into the aquifer for decades after its initial source has been removed. In one startling example, a village in England discovered it was drinking water contaminated by a seventeenth-century graveyard for plague victims.

Water Quantity

Both water quality and water quantity are human value judgments. Water *quantity* may be either too little or too much. The response to *both* problems is usually the same—build a dam. Problems with both drought and flood may be eased by smoothing out the stream flow over time, using reservoirs. There are, however, problems. A little-recognized problem that ensues with water stored in reservoirs is losses by both seepage to underground storage and evaporation into the air. Additionally, poorly con-

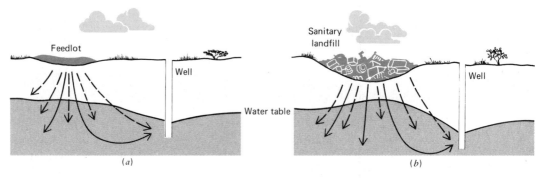

10-11
These cross sections illustrate the concept of groundwater as an open system. Leakage from an animal feedlot or a sanitary landfill may provide fluid contaminants into the water table. If a well is too close to the source of contamination, the water recovered will be polluted.

structed dams, large-volume storage, and earthquake potential are three corners of a dangerous triangle for those who live below the reservoir.

For water in underground storage, different solutions are available. In those parts of the United States where groundwater storage is substantially in *excess* of demand, drainage and piping to improve water removal from the surface area are two of the few alternatives available. As marshlands and other wetlands are drained, we often lose a precious resource of unique life forms and interrupt, with permanent consequences, the web of life within an area of wetland drainage.

In the more arid parts of the United States, the opposite is generally true; removal of groundwater *exceeds* replenishment, and the level of the groundwater table declines. Over much of the arid and semiarid United States, water is being used—mostly for cooling or irrigation—*much* faster than nature replenishes the resource. Such a resource is being *mined* as surely as copper

ore is mined, and there will be no second crop.

Falling groundwater tables lead to various types of problems, such as accelerating drilling costs, declining water quality, higher pumping costs, increasingly salty water, and land subsidence. Over large parts of the southwestern United States, the only answer to the question of where the water is is *down*. As groundwater levels drop, the answer is down *further*—much further with every passing year—and each deepening of the well calls for greater drilling costs, greater pumping costs, and greater consumption of scarce energy to pump still more water from greater depths.

Water *quality* often diminishes with greater depth, not only because the water has been there longer, dissolving out slightly soluble compounds and becoming harder, but also because the water at greater and greater depths may become brackish or salty. Most groundwater at great depth passes into a still deeper reservoir of salty water that was left behind when the rocks formed and were cemented. Fresh water floats, because of its lesser density, on top of this salty water. With excessive use of groundwater, the water table falls and ever deeper wells may begin to withdraw brackish (salty) water; declining water quality and increasing expenses are preventable costs that come along together.

Still another concern becomes reality as water is mined from deeper and deeper aquifers. Often the water in the pores of the rock or soil helps to *support the weight* of the overlying rock, soil, or buildings. As large volumes of water are withdrawn, the upper layers of the earth are artificially dried out; the pore spaces fill with air instead of water, and the land surface slowly collapses as its support is removed (Figure 10-12). Over areas of extreme water depletion, *land subsidence* has become a major construction hazard. Highways buckle and break, building formations crack and deteriorate, buried piping springs leaks, and a whole web of buried utilities begin to fail.

The earth's subsurface can be thought of as a gigantic sponge that absorbs and releases water. Remove the water no faster than nature replenishes it with rain and melting snow, and the sponge stays much the same; its water is a renewable resource. Remove more water than nature provides, and the sponge dries out and may collapse if the granular materials beneath cannot support the land.

In places as diverse as Venice and Las Vegas, the story is the same. Venice has been sinking into the Adriatic Sea as factories on the nearby mainland overuse water, although stringent conservation measures in 1979 may have stopped the subsidence. The Houston-Galveston area of Texas sinks at the rate of about four inches (10 centimeters) a year. Mexico City has sunk a total of 10 yards (9 meters); its sewage must now be *pumped uphill.* Long Beach, California, dropped a similar distance over a 30-year period as *petroleum* was removed. Seawater has been pumped, under pressure, back into

10-12
An example of subsidence from extreme southwestern Kansas in an area once crossed by the Santa Fe Trail. This collapse was due to the solution of underground salt by groundwater; the collapse occurred overnight in 1859. (Photograph by W. D. Johnson, U.S. Geological Survey.)

the dry strata, and the surface has re-bounded—a remarkable example of a coastal city reviving itself.

Las Vegas, Nevada, is perhaps a classic example of human interference in a desert area with limited water resources. Las Vegas is a town of lush, green golf courses, manicured lawns, swimming pools, and abundant trees. It is also a city that will run out of water between 1990 and 2000 unless external sources of water are available. Las Vegas is also sinking into the sands that sustain it; it has fallen a total of nearly 2 yards (not quite 2 meters) in the last 40 years due to compaction of sand as the elevation of the water table drops. The Las Vegas "strip"—an area of plush resort hotels and extravagant water use—is sinking fastest of all.

Ironically, part of the reason Las Vegas is sinking is the recent accumulation of a large reservoir of fresh water nearby. The water trapped in nearby Lake Mead is a 40 billion-ton (36 billion metric ton) deadweight added to the land surface in the last 40 years; its weight is forcing the earth's crust down and also causing minor earthquakes. Most of the reason Las Vegas is sinking into the sand is, however, because of its own profligate use of the water resource stored in the desert sands on which it is built.

It is one of the ironies of our water consumption patterns that water is often wasted exactly where it is most scarce. The greatest population shift in America's recent history is toward the southwestern desert area, with its promise of warm, sunny days, little rain, and no snow, all accompanied by lush, green lawns, large golf courses with impeccable grounds, a giant swimming pool in everyone's backyard, and inexpensive fresh fruit and vegetables from nearby irrigated fields.

Phoenix, Arizona, is one sad example of an area where the rate of decline of the ele-

10-13
Dripstone in Higenbothem's Cave, near Glasgow Junction, Kentucky, in 1925. (Photograph by W. T. Lee, U.S. Geological Survey.)

vation of the water table is very high and is accompanied by massive subsidence failure; some areas have sunk a total of 3 yards (2¾ meters). Phoenix is also a city, set in the midst of a typical desert climate, whose water consumption is, per capita, *twice* the national average. Finally, and not at all surprisingly, it is a city that is desperately interested in the Central Arizona Project—a massive, federally funded water diversion project that, if operating at full design flow, will only *diminish* the total, *current* water overdraft but will *not* solve it. Three centuries ago the English poet Samuel Butler said: "All progress is based upon a universal innate desire on the part of every organism to live beyond its income.''

Karst

Subsidence problems in parts of America's southeastern states often come from a different source. Limestone is a common sedimentary rock; in arid areas limestone may make stark cliffs, since it is often a hard, resistant rock. But anywhere limestone is exposed to even moderate quantities of water flowing underground, it will begin to slowly dissolve, and caverns or caves will form. Groundwater dripping from the ceiling of caves may form networks of beautiful dripstone deposits (Figure 10-13), visible to anyone who climbs into a cave that is above the water table. The dripstone deposits are simply limestone that was dissolved from one area and redeposited in another as groundwater drips and evaporates.

In many areas of silent underground caverns, the solution of limestone can mean potential trouble; the roof of the cave (Figure 10-14), progressively thinned by solution, may eventually collapse and form a **sinkhole.** A sinkhole is a roughly circular depression (Figure 19-12) formed in an area of soluble (usually limestone) bedrock by the collapse of a cavern roof.

In areas of abundant sinkholes, the prevailing topography is rolling, and numerous depressions dot the landscape. In many of these areas, the ground surface is so thoroughly laced with underground solution that water *rarely flows on the surface,* but flows as a series of streams through a connected underground cavern system. The topography of an area of extensive limestone solution is called **karst** topography, after a region in easternmost Yugoslavia where such a landscape was first described.

Lowering of the groundwater table by heavy pumping accentuates cavern collapse, because it promotes solution. As the cavern roof thins, collapse becomes inevitable; the

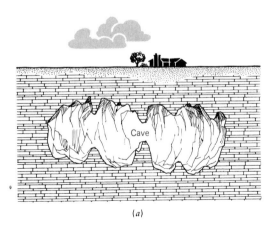 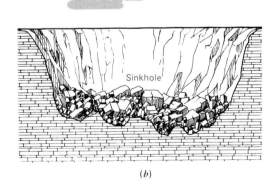

(a) (b)

10-14
Before and after cross sections of an area of limestone bedrock in a humid region. (a) The cavern develops because of solution of the bedrock. (b) After the roof collapses, a sinkhole remains.

rumble of a passing truck may sometimes be enough to cause the unstable cavern roof to collapse. The gaping hole that results may eventually fill with groundwater and become a sinkhole lake, which might be regarded as a resource.

If, however, the collapse occurs under highways, railroad tracks, sewer pipes, or your home, the collapse cannot be considered beneficial. In some areas of central Florida, people have been frantically dialing the mover when their homes collapsed into holes many tens of yards (meters) deep; the cracks that suddenly appeared in walls and ceilings were their only warning. In Shelby County, Alabama, one recent collapse—fortunately in an uninhabited area—left a crater more than 100 yards (90 meters) across and 40 yards (36 meters) deep.

Little can be done about the obvious hazards presented by construction in karst areas except to locate potential sinkholes in an area before construction begins. There are several methods of locating sinkholes that use a variety of sophisticated instruments to recognize the deficiency of mass that occurs when air, instead of rock, is beneath one's feet.

WATER LAW

A substantial body of law envelops both the use of water and the damage resulting from the misuse of water. In the relatively well-watered eastern half (Figure 10-2) of the United States, most water law is concerned with the problem of water pollution and the separate problem of excess water, or flooding. West of the hundredth meridian of longitude, water law generally reflects growing concern over allocation of a scarce resource.

Much water law is quite old; it was embodied as common law and was written long before the physical principles governing the flow of both surface water and groundwater were understood. A review of water law will suggest that water can be alternatively regarded as a treasured resource or as a nuisance—depending on its quantity and quality.

Surface Water

Water, running unconfined across the surface of the land, has long been regarded simply as a nuisance to be disposed of as quickly as possible. Property owners are generally entitled to protect their property from flood by whatever means necessary, including the diversion of storm drainage through natural drainageways across a neighbor's land. In general, modern law recognized that if flood protection *seriously increases* the natural flow into a neighbor's property, the neighbor may sue for damages. This doctrine is often called the REASONABLE USE RULE: you are entitled to use your property in any way you choose, *so long as your use does not injure another*. The reasonable use rule is one of the cornerstones of water law; we will refer to it frequently.

If surface water is confined to a stream, which has a definite channel, a much larger body of law applies. There are two classes of water law governing stream flow: the **riparian doctrine** or **rule** and the **prior appropriation doctrine**. The riparian rule, modified by the doctrine of reasonable use, is the basic water law governing stream water and lake water in the eastern United States; while the doctrine of prior appropriation, with modifications, is the heart of water law in the arid western United States.

The riparian rule stems from French (Napoleonic) law and implies that the landowners adjacent to any watercourse may use the water as they see fit, providing that (1) the water is returned to its ordinary course after use; (2) the water use is reasonable and does not deprive landowners further downstream of their use; and (3) the water flow is neither obstructed nor substantially diminished in quantity or quality.

The riparian rule does provide a system for settlement of disputes among landowners, but it is not an effective system for water *management*. What constitutes reasonable use, pollution, or obstruction is up to the courts to determine; water rights are not absolute and may change at the stroke of a judge's pen or with subsequent legal review.

The prior appropriation doctrine developed from a succession of Indian, Mexican, and Spanish governments. This proposition rests on a simple concept; the person *first* using a resource acquires a right to its *exclusive* use. That right is lost only by abandonment—much like the laws governing western mining claims.

Notice that the right to water does not accompany a property interest in land, as it does by the riparian rule. Instead, a senior user or appropriator has a right, forever, *to the quantity of water previously used* and may transfer that water to any location where its usage is convenient.

Groundwater

For groundwater in the United States, the oldest rule is the **English rule.** It is adapted from ancient common law and states that ownership of the land is *absolute,* vesting an *absolute right to all materials below and above the land:* "He who owns the soil owns from the heavens to the depths." This ancient doctrine was adopted when essentially nothing was known of the flow of water beneath the land; it assumes that unless malice is shown, landowners can produce as much water from beneath their land as is possible, even to the detriment of a neighbor. In many states, this is still the basic rule and, if a landowner dries up a neighbor's wells by intensive pumping, the neighboring landowners have no grounds for court action. All landowners are, however, required not to pollute groundwater and are liable for contamination of the resources of others.

In some states (mostly the more arid western states) the **American rule,** or the reasonable use rule, modifies English rule proceedings. The reasonable use rule may require the groundwater to be used *on the land from which it is taken.* If the property owner transfers water off the land, a legal action may be sustained if the neighboring landowner can show that the excess water transferred elsewhere has caused harm—either through loss of quality or quantity. In this modification, the landowner must use the water beneath the soil *reasonably,* having *due regard for the rights of others.*

California has established a third principle that has been adopted with increasing frequency by other western states. This principle, called **correlative rights,** states that the absolute right to water that comes with landownership is limited to that that will *directly* benefit the land *from which the water is taken.* Any surplus water is available for appropriation; furthermore, in times of shortage, each owner must share in the shortage proportionately to the land area owned.

Added to these laws governing the use of surface water and groundwater is a further system of priorities. In a general category of uses, water for domestic and municipal consumption has the highest priority, with diminishing priorities divided among mining, manufacturing, and agricultural interests.

Water law can be characterized as ancient, interesting, complex, and unscientific, because most water law was codified long before we understood how water flowed either above or beneath the surface and long before an appreciation of how closely tied surface water and groundwater resources are. Few water laws can be viewed as management tools, because the doctrine of water use (and abuse) closely tied to landownership or early appropriation is deeply ingrained.

Basically, water law is state law; each state has its own system of laws and subsequent interpretations. The laws of *water movement* are reasonably well known; a set of legal doctrines that provide for effective *water management* is yet to be formulated.

Until such time, we should operate on a simple premise that is inherently fair: water is a valuable resource to be used prudently and reasonably with due regard for one's neighbor.

SUMMARY

In humid areas the flow of subsurface water to the sea is interrupted by rivers and lake basins; in arid regions the water table, dividing saturated from unsaturated land, slopes away from ephemeral rivers and lakes that carry water only after an infrequent rainfall. Surface water is easy to find, cheap to pump, and more expensive to treat; groundwater is harder to find, more expensive to pump, and often requires less treatment prior to use.

Water problems stem from two basic characteristics of water; water is a remarkable solvent, and its distribution underground and on the surface is tied to climate. Since water dissolves much of what it contacts and is an absolute necessity for life, it inadvertently becomes the carrier of dissolved minerals, hazardous germs and viral colonies, toxic chemicals, and trash. The quantity of water is essentially a function of climate but, even in arid areas where surface streams are absent, huge amounts of water may have accumulated underground over thousands of centuries. The Sahara desert, synonym for aridity, contains millions of cubic miles (kilometers) of water deep beneath its wind-scoured, barren surface.

Water usage falls into three categores: (1) domestic and municipal use, including most light industrial use; (2) irrigation; and (3) cooling water for electric power plants that use fossil or nuclear fuels as their energy source (Figure 10-15).

Agriculture uses more water than any other single industry in the United States; two-thirds of total water use is consumed in irrigation. Ten percent of all farms are irrigated—mostly in the arid and semiarid west—and provide nearly 20 percent of the value of farm crops produced in the entire

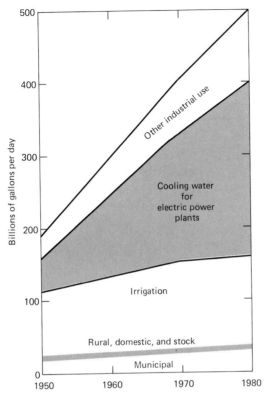

500 —

400 —

Other industrial use

300 —

Billions of gallons per day

Cooling water
for
electric power
plants

200 —

Irrigation

100 —

Rural, domestic, and stock

Municipal

0 —

1950   1960   1970   1980

10-15

Withdrawal of water by major use. (Data from
U.S. Geological Survey, 1974, Circular 703,
and the U.S. Water Resources Council, 1968,
The Nation's Water Resources.)

United States. The extraordinary water (and energy) demands of irrigated agriculture often lead to precipitous drops in the ground reserve accumulated over the centuries.

Water for electricity production is basically used for cooling purposes and may be of lower quality than that used for domestic or agricultural purposes. By 1980, in the face of surging electrical demand (Figure 10-16), the withdrawal of water for cooling electrical power plants will replace agriculture as the greatest single consumer of water in the United States. Water used for cooling may be returned to a variety of source, its temperature raised an average of 10 degress Celsius as a by-product of the enor-

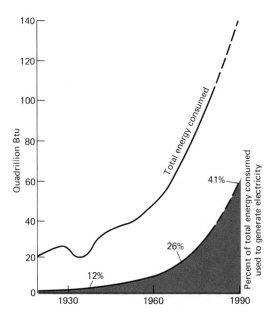

10-16
Chronologic summary of electrical energy
demand as a part of the total U.S. energy
demand from 1920 to 1990. (After U.S. Water
Resources Council, 1974, *Water for Energy
Self-Sufficiency.*)

mous energy waste characteristic of electrical power generation. Such thermal pollution of water constitutes an environmental hazard of growing
proportion; the energy *wasted* in power generation is greater than that
needed to heat all the homes in our country right now, and is 15% of our
total energy demands.

Many forms of pollution characterize our ancient assumption that "the
cure for pollution is dilution." As more and more people produce more and
more goods, water quality in a stressed environment diminishes, although
determined environmental action under newly enacted laws may spread
the enhanced costs of clean water widely over our society.

Problems with overuse of water resources are mostly, but not exclusively, confined to the United States west of the hundredth meridian. Here
overconsumption of ancient, stored resources has led to land subsidence,
deterioration of water quality, higher pumping costs, and an economy
geared to profligate use of water in a water-short land.

Water is a whimsical commodity, despised where it is too abundant and revered where it is too scarce. It is the stuff of life whose use is regulated by a confusion of state laws based on scientific misconceptions, ancient European laws, and frontier justice. Seen from the interminable black void of empty space, water is earth's greatest gift to itself, and to all of us who call earth home.

EXERCISES

1. Through the ages, spring water has often been assumed to have magical or medicinal properties. Can you suggest why?

2. In some areas, the water contains small amounts of dissolved fluoride, a nutrient essential to dental health. Check Appendix A and see if you can figure out the probable mineral source of the dissolved fluoride.

3. It has been observed that many limestone caves form upslope from rivers. Can you reason out why this association is so common?

4. It has also been observed that the lowest part of many caverns is V-shaped and may contain a running stream. Why should the cave be V-shaped in cross section?

5. In some areas, ozone has been promoted as an agent of water purification in place of chlorine, which has been shown to form carcinogenic chemicals when injected into already chemically contaminated water. How could the efficacy of ozone be compared with chlorine?

6. Take a tour of the water treatment plant in your town. Which of the following techniques are in use: sand filtration, addition of alum, addition of lime, use of activated charcoal, chlorination, or superchlorination? Why is each one used?

7. Next time you open your favorite 12-ounce (35-milliliter) beverage can, remember that it required 66 quarts (62½ liters) of water to manufacture the can. *Where* was it all used?

8. The average daily per capita household use of water in the United States in 1970 was 300 quarts (285 liters). Check this figure against that of your campus living unit. How and why does it compare?

9. The average daily per capita use of fresh water for *all* purposes is 20 times the household use. Can you suggest some hidden water uses in the materials you can see at this minute?

10. The prior appropriation doctrine for western water assumed that water was free; natural resources were available for those with the initiative to exploit them. Now there are pricing and marketing structures to attempt to balance supplies and demands. What changes in social structure led to such opposite views of water value?

SUGGESTED
READINGS

Environmental Protection Agency, 1977, *Waste Disposal Practices and their Effects on Ground Water,* Washington, D.C., 514 pp.

  Excellent review of the damage that can be done and how to avoid it.

Environmental Protection Agency, 1976, *Quality Criteria for Water,* Washington, D.C., 256 pp.

  The standard guide for limits to 53 substances and properties that may define water quality.

Leopold, Luna B., 1974, *Water: A Primer,* San Francisco, Freeman, 97 pp.

  Brief, most readable, and thoroughly recommended.

Murray, C.R., and Reeves, E.B., 1977, *Estimated Use of Water in the United States in 1975,* U.S. Geological Survey Circular 765, 39 pp.

  A review, updated every 5 years, of where and how we Americans use water.

Peixit, J.P., and Kettani, M.A., 1973, "The Control of the Water Cycle," *Scientific American,* April 1973.

  Useful review of the interrelated factors that control the movement of water on earth.

Sweeting, Marjorie M., 1973, *Karst Landforms,* New York, Columbia University Press, 456 pp.

  Excellent review of karst, caves, and their origin.

U.S. Water Resources Council, 1974, *Water for Energy Self-Sufficiency,* Washington, D.C. U.S. Government Printing Office, 184 pp.

  Thorough appraisal of the role of water in the production of energy.

U.S. Water Resources Council, 1976, *Staff Report to the National Commission on Water Quality,* Washington, D.C. U.S. government Printing Office, not paginated.

  Comprehensive analysis of federal programs in water pollution control.

KEY
CONCEPTS

Surface water

  Legally controlled by riparian or prior appropriation doctrines; quantity dependent on annual precipitation; quality dependent on runoff basin—easily contaiminated.

Ground water

  Legally controlled by English rule, American rule, and/or correlative rights; recovered by conventional and artesian wells and from springs; problem of hard water, drilling and pumping costs, and declining quality and rising costs if water table level declines.

Water use

Domestic use one-twentieth of total use; major industrial use for cooling, chiefly electric power plants; major use nationally is irrigated agriculture; use is high where water reserves have accumulated for many centuries of sparse rainfall.

Water table

Parallels land surface in humid area, opposite in arid area; level is a function of recharge (water addition) and withdrawal (water subtraction); water movement below water table requires permeability within an aquifer.

A contemporary of Steno here argues against the seventeenth-century idea that fossils were simply curiously "ornamented stones," created from the earth, much like minerals. In this frontispiece, *Sense,* with the eye of Reason, demonstrates to *"Vain Speculation"*—the ghostly figure on the left—the organic nature of fossils, like those within the rock. (From Agostino Scilla, 1670 (1748 ed.), courtesy of the History of Science Collections, University of Oklahoma Libraries.)

Chapter Eleven
TIME

"Space is a concrete idea, but time is abstract."
L. Durrell

Few words define a greater variety of concepts. Time may simply be a flow—from past to present to future—or time may be *counted* by noting and counting some recurring event, such as the rising of the sun. Time may be an interval *between* recurring events—a day, a season, a year, a lifetime. Time may be an interval *since* an event—A.D. 1980. Time may describe a season, one's own heyday, an appointed moment, an occasion, or the period of work, play, sleep, birth, or death. Time may be musical, a rhythm, or a measure of the *rate* at which something occurs.

There are many concepts of time—biologic, astronomic, historic, and geologic. This chapter describes each of them.

Geologic time has been described as the greatest intellectual contribution of geology; geology is a uniquely historical science that is concerned with the *sequence* and the *when* of events as much as the *why*. Geology, which is about the physical, chemical, and biological *changes* within and on the earth and, more recently, its neighboring moon and planets, is a uniquely appropriate science from which to attempt a perspective on a tantalizing question. What is time?

Geology, defined as the study of *changes* within and on the earth, illuminates a first principle of our conception of time: *time marks change*. If there were no change, how could time and its passage be conceived?

Imagine an existence in which you experience no bodily changes, no sense of aging, in an environment uniformly heated, devoid of night and day, season, weather, or any other perceptible change. What you have imagined is not living, but existence. Change is the essence of living. The world of life is the world of time.

BIOLOGIC TIME

It is well known that many organisms, including human beings, experience a daily rhythm of activities that are under the control of an internal clock. It has long been assumed that *daily* rhythms of sleeping, eating, and the like are controlled partly by external influences, such as the rising and setting of the sun. Imagine the surprise of a French biologist 200 years ago who discovered that certain plants, now *growing in total darkness,* daily bent their leaves toward the absent sun. Here was a new concept; organisms show inherited cyclic behavior even when the physical environment is kept constant. There is a clock within us all that programs our daily lives.

An even more amazing discovery is the existence of an *annual* cycle. Squirrels, kept at freezing temperatures in a windowless room under an artificial cycle of 12 hours of daylight and 12 hours of darkness behaved normally until October. At that time, their body temperature dropped to 1 degree Celsius; they entered hibernation and awakened the following April. They then ate normally, gaining weight until the fall, and entered hibernation again in October. Their behavior demonstrated that they had an internal clock that was independent on any external stimulus and unaffected by the invariant temperature or day length in their artificial environment.

The migration of birds is another annual cycle that is apparently preset and continues even when environmental conditions are constant. The shedding of antlers by deer is yet another cycle that is unaffected by artificially controlled day length or temperature. It has long been known that animals transplanted from their native habitat to zoos in totally different climate zones continue the annual cycles typical of their native areas; this is true even of their offspring.

The internal clock provides several advantages. An animal clock provides *advance warning* of a coming change; a hibernator needs to begin depositing extra fat, while a migratory bird needs to start flying toward the equator at a particular time each year. The clock also provides *reliable cues* that the environment may not furnish. How does the hibernator know it is spring? How does the bird, wintering near the equator with its changeless temperature and hours of daylight, know that it is time to fly back to the temperate zone for spring breeding?

Curiously, the internal clock is seldom set at exactly 12-hour or 365-day intervals. Instead, the annual rhythm, in an artificially invariant environment, approximates 11 months. An animal's rhythm would therefore become progressively out of phase with the seasons unless it was corrected, and it is corrected in the natural environment by variations in day length and climate.

Human beings also have cycles. Persons partaking in long-term experiments in uniform environments (for example, researchers who spend 6 months in total darkness over the polar winters) find that they have a daily cycle of eating, waking, and hunger that is not clock-dependent. The monthly hormonal cycle is more obvious in females, but males also experience monthly cyclic changes in sex hormone level and moods. Still longer-term annual cycles—in body weight and hormonal level—have recently been identified.

The implications are obvious and fascinating. Long before you acquired a wristwatch, you inherited a clock. The preprogrammed *changes* within us to which we are biologically bound were the first kind of time we ever knew.

ASTRONOMIC TIME

We know that we have internally controlled rhythms, but the question of what time is remains unanswered. The answer *seems* simple. Our concept of times comes from observation of the relative motion between the earth and other stellar bodies. Let us examine the idea further.

Mean Solar Time

The time we ordinarily keep on clocks and watches is called *mean solar time* and is based on the length of one rotation of the earth on its axis. In practice, this time is based on a 24-hour period and is obtained by noting the time on an extremely precise atomic clock at which certain stars cross an imaginary line each night. The results of long observation of these data are astonishing. The stars cross the line at a slightly later *clock* time every year, because the earth's rotational speed around its axis is *slowly diminishing*.

The decrease in the rate of the earth's spin has been known for as long as accurate time could be determined; the length of each day is increasing 0.002 second every 100 years, or about 25 milliseconds in the last 1000 years. Obviously, such changes hardly affect our watches, but they do affect the keeping of precise time and tell us something unexpected about our earth.

Most of the retardation of the earth's spin is believed due to the frictional effect of the ocean tides. Although tides *do* drain the spin, the earth's rate of slowdown is only one-half the rate predicted from tidal friction. More simply, what *else* is causing the earth's speed of rotation to diminish?

The answers to this question may be hidden deep within the earth. Perhaps the mass within our earth is still settling and heading for the core. Or perhaps the universal "pull" of gravity is weakening; the result would be that all material, including the earth, would expand in size (an idea originally presented in Chapter Seven). A decrease in the pull of gravity has been suggested by a recent comparison of two other kinds of time that are discussed next: *ephemeris time* and invariant *atomic time*. Ephemeris time is dependent on gravity, atomic time is not.

Ephemeris Time

Ephemeris time is defined by the orbital motion of the earth about the sun and is determined by correcting mean solar time for variations in the rate of rotation of the earth. Ephemeris time has always been believed to be uniform. *If* the solar system is experiencing a decline in the acceleration of gravity, ephemeris time is also relative and is slowing with respect to *atomic time* as the earth's orbital path around the sun grows longer.

Atomic Time

Accurate timekeeping depends finally on atomic clocks; they measure the continuum of existence with the apparently *invariant frequency* of certain atomic, transition-induced electromagnetic waves. If atomic time marks the time standard, as it does for the United States and the rest of the world, its rate remains constant to within less than a ten-millionth of a second per day. If ephem-

eris time is compared to atomic time, it seems that the universe is slowly winding down as the acceleration of gravity diminishes.

Perhaps we should have expected it. Chemists once thought the elements were fixed; now we know that some spontaneously decay to other elements. Ptolemy thought the planetary scheme was fixed, and Copernicus and Galileo destroyed that scheme. Biologists once thought that species were fixed, unchanging and immutable with time, but we now know that all descendants change with each passing generation. Geologists once believed that the world was a static place, where only sea level rose and fell gently on a constant earth; now we know that plates steadily move.

What Is a Day?

For all of us, the day is a 24-hour period of time during which the earth makes a complete rotation on its axis. As mentioned, our days grow constantly longer as the earth's rate of spin slowly diminishes. Thus the year will eventually have fewer and fewer days. What about the past?

Paleontologists pointed out some time ago that certain animals involuntarily record growth lines that may record days, months, or seasons. Among the potential record keepers are coral and blue-green alga. Counting the daily growth lines within the shell material left behind and comparing those counts to the evidence of seasons left behind, it is evident that many millions of years ago, the earth's spin speed may have been nearly *triple* what it is now.

More than 2 billion years ago, 1 lunar month probably contained 26 days and there were probably 33 months to the year, be-

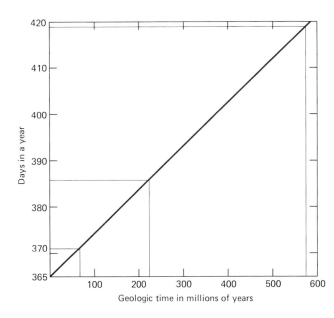

Sixty-five million years ago, there were 371 days in one complete revolution of the earth about the sun; 225 million years ago, 368 days were required; and 570 million years ago, 1 year was 419 days long. (Adapted from John W. Wells, *Nature,* No. 4871, pp. 948–950, 1963.)

cause the year encompassed 800 to 900 days. The day length has grown ever since, as the number of days per year has steadily diminished (Figure 11-1). As a rough approximation, the number of days in a year decreases 5 days every 100 million years, which suggests that about 7½ billion years from now our earth will grind slowly to a *stop*.

Perhaps time *is* the most relative of quantities, precious only when it is limited, measured only when it is needed. Our concern with time leads inevitably to some very human questions. When did it all begin? What is our history?

HISTORICAL TIME

Earliest humans always shrouded the time of the earth's beginning in myth, our oldest defense against the unknown. The earth was presumed to have been created in its present condition. The distinction between historical time and mythical time was vague and blurred. Human curiosity about our place in space and time, our *cosmology,* has been perhaps our oldest philosophical question.

Compared to other forms of life, human beings live an intermediate life span; compared to the range of sizes in the physical universe, we are middle sized. Our concept of space includes atomic-size particles and the awesome immensities of interstellar space; our concept of time includes the fleeting microseconds of some atomic particles and the many thousand of years needed to grow the giant redwoods and the gnarled bristlecone pines—two of the oldest living things on our earth.

The Christian Frame of Reference

The murky haze that enveloped the beginning was, for many people, eliminated with the rise of Christianity. Christ could die for our sins only once; therefore time must have a *beginning and an end*. Time must *flow* from a beginning to an end; the genealogy of Genesis was believed to be a complete and accurate history of the time since Creation. If that were so, the beginning could be revealed by counting backward from Christ to Adam.

By various accountings, Creation occurred a few thousand years before the coming of Christ. Theophilus of Antioch (A.D. 115–183) placed the Creation at 5529 B.C; 1300 years later, Martin Luther (A.D. 1483–1546), giant of the Reformation, called for a date of exactly 4000 B.C. The literal interpretation of the Mosaic chronology reigned supreme; several people even set the day and hour of Creation.

Christians envisioned time and their place in the universe in a totally new way. A human lifetime was now a fair proportion of total time. The whole course of history, in a biblical view that lasted through much of the eighteenth century, comprised six cosmic "days" of a 1000 years each (1 millenium). Four such "days" had elapsed since Creation before the birth of Christ. Another 1700 days passed before the lifetime of eighteenth-century people; only a few hundred years remained until the allotted 6000 years would be completed, to be followed by the second coming of Christ and the Last Judgement. This was to be followed by the promised millenium, completing the seven biblical "days" of the earth's total history (Figure 11-2).

Christian people now had a sense of *direction;* people came *from* somewhere and were *going* somewhere. Time is RECTILINEAR (moves in a straight line).

Our western sense of historical time developed from this Christian sense of history. In a world that has a beginning and an end, there is cause and effect. In a world where there is cause and effect, science is possible, since the basic assumption of all science is that the world is orderly and can be understood. Every effect has a cause, and every cause a potential effect.

Today we cannot conceive of a world that is not historical—where the continuum of existence is *from* a beginning and *toward* a future and time is marked by events that separate eras. Before Christianity people had no such sense of the *direction* of time; there was only the unending present. The past was vague and mystical—a mixture of myth and legend—while the future was only the present, continued.

People in the eighteenth century juggled three fundamental concepts: (1) the earth is a few thousand years old; (2) humans are the center of this young universe and are of supreme importance; and (3) time is unidirectional in a rational world, which can be understood in terms of cause and effect reasoning. The application of the third premise was soon to undo the first two and cause the greatest transformation in the whole history of human thought.

The Eighteenth-Century Challenge

In order to understand the fundamental change that occurred in the human view of time during the eighteenth century, we must first ask how the prevailing concept came about. How did seventeenth-century people form their ideas about the past?

The past is not open to direct inspection, so we must either form conclusions from

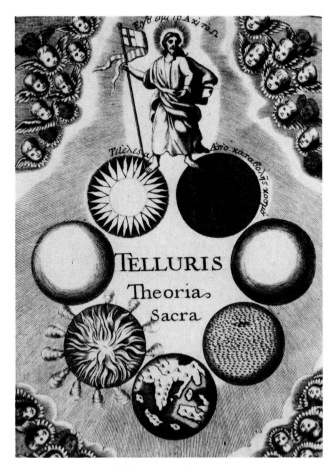

TELLURIS

Theoria

Sacra

11-2
The Christian concept of directional time is depicted by this frontispiece from a popular seventeenth-century text on earth history. Christ's left foot rests on a formless dark earth that, clockwise, takes form and light and is then flooded (notice the ark). The modern earth, at the bottom, is followed by the promised conflagration, the New Earth, and the Consummation, respectively. (From Thomas Burnet, 1680, (1702 ed.), courtesy of the History of Science Collections, University of Oklahoma Libraries.)

available data or depend on the testimony of others.

The prevailing seventeenth-century view had to be based on the testimony of others, because little data about the earth were available from which to reason. The only testimony available was biblical; its Mosaic chronologies were a generally accepted account of a recently created, static world. Seventeenth-century people, from the humblest peasant to the most distinguished scientist, accepted biblical testimony as the

only source of truth. The role of science was simply to *discover* the laws of nature long ago ordained by the Creator.

The eighteenth-century search for *cause* led inevitably away from an earth created fully formed in an instant of time. Georges Louis Leclerc, Comte de Buffon (1707–1788) first attempted to determine the earth's age by estimating the rate of cooling of a molten earth; his was the first of many such estimates. It placed the earth's creation 75,000 years in the past; the age of the *earth* had been freed from its Mosaic bondage to the *age of humans*.

The second third of a revolution had occurred. Copernicus and then Galileo had displaced the earth from the center of a vastly enlarged universe in the sixteenth and seventeenth centuries. Our earth was no longer *unique*. Now the Comte de Buffon and the many followers of his theory argued that the earth was ancient and that humanity was a latecomer. Humans were merely newcomers to an earth that had gotten along quite well for most of its long history without them.

The self-image of human beings absorbed a *third* revolution in the nineteenth century, when Darwin declared that we were hardly unique among other animals, since we were descended from more primitive animals only within a recent, brief instant of time.

Thus, prior to the twentieth century, our ancestors underwent one assault after another on their own image of humanity's place in time and space. Perhaps the greatest shock for twentieth-century people was the stunning views of the earth from space; we have been forced to realize how alone and yet interdependent humans are.

It was not an appeal to the physics of a cooling earth that finally transformed our human perception of time; instead, it was the study of life. Robert Hooke (1637–1703), English chemist and physicist, had recognized that fossils suggested that the earth had changed many times in its history, sea becoming mountain, and mountain becoming sea. Fossils were described as "monuments of nature . . . more certain tokens of antiquity than coins or medals, and though difficult, it would not be impossible to raise a chronology out of them."

The recognition, based on the occurrence

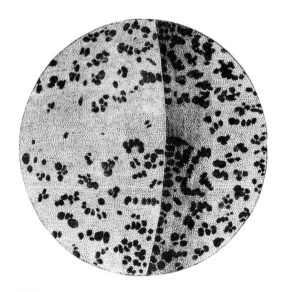

11-3
In 1665 Robert Hooke used a NEW instrument—the microscope—to compare charcoal to petrified wood and thereby prove the organic origin of petrified wood—an issue that was much in doubt at the time. (From Robert Hooke, 1665, *Micrographia*, Plate X, Fig. 1, courtesy of the History of Science Collections, University of Oklahoma Libraries.)

of marine fossils on mountains and fossils of sun-loving plants (Figure 11-3) entombed in deep coal mines, that the earth had changed radically seemed to require time for the changes in elevation of sea and swamp to take place. Time was required not only to allow the earth's surface to move up and down but also to allow a *succession* of living forms to occur. In 1802 French naturalist Jean-Baptiste Lamarck (1744–1829) berated those people who still believed that the earth's history was encompassed by Mosaic chronology.

I am completely convinced that skeleton-secreting [animals] . . . are mainly responsible for the enormously plentiful calcareous material forming the earth's abundant underground layers . . . of limestone. Like the fossil marine shells, these deposits represent indisputable proof that the sea was formerly present in their areas. . . . Has not the sea, which is there today, been in that place more than once?

Oh, how very ancient the earth is! And how ridiculously small the ideas of those who consider the earth's age to be 6,000 odd years!

Lamarck's closing remarks do not conceal his contempt for reasoning from biblical testimony, literally interpreted. He had chosen another path to truth—reasoning from the earth itself.

The history of the last 400 years of science reveals a fundamental change in our attempt to gain knowledge. For 2000 years after Archimedes, *humans learned from authority,* and the advancement of knowledge stood nearly still, embraced by the authority of ancient Greek philosophers and the Church.

In the seventeenth century, Galileo thrust a telescope into the sky; what he learned from the heavens invalidated the theories of Ptolemy (who held that the earth was at the center of the universe) *and* the authority of the Church.

In the eighteenth century, inquisitive people began to examine the earth, and what they learned from the earth nullified the theories of Mosaic chronology. The human view of the earth's place in space and of the earth's antiquity had been transformed; biblical authority was dethroned, and human testimony also was pushed aside. The earth was permitted to speak for itself, and it declared an antiquity unimaginable by human beings who were bound by the human concept of time.

Lamarck envisioned an earth of vast antiquity, an antiquity that was *essential* to his whole system of gradual biologic and geologic change.

The great age of the earth will appear greater to man when he understands the origin of living organisms and the reasons for the gradual development and improvement of their organization. This antiquity will appear even greater when he realizes the length of time and the particular conditions which were necessary to bring all the living species into existence. This is particularly true since man is the latest result and present *climax* of this development, the ultimate limit of which . . . cannot be known.

Lamarck recognized the limitations of people when he later (1805) mournfully suggested: "[man] judges the magnitude of time only in relation to himself and not to nature, [and] will undoubtedly never accept the slow mutations which I have just presented. . . ." Lamarck's "slow mutations," so bitterly contested by Cuvier, were the beginnings of Darwin's theory of "evolution by natural selection," 50 years later.

By the eighteenth century, scientists had learned that historical time was not suitable for describing the earth, but what kind of time *could* describe such an ancient earth?

GEOLOGIC TIME

Geologic time encompasses all time since the formation of a solid earth, a period of time spanning 46 million centuries (4.6 billion years). Within that incomprehensible span of time, the story of the earth can be told in *two complementary arrangements*.

Historically, the oldest scheme involves recounting the *sequence* of events—Adam came before Eve, and so forth. Within the last 50 years, another procedure that involves the *when* of events has become possible. According to one scheme of biblical chronology inserted in the authorized version of the Bible for many years, Adam was created on October 23, 4004 B.C., at 9:00 A.M..

Sequential Time

The concept of placing events in chronologic order is one of our oldest skills. Young children find a dependable sequence or routine an absolutely indispensable part of their security. Sequential time, also called *relative time,* remains an important part of our various functional concepts throughout life. Applied to sedimentary rocks, sequential tim-

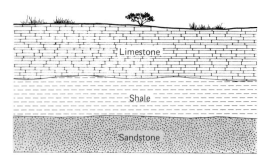

11-4
The principle of *superposition* requires that the sandstone layer was deposited before the shale layer, which was deposited before the limestone layer.

ing depends on three simple ideas (also discussed in Chapter Five), three more ideas about igneous and metamorphic rocks, and one more sophisticated concept that deals with fossils.

Even the simple ideas are only simple in retrospect; at the time they were discovered they seemed revolutionary. Several of these ideas were formulated by Nicolaus Steno (see Chapter Two). The **principle of superposition** states that *in a sequence of flat-lying layered rocks* (Figure 11-4), *the oldest layer is on the bottom, with successively younger layers above.* The basic, underlying assumption is that the rocks formed by the accumulation of sediment, and the sediment must have accumulated *on* something older that is beneath the sediment.

Two corollaries, both described by Steno, developed from the principle of superposition. The **principle of original horizontality** states that in a series of rocks formed and layered by the accumulation of sediment, *the original layers must form a horizontal or subhorizontal unit.* Therefore, if we find large areas of steeply tilted sedimentary rock (Figure 11-5), the rock must have first formed and consolidated and later tilted. Unless the tilting goes beyond vertical, the principle of superposition will still apply. The second corollary is the **principle of original continuity.** Since the layered sedimentary rock is *at the time of the deposition of the layer a continuous sheet in all directions* (Figure 11-6), *the layers now exposed on two sides of a canyon wall must, prior to the erosion of the canyon, have been continuous.*

Working with igneous rocks, other sequential principles apply, including the **principle of crosscutting relation** and the **principle of inclusion.** The principle of crosscutting relation suggests (Figure 11-7)

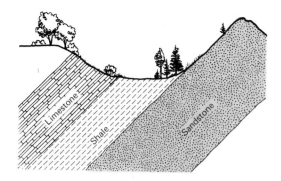

11-5
The principle of *original horizontality* requires that these three layers were deposited as horizontal sheets of sand, mud, and lime particles and then consolidated before tilting. Compare with Figure 11-4. Does the principle of superposition still apply? Is this a humid or arid region? (The answers are at the end of the chapter.)

that an igneous rock is *younger* than any other unit it *affects*. As in Figure 11-7, the igneous material is younger than the surrounding rock it cuts across and bakes.

The principle of inclusion states that a *rock fragment is always older than another rock that includes or surrounds it*. As in Figure 11-7, the fragment of foreign rock in the igneous intrusive is older than the intrusion of magma, because it was undoubtedly a fragment torn away from the side of an opening formed as the magma moved upward. Such fragments of foreign rock, called **xenoliths,** yield their relative age and also give information about what lies beneath an area of igneous activity. They are gratuitous samples; some violent forms of igneous eruption may bring up xenoliths from as far down as the earth's upper mantle.

The **principle of metamorphism** states that the *metamorphism of any rock came later*

than the formation of the original rock. Thus, in Figure 11-7, the baking of the rocks adjacent to the dike must have occurred after the formation of the original sedimentary layers and at the same time as the intrusion of the dike. A metamorphic rock always records a minimum of a two-part history: formation of the parent rock followed by metamorphism.

Each of the six principles just described allows us to infer the sequence of events in any one area, but how do we decipher the relative age of rocks over much larger areas? Nineteenth-century geologists thought that all rocks of the same general appearance were of the same approximate age. Using that premise, igneous and metamorphic rocks were thought to be "older looking," consolidated sedimentary rocks were thought to be "younger looking," and unconsolidated sediment was obviously "youngest looking of all."

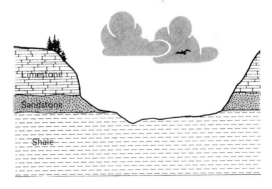

11-6
The principle of *original continuity* would argue that the sandstone layers on each side of the canyon wall were a continuous layer at one time. What is the total sequence of events in this area? (The answers are at the end of the chapter.)

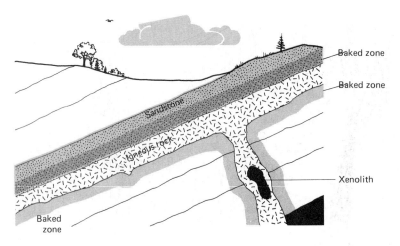

11-7

In this cross section, a fragment of the lowest rock layer is caught up in the magma (now igneous rock), which baked all rocks with which it came in contact. Is the igneous unit a dike, sill, or lava flow? What is the oldest event depicted in this scene? What is the youngest? (The answers are at the end of the chapter.)

During the time when the earth was thought to be only a few thousand years old, classification of rocks by their relative age—based on the assumption that all rocks of a similar type were of a similar age—proceeded quickly. Igneous and metamorphic rocks were called *primitive,* or *primary,* and were assumed to have formed at the Creation. Consolidated, hard, sedimentary rock, usually containing fossils and found on the flanks of high mountains, were called *secondary,* since they formed during the flood endured by Noah and his ark. *Tertiary* (meaning third) rocks included all unconsolidated sedimentary rock lying on top of secondary rocks. Some geologists later added a fourth (*quaternary*) group of rocks; it included volcanic rocks that clearly intruded through tertiary rocks and poorly consolidated sedimentary rocks that contained fossils identical to modern life.

In a world confined within a few thousand years, the assumption that similarity in appearance meant similarity in age might have made good sense; in a brief time span, events happened only once. By the end of the eighteenth century, the three- or fourfold subdivision of rocks based on appearance was widely used; the rocks of the world were neatly tucked into a 4000- or 5000-year history of a static world. The stage was set for revolution.

Sequential Time and Fossils

We know today that similarity of appearance indicates similarity of conditions during rock formation and that similar conditions have occurred *repeatedly* throughout geologic time. Therefore similarity in appearance does not necessarily suggest similarity in time of formation of rocks found in widely separated areas.

The key ingredients that were missing from eighteenth-century minds were the concepts of limitless time and of repetition of environments through time which gave rise to rocks of similar appearance at dissimilar times. How *could* rocks from distant areas be established as time equivalent? The answer lay in the fossils they contained.

From the time of the Greeks, there was speculation on the origin of of fossils. People as diverse as Aristotle, Leonardo da Vinci, and Nicolaus Steno had deduced that fossils were evidence of the life of former times. Steno had recognized in 1667 that certain peculiar fossils—called "tongue stones" at the time—were nothing more than fossil shark's teeth, much like the teeth of modern sharks (Figure 11-8).

The use of fossils in establishing that rocks of unlike appearance in distant areas were age equivalent, rests on a sophisticated idea that must be credited to an English builder of canals, William Smith (see Figure 5-11). During the first decade of the nineteenth century, as he cut canals through the layered, sedimentary rocks of Britain, Smith noted that the rocks often contained fossils. He kept a careful record of what kind of fossils were in each layer and, as he crisscrossed back and forth across Britain, he noted that each layer contained an assemblage of fossils that were unique to it. It therefore became possible, through careful study of fossil assemblages, to **correlate,** or *establish time equivalency between,* rocks of dissimilar appearance that are now widely separated geographically.

A powerful concept for unraveling geologic history had been created. The idea is called the **principle of faunal assemblages** (see Chapter Five); its basic, inherent as-

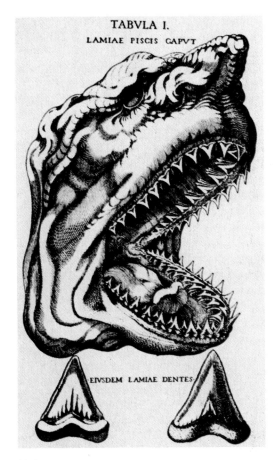

11-8
Steno, who had a lifelong interest in anatomy, dissected the head of a *modern* shark and showed that its teeth were identical to "tongue stones," whose occurrence as common fossils had led others to believe that they had somehow *formed* in the rock. (From N. Steno, 1667, *Elementorum Myologiae,* courtesy of the History of Science Collections, University of Oklahoma Libraries.)

sumption is that fossils differ through time, so that *any one assemblage of fossils can only occur during a short interval of time.*

Imagine for a moment that a volcanic

eruption such as the one that buried Pompeii buried your geology classroom while class was in session. Centuries later, if your school records survived, an investigator could closely determine the time of eruption, because you and your fellow classmates were only together in that room at one particular time during one particular quarter or semester. You and your classmates would have become a fossil assemblage— *a group of individuals unique to a specific time*.

Somewhat later, the recognition dawned that the fossil assemblage in an area is *not only dependent on time, but also on environment*. Fossils from rocks of the same age formed partly in the desert and partly in the offshore sea would look nothing alike—even though the desert-formed rocks and the marine rocks were consolidated, with fossils in them, at the same time. Even today, nearly 200 years after William Smith, establishing time equivalency between fossils in rocks formed in different environments may be a formidable job for *stratigraphers* (geologists who specialize in the study of stratified, sedimentary rock).

No one in Smith's time (about 1802) understood *why* the fossil assemblages changed vertically in sequences of layered rock. Smith's great contribution had been the recognition that the succession of *faunal* assemblages matched the vertical succession of *rock* sequences—an observation now so universal that it is sometimes called the PRINCIPLE OF FAUNAL SUCCESSION. It was difficult enough to accept that fossils changed through time; remember how the citizens of Paris were staggered when Cuvier announced that giant elephants had once roamed the Paris area (see Chapter Five) in relatively recent time.

The fact of fossil change through time was established by Smith and was independently established at almost the same time by Brogniart and Cuvier in France. Cuvier, a devout Huguenot (Protestant), could not reconcile the changes with time that he had so meticulously documented with the prevailing view of instantaneous creation 4000 years before of earth, life, and people. He shrank from the visions of an ancient and changing earth that the fossil record seemed to suggest and called instead for multiple catastrophes to destroy all life many times, with slightly different forms of life re-created after each deluge.

His rival, Jean-Baptiste Lamarck, saw things quite differently. Like Cuvier, Lamarck was impressed by the fact of fossil *evolution* through time. Unlike Cuvier, he believed that changing life forms through time required time (vast amounts of time) and that change in species was accomplished through slow mutations. Lamarck, like Cuvier, saw water as an important agent of geologic change, but he saw no reason to limit its action to a single, or several, Noachian floods. Biblical history, Lamarck argued, was no guide to earth history. The earth's rocks and fossils were their *own* historian and were a reliable record of changes going back an unforseeable distance into time. There was no doubt that there was a beginning; it is doubtful that records of it still remained on a restless earth.

The fossil record clearly described vertical change, or change in life through developing time. The *fact* of change was not doubted, but the *how* and the *why* of change remained a controversy, pending the efforts of Charles Lyell and Charles Darwin.

Lyell and Darwin

Sir Charles Lyell (1797–1875) was one of a group of British geologists who were to establish the foundations of modern geology.

Lyell (Figure 11-9), after extensive field studies in Italy and France, had recognized the fact of gradual change in life; he had also emphasized a striking corollary to an older concept called *actualism*—physical and chemical laws are constant through time. The forces acting on the earth were believed to be constant in time, in type, and in intensity through vast amounts of time.

Lyell's concept (originally proposed by James Hutton) called *uniformitarianism* by one of its many critics, demanded a world of steady change. It was change that went back to another part of the cycle, to the world of Greek Stoic philosphers, which was a world in perpetual motion and change that was going nowhere.

The concept of uniformitarianism was Lyell's reply to biblical literalism. Those who believed that the Bible provided a complete history of the earth came under increasing attack as evidence accumulated that organic change demanded more and more time.

Lyell was not antireligious, as this thought that summed up his life and was placed on his grave marker in Westminster Abbey showed: "O Lord, how great are thy works and thy thoughts are very deep." Instead he saw, correctly, that a science bound by Mosaic chronology was not a science at all.

Science can only deal with ideas that, potentially, can be disproven. Science can neither prove nor disprove topics such as miracles, the existence of a soul, or the existence of God. Science must also treat any concept as proven only until it is challenged by new information. *Nothing* is absolute truth; ideas that have stood many tests may someday fail a new test and be eventually discarded.

Scientific progress comes only from challenging current conceptions. Recall the fate of Jeffreys' theory of a static earth (see

11-9

Charles Lyell, exponent of the uniformitarian approach to geologic processes. (Courtesy of the History of Science Collections, University of Oklahoma Libraries.)

Chapter Seven) as the discovery of continental drift and radioactivity destroyed one of the most widely held "truths" in the scientific community. *That human beings and the earth were created at the same time is a testable hypothesis,* and Lyell and many others saw that Mosaic chronology failed the test.

Perhaps Lyell's greatest contribution, other than eventually disposing of the paralyzing influence of attempts to conform geology to scripture, was his dogmatic insistence that both inorganic and organic change was gradual and demanded great amounts of time. Furthermore, Lyell insisted that the changes went nowhere; that is, life came from nowhere and was going nowhere. The world was, quite simply, in a steady state. Lyell denied the validity of any evidence for a directionally changing earth and a progressively changing life.

Curiously, for a man who fought biblical literalists with great tenacity, Lyell came to these steady-state views partially because he thought they demonstrated the wisdom of the Creator. Lyell's views placed him in direct conflict with many of his contemporaries, who argued that the earth and its life not only changed, but progressed—*that time had direction.* Among those most affected by Lyell was a young English biologist, Charles Darwin.

Charles Darwin (1809–1882) (Figure 11-10) had been given a copy of Lyell's new geology text shortly before he left for a research voyage on the *H.M.S. Beagle* in 1830. Although warned by his professor to read it but not believe it, Darwin found Lyell's ideas immensely suggestive. Darwin had learned some geology as a student of Adam Sedgwick, an English geologist, and he was easily persuaded by Lyell's concept of uniformity. Lyell's insistence on uniformity of process meant, fundamentally, that the earth had a history that could be interpreted without appeals for divine intervention. On the other hand, Darwin recognized, as did many others, that Lyell's uniformity did not explain a basic paleontological question. *Why* did new *species* (organisms capable of interbreeding) of plants and animals appear throughout geologic time?

When Darwin reached Chile, he found ancient beaches now many yards (meters) above the sea level; their surfaces were littered with fossil shells. Darwin interpreted what he saw in uniformitarian principles; the beaches had gradually risen above the sea level in gradual steps. While still in Chile,

11-10
Charles Darwin, exponent of the evolutionary approach to the origin of species. (Courtesy of the History of Science Collections, University of Oklahoma Libraries.)

his ideas were forcibly vindicated by a disastrous earthquake that raised the coastline once again. Darwin followed Lyell in an actualistic interpretation of the physical world; the past could be understood in terms of present-day processes still at work.

Ironically, Lyell's insistence on gradual changes in life undid his insistence that life did not *progress* in any direction. Paleontologists around the world steadily found more and more evidence that the fossil record was a reasonably complete history of life, and that life *did* progress from one group of forms to a higher group of form in general. But how?

Darwin finally had his now famous answer. Since we will refer to *evolution* as the *unifying principle in biology* in many of the following chapters, an extremely brief review of the fundamental concepts in Darwin's theory is now presented.

Darwin's theory of evolution consists of two parts: (1) the concept of EVOLUTIONARY CHANGE and (2) the concept of NATURAL SELECTION.

The concept of evolutionary change is not a difficult one for twentieth-century people to understand, because we recognize that change is the norm for the earth and its life. Darwin, however, lived in a time when the idea of a *recently* formed and essentially *static* earth was dominant. He pointed out *three* major kinds of evidence to demonstrate that animals and plants changed or evolved through time.

First, Darwin noted the changes produced in domestic animals and plants by careful breeding programs. For example, the ancestor of modern corn had ears of hard, bitter seeds and were about 1 inch (2½ centimeters) long. How could anyone doubt that organisms changed through time, when the evidence of deliberate change in historical time was everywhere?

Second, Darwin indicated the major resemblances between living species; the basic bone structure of a human arm, a dog's front leg, and a seal flipper are the same and, indeed, the same bones are present in a bird's wing. In the same way, many species possess nonfunctional structures (like the gills and tails that human embryos have). The simplest explanation for these observations is that many species have descended from a common ancestor and have inherited, with unique modifications, similar structures that perform different functions and some structures that no longer have *any* function.

Third, Darwin cited the evidence from fossils; these preserved remnants of past life provide convincing evidence that the history of life has been a history of change and that the changes were the result of accumulations of smaller alterations in life as generation followed generation. But if the fossil story, similar and nonfunctional structures, and domestic breeding programs all support the reality of the change of life forms through time, what *caused* the changes?

In 1838 Darwin happened to read a book by Thomas Malthus that suggested an answer. Malthus had indicated that populations of humans will grow much more rapidly than their food supply and that famine was eventually inevitable. Darwin also knew that all animals and plants exhibit an enormous *reproductive potential;* a single pine tree may produce millions of seeds during its lifetime, but only a few will grow and survive.

Once Darwin recognized that most offspring die before they can reproduce in the natural world, he had the evidence needed to explain *natural selection.* Survival to reproductive age is *not* a random process. Individuals with a *variation* that gives them a slightly better chance to escape predators or obtain adequate nutrition or to cope generally with their environment stand a better chance of surviving and reproducing. If their slightly altered characteristics are inheritable, these characteristics will become more common in future generations, while less desirable characteristics will be weeded out. In time, inherited characteristics have an unequal chance of surviving, since only the characteristics that give one an advantage are liable to be passed along. Once born, the *individual* does not evolve; the change through time is in the *characteristics* of the *population* that lives to reproductive age.

In summary, evolution depends on five fundamental assumptions and observations.

1. Many more individuals are born than will survive.
2. All individuals are not identical; there *is* variation.
3. Individuals whose characteristics give them a slightly better chance of surviving have a better chance of growing old enough to reproduce.
4. Some of the characteristics that provide an advantage are inheritable.
5. The enormous span of geologic time allows mechanisms of change to produce new species through time, since natural selection operates on populations that are undergoing evolutionary change.

Darwin's impact on geology and paleontology leads directly into two formidable lines of evidence that seemed—late in his life—to doom his evolutionary theories. Darwin was well aware that paleontology could provide the only real substantive evidence that life *had* produced new species in time and, furthermore, that evolution at a higher than species level had provided the great diversity of life, both past and present.

Briefly, the fossil record did *not* provide much evidence of gradual change. It suggested that many changes were *abrupt,* and the evidence for the *gradual* evolution of Darwin was conspicuously absent.

Faced with the lack of such evidence, Darwin could only suggest that the fossil record was *extremely* fragmentary and characterized by substantial breaks in time during which the gradual changes must have occurred. That such changes were always conveniently hidden in missing rock intervals was unacceptable to many scientists of Darwin's day; the problem of the inevitable

"missing link" continues to confound some paleontologists and physical anthropologists today.

In the history of paleontology, many missing links were eventually discovered, particularly in areas where continuous deposition and abundant fossil remains allow the variation between species to be carefully studied. Among the most carefully worked out examples is the evolution of the horse (Figure 11-11), whose abundant, well-preserved fossil remains in North America enabled its evolution to be worked out in detail.

The discovery of *Archaeopteryx,* a reptilelike bird, and *Compsognathus,* a birdlike reptile (see Chapter 14), seemed to demonstrate that even very unlike animals could have common ancestors. Once it was conceded that animals as different as birds and reptiles had a common ancestor, the evidence from embryology, comparative anatomy, and biogeography fitted nicely into an evolutionary framework.

The search for fossil evidence for evolution had been eventually successful at both the specific and intermediate levels, but the largest subdivisions—the *phyla* of life remained discouragingly immune to an evolutionary approach. How could the enormous variations among the phyla be explained? And could the fact be explained that in very old fossiliferous rocks (Chapter 13), many animals already were surprisingly complex? Among the older animals known are extinct types of arthropods known as *trilobites,* which are extraordinarily complex animals that are distant cousins of the modern crab. How could the presence of complex, vertebrate fish in relatively old rocks be explained? If life progressed, what were these complex forms (Chapter 13) doing in such old rocks, and where had they come from if evolution was operative?

For Darwin, Lyell, and many others the

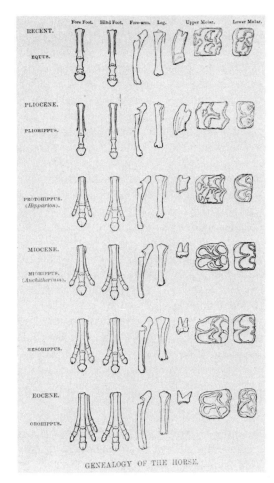

11-11

This graph shows the evolution of the feet, legs, and teeth of the horse for the last 60 million years. This original presentation of the evidence is now known to be far too simple, but it still illustrates the kinds of evidence pointing to evolutionary development within a group. (From O. C. Marsh, 1871, courtesy of the History of Science Collections, University of Oklahoma Libraries.)

answer was to suggest that the record of differentiation of organisms into discrete phyla had occurred when the *most* ancient rocks (Chapter 12) were being formed, and that

these ancient rocks had long ago been metamorphosed, or melted, into a modern, unfossiliferous state. This was once again the appeal to negative evidence; the events occured but, fortuitously, the evidence was gone. We now know, from fragmentary evidence, that much of the evolution proposed by Darwin *did* occur before animals developed skeletons and, therefore, were preserved (Chapter 12).

Near the end of the nineteenth century, the answers to the problems of missing links, variation among phyla, and the sudden appearance of complex life in early earth history seemed to be reasonably well worked out. Missing links within and between species were only missing if the appropriate rock unit had yet to be found. Variation among phyla had occurred early in earth history; the record of that variation had been destroyed due to melting and metamorphism of these ancient rocks or not preserved in animals without skeletons. The sudden appearance of complex life was similarly explained; in the vast stretches of time that preceded the formation of fossiliferous rocks, evolution in some phyla had proceeded toward a great complexity, but the evidence of *that* evolution had also been destroyed by the melting and metamorphism that pervaded the ancient rocks or by lack of preservation of soft-bodied organisms. The answer to all questions was time—limitless time—in which all the necessary events could occur.

Enter Lord Kelvin

The assumption of vast amounts of time had come under severe attack by the English physicist William Thomson (1824–1907), better known as Lord Kelvin (Figure 11-12). Using the best available physical data on the

11-12
William Thompson (Lord Kelvin) as he appeared in 1897. (Courtesy of the History of Science Collections, University of Oklahoma Libraries.)

rate of temperature increase from the outer crust into the earth, and *assuming that the earth had cooled from an original molten state,* Kelvin suggested the earth's crust became solid sometime between 20 and 400 million years ago. Considering the cooling necessary for a recently solidified crust to become habitable by life, life might first have colonized the earth 100 million years ago—but *no more.*

Kelvin's arguments, clothed in mathematical rigor from the most fundamental of all the sciences, had the same devastating effect as Jeffreys' assault on the theory of continental drift (see Chapter Seven). The effect was withering: Lyell's steady-state earth of cycle after cycle—a perpetual motion machine—was crushed. Darwin's argument for a vastly old earth in which gradual selection under population pressure could produce all known forms of life was quashed.

The concept of evolution was shelved until the discovery of radioactivity several decades later. Darwin came to doubt his own theory more and more. Within a now-restricted time scale, agreed on by almost all geologists, time was simply unavailable for the processes of gradual change described by Lyell and Darwin.

Geologic time, freed from the constraints of literal biblical interpretation, had become unlimited; the concepts of uniform change first suggested by Hutton now embraced the concept of the origin and evolution of life. Kelvin single-handedly destroyed, for a time, uniformitarian and evolutionary thought. Geologic time was still restricted because the laws of physics bound as tightly as biblical literalism ever had.

The earth's existence was again brief and finite. The earth, once molten, was cooling down; its past was brief and its future as a life support system briefer. The earth, shorn of antiquity, uniformity, and evolution, was simply running down. The immutable laws of physics had again prevailed.

Chronologic Time—Early Attempts

In retrospect, Kelvin did geologic inquiry a favor, even though he shattered its intellectual foundations in the late nineteenth century. He had forced geologists to ask a vital question. How old *is* the earth?

To Hutton, Lyell, and Darwin, the earth was incomprehensibly old, and a moment's reflection suggested that gradual, modern processes could shape any coastline, modify any animal, and cut any valley. With Kelvin's theory, the age of catastrophism and biblical imprisonment were dead, but the idea of a world without beginning or end had also died. What could replace it?

The new world would have to be built on the concept of chronological time, so the age of the earth and the age of its rock units would have to be known. *But how is chronologic or absolute time measured?*

Today we measure conventional time with some type of clock; its *rate* of advance is held constant by various mechanical and electrical means. For even more accurate time, we measure time as the *rate* of the earth's rotation on its axis or as the *rate* of the earth's orbital motion around the sun. If we require still more accurate chronologic time, we measure the frequency (*rate*) of certain electromagnetic waves produced by atoms; these atomic clocks are capable of accuracies of greater than one-ten millionth of a second per day.

Chronologic time always depends on some process happening at a dependable RATE, so it is a statement of the *length of an interval since an event;* the *extent* of the interval is measured by any device of *constant rate*. The statement that "this is 1980" therefore implies that it has been 1980 years since a singular event in the world's history. The interval chosen is the *year*, the period of time required for the earth to make a complete revolution around the sun. Thus, since the birth of Christ, the earth has made 1980 revolutions around the sun.

As we will soon see, an interval that seems as absolute to us as a year becomes a unit of relative time when it is measured by other series of intervals—hours and days. Currently, the year consists of approximately 365 days, 5 hours, 49 minutes, and 12 seconds, but this was not always so. Several billion years ago, the earth's year probably contained 800 to 900 days, as previously discussed.

A natural process is required to allow us to assign chronologic ages to the rocks of the earth; its *rate of change is absolutely unchanging throughout any length of time, is unaffected by changes in the environment and can be accurately measured, and its beginning coincides with the event whose age we wish to measure.* These seem to be an impossible list of requirements for any natural process. The search for a suitable process failed many times; a review of one these failures follows.

Since Kelvin had estimated the age of the solid earth at around 100 million years, let us probe the assumptions that lay behind his historic estimate. The *first assumption* was that the earth started life as a molten body; this was a common assumption of Victorian science. It seemed to be correct, because the oldest rocks were mostly igneous and metamorphic. The *second assumption* was that the only energy source available to the sun and earth was gravitational energy that was acquired as they formed and that *dissipated* ever since in various physical processes.

Kelvin was the codiscoverer of *the second law of thermodynamics,* which states that the total amount of energy available in the universe remains constant, but that every energy conversion occurs with the loss of waste heat, which cannot be recovered. Therefore every physical process wastes a small part of the available finite energy resource, and *the universe is running down.*

The *third assumption* stated that the *rate* of heat dissipation from both the sun and the earth was *constant;* working backward, it should have been possible to determine the time necessary for the primitive, molten earth to cool to its solid, modern state. Kelvin made the calculations and presumed the matter closed.

Notice that three assumptions, all of which *could* be tested, lay behind Kelvin's age of the earth estimate and the mathematical derivations of the estimate. With the superb vision characteristic of hindsight, we would state that Kelvin's first assumption could be challenged and his second assumption is absolutely erroneous for both the earth and the sun, thereby invalidating the third assumption completely. We will soon see why Kelvin's calculations were merely good deductions based on fallacious assumptions.

There were many other schemes for estimating the probable age of the earth, but they all foundered on one inescapable fact; through the earliest part of the twentieth century, no one knew of any processes whose *rate* was assuredly *constant* throughout *all* time and *all* conditions. Thus, when such a process was discovered, Kelvin's model of an earth that was running down was completely destroyed.

Radioactivity—The Modern Answer

In 1895, a German physicist (Roëntgen) working with electricity in a vacuum tube discovered that mysterious rays (called X rays) from the tube were capable of exposing photographic film *through* lightproof paper. A year later, a French physicist discovered that a metal called uranium affected photo-graphic film just as the newly discovered X rays did. Two years later, another French chemist, Marie Curie, isolated the element radium from a uranium mineral. The radiation from radium was very intense, and the spontaneous emission of rays was called **radioactivity.**

Four years later, a British physicist (Lord Rutherford) showed that the rays from radium and other radioactive materials consist of three kinds of rays: the alpha ray, the beta ray, and the gamma ray. The gamma (γ) ray is an uncharged particle, identical to the X ray, and passes readily through most material. The alpha (α) ray passes through only a few inches (centimeters) of air and consists of small, composite particles charged with positive electricity; they are indistinguishable from the nucleus of a helium atom. The beta (β) rays are **electrons,** negatively charged atomic particles that, inside an atom, can be thought of as revolving around the atomic nucleus like planets about the sun; however, this is an enormous oversimplification of the actual situation (see Appendix B). Beta rays are charged, small, atomic particles; their range of penetration is much greater than that of the alpha particles.

No radioactive element, such as radium, which emits particles of itself, can remain the same; it must be *changed into* something else as the parent substance strews the surrounding air with atomic particles. This capsulizes the discovery that atoms of one chemical element may be formed by the decomposition of another element. The process of change from one parent element to another is called **radioactive decay,** a process that releases large amounts of *heat.* Radium itself is a product of decay, since it formed from the decomposition of uranium. As radium continues its own decay, emitting gamma rays, helium nucleii, electrons, and X rays, it changes through a series of inter-

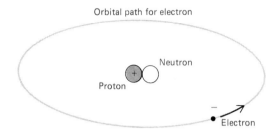

Orbital path for electron

Neutron

Proton

+

−

Electron

11-13
Schematic sketch of a deuterium atom, whose nucelus consists of an uncharged neutron (open circle) and a proton (colored circle). The nucleus is orbited by a single electron that has a negative charge. Deuterium is an isotope of hydrogen and has an atomic weight of two; the atomic number is one.

mediate elements until, finally, a stable end product is formed. The end product is a form of lead.

To analyze what has occurred, we must know more about the nature of the atom. Atoms of all elements consist of a *nucleus* that contains almost all of the mass of the atom; the nucleus contains both positively charged **protons** and **neutrons,** which are particles of electrical neutrality. Surrounding the nucleus is a cloud of orbiting, negatively charged electrons; the number of electrons equals the number of protons. The **atomic number** of an atom specifies *the number of protons and electrons in the atom.* The **atomic weight** (*mass*) of an atom is the *average* weight of one atom of the element, usually expressed as a weight relative to one atom of carbon, which has a standard weight of 12.

All atoms of the same element have the same atomic number; THE NUMBER OF PROTONS OR ELECTRONS IS WHAT SEPARATES THE ELEMENTS FROM ONE ANOTHER. The atomic number of potassium is

19, and that of calcium is 20. Potassium has one less proton in its nucleus and one less electron surrounding its nucleus than calcium does.

Within a single element, the number of neutrons in its nucleus may vary; this fact was recognized early in the twentieth century when precisely determined atomic weights turned out to be nonintegral numbers; the atomic weight of hydrogen is 1.00797, for example (it would be 1.0000 if all atoms had only one proton and no neutrons).

In an ordinary hydrogen atom, a single proton forms the nucleus, which is orbited by a single electron. Add a neutron (Figure 11-13) to the nucleus, and the atomic weight increases to two, while the atomic number *remains at one.* The new form of "heavy" hydrogen, called *deuterium,* is an **isotope—** a *neutron-number variety of a given proton number.* Add still another neutron and another hydrogen isotope, called *tritium,* forms; it has an atomic weight of three, and the atomic number remains at one. Hydrogen gas consists of ordinary hydrogen, written H^1, and extremely small amounts of hydrogen's heavier isotopes, written H^2 and H^3. Averaging together the large amounts of ordinary hydrogen and the tiny amounts of its heavier isotopes that are normally present yields an atomic weight of 1.00797—the average weight of the combined three isotopes of hydrogen.

The atomic weight of one isotope of uranium is 238, written U^{238}. The atomic weight of helium is 4, written He^4. During the complete process of radioactive decay of uranium through intermediate steps to lead, eight nucleii of helium are emitted. The lead formed from the disintegration of uranium has the atomic weight 206, written Pb^{206}. The following mathematics explain why. $U^{238} - (8 \times 4) = Pb^{206}$. U^{238} thus changes

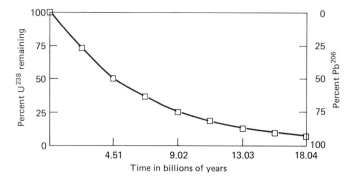

Decay curve for U^{238}–Pb^{206}. All decay curves follow this general form. In EACH successive half-life period, the number of atoms of the parent (in this case U^{238}) element present at the beginning of that half-life period is halved.

into Pb^{206} in eight steps; each step involves the loss of four units of atomic weight (the helium particle): $238 - 32 = 206$.

Ordinary lead consists of four isotopes (Pb^{204}, Pb^{206}, Pb^{207}, Pb^{208}) and has an atomic weight of 207.19. Three of the isotopes of lead are formed from radioactive decay; Pb^{204} is not. Pb^{206} can *only* form from the decay of U^{238}, Pb^{207} from U^{235}, and Pb^{206} from Th(orium)^{232}.

The time required for the original number of atoms of a radioactive parent to be reduced by one-half is called the **half-life.** The half-life of U^{238} is 4.51 billion years; one-half of the atoms of U^{238} will have changed to Pb^{206} after one half-life (4.51 billion years) has passed. The end of one half-life is the beginning of another. After 9 billion years (Figure 11-14), three-quarters of the parent uranium isotope atoms will have changed into lead atoms.

Mineral Clocks

From the combined creative efforts of German, French, American, and English physicists and chemists at the beginning of the twentieth century, two startling discoveries ensued. Early estimates of the quantity of heat produced by the naturally occurring ra-

dioactive minerals in the earth demonstrated that the heat lost from the earth was largely the product of radioactivity. Heat was no longer residual, and the earth was no longer doomed to a slow death by frostbite. Instead, heat was and is constantly being produced in the earth by radioactive decay; its prodigious energy is apparently the cause for the mysterious force that drives continent against continent (see Chapter Seven), renewing and consuming the seafloor.

The sun, too, was no longer doomed to death; instead of dwindling like a coal fire, its searing energy from radioactive changes (*fusion*) has remained nearly constant for at least the last 4 or 5 billion years. Kelvin's elaborate assumptions had collapsed with the discovery of radioactivity, but the old question still remained. How old is the earth?

The answer to this question was in the rocks themselves. In 1907 an American chemist demonstrated that in minerals of known *sequential* age, the uranium-to-lead ratio was *progressively* different. *The older the mineral, the greater the uranium-to-lead ratio.*

Radioactivity, whose rate of change is unaffected by any event, became the ultimate tool for measuring the age of rocks. In practice, radioactive minerals from igneous and metamorphic rocks are separated from the rock, and the ratio (Figure 11-14) of the "daughter" element (the product of radioactive decay) to the radioactive "parent" is obtained by precise chemical analysis.

Radiometric dating, as the process of *finding chronologic time from radioactive timekeepers* is called, also operates on some fundamental assumptions, as does any other idea. There are three critical assumptions implicit in radiometric dates: (1) the rate of decay is *invariant, regardless of conditions;* (2) *no atoms of the daughter isotope were present when the mineral formed* (or the amount originally present can be determined); and (3) the mineral or rock has remained a *closed system since it formed;* nothing has leaked in or out. The first assumption has been tested many times and so far seems to be correct. The second assumption may or may not be true but, by various techniques, the existence of daughter products at time zero usually can be recognized. The third assumption may or may not be true; the leakage of parent or radioactive offspring from the rock system is one of the chief sources of inaccuracy in radiometric dates.

In order to cross-check the validity of a single radiometric date, accurate dating techniques require that more than one parent-daughter isotope pair from the same rock be analyzed, allowing comparison among the dates obtained. Fortunately, many radioactive isotopic pairs are known. A few are shown in Table 11-1, along with their half-lives.

As can be seen, six isotopes provide essentially all of the available radioactive ages; these isotopes are C^{14}, U^{238}, U^{235}, Rb^{87}, Th^{232}, and K^{40}. Other isoptotes are simply too rare, too long lived, or too short lived to be of practical use, except in special situations.

Chronologic Age Determination

Carbon-14 (C^{14}) is continuously created in the atmosphere by cosmic ray bombardment, causing nitrogen-14 (N^{14}) to absorb a neutron, emit a proton, and thus change to C^{14}. Once formed, C^{14} is incorporated into carbon dioxide and into all living substances. When a plant containing C^{14} dies, it no longer absorbs carbon dioxide and, with

11-1
Radioactive Isotope Pairs

Parent Isotope	Half-Life (years)	Daughter Isotope	Source of Material
Carbon-14 (C^{14})	5,730	Nitrogen-14 (N^{14})	Organic matter
Uranium-235 (U^{235})	713,000,000	Lead-207 (Pb^{207})	Zircon; various uranium minerals
Potassium-40 (K^{40})	1,300,000,000	Argon-40 (Ar^{40}) + Calcium-40 (Ca^{40})	Whole volcanic rocks; micas, feldspars, and amphiboles
Uranium-238 (U^{238})	4,510,000,000	Lead-206 (Pb^{206})	Same as U^{235} (zircon)
Rubidium-87 (Rb^{87})	47,000,000,000	Strontium-87 (Sr^{87})	Whole rocks; feldspars and micas

time, the amount of C^{14} present diminishes. The age of organic material is *not* determined using the parent-to-daughter ratio, but by measuring the radioactivity of the remaining C^{14} in the sample. This radioactivity diminishes rapidly with time, since the half-life of C^{14} is so short (see Table 11-1) and samples over 40,000 years old are difficult to date accurately.

This unique method of dating allows separation of events within the last flicker of geologic time, and the method has been of immense value to geologists interested in recent earth history, anthropologists, and historians. This dating technique has been applied to sizable samples of mummy cloths, manuscripts, clamshells, bone, leaves and stems, hair, and rope—in short, anything that once lived.

The basic assumptions behind C^{14} dating are that the life span of the organism was short relative to the half-life, and the rate of production of C^{14} has remained essentially constant. Cross-checks with other dating methods have shown these assumptions to be basically correct, although there seem to have been minor modifications in the C^{14} production rate through time.

A new method of C^{14} dating measures the amount of C^{14} directly. A cyclotron (a circular atomic particle accelerator) is used to separate the isotopes of carbon, whose ratio may then be measured directly. This method requires extremely small samples, so that the object being dated need not be severely damaged in the dating process. It also seems to offer greater precision and the inherent possibility of routinely obtaining radiocarbon dates from materials up to 100,000 years old.

An offshoot of this cyclotron method has been the separation of other isotopes; this method was not previously used in radiometric dating for various technical reasons. Among the most promising of the isotopes is beryllium-10 (Be^{10}). Its half-life is 1.5 million years; events within the last 20 to 30 million—an interval poorly covered by current methods—seem to be the prime target for this developing method.

Both of the two radioactive isotopes of uranium (U^{235} and U^{238}) decay with vastly different half-lives (see Table 11-1) to unique isotopes of lead. Thus, almost any mineral containing uranium contains *both* radioactive isotopes and *both* isotopic forms of lead as daughter products. Typical radiometric dating techniques of samples that contain uranium involve obtaining the parent-to-daughter ratio on *both* sets of uranium-lead pairs. If the rock involved has had no leakage of materials, both ratios should yield the same age (Figure 11-15), and the ages are said to be *concordant*. The *pair* of ratios plot on Figure 11-15 at a point on the *concordia curve;* different points along this curve represent different ages (and their corresponding Pb^{206}-to-U^{238} and Pb^{207}-to-U^{235} ratios).

Original lead in a uranium-bearing mineral will, of course, cause the radiometrically determined age to be greater than the true age. If nonradiogenic lead-204 (Pb^{204}) is originally in the mineral, other isotopes, including lead-206 (Pb^{206}) and lead-207 (Pb^{207}) must also have been present. Since the ratios between the various isotopes of lead at the time of formation are known, the quantities (from studies of ancient meteorites) of lead isotopes are calculated from the Pb^{204} amount, and then subtracted from the total Pb^{207} and Pb^{206} amounts before calculating the parent-to-daughter ratio.

The uranium-lead method is one of the oldest radiometric dating methods; it is suitable for older rocks that contain the mineral

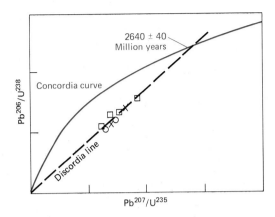

11-15

A typical concordia plot. The colored curve plots the changing ratios of uranium and lead isotopes through time in a uranium-mineral sample. The concordia curve is plotted so that the amount of radiogenic (produced by radioactive decay) lead increases upward for Pb^{206} and to the right for Pb^{207}. The dashed line (discordia line) is drawn through the results of chemical analyses of several different uranium-bearing minerals from one deposit. The interception of the discordia line with the concordia curve yields the age when the uranium minerals formed; this is the age of the deposit. (Example after K. R. Ludwig and J. S. Stuckless, 1978, *Contrib. Mineral. Petrol.*, *65*, pp. 243–254, with permission.)

zircon or other uranium-bearing minerals (young rocks do not contain enough radiogenic lead to be accurately analyzed).

Any argon-40 (Ar^{40}) in minerals that contain potassium results from the radioactive decay of potassium-40 (K^{40}). Ar^{40} is an inert (unreactive) gas, and thus may escape from minerals that have been heated above 200 degrees Celsius. The loss of Ar^{40} from the mineral yields apparent radiometric ages that are too low; potassium-argon ages are usually considered as *minimum* ages, unless it can be demonstrated that the rocks have never been intensely heated.

With a half-life of more than 1 billion years (see Table 11-1), potassium-argon dating is suitable for the oldest rocks on earth—and for the moon as well. All that is required is that the gas-tight mineral being analyzed contains some potassium, an abundant element in many crustal minerals. Because very small amounts of argon can be readily measured, potassium-argon dating has also been applied to rocks no more than 50,000 years old that contain potassium-rich minerals.

The decay of the rare isotope rubidium-87 (Rb^{87}) into strontium-87 (Sr^{87}) furnishes another parent-daughter pair whose ratio is a function of age. The Rb^{87}–Sr^{87} method, with its sizable half-life, is suitable for the oldest igneous and metamorphic rocks known (see Table 11-1).

The method analyzes the Rb^{87}, Sr^{87}, and Sr^{86} contents for a number of minerals from the same rock; each mineral generally contains different original amounts of rubidium and Sr^{87} and Sr^{86}. At the time of crystallization of, say, a magma, the ratio of radiogenic Sr^{87} to nonradiogenic Sr^{86} was constant throughout the whole rock. With time, in each mineral, this ratio increases as the content of radiogenic rubidium decreases, and the amount of radiogenic strontium increases (Figure 11-16) at a rate that is proportional to Rb^{87}-to-Sr^{86} ratio in each mineral. The series of analyses, plotted on a graph, define a line called the *isochron* (equal time), whose slope defines the rock age; the isochron intercept with the Sr^{87} to Sr^{86} axis defines the initial ratio, which otherwise would be unknown.

Radiometric ages define the time at which the mineral that contains radioactive parent elements *formed or crystallized*. For that

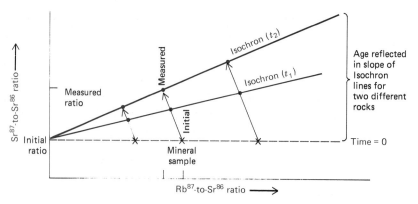

11-16

Rubidium-87 decays to strontium-87; both parent and daughter isotopes are shown here as a ratio to strontium-86, *not* produced by decay and hence constant. At the time of crystallization of a magma ($t = 0$), the ratio of Sr-87 to Sr-86 in all the minerals was a constant value. This value depends on the *source* of the rock. If the minerals in the rock contained *no* rubidium, the ratio (Sr-87 to Sr-86) would *remain* constant as time passed. If the minerals in the rock *do* contain rubidium, with the passage of time (to time t_1), the amount of Sr-87 increases while the amount of Rb-87 diminishes for *each mineral sample.* The plots of the isotope ratios of three minerals are shown; they establish a line whose SLOPE is a function of the length of time the Rb-87 to Sr-87 decay has been going on. The interception of the sloping line with the Sr-87 to Sr-86 axis establishes the *initial ratio,* which tells us the probable rock source. At a still later time (t_2), the *measured ratios* will be still higher, since more time passed and more Sr-87 was produced. The slope of the line will be greater the older the rock is.

reason radiometric dating is nearly restricted to young organic matter that once contained C^{14} and to igneous and metamorphic rocks whose crystallization resets the radiometric clock to zero. The dates available from radioactive parent-to-stable daughter ratios are the date of *crystallization* (freezing) for igneous rocks and the date of cooling for metamorphic rocks. If a rock is metamorphosed more than once, numerous complexities may occur, because the radioactive mineral "clocks" are totally or partially "reset."

Setting or completely resetting the radiometric clock always involves some reconstitution of the mineral. The new mineral begins its life with a limited amount of radioactive "parent" elements present within it; the amount diminishes geometrically with time. Melt the rock or strongly metamorphose it, and the new minerals formed start the process of radiometric decay all over again.

How might we determine the radiometric age of sedimentary rocks? Obviously, conventional radiometric dates of the minerals in a sedimentary rock would simply yield the date when their igneous or metamorphic *source,* later weathered and eroded to make the sediment, formed. Only one mineral exists which, if it is *formed* during sedimentation, has a potassium content that makes it suitable for potassium-argon dating. This mineral is *glauconite,* which often displays poor argon gas retention. There is no other method of *directly* arriving at deposition dates for sedimentary rocks. However, sedimentary rocks may be indirectly dated by dating the igneous rocks that intrude, overlie, or underlie them (Figure 11-17).

Among numerous other dating methods available, *fission track* analysis is a versatile new technique that is also dependent on radioactivity. When uranium, in the form of the highly radioactive U^{238}, decays, the heavy, high-energy fission fragments that result, as the atomic nucleii split into fragments (*fission*) damage the crystalline or glassy material through which they pass; etching highly polished mineral surfaces with acid brings out the damage as a series of "tracks" left behind by the high-energy fragments. This method requires that the number of tracks per unit area be counted; the track density is a direct function of the age of the material and the U^{238} content, which must be measured.

The radiometric systems just described measure the *product* of decay—the daughter isotope; the fission track method describes the *effect* of decay. Depending mostly on the amount of U^{238} originally present in the specimen, the ages obtainable from fission track dating range from a few years to many billion years. Material that has been dated includes crystals from many rocks, amber, volcanic ash, obsidian, and pottery.

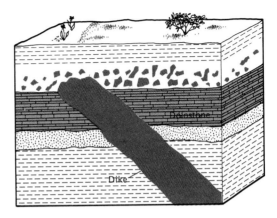

11-17

This hypothetical section illustrates one way in which igneous rocks can be used to date sedimentary rocks. The dike intruded the dolostone (colored layer) and was then weathered and eroded (note fragments) as the upper layer was deposited. If the fossils show that the two layers are of very similar age and radiometric dating of the dike yields a rubidium-strontium date of 220 million years, the dolostone is very slightly older than 220 million years and the upper layer is very slightly younger than 220 million years. Continued comparisons of the *same* layers elsewhere may allow their age to be ever more precisely bracketed.

The science of tree ring dating, called *dendrochronology,* depends on the old idea of counting the number of rings in the trunk of a tree to learn the tree's age. The variation in width of the annual rings is a function of climate. If distinctive patterns of wide and narrow rings are present, one then matches the annual pattern of one tree with corresponding patterns in another. By finding very old trees, or dead trees, that overlap in time the trees whose rings have been dated, it is possible to go back to nearly 8000 B.C.

Tree ring chronology has made it possible to recalibrate C¹⁴ dates by obtaining dates from wood fragments with both methods. In material formed about 6000 years ago, C^{14} dates systematically erred by as much as 1000 years. Tree ring dates made it possible to calibrate the long-suspected error (variation in C^{14} production in the ionosphere) to produce an error correction factor that is now routinely applied to radiocarbon dates.

A fairly new dating technique depends on the recognition that after death, some of the amino acids in an animal's bones slowly shift their structure from one form to another; this new form is unknown in living things. The rate of change seems to be constant, and age determinations using the method, called *amino acid racemization,* have correlated well with C^{14} dates from the same specimen. Racemization dating is a promising concept because smaller bone samples yield dates within reasonable limits of error within the last 100,000 years.

Still another new technique, useful for dating material worked by humans within the last few thousand years, is *obsidian hydration.* This technique depends on measuring the length of time since the creation of a fresh surface on obsidian (see Chapter Three), which is a type of volcanic glass. Any event that *causes* a fresh surface—including the purposeful chipping of obsidian into a tool by an ancient artisan—can be dated.

The dating method depends again on a rate process; the rate of hydration (addition of water) of the fresh surface is proportional to the square root of time. The longer the surface has been exposed, the thicker the *hydration rind*—an altered zone where water has been added that worked its way from the surface inward.

THE GEOLOGIC TIME SCALE

With the recognition that rocks of identical appearance could be of widely varying age, the old terms—primary, secondary, and tertiary—lost their explanatory power. Knowing that animals and plants changed through time and that each sedimentary layer contained a unique assemblage of fossils made it possible to *correlate* rocks of unlike appearance—that is, to recognize that they were of the same age.

With *rocks now divided on the basis of fossil content* instead of appearance, new subdivisions of geologic time were needed. These broad subdivisions, called **eras,** would be made using fossils characteristic of each division.

The era whose rocks contained ancient marine and amphibious life forms was called the **Paleozoic era** (from two Greek terms meaning "ancient life"). Rocks whose fossils suggested somewhat younger life forms, including the reptiles, were formed in the **Mesozoic era** (the term means "middle life"). The youngest group of rocks, whose fossils became more and more like modern life forms, including the mammals, is the **Cenozoic era,** (meaning "recent life"). The oldest of all the rocks, underlying all others and containing only sparse, primitive life forms, and few fossils formed during the **Precambrian** era.

Further subdivisions of each of the younger three eras into briefer units of time, called *periods,* was possible using more refined distinctions between fossils. Finer and finer subdivisions of time, called *epochs* and *ages* (see Figure D-3 in Appendix D), reflected still greater refinement in classifying fossil assemblages and recognizing their counterparts around the world.

Although the world of fossiliferous sedimentary rocks had been thoroughly subdivided by 100 years or more ago, geologists were still developing more refined units of sequential time. As radiometric dates became available early in the twentieth century, it was immediately clear that chronologic dates would check the assumptions inherent in any sequential time scale and also provide the long-sought chronometer for the geologic time scale (Table 11-2).

Geologic time is divided into four unequal divisions; each older division is progressively longer. The Precambrian era encompasses 4 billion years—seven-eighths of all earth history. Within this vast span of time, the sparse fossils are unicellular and generally unsuitable for correlation, although fossil algae have served in some areas. Within the Precambrian era, there are no generally agreed on subdivisions around the world because of the lack of fossils suitable for correlation. Precambrian rocks can be subdivided using radiometric techniques, but worldwide correlation of Precambrian rocks is hindered by a confusing morass of local names and events and the lack of internationally adopted standards.

The Paleozoic era comprises almost 350 million years of earth history. The rich collections of fossils in many Paleozoic rocks have enabled them to be subdivided into seven periods (see Figure D-3), recognized around the world, and each period has been further subdivided into epochs and ages. Life in early Paleozoic rocks is a rich trea-

11-2
The Geologic Time Scale

Era	Length of Time (million years)	Major Biologic Events
Cenozoic	0–65	Dominance of mammals and flowering plants
Mesozoic	65–225	Rise of reptiles and conifers, also primitive birds; last of the seed ferns. Rise of flowering plants
Paleozoic	225–570	Development of hard parts by invertebrate marine animals; first land plants and amphibians. First vertebrate animals (fish). Seed ferns, ferns, and primitive land plants
Precambrian	570–4600	Development of life. Earliest life bacterial, then algal, with profound modification of the atmosphere. Development of nucleated cell

sure of *invertebrate* (lacking backbones) animals that lived in the ocean, plus a few vertebrate fish. About the middle of the Paleozoic era, the rocks reveal that amphibian and plant life had colonized the continents for the first time; apparently the first 3 billion years and more of the evolution of life took place entirely in the world's oceans.

The Mesozoic era includes approximately 160 million years. Although abundant marine invertebrate and vertebrate life remained in the ocean and an amphibious animal life and an abundant plant community had colonized the land, we think of the Mesozoic time mostly in terms of just one dominant group of animals—the *reptiles*. Among the reptiles who dominate the fossil record of this time, none have so captured our imagination as the dinosaurs. Reptiles also took to the ocean and to the air, and they dominated life on land, but many mysteriously disappeared toward the end of that era.

The Cenozoic era encompasses the last 65 million years. During this time, fossil remains became progressively more like modern life. This was the age of development of *mammals;* the last few million years of the Cenozoic era witnessed the development of

a unique mammal species called *Homo sapiens* (human beings).

The eras record an early interpretation of the fossil record that contains major breaks in the history of life. The oldest break, between the Precambrian and Paleozoic eras, comes near the development of multicellular life and is approximately coincident with the development of a skeleton. The second break records the evolution of the reptiles, and the last break documents the rise of mammals.

Within each of these great eras are a series of physical and biological events whose interpretation occupies the remaining chapters of this book.

Seen from a human perspective, the story of the earth is similar to an old-time movie. The actors seem to move on and off their earthly stage at a dead run, while the seas roar in and out, and mountains pop up in the air like a blister on a cheap tire. The pace of change only seems rapid because of our perspective; if we were to live for 100 million years, the skidding of continent into continent, the rise and fall of the sea, and the prosperity and death of the dinosaurs would hardly be noticed.

Even chronologic time, then, is relative.

SUMMARY   In the history of life, the earliest sense of time was kept by plants and animals themselves; their lives were controlled by internal biologic clocks whose origin and location still remain a mystery today, even though we humans also have such internal clocks. For earliest people, it was enough to conduct life in the present; myths were created to explain the misty past, and little thought was given the future.

The rise of Christianity affected the western world as did no other event; it established the birth of Christ as the basic reference point from which chronologic time is kept. Additionally, Christian faith established time as having *direction,* proceeding from the creation of Adam a few thousand years before, through the death of Christ, toward a promised second coming that was at most a few hundred years in the future. Thus human time was supposedly constrained to about 6000 years and, since humanity and the earth were believed to have been created together, the world, too, was envisioned as being only a few thousand years old.

In a world a few thousand of years old that possessed high mountains, giant volcanoes, deep valleys, and roaring rivers, only one of the following concepts could be accepted: the world was static and little changed since its recent creation, *or* the world was changed by catastrophic events as mountains were created, valleys split apart, and so forth.

Stating that *neither* a static nor a catastrophic earth was plausible, many eighteenth- and nineteenth-century scientists saw that the sequence of life, preserved as fossils, needed great amounts of time for changes to occur; however, the *cause* of change eluded them. The golden age of science had begun; people were questioning the earth instead of listening to human or biblical authority.

Fossils allowed scientists to place rocks in correct *sequential* order, as did many other commonsense principles such as superposition, original horizontality, original continuity, intrusion, inclusion, and metamorphism. The concept that rocks of similar appearance were of similar age had been cast aside; fossils were the supreme indicators of relative age and tools for *correlation*.

Understanding the *why* of fossil change in a vertical sequence of rock required the use of limitless time and natural selection under population pressure; both theories were the result of a lifetime of work by Hutton (and his champion, Lyell) and Darwin. Kelvin temporarily undid their theories by providing mathematical evidence derived from assumptions on the earth's cooling rate. This evidence *required* the crust of the earth be around 100 million years old; this period of time (Figure 11-18) was impossibly short for the gradual evolution of landscapes or life by uniformitarian processes.

Kelvin's dogmatic denial of Lyell's concept of uniformity of process was based on sound physical principles, *given the knowledge of the late nineteenth century*. Uniformity of process through endless time demands a nearly inexhaustible source of energy—and no such source was known for either the earth or sun. Kelvin had destroyed the concept of uniformity and the concept of organic evolution as surely as Jeffreys had destroyed continental drift—*and for the same reason*. In an earth whose original energy source is running down, neither continental drift, uniformity of process, nor *gradual* evolution of life is possible.

The discovery of radioactivity gave the sun billions of years of life, fueled the earth's own internal engine, and allowed, once again, the gradual development of life on a sunlit earth. The earth acquired, all at once, the

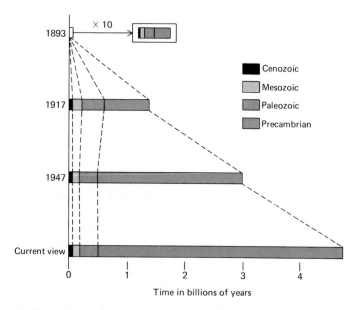

11-18

Illustration of changes in the concepts of geologic time. The sizable jump between 1893 and 1917 was due to the advent of radiometric dates, which quickly overturned the 1893 estimate of 55 million years. Notice that most of the increase in the estimates of the length of geologic time is due to increases in the length of the Precambrian era, as older and older rocks (including meteorites) have been located and dated. (After H. L. James, 1970, *Am. Jour. Sci.* (Bradley Volume), Vol. 258-A, pp. 104–114, with permission.)

energy to change itself constantly through nearly endless time and the invariant solar energy to allow life to form and change. But did the earth have endless time?

Radioactivity also answered that question, because the ratio of stable offspring to radioactive parent is a direct function of the length of time that radioactive decay has proceeded. Chronologic time, from radiometric means, yielded an earth billions of years old; this great amount of time was now divided into four eras based on the dominant life form during each era.

Earth time is hardly limitless now, but it is still inconceivably vast. Earth time also turns out to be relative—relative to the heavenly bodies that surround us. Clock time must gradually slow as the earth's ponderous spinning mass, braked by the tides and other speculative forces, slows and enlarges its orbit about the sun.

Time turns out to be the most relative of concepts.

The concept of geologic time, in all its vastness, is geology's greatest contribution to human culture, and it brings us quickly to a realization of our human insignificance. Perhaps what our thoughts about time teach us is that everything is relative, except those things that cannot be measured.

The greatest mystery for us is not that we are here, but that we should find within ourselves the skill to interpret what came before, and thus deny our own insignificance.

ANSWERS
TO FIGURE
PROBLEMS

Figure 11-5

Deposition of the shale, sandstone, and limestone, in that order; erosion of the valley, which is continuing; flight of the bird.

Figure 11-6

The intrusion is a dike, which becomes a sill. Notice that the intrusive bakes the rocks *both* above and below it; therefore the igneous rock formed *after* the formation of all the sedimentary layers. If the igneous material had been a lava flow, it would have baked *only* the material beneath it, since its upper surface would have been open to the sky.

Figure 11-7

The oldest event is formation of black layer; the intrusion of the magma that formed the sill is younger than formation of sandstone layer. A dike fed magma to the sill.

EXERCISES

1. Certain kinds of fossils are essentially useless for correlation purposes, because they are found in a specific rock type instead of in a specific time interval. Why would a particular group of life forms be unique to a specific sedimentary rock type?
2. Suppose you found the hard parts of both marine and continental animals mixed together in an assemblage of fossils within a single sedimentary rock. What could you conclude?
3. Fossil shark's teeth were said by Pliny (A.D. 23–79) to be objects that fell from the sky during eclipses of the moon. Others believed they were tongues of serpents and, therefore, might be powerful remedies against snakebite. Since both ideas were demonstrably false, why did it require 16 centuries to discover what shark's teeth really were?
4. If the mythical element *nazanium* had a life of 10 minutes, of the 10,000 atoms originally present, how many would remain at the end of 1 hour?
5. Why would very small fossils be of particular value in correlation in

comparing various rocks penetrated by one oil well with those penetrated by another well?

6. In a specimen 16,800 years old, what percentage of the original C^{14} would remain?

7. Suppose that in a rock of unknown age, after chemical analysis, the ratio of Rb^{87} to Sr^{87} is 50:50. How old is the rock (in millions of years)? In what era would this rock be placed? What kind of fossil life might be present?

8. Theories that suggest that the force of gravity is weakening through time would predict that the earth's diameter must therefore be expanding at the rate of about $\frac{1}{2}$ inch ($1\frac{1}{3}$ centimeters) every 100 years. How could such a prediction be checked?

9. If the length of the terrestrial day is increasing by 0.002 seconds every 100 years (2 seconds every 100,000 years), how long was the "day" when the earth was formed 46 million centuries ago?

10. In a remarkable recent study, a person blind since birth was shown to have a biologic cycle of 24.9 hours, which is the period of the lunar day. Sleep onset was "remarkably coincident . . . with a local low tide." Comment?

11. U^{235} is now 0.72 percent of natural uranium. How could we compute its abundance at the time of earth formation? (It can be done, and you may want to do it. The answer is 17 percent).

SUGGESTED READINGS

Albritton, Claude C., 1967, *Uniformity and Simplicity,* Geological Society of America Special Paper 89, 113 pp.
   A symposium on the modern meaning of uniformity.

Albritton, Claude C., 1975, *Philosophy of Geohistory: 1785–1970,* Stroudsburg, Pa., Dowden, Hutchinson & Ross, 386 pp.
   Reprinting of some important papers representing nearly 200 years of geologic thought; highly recommended.

Berry, W.B.N., 1968, *Growth of a Prehistoric Time Scale,* San Francisco, W. H. Freeman, 158 pp.
   Excellent review of the clash of concepts that eventually led to development of the modern geologic time scale.

Harper, C.T. (ed.), 1973, *Geochronology: Radiometric Dating of Rocks and Minerals,* Stroudsburg, Pa., Dowden, Hutchinson & Ross, 435 pp.
   Thorough review and updating of the major methods.

Porter, Roy, 1977, *The Making of Geology,* Cambridge, England, Cambridge University Press, 288 pp.
   The history of geology in Britain from 1660 to 1815. Thorough scholarship, no illustrations, and an exhaustive bibliography.

Toulmin, Stephen, and Goodfield, June, 1965, *The Discovery of Time*, New York, Harper & Row, 286 pp.

Probing, insightful scholarship on the meaning of time and the role of geology in human thought.

KEY
CONCEPTS

Time

Internal; astronomic, historic; geologic.

Sequential or relative; chronologic or absolute.

Chronologic or absolute time

Rate dependent.

Radioactive decay the only independent rate.

Geologic time scale

Subdivided into eras, based on major biologic events; exact chronology developed by radiometric means; concept of half-life; parent-to-daughter ratios.

Geologic time

Dethroned biblical chronology.

Concept of static earth, a few thousand years old; humans and earth created at same time; earth provided by God for the pleasure of people.

In place of biblical authority, authority from the rocks.

An earth of uniform change, incredibly old; an earth where, with time, life forms evolve; an earth where people follow nearly 4 billion years of other life forms; an earth where we have no dominion, but must live in harmony with other, older life.

Much about geology has changed since 1890, when this photograph of geologists at work in Yellowstone National Park was taken. The discoveries outlined in this chapter have depended on some of the most sophisticated scientific equipment available, but also on mules, backpacks, and boot leather—commodities that are still much used by geologists today. (Photograph by J. P. Iddings, U.S. Geological Survey.)

Chapter Twelve
DAWN
the precambrian

"Repetition is the only form of permanence that nature can achieve."
Santayana
"Life is an offensive, directed against the repetitious mechanism of the universe."
A. N. Whitehead

Precambrian time spans about 4 billion years, or seven-eighths of all earth history. Many of the details of the history of this period are not known; most of the rocks of this age are of igneous and metamorphic origin, and their history is difficult to decipher. Igneous and metamorphic rocks do, however, tell us about the chemical events within the early earth, and radiometric dating of their minerals has furnished us with the beginnings of a Precambrian chronology. These ancient rocks also provide the great majority of the world's mineral wealth.

Precambrian sedimentary rocks are rare, because most of them have long ago been recycled into other rocks. Their remnants yield extraordinary information about the accumulation of the earth's atmosphere and ocean. These old rocks also contain the record of earth's most unique resource— life.

The beginning and evolution of Precambrian life is one of the many exciting research frontiers in geology; perhaps the greatest lesson to be learned from Precambrian life is the marvelous durability and adaptability of life. The history of life is the history of meeting challenges. From each challenge, life emerges, changed and triumphant.

In this chapter and the ones that follow, we will reflect on two basic concepts: (1) the dominant physical events of the Precambrian, and (2) the history of life. Within each theme, we will occasionally digress to look at the "how" of history. *How* do we know is a vital corollary to the historical query *what* do we know?

Geologists find their chief satisfaction in deciphering the relation between pattern and process. For interpreting the past, the patterns observed *imply* process; for example, an ancient accumulation of unsorted boul-

ders, grooved, scratched, and battered would suggest glaciation. We may also use current patterns to predict future processes, as when a geologist warns that conditions are such that a disastrous landslide might occur. Observing the *sequence* of changes in ancient patterns allows the geologist to describe process through time; we call the results geologic history.

Understanding earth (and planetary) history and the history of life is the chief academic goal of the geological sciences. Let us consider some of the results.

THE OLDEST EVENTS

Much as human history merges into prehistoric history and anthropology, the geologic study of the earth merges into *astrophysics*—the science that studies the origin of stars and planets. Both astrophysical and geologic knowledge sets limits as to what reasonable schemes for planetary evolution must look like. Astrophysical data require that any scheme for forming the earth must also be compatible with its distance from the sun and neighboring planets, its orbital path, its density, its diminishing spin rate, and its spin direction. Geologic data constrain any model to one that will form an earth with its known chemical composition and to one model that causes internal separation into shells of increasing density into earth's center. Also, the chemical distinctiveness of the earth as compared with the universe and with other planets must be explained; we might particularly ask why *only* the earth has an ocean and an oxygenated atmosphere. Finally, any system of earth formation must give the earth its radioactivity—the internal heat engine that allows the earth to continue to evolve.

Only one of several schemes need be presented here, but it is only one of several models or hypotheses that satisfy the limits imposed by our current store of astrophysical and geologic data. As that storehouse of data continues to expand, the limits to theories of planetary and earthly evolution will continue to contract, forcing us to adopt better and better approximations of the sequence of events that formed our earth.

Many theories of planetary formation begin with the common astronomic observation that space consists of something rather than nothing. Minute quantities of interstellar dust, made up of ice crystals, mineral crystals, and organic molecules, have been detected, as have small amounts of gases (mostly hydrogen and helium). Stars spew great quantities of this dust into space as they evolve, and it is of this dust that new solar systems, and life, are formed.

As gravity began to act on a slowly rotating cloud of interstellar dust and gas about 5 billion years ago (we call modern examples of these clouds *nebulas*), a dense mass of gas at the center of the nebula, driven inward on itself by gravitational attraction, reached temperatures so high that it became luminous. That central body (our sun) is still luminous today; its energy is derived from the conversion of immense stores of hydrogen to helium by a process (fusion) duplicated in thermonuclear bombs.

As this giant nebular disk cooled, aggregations of matter began to collide and stick together (due to gravitational attraction) to form a series of planets about the sun. Collisions must have been frequent, with protoplanets forming and breaking up but, eventually (by about 4.5 billion years ago), each planet had formed as a solid body after its gravitational attraction swept surrounding space reasonably clean of litter. Bits of interstellar debris left over from the formation phase of the solar system are still being collected by the earth's gravitational attraction; we call these bits of "space junk" *meteorites*.

Radiometric dates from meteorites cluster around 4.6 billion years, a date consistent with the oldest lunar rocks as well. The abundance ratios of lead-206 and lead-207 also form a pattern in earthly rocks consistent with an origin of 4.6 billion years ago. Thus we obtain our first evidence of a *solar system* that contained solid, rocky material 46 million centuries ago.

As the earth formed, it was probably never truly molten *throughout;* if it had been, it would have lost water and oxygen as gases into interstellar space. Instead, chemically reactive gases such as water vapor and oxygen were retained as dissolved gases and mineral compounds in the early magma and rocks of the earth. Chemically inert gases (that could not combine into compounds) such as argon and neon mostly escaped, and their abundance on earth is now a tiny fraction of their abundance in the total universe.

What we have now is a *model*—one of several—for producing the primitive earth 4.6 billion years ago. The early earth must have looked nothing like the modern earth; it presumably had no oceans, no atmosphere, no continents, no ocean basin, no mantle, and no core. In short, most planetary evolution models produce a rather cool, solid, homogeneous earth composed of oxides and silicates of metals (chiefly iron and magnesium) plus far smaller amounts of the other common elements. It was an earth resembling the modern earth only in its *overall* chemical composition; it was an earth formed from catastrophe and was awaiting another catastrophe of its own making.

Differentiation

The primitive earth was a solid, homogeneous body, intensely heated by collision, gravitational attraction, and radioactive decay. But how could the growing source of heat be released?

SOLIDS can only transmit heat by *conduction*, which is the flow of heat from a hot source to a cooler receiver. Some solids, including most metals, conduct heat well others do not, which is why metal skillets may have wooden handles. Rocky material conducts heat poorly, so several geologic substances, including gypsum, brick, stone, mica, and asbestos, are used for insulation.

In a *solid* earth comprised mostly of insulating materials, the emission of heat within it could only mean that the *temperature would rise,* because the heat was generated faster than it could flow away.

As temperatures continued to rise, the earth began, in part, to melt. Metallic iron was among the most abundant components, and the melting (iron has one of the lowest melting points of any component) of heavy iron allowed it to begin sinking and displacing lighter material. As melting iron sank, large amounts of gravitational (kinetic) energy were released, heating the earth still further and causing most of the earth to melt.

In a *fluid* earth, two processes, each a key to the evolution of the *modern* earth, occurred simultaneously. FIRST, the earth *differentiated into a core,* which was formed by the aggregation of the iron as it melted and sank, *and an overlying mantle* (Figure 12-1), which was composed mostly of iron and magnesium silicates. The still lighter material, composed primarily of silicates of potassium, sodium, aluminum, and calcium, floated to the surface, *forming the earth's*

(*a*)

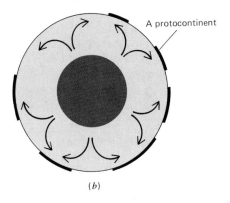

A protocontinent

(*b*)

12-1
(*a*) The originally homogeneous earth, heated above the melting point of iron by *conduction,* melts iron, which starts falling toward earth center under the influence of gravity. The infalling iron displaces less dense material, which moves upward. (*b*) After the melting and density differentiation event is complete, the earth has a core and a viscous mantle, which release heat to the surface by *convection.* A few primitive continental granitic masses are shown on the surface as thin, dark lines to complete the picture.

first crustal fragments. Within a period of perhaps a few hundred million years, *the earth had restructured itself, under the pervasive influence of gravity, into a layered earth, and each deeper layer was a successively denser one.* The earth had destroyed its early homogeneous state and had become an evolving, differentiated planet.

The SECOND process was to give the earth its unique dynamism; a partially *molten* earth releases and transfers heat by *convection,* a process discussed in Chapter Seven. Convection is a *far more efficient method of heat transfer* than conduction (Figure 7-6), and the heat formed within the earth, usually by its own radioactivity, was rapidly transferred to the surface. Now the earth cooled rapidly. The fragments of granitic crust, (or parts of it), formed by fractional crystallization of the mantle, became solid by 4 billion years ago; we know this because radiometric ages for a few crustal igneous and metamorphic rocks approach 4 billion years.

Convectional overturn continues in the mantle today, still transferring the heat upward from the earth's partially molten core and the heat from the radioactive decay of elements within the mantle and crust. That heat, dissipated within the mantle and crust by convection, drives the grand schemes of plate tectonics described in Chapter Seven and causes our planet to continue to evolve.

At this stage, the earth might have looked slightly more like the modern earth, but it lacked three components that distinguish it from *all* the other planets in our solar system: (1) an oxygen-rich atmosphere; (2) an ocean; and (3) life.

Origin of the Atmosphere

The melting event just described may be said to start the earth's geologic history, since geologists can say little about the earth until a rock record exists. The crustal record begins nearly 4 billion years ago, and that re-cord consists of strongly metamorphosed *sedimentary* rock. The character of these ancient sediments suggests two bold reconstructions, since *sediments* can form only where there is water, and, an atmosphere.

Briefly, the chemistry of the minerals in the earliest rocks suggest that the early atmosphere may have been rich in nitrogen, carbon, and hydrogen in combined forms, but the atmosphere was *essentially devoid of oxygen.*

The earliest rocks also indicate that crustal temperatures were still very high; radioactive heat production was probably four or five times that of today (Figure 12-2), since many radioactive elements have gone through numerous half-life cycles of decay by now. Perhaps Kelvin was correct; the earth *is* running down, but its store of radioactive energy is still immense and capable of causing forces in the mantle that move continents and oceans about with equal ease.

How, then, can we make sense of an earth whose primitive atmosphere seems to have been lacking in oxygen and rich in carbon, hydrogen, and nitrogen and whose heat loss may have been several times that measured today?

The answer seems to lie within the question itself. Estimates of the proportions of sedimentary rock as a function of age (Figure 12-3) suggest that sedimentary rock of *volcanic origin dominates the early Precambrian era.* We know that volcanoes and geysers are, today, one of the methods of venting internal heat; since far larger amounts of heat were produced in the past (Figure 12-2), the early earth must have been *intensely volcanic.*

The nearest planetary analogy we have is Jupiter, which may be a reasonable thermal model of the earliest earth. Its atmosphere is rich in methane and ammonia, which are

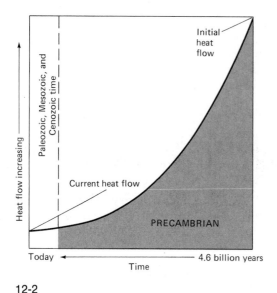

12-2
A hypothetical curve displaying change in heat flow through time. Such curves assume that the heat generated by gravitational contraction of the protoplanet earth, plus the heat generated by massive meteorite impacts (our moon still records this phase in earth history, which has been almost obliterated by subsequent weathering and erosion) and radioactive heat production (about five times modern radioactive heat flow) were the sources of heat energy available in the primitive earth.

compounds of nitrogen, carbon, and hydrogen. Add to such an early atmosphere the components of earthly volcanism—mostly *water vapor,* and some carbon dioxide, nitrogen, and various sulfur oxides—and we *create* the earth's primitive atmosphere.

Volcanoes *are* the basic method by which the earth vents its internal gases, and it seems that early venting of volcanic gases gave the earth its first primitive atmosphere. An atmosphere composed of ammonia,

methane, water vapor, and minor sulfur oxides would be a reasonable legacy of an extremely hot earth that vented its radioactive heat and its lightest weight gases through volcanoes, *but it is certainly not today's atmosphere.*

Obviously, if volcanoes gave the earth its earliest gaseous shell, that shell has been extensively modified since then. What happened to all the carbon and sulfur, which are both trace components of the modern atmosphere? And from where did all the oxygen come? What happened to all that water vapor? In such a primitive atmosphere, modern life would die instantly; how could life have formed? The answers are all interrelated, and the best available ones follow.

Origin and Characteristics of the Ocean

Nearly three-quarters of the earth's surface is water, home to *all* life for the first 3 billion years of earth history. The origin of this immense body of water is not difficult to explain, because water vapor is approximately *three-quarters of the gas produced by modern volcanoes.* The oceans, too, were the product of volcanoes.

Since their origin from the incessant volcanism that must have characterized early earth, the ocean's enormous volume has had a stabilizing effect on the earth's climate, atmospheric chemistry, and crustal chemistry. The ocean is essentially a gigantic buffer whose sheer volume defies any wholesale change as it interacts with the rocky crust, the atmosphere, and life. The salt in seawater comes from submarine volcanism and weathering of sodium-rich minerals, and numerous other chemical reactions apparently

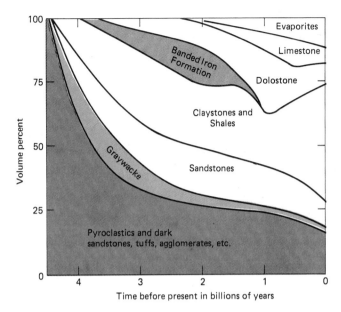

12-3
Relative proportion of the major sedimentary rock groups through time. (Adapted from R. B. Hargraves, 1976, *Science, 193,* pp. 363–371, copyright © 1976 by the American Association for the Advancement of Science, which was adapted with permission from F. T. MacKenzie, 1975, in J. P. Riley and J. Skirrow (eds.) *Chemical Oceanography,* Vol. 1, p. 309, copyright by Academic Press, which was derived from data from Alexander B. Ronov, 1964, *Geokimiya, 8,* p. 715. Published with permission from all cited sources.)

have kept the chemical composition of seawater nearly constant for billions of years.

The implications of the constancy and volume of seawater to the development of life can hardly be overemphasized. As we will soon see, life had its beginnings in the ocean. Oceanic life is born, feeds, mates, and dies in a single, interconnected medium that resists change. Chemically, the sea is a strong salt solution whose other subtle chemical reactions take place in solutions of immense dilution. Physically, seawater absorbs and releases heat very slowly, so its temperature is little affected by climatic changes.

Life in the sea, like all life, is fueled by the sun. A minute fraction of the sun's energy is converted on land, by plants, into carbohydrates, proteins, and fats that form the food for all other continental life. In the sea, the same tiny fraction of solar energy allows the growth of single-celled plants called **phytoplankton** in the upper, sunlit part of the sea.

These phytoplankton are the basic food resource of the sea; they are consumed by slightly larger animals that, in turn, are consumed by diminishing numbers of larger and larger animals. Each larger animal in the *food chain* passes on about 20 percent of the energy it consumes to its consumer; the larger few, such as human beings and whales, live on the combined nutrients of the smaller many.

The zones of life within the sea include free-floating and swimming forms in the sunlit open sea and other forms that live near, on, or burrowed into the ocean floor at depths ranging from near sea level to the deepest ocean floors. Other areas of shallow water, including continental shelves, banks, and atolls, constitute about 10 percent of the total area of the ocean, but furnish an incredibly rich harvest of life in complex communities.

It was not always this way. Billions of

years ago, an EVENT occurred in the sea that was to modify the sea and totally change the atmosphere above it. That event, singularly confined to our earth, was the origin of life.

THE FIRST LIFE

Perhaps no question has perplexed us more than the origin of life. Every culture has had its own myths, but has also observed that life came from life by sexual reproduction, too. Over 100 years ago Louis Pasteur, a French biochemist, showed that life could *not* come from nonlife, that life did not generate spontaneously as so many had thought. If life came from life, how could the first life have formed? To understand this question, we must ask another. What *is* life?

If we analyze living matter, it may include about 24 elements, of which hydrogen, oxygen, and carbon are overwhelmingly dominant. Other critical elements, in much smaller amounts, include nitrogen, phosphorous, and minute amounts of sulfur. Living matter is thus very much like water in composition, but it is vastly enriched in carbon, somewhat enriched in nitrogen and phosphorus, and unenriched in sulfur. Essentially *life, chemically, is little more than water plus carbon;* we call such a compound a *carbohydrate.*

If we attempt to write a molecular formula for living matter (the formula for water is, of course, H_2O), it resembles $H_{2960}O_{1480}N_{16}P_{1.8}S$. The formation of living tissue is the most intricate known feat of chemical engineering. How did it occur?

The basic building blocks of life are *amino acids,* nitrogen-enriched carbohydrates from which *proteins* are made. Proteins occur in all living matter and are essential to the growth and repair of living tissue, but they

are not life. The formation and replication of protein is controlled by various *nucleic acids* (chiefly DNA and RNA) and by complex compounds of hydrogen, carbon, nitrogen, oxygen, and phosphorus. These nucleic acids form the chemical pattern that causes each cell to replicate itself in its own unique fashion. Once a protein has been produced that is capable of reproducing itself from its internal store of nucleic acids, we call that protein alive; *life is separated from nonlife only by the ability to reproduce itself.*

In an early earth, the formation of amino acids was not a difficult feat. In an atmosphere rich with carbon, hydrogen, nitrogen, and water vapor, lightning could have readily formed amino acids from the available inorganic materials. Laboratory experiments, some dating back nearly 30 years, have formed a host of complex organic molecules by exposing ammonia, methane, carbon dioxide, and water to artificial lightning or to ultraviolet radiation. Lightning must have been common on a volcanic earth, and an earth with a primitive, oxygen-free atmosphere would admit intense ultraviolet radiation.

The primitive environment, predicted on chemical data, thus turns out to be the *ideal* environment for the formation of amino acids and complex organic molecules. The necessary chemistry was present, and the energy sources—lightning and ultraviolet rays—were abundant. *Very important was the fact that oxygen was absent;* if oxygen had been present in any appreciable amount, the organic molecules would have quickly been oxidized and thus destroyed.

The jump from protein molecules to life is still awesome, and that phase in the history of the chemical evolution of life is still highly speculative. The synthesis of DNA and RNA remains a potent piece of biochemistry, and no one has yet figured out what the intervening stages between complex organic proteins and living, replicating proteins were like.

We can, however, make some statements about what the first life would have had to be like. It would have had to be quite small, exposing a maximum of surface area to the sea to maintain its internal temperature. It would have had to be *anaerobic,* capable of living without oxygen. It would have to have been *heterotrophic,* deriving its nutrition from the consumption of other organic molecules, just as we do today. It would have had to be *marine,* because no living matter could have survived on the continents, which were bathed in intense ultraviolet radiation; the chemistry of life is still essentially similar to the chemistry of seawater.

We now turn to a discussion of the world of fossils in order to learn what the first life was really like.

The Prokaryotes

The most popular categorization of life divides all life into five kingdoms: plants, animals, fungi, protists (single-celled organisms with cell nuclei, such as amoeba and paramecia), and prokaryotes (sometimes called *monerans*).

The **prokaryotes** are distinguished from all other life by the *absence of a cell nucleus* (the control center of the cell); prokaryotes include bacteria and blue-green algae. Most biologists regard the split between prokaryotes and *all* other life (whose cells have nuclei) as the FUNDAMENTAL *subdivision of life;* this is a far more important system than the old subdivision of life into plant or animal (Appendix F).

Within the prokaryotic group, the prime candidate for being the earliest life form is clearly a group of bacteria that share the requirements that we have outlined for earliest life. The methane-producing bacteria—recently christened *methanogens*—are so unique that they may not be bacteria at all, but a new group within the prokaryotes. They are also perhaps the most ancient of all life, *although they have not yet been found as truly ancient fossils.* On fragmentary evidence the methanogens seem to be a separate evolutionary group from fellow prokaryotes blue-green algae and bacteria; all three groups were preceded by some type of common ancestor.

The methane-producing bacteria are *anaerobic;* they cannot live in the presence of oxygen. They grow by oxidizing hydrogen and reducing carbon dioxide, thereby producing methane. Thus the early primitive atmosphere was *exactly right* for methanogens; they may well have been among the earliest of all life. Modern methanogens are a minor fragment of the tree of life; they are found in a few hot springs and in stagnant mud, and their days of dominance are billions of years past.

But what, then, is our first real fossil evidence? The oldest known unmetamorphosed Precambrian sedimentary rocks are, of course, the place in which to search for the oldest fossils. The oldest studied up to now, at 3.4 billion years of age, is a chert from the Swartkoppie Formation at the base of the Fig Tree Group of South Africa. Bedded chert is an *ideal* sedimentary rock in which to look for microscopic fossils; it is composed of minutely crystalline silica, which is an ideal substance in which to preserve exquisite detail. It was in the Fig Tree cherts that the oldest fossil life known was found.

The Fig Tree organisms are tiny microspheroids (Figure 12-4) that are similar to modern algal materials. Preserved in minute detail, the algalike microstructures have the following characteristics.

1. They are within the size range of modern prokaryotes.
2. They have a size distribution similar to modern prokaryotes.
3. Exhibit forms like modern and fossil prokaryotes.
4. They yield carbon-isotope ratios like that of photosynthetic organisms.
5. About one-quarter of the microfossils have been "caught" in several stages of cell division.

On these bases, prokaryotic algal life is well documented from rocks 3.4 billion years old.

The occurrence of life in the oldest known rocks that could have preserved the record of life yields fascinating perspectives. The Fig Tree microfossils are obvious evidence that chemical evolution had passed into the organic evolution of life: they are also evidence that a layered earth and life *came together;* the formation of a layered earth was rapidly followed by the formation of life.

If still older, unaltered sedimentary rocks are ever located, which is an unlikely event, perhaps we will someday receive a glimpse further back in time to even more distant beginnings.

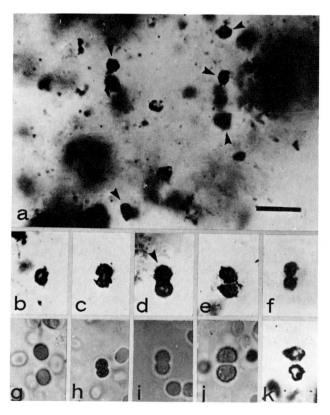

12-4
Arrows in part *a* point to microfossils in the chert. Parts *b* to *e* show stages in cell division preserved as fossils in the chert. Parts *f* and *k* are fissioned cells. Parts *g* to *j* are examples of binary cell division in *modern* prokaryotes. All photomicrographs × 1600. (With permission of Andrew H. Knoll and Elso S. Barghoorn, from A. H. Knoll and E. S. Barghoorn, 1977, *Science, 198,* Fig. 1, pp. 396–398, October 28, 1977. Copyright © 1977 by the American Association for the Advancement of Science. Used with permission.)

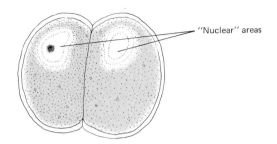

"Nuclear" areas

12-5
Sketch of idealized prokaryotic cell. As drawn, two cells are shown undergoing binary fission. The lighter-colored areas in the upper part of each cell are the very poorly defined nuclear areas that are devoid of a cell wall. "Nuclear" material has been exactly split between the two daughter cells. Compare with Figures 12-4 and 12-8.

Prokaryotic cells (Figure 12-5) (prokaryote means *prenuclear*) have their genetic material somewhat diffused throughout the cell, and they are sexless. Prokaryotes lack chromosomes (major genetic bodies) of the sort seen in all other cells, and chlorophyll, if present, is diffused throughout the cell. All prokaryotes reproduce by **binary fission;** the genetic cell material (one chromosome) is equally divided, and each new daughter cell is an *exact copy of the original.* Reproduction is thus totally asexual, since there is no mingling of genetic material from two different parents. The offspring are *exact* copies of the single parent cell. Little change from generation to generation is possible.

The prokaryotic bacteria and blue-green algae are so unlike any other living thing that at their primitive level of cellular organization, they are neither plants nor animals or, they are both. They are the most primitive life form known on earth, and they survive to this day.

We know about bacteria primarily because some of them make us sick; blue-green algae are the greenish scum on ponds. All blue-green algae are not blue-green in color; a reddish version of them gives the Red Sea its name. Other colored versions of them live in hot springs whose temperatures may approach boiling (Figure 12-6), and still others live with fungi in the plant group we call *lichens.*

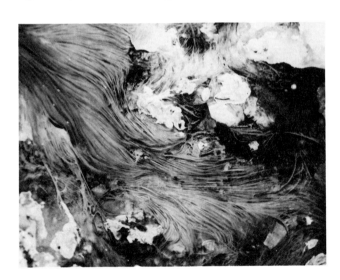

12-6
Calcareous algae floating in a hot spring, Yellowstone National Park, 1897. Such algae may cause the deposition of large amounts of lime mud. (Photograph by Charles D. Walcott, U.S. Geological Survey.)

The First Life   **405**

All blue-green algae and many modern bacteria are *photosynthetic;* they provide their own food by the reaction of the sun with water, carbon dioxide, and chlorophyll in their cells. *If* the oldest fossils recognized until now include blue-green algae, then life had not only overcome its first hurdle, the transition from dead protein to replicating (living) protein, but had also overcome its second hurdle, finding enough food for itself. If the earliest speculative fermenting life only fed on the organic molecules in the oceanic broth that surrounded it and multiplied, it would soon have eaten itself out of existence. Thus earliest heterotrophic life must soon have become *autotrophic* (providing its own food), and the sun was the obvious source of energy. Thus photosynthesis *may* have begun over 3 billion years ago; in fossils as young as 2 billion years old there is no doubt that the life is algal and, therefore, photosynthetic.

By 3 billion years ago, prokaryote life had no trouble existing. The sun provided it food, the ocean provided it a stable home, and there were no predators except the intense ultraviolet radiation from the sun itself. Life must have been easy, because the miracle of photosynthesis guaranteed an unending supply of food. Unfortunately, photosynthesis also required that the algae give off oxygen as a waste product, just as plants in sunlight do today. And for ancient life just *as for modern life, including human beings,* oxygen is a *poisonous* gas. The algae had become the earth's first air polluter, and the consequences were enormous.

Oxygen and Life

We have seen that the origin, proliferation, and development of life occurred under *anaerobic* conditions; there must have been

less than 0.1 percent free oxygen in the early atmosphere. Oxygen would have *destroyed* the early amino acids and complex organic molecules until they were safely shielded by a cell wall. Curiously, however, life could only have *started* in an oxygen-free atmosphere.

For all breathing animals, oxygen represents both a resource and a deadly challenge. This gas, whose presence is now absolutely *vital to most life, is also deadly to all life.* We only survive in an oxygen-rich atmosphere by virtue of an elaborate defense mechanism that is comprised of the proteins in our blood (which we call *hemoglobin*) and certain enzymes (proteins that enhance chemical reactions) present in every cell.

The toxicity of free oxygen is due to its reactivity, which is so great that it will destroy cells unless it is reduced. We can see this toxic effect in the use of hydrogen peroxide (an oxygen source) as an antiseptic and in experiments with space and deep-sea investigators. The results of such studies are unanimous; increased amounts of oxygen are toxic to life, and toxicity increases as a function of oxygen concentration. Indeed, in spite of our body's elaborate defense mechanism, a constant, low level of oxygen damage does seem to occur; many biologists believe that aging is fundamentally cumulative oxygen damage to our cells.

The very reactivity that makes free oxygen so toxic also makes it an extraordinary resource for life. The opportunity that oxygen presented to life for exploiting it for energy use is phenomenal; our whole system of metabolism and growth is based on oxidizing our food intake and yielding carbon dioxide and water as the major waste products.

The blue-green algae, more than 3 billion years ago, *had begun a major change in the composition of the earth's atmosphere*. A change away from the inefficient metabolism by fermentation of other organic matter to more efficient metabolism by photosynthesis was underway. The algae, in time, became much more abundant; they are preserved in rocks as *stromatolites*, reeflike masses (Figure 12-7) of limestone that formed when the metabolism of algae caused lime muds to be deposited around their tissues.

Earliest life had surrounded its substance with a cell wall by over 3.4 billion years ago. That was the *first* major step: from chemical to organic evolution.

The *next* step was the swing from fermentative to photosynthetic metabolism and the production of oxygen. As the oxygen content of the atmosphere gradually began to rise, the earth slowly acquired an ozone layer. Ozone (O_3) is an unstable form of oxygen, produced by lightning (you have probably smelled it during a thunderstorm) or by ultraviolet radiation of ordinary oxygen.

As the ozone layer built up in the earth's atmosphere, its major effect was to *block* most ultraviolet radiation from reaching the earth. The earth had acquired its own shield from the radiation that probably permitted life to originate, but that also *damaged* any form of life that was exposed directly to the unshielded rays of the sun.

The timing of the first photosynthesis could be as old as the Fig Tree rocks—over 3 billion years. If the spheroidal microfossils within the Fig Tree rocks are *not* algae, photosynthesis must have occurred at some later date. Among somewhat younger rocks, the Gunflint Chert from Ontario, Canada, has been radiometrically dated at around 2 billion years; it contains marvelously preserved fossils of blue-green algae. In the Gunflint rocks, there is no doubt that stromatolitic algal colonies are plentiful and that the algae are photosynthetic. Older rocks (2.8 billion years) have since been found that also contain what seem to be stromatolites.

Oxygen thus *supports life* and *also arises from life*. The oxygen we breathe is of wholly biologic origin. Ultimately, it is derived from water, decomposed by light energy in photosynthesis, and by ultraviolet energy, which cause hydrogen to separate from oxygen. Thus, while water and the ancient primitive atmosphere came from volcanoes, the *modern* atmosphere that makes our life possible comes from life itself.

Oxygen makes extraordinary energy available to us; oxygen-based respiration releases more than *10 times* the energy from the same source as anaerobic fermentation does. The shift from fermentative feeding on other organic molecules to oxygenative respiration eventually allowed the evolution of advanced forms of life, including *Homo sa-*

12-7

Stromatolites such as this one (shown here in a polished cross section to illustrate the details of layering) are formed as algal respiration causes the precipitation of lime mud in layers. Stromatolites are fairly common fossils from the middle Precambrian onward. (Photograph by W. H. Bradley, U.S. Geological Survey.)

The First Life **407**

piens. Without photosynthesis, life could never have grown large or complex or have lived on the continents as they evolved and grew in size. The earliest biologic world was a world limited by the intense ultraviolet rays of the sun and the inefficient metabolic process called fermentation, whose waste products are ethyl alcohol or lactic acid.

Before we totally condemn fermentation as primitive and inefficient, we might first remember that an enormous beverage industry is built on fermentative processes. Second, when our own tissues, during heavy physical activity, require more oxygen than breathing will allow, fermentative processes provide that "extra push" at the expense of lactic acid accumulation in the muscles, which causes muscle fatigue. The oxygen debt must eventually be paid back, usually by panting, and the products of fermentation are now metabolized by the more efficient oxidative respiration.

The Eukaryotes

The prokaryotic cell has several disadvantages. Its genetic material is not surrounded (Figure 12-5) by a nuclear membrane, as in all other types of cells. Reproduction does not involve a reassembly of parental genes, but only the sharing of a single chromosome—essentially one long DNA molecule. The organization of hereditary material means that reproduction produces an offspring *exactly* like the parent. Thus the bacteria *Kakabekia umbrellata,* a fossil found in rocks about 2 billion years old, looks very much like a umbrella-shaped modern bacteria, and many living species of blue-green algae are indistinguishable from those preserved as fossils billions of years ago.

The prokaryotes are thus a genetically conservative group; they have survived with little alteration for billions of years. For change to be possible, totally asexual reproduction must be replaced by sexual reproduction; this reproductive method implies immense benefits stemming from the potential for change. For all of us who live in a society that is preoccupied with sex, it may be a shock to discover that sex was invented billions of years ago by *green algae,* which are still found today in both seawater and fresh water!

In order to provide for sexual reproduction, an entirely new organization of matter on the cellular scale was necessary; a cell capable of sexual reproduction *must have a nucleus*—a central area in the cell where the genetic material is enclosed within its own membrane. Such a cell is called eukaryotic—*truly nucleated.* ALL LIVING MATTER, EXCEPT BACTERIA AND BLUE-GREEN ALGAE, IS COMPOSED OF ONE OR MORE EUKARYOTIC CELLS.

In many ways, all life is miraculously alike; life forms as different as people and mushrooms have similar nucleic acids and proteins that are composed of an identical 20 amino acid units. They share similar enzyme systems and methods of obtaining energy from food.

The eukaryotic cell contains numerous internal bodies, called *organelles,* that perform highly specific functions, including reproduction, digestion, and excretion. The prokaryotic cell lacks all of them; even the chlorophyll in photosynthetic prokaryotes is diffused throughout the cell. *How* did the change from prokaryote to eukaryote occur? *Why* did the change occur?

The answers to these questions are somewhat speculative, since the meager fossil evidence can be interpreted in several ways. The why of change must remain speculative, but one reasonable answer is that the formation of nucleii gave cells better protection against oxygen by isolating their vital processes behind a second membrane.

If that concept is accepted, we must marvel that life had survived another challenge: defending itself against its own toxic waste product—oxygen. The process of change may have occurred by successive incorporation of free-living organisms into mutually beneficial, cooperative organisms living within an enclosing cell wall. These organisms then gradually lost their own identity; they are the organelles of the modern eukaryotic cell.

As cells slowly incorporated other specialized cells in a mutually beneficial arrangement, the end product of these experiments, which may have spanned 1 billion years, was the eukaryotic cell (Figure 12-8). The eukaryotic cell represented a great advance over its prokaryotic precursor, because eukaryotes are capable of **mitotic cell division**—and *that* was the key to the future of life.

Recall that prokaryotes carry out cell division by a simple splitting called *binary fission*. Genetic material is replicated, and one set of genetic blueprints is included in each identical daughter cell. In eukaryotic cells, cell division involves one or several series of elaborate nuclear changes; cell division is much more than a simple replication and splitting of genetic information. *Mitotic cell division,* commonly an early stage in cell division of eukaryotes, *is still asexual reproduction;* it is an elaborate mechanism for splitting and replicating the genetic material and the tissue of the parent cell. Thus offspring *cannot* differ from the parent; there is no way for the genes (the basic units of heredity) from one individual to be combined with the genes of another.

However, mitotic cell division is often the precursor to **meiosis**, a highly specialized division of the genetic material that alternates with sexual fertilization. Sexual reproduction, with its meiosis and fertilization, allows *random* chromosomal pairing, which means that each offspring is different from its parent. Sexual reproduction makes genetic recombination possible by *increasing the potential for variation among individuals* in a group.

Without genetic variation, there could be little or no evolution; variation among individuals, acted on by natural selection, is what causes populations to evolve. Evolution can only act on life where variation is present; if environments change, survival depends on the ability to respond to change. Variations that enhance survival are retained; variations that weaken the chance of survival are progressively weeded out.

The development of the eukaryotic cell is then one of the major milestones in life history; it allowed for mitosis and meiosis and also allowed for genetic variation, which led to the great variation of life forms we all accept as normal today. Without the development of eukaryotic cells, the earth would still be populated with only two types of life: bacteria and blue-green algae. And where would that leave us?

When Came The Eukaryotes?

If the development of the eukaryotic cell is the key to everything that follows it, the timing of the origin of cell nucleation is obviously an event that geologists would like to document. Almost 20 years ago, well-preserved eukaryotic algae were found in Australian and Californian rocks nearly 1.5 billion years old. Therefore the formation of

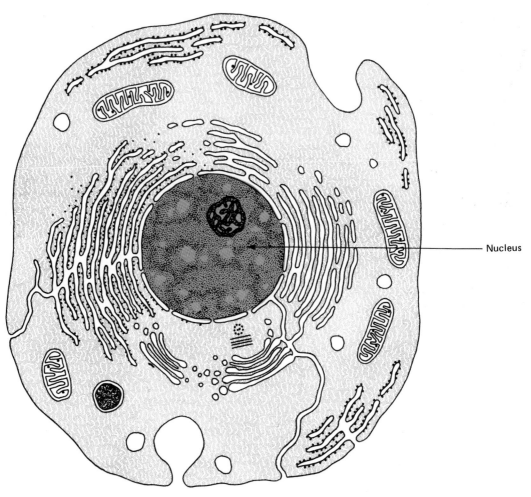

————— Nucleus

12-8
Sketch of an idealized eukaryotic cell. The faintly colored central area is a
well-defined *nucleus* that has a surrounding nuclear membrane. Within the
nucleus are *chromosomes* and other genetic material. The outer cell wall
surrounds a variety of *organelles*, highly specialized cellular components.
Compare with Figure 12-5.

eukaryotic cells was assumed to have been
complete by 1.5 billion years ago.

In 1978 E. S. Barghoorn, one of the discoverers of the proposed eukaryotic fossils,
questioned his own discovery. It seems that
as modern blue-green algae die and degrade,
they create central structures of degraded
organic matter that are identical in detail to
the supposed nucleii of the fossil "eukaryotes." Therefore the fossil record of eukary-

otic life has been seriously misread, because there is no way to recognize undoubtedly eukaryotic life from its microscopically identical, degraded procaryotic ancestor. Nature has played an ironic trick on us; at this time all supposed eukaryotic Precambrian fossils must be regarded as suspect.

There is, however, a partial answer to our persistent question as to the origin time of eukaryotic life. *All* life to which we have referred so far is unicellular; each organism consists of a single, independent cell that carries on all of its life processes by itself. We can now also say that there is no *undoubted* evidence that any of the life forms we have discussed are eukaryotic. All life discussed until now may have been prokaryotes that decayed in such a way that their remains *seemed* to have nucleii.

The vision of scientists challenging their old conceptions with new evidence is a modern model of how science works. As William James said, "Science, like life, feeds on its own decay. New facts burst old rules; then newly defined conceptions bind old and new together into a reconciling law." Where is the reconciling law for the origin of eukaryotes?

METAZOAN LIFE

Fashioning a eukaryotic cell must have been completed before the advent of **metazoa**— organisms that consist of more than one cell. ALL METAZOAN LIFE CONSISTS OF EU-KARYOTIC CELLS; therefore, if we can find the oldest fossil metazoan, we can be certain that eukaryotic cells had formed earlier.

If we accept the apparently nucleated cells from 1.5 billion-year-old rocks as *genuine* eukaryotes, our search is complete. These old fossils have been identified as *green algae,* generally regarded as the group from which all more complex plants and animals developed.

Some types of green algae are unicellular eukaryotes that reproduce asexually by mitosis and sexually by a primitive form of meiosis. Others are equally unicellular, but they live in large colonies of hundreds to thousands of cells, many of which have become specialized for reproduction, feeding, excretion, and the like. In these colonial forms of green algae, the cells are so dependent on one another that they cannot live alone; the colony will die if it is disrupted or if cells are removed from it.

The study of modern green algae may reveal one way in which multicellular plants and animals may have developed. It becomes an entirely arbitrary decision at what stage one calls a colony of cells, which are so interdependent that they cannot live apart from one another, metazoan. As cells began to specialize (to differentiate their functions), unicellularity, colonial unicellularity, and multicellularity become gradational steps in the continuing evolution of life.

If we do *not* accept that the apparent nucleii in algal remains come from 1.5 billion-year-old rocks, we must search for evidence of *undoubted* metazoan life in much younger rocks and be content with knowing that eukaryotes developed at some time long before. In England, Newfoundland, Russia, North Carolina, and South Australia, undoubted, complex, metazoan animal life is well preserved as fossil impressions in rocks that are 600 to 800 million years old.

The most spectacular find of all is in the Pound Quartzite from the Ediacara Hills in South Australia. These ancient tidal flat deposits, around 700 million years old, record the impressions of soft-bodied metazoan animals. Included in this find are a variety of worms, jellyfish, echinoderms, arthropods, and some other forms that are unlike anything still alive.

These are remarkable complex multicellular animals, but they entirely lack skeletons. They give us a glimpse at the astonishing diversity of life in the youngest Precambrian and suggest that the development of the eukaryotic cell either occurred long before 700 million years ago or that the development of the eukaryotic cell—with its capacity for variation—led to nearly explosive filling of numerous ecological niches shortly after the development of sexuality.

Our view of the development of Precambrian life permits us occasional glimpses at long intervals and, to date, offers little evidence of what went on between the periods that we do know about.

This reflects three facts surrounding the investigation of Precambrian life. FIRST, analysis of Precambrian microfossils had to await advances in optical and electron microscope technology. SECOND, because of the first restraint, investigation of Precambrian life has been confined to the last 20 years. THIRD, the majority of Precambrian rocks were long ago melted, metamorphosed, or recycled into other rock (Chapter Five). The fossil record is sparse, because there are relatively few rocks remaining in which life could be preserved.

A Tentative Summary

As time continues, more information about early life will become available to explain what went on in the as yet unexplored Precambrian periods. It is doubtful that the following observations will, however, be changed by new data.

Life began as a unicellular, fermentative form but, in time, evolved into a photosynthetic form. Photosynthesis released oxygen into the primitive atmosphere, thereby slowly increasing its oxygen content. Life met the challenge of this reactive gas by developing the eukaryotic cell to protect its reproductive material; in doing so, it changed its reproduction method from asexual to sexual. In the presence of elevated oxygen levels, eukaryotic photosynthetic organisms diversified into more complex plants and animals whose more and more specialized cells led to metazoan life (Figure 12-9). Metazoan green algae *may* stretch back 1.5 billion years; complex metazoan animal life definitely stretches back at least 700 million years.

The interval before the appearance of complex metazoan organisms was undoubtedly the interval during which primitive eukaryotic plants, probably flagellated green algae, evolved into complex marine plants and animals. This long period of time— nearly 1 billion years—has yet to be recorded by a fossiliferous rock unit. The form of evolution during this time is still an unknown but, by 700 million years ago, its end result was incredibly diverse soft-bodied faunas that awaited the next profound evolutionary step—the development of a skeleton.

Multicellularity had many advantages. Unicellular life is severely limited in size to the maximum size through which food may diffuse in and wastes may diffuse out. Because of multicellularity, cells could specialize and become interdependent; this led to much greater size. Increase in size is a common evolutionary trend; it permits much greater stability of life processes in the organism, greater feeding and reproductive capacities, and increased longevity. Regulatory mechanisms had to be developed to

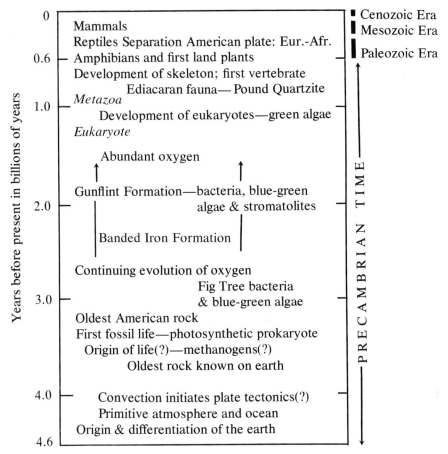

0
Mammals
Reptiles Separation American plate: Eur.-Afr.
0.6 — Amphibians and first land plants
Development of skeleton; first vertebrate
Ediacaran fauna— Pound Quartzite
1.0 — *Metazoa*
Development of eukaryotes—green algae
Eukaryote

Abundant oxygen

Gunflint Formation—bacteria, blue-green
2.0 — algae & stromatolites

Banded Iron Formation

Continuing evolution of oxygen
Fig Tree bacteria
3.0 — & blue-green algae
Oldest American rock
First fossil life—photosynthetic prokaryote
Origin of life(?)—methanogens(?)
Oldest rock known on earth

4.0 — Convection initiates plate tectonics(?)
Primitive atmosphere and ocean
Origin & differentiation of the earth
4.6

Years before present in billions of years

PRECAMBRIAN TIME

■ Cenozoic Era
▮ Mesozoic Era
▮ Paleozoic Era

12-9
A chart of some of the major events in the history of the earth. Speculative
events are shown with a question mark. Origin of eukaryotes is not well fixed
in time.

keep all the cells working in a coordinated manner so that, in terms of greater efficiency, the advantages of specialization could be realized.

Establishment of the sexual process for reproduction also accelerated the rate of evolution of multicellular life, because (together with mutation) it yielded an essentially unlimited number of variations on which the environment could act. The incredible variation in life is obvious even within the highly restricted group known as humans; among the billions of humans alive today, not one is exactly like another.

The development of sexuality about 900 million years ago led to an enormous diversification in life. We first see the results of this explosive increase in diversity in worldwide rocks formed 600 to 700 million years ago.

These faunas, known collectively as the *Ediacaran faunas* (named after the Ediacara Hills in South Australia), yield soft-bodied examples of many of the major modern forms of animal life. They are only a prelude; the major unfolding of the more complete *fossil* record had to await the development of a preservable skeleton, and that event was to coincide approximately with the beginning of the Paleozoic era. To restate this more properly, the Paleozoic era was defined as the era in which preserved fossils were both metazoan and skeletonized.

Oxygen and Metazoa

One other event must be described before the discussion of Precambrian life is closed. Recalling that photosynthetic algae began placing oxygen in the atmosphere several billion years ago, we can fit one last piece into our story. At the beginning of oxygen emission iron, one of the earth's most abundant elements, absorbed huge volumes of oxygen as it changed from its soluble form to its insoluble form. Iron, which had moved freely into the early ocean in dissolved form, now began to enter the ocean as *particulate* matter; the unique sedimentary rock that resulted is called the *banded iron formation* (Figure 12-10). This type of rock, a worldwide iron ore, is found *only* in rocks older than 1.8 billion years (Figure 12-9) on nearly every continent on earth. After this watershed date, the banded iron formations do not occur; they required the peculiarly low-level oxygenated atmosphere of the primitive earth in order to form.

As oxygen continued to enrich the atmosphere, the formation of the atmospheric ozone shield should have occurred when the oxygen content of the atmosphere reached 1 percent. Since harmful ultraviolet radiation was now screened out, photosynthetic organisms would have multiplied rapidly, no longer requiring elaborate defense mechanisms against the destructive potential of the ultraviolet rays. As the dominant life forms shifted from fermentative to oxidative respiration, oxygen furnished an increasingly valuable resource for life.

The oxygen produced by photosynthesis accumulated slowly; life had to segregate oxygen to form carbohydrates or to set it apart in its inorganic form (limestone) as oxygen was evolved. Oxygen not taken into organic or inorganic compounds was simply recombined at night, just as modern marine plants do today. Thus oxygen could only build up when there were no carbonaceous compounds to absorb it; life required *more* life to partially absorb its own waste product.

As oxygen continued to increase, the eukaryotic cell effectively met its toxic challenge and exploited its reactivity in oxygenbased respiration. It also seems that increasing oxygen levels fueled an explosive metazoan evolution that was based on the diversity furnished by sexual reproduction. Size could now increase, because oxygen respiration and cellular differentiation provided much higher levels of efficiency. The minute size of early Precambrian life that was to make its recognition and study so difficult soon gave way to a rich store of metazoan life of constantly increasing size that required the development of a skeleton. We will discuss that in Chapter Thirteen. We next consider the physical events of the first seven-eighths of our earth's history.

12-10
A banded iron formation is a rock composed of alternating layers of magnetite (the dark layers) and hematite (lighter layers) in a matrix of finely crystalline silica. The layering in this specimen, which is about 6 inches (15 centimeters) across, is gently folded; the specimen was collected near Ely, Minnesota. Around the world, rocks of this type are found in only one interval of middle Precambrian time, suggesting that these rocks represent a unique transitional chemical system and were formed only at the time that oxygen first became abundant.

PRECAMBRIAN PHYSICAL EVENTS

It is difficult to encapsulate the physical events that cover 4 billion years into a small part of one chapter. Although they are difficult to work with and often geographically inaccessible, Precambrian rocks around the world have yielded a remarkable history of continental and oceanic events. Instead of summarizing everything that is known on the subject, this discussion centers on two fundamental geologic questions. How did our continents and ocean basins originate? How have they changed through the 40 million centuries recorded in the rocks themselves?

We must first find out what the oldest rocks are; then we must interpret the stories they record. This will severely test our uniformitarian principles, because we may be reaching back into a past so different from today that we cannot understand it in terms of modern processes. However, this is not necessarily so; we may find that today's processes explain even the oldest record we have.

The Oldest Rocks

Rocks more than 3 billion years old occupy a little less than 10 percent of the total area of the world's continents. Areas of ancient igneous and metamorphic rocks that contain these very old radiometric ages include part of Labrador, southeastern Africa, northern Norway, southern Minnesota and, especially, western Greenland. These oldest rocks consist of metamorphosed basaltic volcanic and sedimentary rocks and lighter-colored granitic gneisses.

The oldest come from strongly metamorphosed rocks on the west coast of Greenland; they yield a radiometric date of about

3.8 billion years. Like other rocks older than 3 billion years, the Greenland rocks contain within them fragments of still older rocks that cannot be dated, but these fragments must be even older. Perhaps the greatest lesson to be learned from these ancient rocks is that they are much like other rocks billions of years their junior. The concept of uniformity still applies.

The second lesson they suggest is that continental crust had formed by 3.8 billion years ago and has remained ever since. As discussed in Chapter Seven, continental crust is of too low a density to be incorporated into either denser oceanic or mantle rocks. Once formed, continental crust is permanent. It may be eroded and redeposited, sliced into ribbons, glued onto another continent, and severely deformed—but it cannot be totally destroyed. Thus continental rocks stretch back nearly to the beginning of the earth and record essentially all of its history.

As noted in Chapter Seven, the counterparts of continental rocks, the ocean floors, record only the last 200 million years of history; rocks of the ocean floors are geologically transient visitors to the surface of the earth, doomed to subduction and remelting.

If continental crust *is* permanent, other pertinent questions must be asked. *From where* does continental crust come? How is continental crust *first* formed?

We know that the plate tectonic processes that have so obviously dominated the last one-twentieth of the earth's history make continents out of ocean crust; we have observed that such a process is happening today along the west coast of South America, where the westward-drifting American plate is overriding the Pacific Ocean (see Chapter Seven). Along such a consumptive plate margin, modern *ocean floor* is forced beneath the continental mass, and its lower-melting-point components are *added to the continents by volcanism* to construct a part of the Andes. Could the continents in the past also have been formed from continuing differentiation from the heavier rocks of the mantle? Could plate tectonics really have worked that long ago?

Let us *assume* for a minute that plate tectonics was at work soon after the earth's differentiation into crust, mantle, and cores. Let us predict what the plate tectonic model would produce in a few billion years and then check that prediction against what is known of the Precambrian crust. Also, we will investigate what process or processes might have formed the oldest sliver of rock that we have left to work with.

The oldest rocks known are, as mentioned, strongly deformed igneous and metamorphic rocks. Their parentage seems to be volcanic basaltic rock and fairly average types of sedimentary crustal rock. Thus the oldest known rocks correspond with oceanic crust and typical continental crust. How either type of crust originally formed is open to conjecture, but two other results are not. These oldest rocks, in part originally sedimentary, tell us that the earth *had an ocean* 3.8 billion years ago. Furthermore, they tell us that the earth *had a crust* composed of basaltic and intermediate types of rock. Differentiation from the mantle *could* have formed the oldest crust.

If all of the earth's continental crust, or a great part of it, had been formed in the earliest history of the earth, it should still be around. It might be profoundly altered by later events, but it could never be totally destroyed once formed. Detailed examination of younger Precambrian rocks show that their strontium isotope ratios (see Chapter Eleven) are inconsistent with their formation through remelting of older continental crust but the ratios are consistent with rock formation as differentiates of the upper mantle.

Examination of areas of crustal rock in North America (Figure 12-11) presents information similar to that of other continents. Less than 10 percent of the area of the North America continent contains rock older than 3 billion years.

Apparently the earliest continental blocks were quite small; they are surrounded by other blocks of generally *progressively younger* age. It paradoxically seems that the earth's continental blocks were growing outward from a central, older core, adding layer after layer.

If we check the continental rocks of North America (Figure 12-11), perhaps as much as one-half of them are older than 2.5 billion years; *one-half* of North America existed 2.5 billion years ago—and these rocks have changed little since.

Could we be seeing genuine growth of the land area of a continent through time? If so, from where is an increasing volume of rock coming? Will the process continue? An expansion of ideas already discussed in Chapter Seven will provide some remarkable, tentative answers.

Continental Margins

From the theory of plate tectonics we have learned that continental margins that face rift oceans—oceans growing larger in area by addition of basaltic seafloor at the oceanic ridge—are passive and quiet. Such margins are the site of modern geosynclines, as discussed in Chapter Seven. A geosyncline is the name given to sites of sediment accumulation on the modern *continental shelf* and *continental slope* or *rise*.

The sediments deposited on the modern continental shelf are characteristically clean, well-sorted fossiliferous sediments, deposited in shallow water. Continental shelves comprise about 10 percent of the earth's total surface area and are broad aprons of sediment accumulation stretching from shoreline to a prominent break in slope at depths averaging around 600 yards (550 meters). The wedge of sediments is generally coarser grained near the shoreline and somewhat finer grained further offshore. The wedge of sediments thickens seaward; total thickness ranges up to 3 miles (5 kilometers) near the shelf edge. At the shelf edge, the sediment wedge is abruptly truncated by the break in slope, which passes into the much deeper zone of sediment accumulation that we know as the continental slope or rise.

The continental shelves of the world receive over 40 trillion tons (36 trillion metric tons) of sediments from the continents annually and spread this vast load over the shelves under the influence of current and wave action. These vast collections of winnowed sediment, deposited in *shallow,* sunlit water form about one-half of the total geosyncline; the shoreward section is called the **miogeosyncline,** or miogeocline.

Seaward from the continental shelf, miogeosyncline is a totally different domain of sediment accumulation known to oceanographers as the continental rise and to geologists as the **eugeosyncline,** or eugeocline— the *deep water part of the geosyncline.* The continental rise typically stretches seaward for hundreds of miles (kilometers), gradually grading into the deep ocean floor (Figure 12-12).

The rise is the site of accumulation of sediments that may be up to 6 miles (10 kilo-

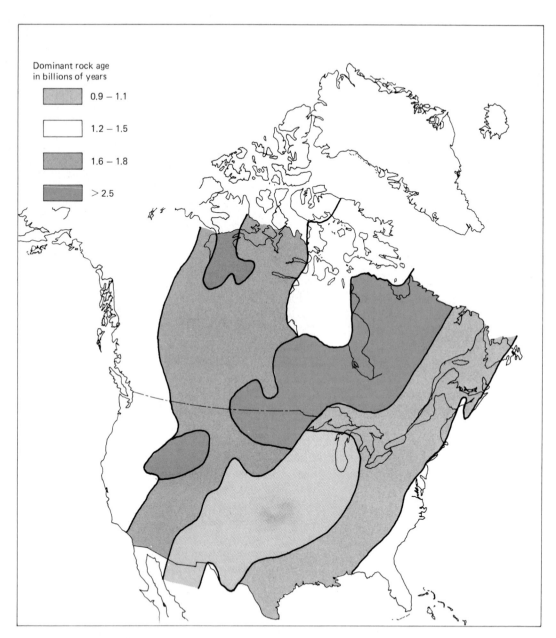

**Dominant rock age
in billions of years**

- 0.9 – 1.1
- 1.2 – 1.5
- 1.6 – 1.8
- > 2.5

12-11

Major age provinces of Precambrian continental platform rock in North
America. Data are *highly* generalized from numerous sources; small areas of
rock of differing ages are within the larger provinces shown.

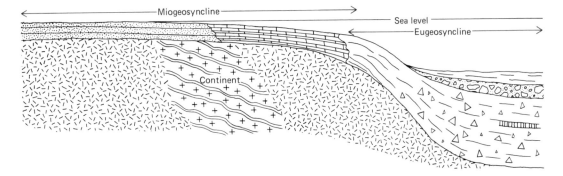

12-12
Modern concept of a geosyncline. The miogeosyncline encompasses the continental shelf, and the eugeosyncline includes the continental rise. The continent is made up of older, highly deformed geosynclinal material that comes mostly from the eugeosyncline plus volcanic material added from the mantle. The folding, metamorphism, and intrusion of the geosynclinal material comprising the continent *predates* the *formation* of the modern geosyncline shown by many millions of years

meters) thick, deposited on the rise as muddy sand cascades from the continental shelf. The sediments are termed *turbidites,* because they flow onto the rise as a turbid (cloudy or muddy) suspension from above, much like an ash cloud (Chapter 3) suspension from a volcano. Interlayered with these turbidites are typical deep water fine clay beds, dark, thin limestones, and cherts. Fossils are sparse and include siliceous marine animals.

It was suggested in Chapter Seven that geosynclines were mountain ranges waiting to be born. It has long been recognized that modern fold mountain ranges, such as the Appalachians, Ouachitas, and Rockies, are areas of former geosynclinal sediment accumulation. As suggested, the mighty fold mountain ranges of the world seem to have been inched up into the sky as the passive, geosynclinal continental margins reversed

their tectonic role and became convergent plate margins, crushing and compressing the former geosynclinal sedimentary prism along oceanic subduction zones of areas of continent-continent collision. These ideas will now be discussed in more detail, because they seem to be the key to how continents are made.

Continental Construction

First, imagine a geosynclinal margin, composed of both the eugeosynclinal and miogeosynclinal units, caught up in a convergent oceanic subduction zone. The best modern example is the west coast of South America, and the formation of the Andes. In such a zone of subduction, the basaltic seafloor plunges beneath the continent and is melted and consumed; its lighter-weight fractions are added to the continental crust as andesitic volcanoes.

The eugeosyncline sediments, which rested on the ocean floor, are intensely crumpled, compressed, and metamorphosed at high pressure. The resulting rock group consists of detached slices of altered ocean floor basalts interlayered with crumpled, metamorphosed eugeosynclinal rocks. This suite or group of intermingled, deformed ocean floor basalts and eugeosynclinal rocks is called an *ophiolite suite*. Ophiolitic rocks are a part of many high mountain ranges today; they mark the former juncture of sea-floor and eugeosyncline.

The intense compression and alteration that are characteristic of either a subductive convergent plate margin or a zone of continent-to-continent collision forces the former eugeosynclinal rocks onto the continent; this literally *welds* these rocks to the continental landmass from which they formerly came as sediments. By contrast, volcanic additions from the mantle and from the former sea-floor represent *new* material added to the continent for the first time from the mantle.

The addition of low-melting-point light-weight material from the mantle to the continent is the process by which continents grow in size through time. This process is irreversible; once the granitic and andesitic material of lower density is added to a continent, *it can never be returned to the mantle.* It may be weathered, eroded, and deposited on a continental shelf or rise, but its fate is assured; the next round of convergence will metamorphose it, melt it, and jam it right back onto a continent. Once added and safely inland, it is little altered throughout the rest of geologic time.

If continents grow in size by adding on successive belts of eugeosynclinal material to their margins, what of the miogeosyn-clinal material? The shallow water sedimentary rocks of the miogeosyncline are deposited *on* older metamorphic and igneous rock of intermediate to granitic composition. This rock is collectively called the **basement** by geologists, because it forms the foundation for everything above it. Basement rock is merely older eugeosynclinal rocks welded onto the continent in the past and then worn down to serve as the foundation for new deposition.

Thus, as a continental mass grows outward, its margin facing a rift ocean is always the site of geosynclinal accumulation; the miogeosynclinal sediments accumulate across an older, deformed, eroded eugeosynclinal mass (Figure 12-13).

The compression that so profoundly alters and intermingles eugeosynclinal rocks and ocean floor basalts has a different effect on the miogeosynclinal prism sitting up on top of low-density basement rock. The miogeosynclinal rocks are thrown into a series of folds and faults, and the intensity of the deformation dies out landward. Metamorphism and melting are uncommon; instead, the sediments of the miogeosyncline are kicked into great open folds.

A Tentative Summary

The essential resistance to subduction and the indestructibility of continental crust are the most fundamental facts about our earth. Because of their low density, continental rocks cannot be recycled into the mantle once they have formed from it. Continental rocks are rarely totally remelted; strontium isotope data indicate that the majority of continental rocks have continued, through geologic time, to originate from the upper mantle, whose strontium isotope ratio is

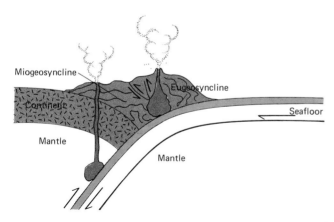

Miogeosyncline

Eugeosyncline

Continent

Seafloor

Mantle

Mantle

12-13
During a continent-ocean basin collision, the miogeosynclinal sedimentary rocks were squeezed and faulted upward into large fold mountains, like the Appalachians. Volcanism beneath the continent along the Benioff zone adds mantle material to the continent, while ophiolite and blueschist zones (Chapter Five) may form where eugeosynclinal sediments have been metamorphosed, melted, and welded onto the continental margin.

changing due to radioactive decay (see Figure 11-16).

The continents are self-healing. They recover essentially all the sediment washed out onto their margins in each convergent event and weld that metamorphosed and melted sediment onto the continent; they also form strongly folded mountains from the former rocks of the entire geosyncline. Each fold mountain range records the successive readdition of the continent's own material to its convergent margin.

But *if* these retrieving and altering processes were the *only* ones at work, the continents would *simply retain their size, endlessly realtering their own material.* Instead, radiometric dates indicate that continents *add to their own area throughout time by welding on successive geosynclines* at their convergent margins *and by adding new material from the mantle by igneous activity.* This latter process provides each continent with new volumes of granitic material from the mantle.

We might speculate that if such a process has been operating for 4 billion years, pro-

viding the continents with progressively younger volumes of granitic rock, the mantle itself would be changing in composition. But the entire earth's crust, which seems very important to us, since we live on the fractional continental part of it, is only about four-hundredths of 1 percent of the mass of the earth; the mantle could manufacture all of the continental crust thus far created without any measurable change in its own chemical composition.

People have been confronted with their insignificance once again. The continents on which we live are little more than the thin skin of granitic slag on the surface of the boiling mantle. Our continents are sent spinning lazily across the surface. Their collisions with other continents or ocean basins force their debris back up into the sky once more; this process is punctuated by igneous events that add more material each time. The continents then reverse their motion and slowly ram into other antagonists. They emerge triumphant from each collision; their light weight always keeps them on top of the convecting mantle, although driven by it.

From each collision, they also emerge enlarged because of the addition of lower-melting-point silicates from the mantle beneath; their boundaries are extended into the ocean basins that feed them.

Implications Of The Model

If our model of growing continents is real (and not all geologists would agree that it is), it would imply that the earth, too, is evolving. Early continents would have been quite small and, on an isostatic earth, thin. The type of metamorphism observed in our oldest rocks supports this idea; most Precambrian metamorphism is of a type characterized by low pressure but high temperature. Only in the ophiolite zones, the ancient margins of land and sea, is the sequence sometimes reversed; here the powerful pressures of convergence have left glistening *blueschists,* metamorphic rocks (Chapter 5) whose unique mineral content forms only under extreme pressures but comparatively low temperatures.

As continents grow in area against the seafloors, they also gradually grow in thickness, standing, in a very general way, progressively higher above the sea. It is as if, with time, the continents are becoming better defined and better separated from the seafloors that furnish their substance.

Rifts in the seafloor may tear continents apart, as Africa and the Arabian Peninsula are experiencing today. Each new fragment goes its own way; in time it, too, joins with a different partner for a time. The gliding motions of the lithosphere may force continent against continent, as India and Asia are today squeezed into a new comradeship. Continents may be slowly shredded into fragments along planes of rotational slip, as southwest California continues its lonesome journey toward the Aleutians today. But

nothing can *destroy* a continental mass; each continent is a combination of fragments of lightweight substances and is jammed into geosynclinal collision by distant events.

As long as the radioactive fires within the mantle continue to fuel the earth, the cycle of accretionary growth, punctuated by rifting and shredded by transform faulting, will continue. The ancient rocks have told their story of triumphant growth from an inauspicious beginning nearly 40 million centuries ago. The story of mountains, continents, and ocean floors, briefly outlined here, is presented in more detail in the chapters that follow. First, however, a brief glance at other treasures hidden within these most ancient of rocks is in order.

PRECAMBRIAN WEALTH

More than history lies within Precambrian rocks; they are the greatest storehouse of mineral wealth for the world. Forming as they do the basement for Paleozoic and younger rocks, Precambrian rocks form the stable platform on which the last 600 million years of life and events were to be played out.

These great platforms of Precambrian rock, underlying almost all of North America and other continents, are called **shields** or **cratons.** Cratonic rock, bounded by either active or passive continental margins, includes deposits of iron, chromium, nickel, diamond, copper, uranium, gold, and many other substances vital to our technological way of life.

Iron

No resource dominates the Precambrian cratons of the world as does iron, the fourth most abundant element in our crust. The iron ore deposits in the Minnesota-Michigan area have satisfied our needs for this most used of all metals for over 100 years, and they are far from exhausted. Worldwide, Precambrian iron ore deposits exist on essentially every continent; for example, banded iron ores (Figure 12-10) are found in Labrador, Brazil, Greenland, and western Australia.

This unusual rock is present throughout the world in Precambrian rocks; it is never found in younger rocks. Its uniqueness lies not only in its restricted age of formation and worldwide abundance, but also in its richness. Banded iron formation may be more than one-half iron, an extraordinarily rich ore.

This lucky accident of ancient chemistry creates an ore so rich and so abundant that iron and steel form the basis of industrial technology around the world. Raw iron costs us less than dog food and is therefore little valued. Each of us uses somewhat less than 1 ton ($^9/_{10}$ metric ton) each of iron and steel *every year*. Our needs continue to be met primarily from the banded iron formation and allied rocks of the Lake Superior region.

Since iron and steel account for over 95 percent of all metals used in the world, and since most iron comes from Precambrian rocks, the importance of Precambrian resources to our world cannot be overemphasized. The worldwide reserves of Precambrian iron ore are many trillions of pounds (kilograms), enough for many centuries of reliance on the ancient sources of this modern metal.

Uranium

The richest reserves of uranium in the United States are in young sedimentary rocks in Colorado, Wyoming, Arizona, and New Mexico. On a worldwide basis, most uranium does not come from deposits of this type, but from igneous and metamorphic rocks that contain the mineral substance sometimes called *pitchblende;* this is the raw material from which radium was first isolated. Pitchblende (uraninite) deposits occur in Precambrian rocks in several regions of Canada and Africa.

As fuel for the future, these reserves are critical; an intensive worldwide search for uranium has revealed far less of this radioactive element than one might have hoped.

Gold

Gold, precious metal and gift to kings, is essentially indestructible. Most of the gold ever recovered is still available for our use, because no one is careless with gold. Therefore the gold in your dental filling may once have graced an Egyptian Pharaoh's arm as part of a bracelet.

Most of the world's gold comes from Precambrian gravel deposits, many of which also yield small amounts of diamonds and uranium. The largest gold mine in the United States is the Homestake Mine in South Dakota, where gold occurs in Precambrian metamorphic rock.

Nickel

Nickel is used to alloy steel and give it desirable noncorrosive properties and great strength at high temperature. The majority of the world's supply of nickel comes from mineral segregations in dark-colored plutonic Precambrian rock. One mine in southern Canada furnishes somewhat less than one-third of the world's total nickel produc-

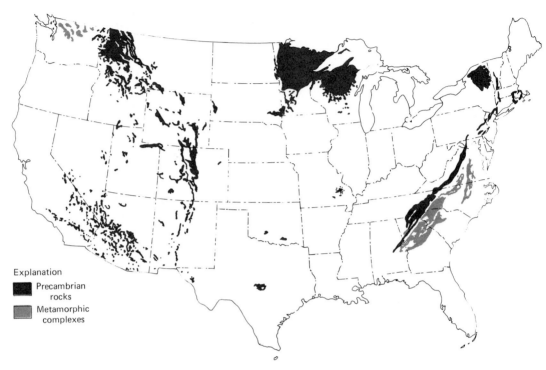

12-14

Surface exposures of Precambrian rocks. Also shown are metamorphic complexes that probably include rocks of Precambrian age. (From P. B. King, 1976, U.S. Geological Survey Professional Paper 902.)

tion from deposits in a Precambrian gabbroic body.

DISTRIBUTION OF PRECAMBRIAN ROCKS

Precambrian rocks underlie most of North America, but they are almost hidden by overlying younger sedimentary rocks. The Adirondacks of New York State are one area where the Precambrian rocks of central Canada reappear from under their sedimentary cover. The Blue Ridge zone in the Ap-

palachians and areas throughout northern Minnesota and Michigan also expose Precambrian rocks. The Black Hills of South Dakota, the Arbuckle Mountains of Oklahoma, and the Central Mineral Region of Texas also provide isolated glimpses. Precambrian rocks are well exposed all up and down the Rockies and in numerous other areas all the way to eastern California. These exposures (Figure 12-14), combined with the recovery of numerous samples of Precambrian rocks from deep wells, give us a reasonably complete glimpse of the foundation of our continent.

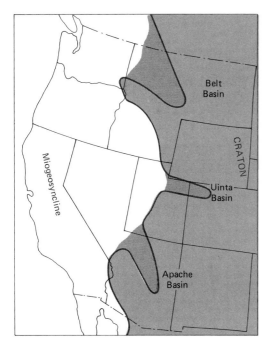

12-15

A reconstruction of the probable western shoreline of the United States approximately 800 million years ago. The continental platform had three major bays in which thick muddy and limy sediments were deposited during late Precambrian time. (After Jack E. Harrison, et al., 1974, U.S. Geological Survey Professional Paper 866.)

Among the best places to study the terminal events of the Precambrian era and to study a large exposure of Precambrian rock is in Glacier National Park in Montana. The rocks of Glacier National Park are primarily of young Precambrian age and were apparently deposited in a marine reentrant (bay) into the North American craton between 800 and 1600 million years ago (Figure 12-15). Similar rocks of this age were deposited in Utah and Arizona, also in comparable reentrants and at approximately the same time. The best modern analogy we have of such a cratonic seaway would be the Gulf Coast embayment.

Sediments deposited in the Gulf of Mexico today reach up to 9 miles (15 kilometers) in thickness and consist of generally fine-grained sediments furnished to the basin by numerous rivers draining the heartland of the United States. Picture our western shoreline, as reconstructed from evidence in the rocks themselves, about 800 million years ago (Figure 12-15). Along embayments in that shoreline, up to 12 miles (20 kilometers) of silt and mud, along with some fine-grained limestone, was deposited as North America prepared for a new era—the Paleozoic.

Rocks formed in those old basins now have many names, and they form scenery as diverse as Glacier National Park, the Uinta Mountains, and a lower part of the walls of Grand Canyon. They record sedimentation in an environment like our modern Gulf of Mexico over a period lasting 800 million years. By the end of the Precambrian time, the western shoreline of North America roughly paralleled the western boundaries of modern Utah, Idaho, and Arizona (Figure 12-15).

SUMMARY   Our solar system originated approximately 4.6 billion years ago, perhaps by the accumulation of interstellar matter in a nebular system. As the solid matter that was to make the earth accumulated to make a larger and larger body, radioactive decay produced more heat than a solid, rocky body could conduct away into space. The early earth then mostly melted, and its heavy iron-rich material gravitated toward its center to form the core. Progressively lighter material made the mantle and the first bits of crust.

The mantle then began releasing internal heat by convection, and this more efficient process allowed the earth to cool. Intense volcanism released great quantities of water vapor and carbon- and hydrogen-rich compounds to make the primitive oceans and atmosphere. This happened almost 4 billion years ago.

Within that early ocean, lightning and intense ultraviolet radiation formed more and more complex organic molecules, but the awesome change from these molecules to actual life forms is still largely unexplained by science. The first life, probably a unicellular, prokaryotic, fermentative-heterotroph, likely formed more than 3.5 billion years ago. Its descendants soon switched to a more efficient method of feeding; they developed the process of photosynthesis and thereby released oxygen into the primitive atmosphere.

Oxygen changed everything. It eventually shielded life from the potentially damaging radiation that may have helped form it and provided a much more efficient system of energy conversion. In response to rising oxygen levels, critical organelles (specialized subunits of a cell) began to share a central nuclear membrane. The newly organized eukaryotic cell discovered the secret of sexual reproduction, which would permit the enormous diversity of life that was to follow. That diverse life included entirely soft-bodied creatures that were poorly preserved in natural environments; however, the fragmentary record that remains suggests that evolution occurred rapidly in the several hundred million years immediately preceding the beginning of the Paleozoic era.

Life met challenge after challenge—ultraviolet radiation, the need for oxygen, and the need for food. Photosynthesis, nucleation, mitosis, and meiosis were some of the responses to these challenges. The rate of change speeded up dramatically once sexual reproduction was possible, and it remains high today. The genetically conservative prekaryotic ancestors still exist alongside their modern offspring.

The earliest continental landmass was driven by convection within the underlying mantle, much as continents are driven today. The mantle provided the fuel for motion and additional rocky material of lower melting point and density as the mantle continued to differentiate. Continents, adding their own sedimentary wedges and newly formed volcanic rocks to their margins, slowly grew in area and have become distinctive from the seafloors that feed them.

By the beginning of the Paleozoic era, the North American craton had grown outward from its oldest core in the modern Hudson Bay area to underlay most of North America. The changes that produced this pattern were not uniform; continents were repeatedly sliced, rifted, and rejoined with other continents, but the basic pattern of growth is fairly clear, and the processes are uniform.

Within the cratons of the world is most of our mineral wealth, including gold, nickel, uranium and, most important, vast supplies of iron ore. The rocks of the Precambrian are exposed over most of central Canada and in more isolated areas in the United States, separated by large areas of younger sedimentary rocks.

The Precambrian is a prelude; the events that shaped North America were still to come, and only a few modern life forms stretch back to the Precambrian. The great lesson of the Precambrian is that the earth, too, is evolving (its continents are growing), and its evolving life is incredibly tenacious and adaptable. Perhaps this fact is reassuring; human beings are the culmination of almost 4 billion years of life that met many deadly challenges by coping and changing.

Of course, not all life successfully adapted; an estimated 100 million species of plants and animals are known only as fossils, because they are long extinct. What made the difference between those that could cope and those that could not? This question, which has implications for all of us, is answered in the following chapters.

EXERCISES

1. Referring to Figure 5-1, why is it so difficult to find unmetamorphosed oldest Precambrian rock?
2. If Precambrian heat flow was extremely high, why would the assumption follow that early continents were extremely thin compared to today's continents?
3. What are the limits, if any, to the lateral extent of continents?
4. See Figure 7-5b. Does the relative size of continents bear any relation to their antiquity? How could this be tested?
5. A plot of radiometric dates versus distance from continental margins for North America reveals a rough linear relation. How could you account for the dependency of these two variables?
6. The earliest known fossil life is spherical. What are the advantages of being spherical to a tiny life form in the ocean?
7. During the earliest Precambrian, the year might well have had over 1000 days (see Figure 11-1). The moon would have been much closer to the earth. How would all this have affected ocean tides? How would the tidal effect affect life?

8. Recently researchers have suggested that various varieties of ordinary clay preferentially cause chains of amino acids to form from inorganic materials. In order to have clay available, what processes must intervene?

9. Given your knowledge of the relation between igneous activity and ore deposits from Chapter Two and the relation between oceanic rift zones and ore deposits developed in Chapter Seven, give two distinctly different reasons why Precambrian rocks should hold the majority of the world's mineral wealth.

10. We have direct evidence of photosynthetic life in the oldest rocks that could preserve it and, by tenuous inference, a probability that methanogens predated the Fig Tree algae. Life, then, seems to have arisen on the earth as soon as the earth was cool enough to allow it. What philosophical implications do you draw from this? Does this statement say anything about the chances of finding life in other solar systems?

SUGGESTED READINGS

Hargraves, R. B., 1976, "Precambrian Geologic History," *Science, 193* (4251), pp. 363–371.
  A different approach to continental evolution than the one presented here; excellent reading and bibliography.
King, Philip B., 1976, *Precambrian Geology of the United States: An Explanatory Text to Accompany the Geologic Map of the United States,* U.S. Geological Survey Professional Paper 902, Washington, D.C., U.S. Government Printing Office, 85 pp.
  Thorough review and bibliography; excellent appraisal by region of U.S. Precambrian rocks and history.
Ponnamperuma, Cyril (ed.), 1977, *Chemical Evolution of the Early Precambrian,* New York, Academic Press, 221 pp.
  A delightfully rich book, a bit technical at times, with a good review of earliest Precambrian events and concepts.
Windley, Brian F., 1977, *The Evolving Continents,* London, Wiley, 385 pp.
  Masterful review of the course of evolution of the continents; heavy emphasis on Precambrian events, and an exhaustive bibliography.

KEY CONCEPTS

Continental evolution
  Earliest accretion, conduction led to temperature rise; melting, iron catastrophe, and differentiation with convection; differentiation of

upper mantle to produce granitic continents still continues; continents grow larger and thicker, therefore higher above sea level with time; accretion of geosynclines the basic growth mechanism.

Ophiolites and blueschists; upper mantle volcanism.

Evolution of life

Methanogens may (?) predate oldest known fossils: oldest life is photosynthetic prokaryotic algae; bacteria also an important Precambrian fossil type; shift to eukaryotic cell difficult to date, may have occurred by 1400 million years ago, certainly by 700 million years ago; eukaryotes a defense against oxygen; eukaryotes provide sexual reproduction and genetic variability.

Precambrian rocks the storehouse for world mineral wealth

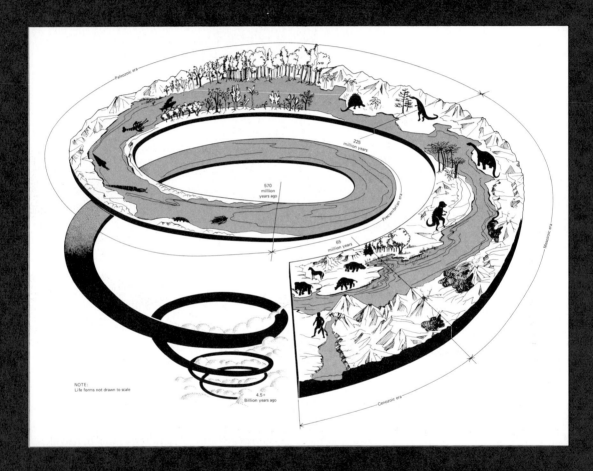

This spiral depicts in highly schematic form the parade of events and life within the past 570 million years. (From W.L. Newman, *Geologic Time*, U.S. Geological Survey.)

Chapter Thirteen

MORNING

the paleozoic

"Knowledge consists in understanding the evidence that establishes the fact, not in the belief that it is a fact."
Charles T. Sprading

The boundary between the Precambrian era and the Paleozoic era was originally defined as the boundary between nonfossiliferous rocks and rocks containing many fossils. Thus the concept of a lifeless Precambrian remains a holdover today; many geologists still classify any nonfossiliferous rocks found under early Paleozoic fossiliferous rocks as Precambrian.

The recent discoveries of sparse unicellular and colonial life, plus soft-bodied multicellular life in Precambrian rocks have raised an interesting issue. Since life forms are, apparently, gradational from Precambrian to Paleozoic time, how can this gradation be interrupted in a classification scheme? Some geologists insist that the dawn of the Paleozoic should coincide with the origin of differentiated cells and multicellular life. Unfortunately, multicellularity is also gradational, as we have already observed, and soft-bodied metazoans are found in rocks that are older than those conventionally called Paleozoic.

Older schemes separated the Paleozoic from the Precambrian based on the extent of skeletal development. The result seemed to be a sudden development in the evolution of life; once skeletons had been developed, their preservation as fossils was much more certain. The apparent explosion of life at the beginning of the Paleozoic was only an artifice of the classification scheme; the abrupt adundance of life at the beginning of the Paleozoic was nothing more than sudden *preservation* of a much higher percentage of life that had long been evolving.

There is no totally satisfactory way of drawing classification boundaries through gradational events; one method advocates establishing a standard and proceeding from there. *Eocambrian* has long been used to refer to rocks that are older than those conventionally assigned to the Paleozoic but that contain multicellular complex life forms as fossils. Such rocks may yield radiometric dates of 700 to 800 million years.

By whatever term we begin it, this chapter deals with the rich history of the physical events that shaped the North American continent and the life that inhabited its marginal seas, which partially flooded the continent many times. At the midpoint in this era, life met still another challenge as it placed plants and animals on the barren continents.

As we deal with younger and younger rocks, the details of geologic history become progressively clearer, because each succeeding era covers a briefer and briefer time span. The *details* of the record, with which we will occasionally deal, are used in this book only to illustrate *how* geologic history has been interpreted, not to bury you under facts; as Bertrand Russell, a modern British philosopher, once said, "A fact in science is not a mere fact, but an instance." Our brief discussion of geologic and biologic history will include some detailed digressions into the *how* of historical and biologic reconstruction.

PHYSICAL EVENTS

At the beginning of the Paleozoic, the North American craton (Figure 13-1) was a vast land area, approximately 80 percent of its current size, surrounded by marginal seas. Eocambrian strata are common in the sediments deposited in these marginal seas, but they are nearly unknown in the central part of the continent. The western continental boundary very approximately (Figure 13-2) trended south from the Washington-Idaho boundary, meaning that Washington, Oregon, and most of Nevada and California

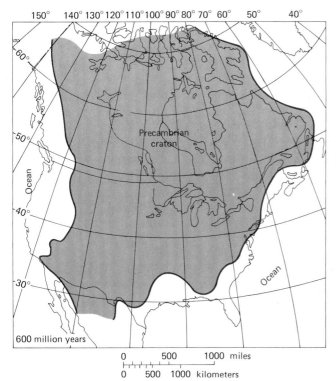

Precambrian
craton

Ocean

Ocean

600 million years

0   500   1000 miles

0   500   1000 kilometers

13-1
North America, 600 million years ago.
Continental crust outside the colored
area shown has been added to the
North American continent since
Precambrian time. (After P. B. King,
1976, U.S. Geological Survey
Professional Paper 902.)

were shelf and seafloor when the Paleozoic
era began.

Let us follow the earlier evolution of the
western margin of our continent to see how
history can be read from rocks and from the
evidence of life within them. As a fundamental concept, we should first reflect that pa-
leomagnetic evidence suggests that at this
time the equator ran from the Great Lakes
to the Gulf of Mexico (Figure 7-3). What is
now the eastern half of the United States
would have been the southern half, and the
present western half was the northern half.
The United States would have been enjoying
a climate something like that of modern Africa, because the geographic position of
North America was bisected by the early Paleozoic equator.

If we examine only one instant in time,
one corresponding to about 540 million years
ago, we can form a mental image of what the
western shores of the United States looked
like at that time. Such a map (Figure 13-3) is
drawn by plotting the distribution of rock
types of the same geologic age. This map,
here *highly* generalized, is the result of the
work of many hundreds of geologists and
perhaps 100 years of intermittent effort at
understanding these old rocks. As you can
see, the broad patterns are remarkably simple; sandy sediment graded east into a zone
of nondeposition (land) and west into shale.
Still further west, the rock type gradually
changed from shale to deeper water marine
limestones.

If we examine a modern continental shelf

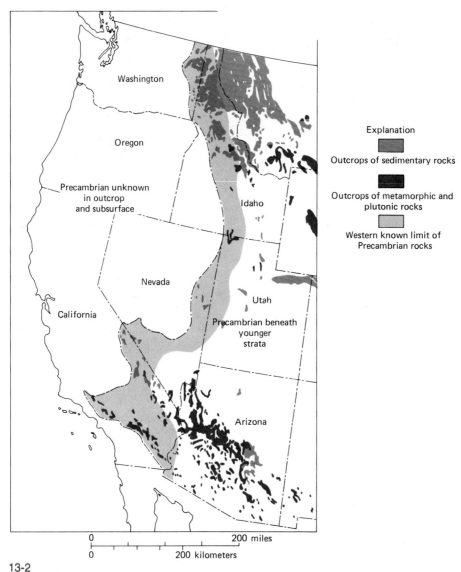

Explanation

Outcrops of sedimentary rocks

Outcrops of metamorphic and plutonic rocks

Western known limit of Precambrian rocks

13-2

The western continental boundary at the end of the Precambrian era, based on the distribution of surface exposures of Precambrian rocks plus penetration of Precambrian rocks in deep wells. (After P. B. King, 1976, U.S. Geological Survey Professional Paper 902.)

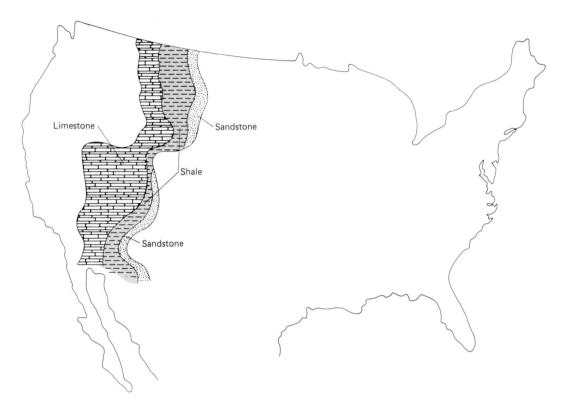

13-3
Highly generalized map of distribution of major rock types, whose age is approximately 540 million years, in the western United States. (Data compiled and generalized from several sources.)

(for example, the Gulf of Mexico), the same pattern of gradational rock types is observed. Sand grades shoreward to dry land and seaward to silty muds and lime muds. Taken together with the kinds of fossils contained in the ancient western sequence of rocks being discussed, we can see that the western rocks are a former continental shelf whose contact with dry land ran nearly due north-south.

If we draw a diagrammatic east-west cross section across the western United States (Figure 13-4), we see that the sand near the inferred old shoreline is quite thin, having been deposited directly on the old, mostly igneous and metamorphic Precambrian rocks of the craton. Further west, the shaly and limy units thicken, becoming much thicker seaward. Again, such a cross section would be nearly identical to a cross section drawn due south from New Orleans; the present *is* one key to the past.

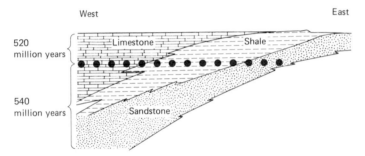

13-4
A highly diagrammatic cross section across the western United States
showing changes in thickness and rock type for two broad time intervals.
Depositions during the 20 to 30 million-year interval shown was essentially
continuous; dates given are simply averages. The series of colored dots
marks a distinctive index fossil that allows fairly precise separation of time
intervals. During any one brief time interval, sand was being deposited near
the shore, mud further offshore, and limy material still further offshore. *One
single rock type is not the same age everywhere, but becomes progressively
younger toward the continental platform or craton.*

If we make a somewhat more elaborate cross section for the whole of time from approximately 500 to 700 million years ago (Figure 13-5), we can read a series of sequential events, or *history*. Notice that the oldest sedimentary rocks are confined to the marginal sea and are absent to the east on the craton. Progressively younger rocks encroach further and further east onto the craton.

The Early Paleozoic Transgression

The rocks in Figure 13-5 and the fossils they contain tell us that throughout this time, sea level rose against the land and flooded the margin of the craton. The story is essentially the same all around our continent. Progressively younger Paleozoic rocks are located inward toward the center of the Precambrian craton; sandy rocks always occur on the cra-

tonic side of the shale and limestone. Geologists call such an encroachment of the sea onto a continent a **transgression.**

If you had stood up at any one point throughout the episode just described, the seawater would have gradually gotten deeper around you. Coincident with becoming deeper, first sand, then mud and, finally, lime (calcite) would be the dominant material swirling around your body. This is true because, in general, the vigorous wave action near the shore allows only the coarser sand to settle out while moving finer-grained silt and mud further offshore. Still further out at sea, where little sediment arrives from the land, is the place of maximum shallow water life and maximum production of limestone. As already observed, the distribution of these three most common sedimentary rocks is, in a *highly generalized* way, a function of the distance from shoreline and the water depth.

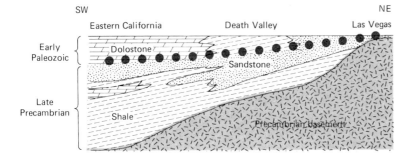

13-5

A geologic cross section from Las Vegas, Nevada, to eastern California. The colored dots define the strata that contain fossils marking the boundary between the Precambrian and Paleozoic. Late Precambrian rocks *average* 700 million years old; early Paleozoic rocks *average* 570 million years old. The inferred shoreline must have been just east of Las Vegas, Nevada, about 570 million years ago. (After P. B. King, 1976, U.S. Geological Survey Professional Paper 902.)

Now we can provide you with one of the chief tools for recognizing an ancient transgressive sea from the rocks it leaves behind. If a series of marine rocks grades upward from sandstone through shale to limestone, it is pretty good evidence that the sea *at that point through time* became deeper, and the same point progressively was further from the shoreline. *A vertical sequence of marine rocks, deposited by a transgressive sea, becomes progressively finer and more limy upward.* As the sea retreats, or **regresses**, from the land, the vertical sequence is reversed (Figure 13-6) and the rocks in *any one locality become coarser grained upward.*

Regression always involves the production of a gap (due to nondeposition and erosion) in the rock record. Such a gap is called an **unconformity**; the amount of time represented by the gap (or *hiatus*) increases toward the former shore. Marine rocks are replaced upward by continental rocks of similar age as the exposed land area increases. Regressive sequences of rocks are often truncated, because the upper, young surface of the deposit is attacked by continental erosive processes as the sea depth declines to zero.

The Cratonic Record

In the following parapgraphs, we will see repeatedly that the record of sedimentary rocks deposited on the craton is sporadic. Continental rocks, once deposited, are immediately subject to erosional processes that may eventually wash them back into the sea. The sea may transgress onto the land for perhaps 100 million years but, eventually, it always retreated to a marginal position, leaving its former thin deposits exposed to the mercies of numerous erosional systems.

The history recorded in the sedimentary rocks on the central part of the craton is about as sporadic as the Precambrian record of life. Paleozoic and younger rocks on the craton give us only glimpses of what was

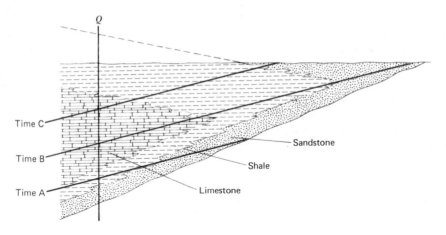

13-6
A diagrammatic transgressive-regressive sequence of rocks, shown in cross section. The colored lines represent time planes or *lines of equivalent time.* At Time A, a sand, mud, limy mud transitional series of sediments was being deposited. The seas then transgressed from Time A to Time B as marine deposition moved onto (onlap) the land. Time B is the time of maximum transgression, followed by regression to Time C. Notice that at locality *Q,* the *vertical* sequence of deposits is increasingly finer grained upward and then coarser grained upward. The entire sequence of transgressive-regressive rock units is bounded by an erosional interval during which the upper part of the regressive sequence was eroded away.

happening during the time the seas reached that far inland, and each glimpse is usually *bounded above and below by an unconformity.* The cratonic record—thin, discontinuous, and riddled with unconformities—is fundamentally different from the record furnished by rocks deposited in the marginal seas, because there the record provided by deposition is nearly continuous.

In recognition of the discrepancy between the completeness of the cratonic and marginal sea records, L. L. Sloss, an American geologist, has proposed that cratonic rocks provide a sixfold division of all time since the Precambrian, each division—called a **sequence**—corresponding to one major advance and retreat of the sea. A sequence (Figure 13-7) encompasses the time between

the beginning of the advance and the end of the following regression of the sea.

As Figure 13-7 suggests, the entire last 700 million years of cratonic history can be described as a series of six major advance-retreat couplets, or "packages," of cratonic history, each package of rock record bounded above and below by major unconformities. One major transgression, whose evidence we examined only at the continent's western margin, began early in the Paleozoic era and lasted for nearly 150 million years. At its greatest extent, the early Paleozoic seas covered two-thirds of the North American continent.

The marginal seas to the west and south of North America were apparently passive, stable areas that continuously received sed-

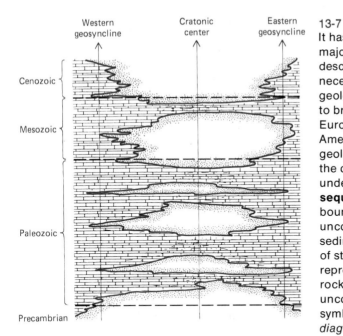

Western geosyncline
Cratonic center
Eastern geosyncline

Cenozoic

Mesozoic

Paleozoic

Precambrian

13-7
It has long been recognized that the major intervals of geologic time, first described in Europe, do not necessarily "fit" the North American geologic units of rocks. In an attempt to bridge the gap between the European time scale and the North American rock record, American geologist L. L. Sloss suggested that the cratonic record was best understood in terms of major **sequences** of thin rock units, bounded by unconformities. These unconformities divide cratonic sedimentary rocks into "packages" of strata. The colored blank areas represent the extent of the *missing* rock record (the cratonic unconformities), while the rock symbols display, *highly diagrammatically,* the kind of rocks being deposited at the time in various areas. The only place the sedimentary rock record is reasonably complete (with relatively few unconformities) is in those rocks formed in the marginal geosynclines. (Adapted from L. L. Sloss, 1963, with permission. Printed by permission from the Geological Society of America, Inc. Copyrighted 1963.)

iment throughout the earliest Paleozoic and then gently subsided. The western geosyncline was to maintain its passive character for several hundred million years longer.

The eastern geosyncline, however, was slowly reversing its passive character as Europe, Africa, and America moved toward one another, consuming the *former* "Atlantic" Ocean floor, which fed the volcanoes that were erupting near what would eventually become the Appalachian Mountain chain.

The Appalachian Record

About 450 million years ago, the quiet, steady sedimentation in the eastern marginal sea was ended by abundant volcanic outpouring—some of it submarine—accompanied by deposits of coarse conglomerates and by igneous intrusions and metamorphism. This activity produced numerous angular unconformities, where tilting of the underlying beds preceded deposition of the overlying layers (Figure 13-8). The source of sediment had abruptly changed from craton to volcanic island arcs as the Appalachian geosyncline was forced over the former Atlantic Ocean Basin, subducting and consuming it (see Figure 12-13). Other sediments from this same time are coarse, continental (oxidized) reddish rocks, devoid of marine fossils—a remarkable contrast to the hundreds of millions of years of tranquil marine sediments beneath them.

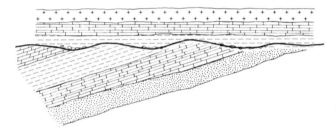

13-8
A cross section of a group of sedimentary rocks containing an *angular unconformity.* The colored line represents a buried erosion surface, which once cut across previously tilted sedimentary layers. Deposition of horizontal layers buries and preserves the old erosion surface as an angular unconformity.

Land had been raised, primarily because of igneous intrusions, within the geosyncline, and sediments rich in feldspar and quartz poured off the flanks of the newly raised land. An event that geologists call the TACONIC OROGENY had begun, about 450 million years ago. **Orogeny** means mountain making, and the Appalachian geosyncline was making mountains; their remnants are buried under younger sedimentary rocks along our east coast today.

The Appalachian geosyncline had received its first "bump," and the rising Taconic landmass began shedding a coarse, continental sedimentary sequence collectively called the *Queenston delta* into the western portion of the miogeosyncline and volcanic debris into the much deeper waters to the east. The Taconic Range, parts of which are still exposed in the Taconic Mountains of eastern New York State and western Vermont, had been formed. The first encounter was not to be the last, because more encounters were to come.

About 350 million years ago, Europe and North America, which had been moving toward each other for at least 100 million years, collided. Mountains, probably similar to the Himalayas, were slowly formed along

the east coast of North America and Greenland and along the west coast of northwestern Europe. The evidence is quite similar to that produced during the earlier, milder Taconic event. The contrasts are interesting, however; the Taconic event is characterized by much basaltic volcanism caused by ocean floor subduction under the continent. The ACADIAN OROGENY (called the *Caledonian orogeny* in Greenland and Europe) was a much more intense event that involved a head-on continental collision between Europe and America. Enormous deposits of coarse, feldspar-rich reddish rocks, called the *Catskill delta complex,* were shed from the newly elevated mountains and, like the older Queenston rocks, became coarser and thicker toward their mountainous source to the east.

The Acadian orogeny generated large volumes of granite and intense metamorphism, because plutonism and metamorphism were superimposed on the rocks affected by the older Taconic orogeny and on an even older 1 billion-year-old Precambrian orogenic event. Unconformities between strongly unturned 350 million-year-old rock and slightly younger horizontally bedded rock laid across it allows fairly precise determination of the timing of the Acadian orogeny—the most severe orogeny affecting the Appalachian geosyncline.

Mountain uplift and compression continued intermittently in the Appalachian region throughout the late Paleozoic, but the site of intense deformation shifted southward from the northern Appalachians. This last southern phase spans the time interval from roughly 350 to 300 million years ago. Within the northern Appalachians, the main result of this later event (known in North America as the ALLEGHENY or APPALACHIAN OROGENY and in Europe as the *Hercynian* orogeny) is renewed folding of previously deformed rocks. Still further south, the Ouachita geosyncline, which had persisted through all the previous Appalachian events in deep water tranquility, was also crushed and shoved to the north, forming the Ouachita Mountains of Oklahoma and Arkansas and the Marathon Mountains of west Texas.

This last, primarily southern event raised the entire former Appalachian and Ouachita-Marathon geosyncline above sea level, causing most of North America to be exposed by the end of the Paleozoic era. The source of energy from the south that generated the late Paleozoic Appalachian orogeny was apparently the collision of America with Africa, a relative latecomer to continental collision.

During the late Paleozoic, Europe also collided with Asia, forming the Ural Mountains, while southern continents were likewise colliding and uniting. By the end of the Paleozoic, the world's continents had grouped together to form one huge continental mass called *Pangaea* (Figure 7-1).

The breakup of Pangaea was to be one of the major physical events of the Mesozoic, much as its formation provides an ending to our brief history of the Paleozoic era. Before we leave the Paleozoic, we will briefly consider what was happening west of the Appalachians throughout Paleozoic time.

The Stable Interior

Sediments deposited on the North American craton have been divided into six sequences (Figure 13-7) that span all geologic time since the Precambrian. Among these six, four include the events of the Paleozoic era.

The basal formations of most sequences are remarkably clean quartz sandstones. Analysis of ancient current directions, recorded in the rocks as cross stratifications and other kinds of sedimentary structures, suggests that the source of the sand was the cratonic center—the Precambrian shield. The surface of the craton, which stretched from western New York State to Colorado, was a series of gentle rises and basins often called the *stable interior;* one major rise stretching from the Great Lakes region southwest to southern California has been called the *Transcontinental Arch.*

At no time since the Paleozoic have widespread shallow seas left behind such extensive, cratonic sandstone deposits. These rocks, which form the surface for most of the central United States, are typically clean, well-washed, thin, and richly fossiliferous. An analysis of just one area will illustrate the marvelous diversity of life and environment entombed in these cratonic rocks.

By about the middle of the Paleozoic era, a roughly circular basin, centered on what was to be Michigan, began to subside slowly. Around this shallow basin, known as the *Michigan Basin,* large coral reefs began to grow. Like modern reefs, these ancient reefs were composed of limestone skeletons secreted by animals that lived in shallow, sunlit water (Figure 13-9). These animals in-

13-9
An example of reef material from a reef limestone, 370 million years old, now in central Arizona. Life types include sponges, corals, and stromatoporoids. (Photograph by Curt Teichert, U.S. Geological Survey.)

cluded sponges, stromatoporoids, some algae, and the corals. Other animals, such as gastropods (snails), pelecypods (clams), and crinoids (sea lilies), lived in or on the reef; after their death they also contributed their calcareous skeleton to the reef mass.

As the basin subsided, the reef-building animals, which needed light to live, built their limestone homes up higher as the depth of water increased, thus providing a substantial mound of reef rock that was continuously built up to near sea level. As the animals continued to compensate for subsidence, the reef rock became 100 yards (about 90 meters) or more high and formed substantial physical barriers. The reefs of the Michigan Basin grew around the roughly circular periphery of the basin and are of the same age as the limestone that forms the lip for Niagara Falls and the surface rock for part of the upper Midwest.

The patchwork of reefs also restricted the flow of seawater into the interior of the basin. The climate must have been tropical, because Michigan was near the equator at that time, and the seawater within the restricted basin evaporated almost as rapidly as the ocean refilled it (Figure 13-10). As evaporation continued, the water within the basin became more and more saline, and deposits of gypsum (Appendix A), anhydrite and, finally, rock salt, formed. These massive salt deposits are mined today and furnish salt for the chemical industry, ice cream, water softeners, road and sidewalk ice clearing, and table use. If you live in the Midwest, the next time you sprinkle salt on your food, reflect that it most likely was deposited about 400 million years ago and has been waiting ever since for you to recylce it.

The association of evaporite deposits with fringing reefs is a common one, occurring somewhat later during the Paleozoic in Alberta, Canada, and at the end of the Paleozoic era over a large area of west Texas and southeastern New Mexico. Not only are the reef evaporites for salt and gypsum, but the reefs themselves, rich with fossil life and thoroughly porous and permeable, are often the site of important oil accumulations.

Near the end of the era, as the Appalachian Mountains continued their rise, a vast area of the eastern and central craton was covered by repetitive, cyclic sequences of nonmarine strata that *contained coal* and marine rocks. These rocks, which at one time must have covered most of the United States from central Oklahoma to the east, are represented on other (presently) northern continents by similar cyclic rock sequences of the same age. How could such remarkably uniform, cyclic sedimentation occur over large parts of several continents at the same time?

The answer is still controversial. One re-

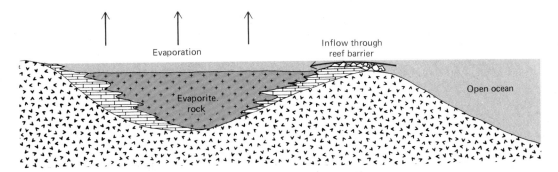

13-10
An example of an evaporite basin such as the ancient Michigan Basin and the modern Persian Gulf. Seawater enters the basin through a fringing barrier reef. As evaporation occurs, the remaining water becomes denser and sinks. Now trapped, evaporation continues with the deposition of evaporite minerals that grade laterally into reef limestones around the basin.

cent suggestion is that worldwide cyclic changes in sea level are best accounted for by episodic volcanism along the world's oceanic ridges. As the ridges are inflated with magma, the space now occupied by the inflated oceanic ridge is accommodated by raising the sea level, which floods the continents. As the ridge cools and contracts, the sea level slowly falls. Others have suggested cyclic changes in climate, perhaps related to widespread glaciation occurring at this same time in the Southern Hemisphere, notably known from evidence in northern Africa, as the answer.

Whatever the reason for their origin, these cyclic deposits, formed in a tropical climate approximately 300 million years ago, contain a major coal resource for much of the United States. The eroded remnants of rocks of this age stretch from Rhode Island to Oklahoma (Figure 13-11) and provide an important part of the industrial energy for the heartland of the United States. The reserves from this great coal belt should last for several centu-

ries, and our energy-hungry society is placing increasing reliance on them.

Within the coals, (often exquisitely preserved) are fossils of advanced plants, including true ferns, seed ferns, horsetail rushes, scale trees, and other advanced forms of plant and animal life. From where had they all come?

PALEOZOIC LIFE

As we pass from the sparse, unicellular plant world of the Precambrian to that of the earliest Paleozoic era, one might reasonably expect a gradual change in diversity because of the species variation produced by sexual reproduction. The rate of diversification, or change, can be well approximated if we deal with relatively modern fossil life. For example, it required 10 million years for the evolution of all of the placental mammals (those that nourish the fetus through a placenta),

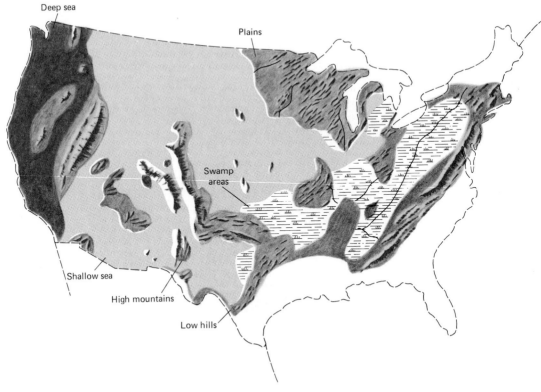

Deep sea

Plains

Swamp areas

Shallow sea

High mountains

Low hills

13-11
A reconstruction of the geography of the United States 300 million years ago.
The area shown as swamp is the area where major coal deposits occur today.
The coal reserves, which formed in those swamps, total about 450 billion tons
(410 billion metric tons), about one-quarter of total U.S. coal reserves.
Compare with Figure 14-4. (Map from U.S. Geological Survey.)

and 10 million years is *one-thirtieth* of all Paleozoic time.

Close examination of the fossil record reveals that undoubted metazoan life stretches back in soft-bodied form to at least 700 million years ago. This remarkably complex life consisted of life forms that swam or floated in the ocean; they, like the modern jellyfish, would have found a skeleton useless.

As time progressed, some forms of animal life began to prey on others. The response to predation was much like earlier responses to earlier challenges: to armor oneself against the problem.

The First Skeletons

About 600 million years ago, some *trilobites* (Figure 13-12) developed an external skele-

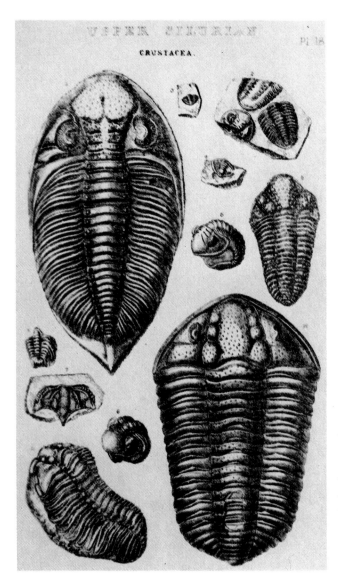

CRUSTACEA.

Pl. 1A

13-12
Notice the resemblance between these *trilobites,* taken from 410 million-year-old rocks, and modern crabs. The head has two eye sockets, the body has numerous segments, and the tail segment is here poorly developed. (From Roderick Murchison, 1872, *Silurian System,* courtesy of the History of Science Collections, University of Oklahoma Libraries.)

ton of *chitin,* a substance similar to the exoskeletons of many insects and to human fingernails. Seafloor life developed skeletons of limestone or phosphatic material, which increased the probability of their preservation as fossils.

Skeletons provide many advantages. External skeletons are an effective defense against being eaten by one's neighbors unless, of course, *they* develop an even better offense against that skeletal defense! Skeletons also provide a rigid framework from which muscles can be attached; this allows increases in body size and coordination. The weight of a skeleton, is, however, an evolutionary disadvantage to some degree: it represents mass that must be moved around without providing its own energy.

The life histories of many forms show that they grow larger through time; size provides advantages in longevity, productivity, protection against longer periods of starvation, defense against predators, and effective maintanence of body temperature. The first increase in size became possible only when cells adopted the colonial life-style and groups of cells progressively became specialized.

Still another advantage of a skeleton is that it dramatically increases the chances that any life form will be preserved as a fossil. When one considers that erosion, weathering, bacteria, and scavengers attack any dead life form, the odds against preservation are exceedingly high. Those odds are much improved if a hard skeleton is available and if the life form is *quickly buried*—either in tar, quicksand, ice, tree resin, volcanic ash or, far more often, under a continuous rain of sediment on the seafloor. Rapid burial denies access to the remains to scavengers and slows down the decay process.

After the death of a skeletonized organism, the soft tissue eventually decays, but the empty shell or bare bones may slowly be changed to hard stone by the addition of compounds of iron, silica, or calcium carbonate by water flowing through the area. Pore space may be *filled* with harder minerals and the shell or bone preserved, or the original substance may be totally removed and *replaced* by mineral mater; petrified trees are a familiar example of this process. Skeletons and shells may also leave impressions of themselves in softer material, and the vacant *molds* may be preserved. If the molds are later filled by mineral matter, *casts* are formed that may display intricate details of the original texture of the shells or bones.

Soft-bodied animals are not so lucky; they are infrequently preserved. Some soft tissues may be converted to pure carbon and the *imprint* of the animal is preserved, sometimes in detail, as a blackened film of carbon within the rock. Other soft parts may be preserved in the sticky *resin* of pine trees or *frozen* in the ice (such as the several finds in Siberia of Ice Age mastodons). The bones and skins of many other Ice Age animals have been found in *tar seeps,* where they have been effectively mummified, or pickled. As mentioned in Chapter Twelve, the preservation of the delicate structures of bacteria and algae has often depended on their *replacement* by finely crystalline silica, or chert.

There is no reliable way to estimate what percentage of life that has ever lived has been preserved as fossils, but a reasonable figure must be only a few percent. Much more has come before us than we can ever know.

Early Paleozoic Life

By Eocambrian time, life included bacteria, blue-green algae, eukaryotic algae, jellyfish, corals, worms, and other creatures of uncertain affinity—perhaps soft-bodied mollusks or echinoderms (spiny-skinned invertebrate animals such as the starfish). For a description and classification of life, see Appendix F, which classifies, in simplified form, all the types of life that we will study in these chapters.

As time moved on, diversity among animal groups increased, and animals gradually acquired the ability to make shells for themselves. The evolution of external shells was not a sudden event; it required at least 60 million years to become a widespread phenomenon.

The fossil life forms found within the first one-third of the Paleozoic era represent marine life that adapted to shallow water. With the exception of early armored fish, all of these animals lacked backbones—they were **invertebrates.** One might reasonably expect that early life forms would be primitive, and some of them, such as the sponges, were. Instead, nearly one-third of all early Paleozoic fossils are *trilobites* (Figure 13-12), members of the arthropods, an immense group (Appendix F) of complex animals that comprises over 80 percent of all living animals today.

Arthropods generally possess chitinous exterior skeletons (like lobsters or crabs), segmented bodies, highly specialized sensory organs, and paired, jointed appendages. Trilobites had all of these; the segmentation of the trilobite body into *three lobes* is the source of its name. Early trilobites were probably scavengers that ate decaying dead material from the the seafloor, much as some crabs do today.

Of the many remarkable features of trilobites, the most impressive to those who collect them as fossils is their eyes; they developed the most sophisticated fossil eyes ever known. The lens elements of trilobite eyes were made of single crystals of calcite and came in both compound and simpler forms that were composed of *doublet lenses;* this lens form so highly corrects for various optical defects that it was not discovered by humans until the seventeenth century. Trilobites had accomplished this optical miracle 0.5 billion years earlier; they created lenses of such optical perfection and efficiency that they have never been naturally duplicated again.

The unblinking eyes of *fossil* trilobites are the earliest eyes known, and they now stare vacantly at a world so unlike the one they knew that only thinking humans could reconstruct it.

Among the earliest of all Paleozoic life were the *archaeocyathids,* extinct animals whose biologic affinities (Appendix F) are so uncertain that they are considered a group by themselves (Figure 13-13). The *brachiopods* (Figure 13-14) are shelled animals that look something like clams and are often called "lampshells," because many are shaped like old Roman oil lamps. They inhabit shallow seas today and are attached to the seafloor by fleshy stalks.

More than 30,000 fossil species of brachiopods are known, and they constitute a large and growing percentage of all life in the early Paleozoic. Brachiopods differ from their lookalikes, the clam, in several ways; the most obvious is that the plane of mirror symmetry of brachiopods is *perpendicular* to the hinge line between their two shells (Figure 13-14), while the shells of a clam are usually symmetrical *parallel* to the hinge line.

The clams belong to the large group of animals known as *mollusks.* Their descendants form the second largest group of living animals. Mollusks include *gastropods* (snails) (Figure 13-15), *chitons, scaphopods* (tusk shells), *pelecypods* (clams) (Figure 13-16), *cephalopods* (squids and octopuses), and *monoplacophorans,* an almost extinct group of primitive, limpetlike mollusks that seem to resemble segmented worms. Monoplacophorans, clams, and snails form the bulk of early Paleozoic mollusk fossils.

Other groups include worms, sponges,

13-13
These are cross sections across *Salterella conulata,* a cone-shaped earliest Paleozoic fossil archaeocyathid several inches (centimeters) long; this was an animal of uncertain biologic affinity. (Photograph by E. L. Yochelson, U.S. Geological Survey.)

13-14
Here are a variety of views of a brachiopod, *Leptocoelia,* fossilized in rocks 390 million years old. Its shells are intensely wrinkled, probably to provide strength. The two shells are commonly dissimilar in size and are symmetrical about a plane *perpendicular to* the hinge line where the shells join. (Photograph by C. W. Merriam, U.S. Geological Survey.)

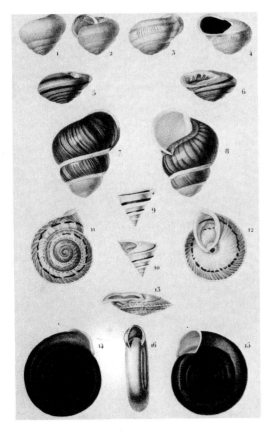

13-15
Here are various kinds of coiled gastropods; some are coiled in cones, while others coil in a single plane. Coiling is the result of displacement of the body of the animal from its foot; it offers advantages in streamlining and water flow. (From A. D'Orbigny, 1849, courtesy of the History of Science Collections, University of Oklahoma Libraries.)

13-16
Here are several views of pelecypod shells. No one shell is symmetrical, but each shell is the *mirror image* of the other; the plane of symmetry *parallels* the hinge line where the two shells join. Compare with Figure 13-14. (Photograph by W. P. Woodring, U.S. Geological Survey.)

echinoderms, and coelenterates. The sponges are a particularly interesting group and comprise one of the most primitive forms of life still alive today. Among the coelenterates, sea anemones, corals, and jellyfish are common in the sea today; they, too, are fairly primitive animals. Corals entered the fossil record early in the Paleozoic and became important members of reef communities in the middle and later Paleozoic (Figure 13-17).

By 500 million years ago, all of the major types of invertebrate animals had evolved, and the shallow seas that gradually encroached on the North American craton were rich with life. Reefs became more and more common in the shallow, cratonic seas;

13-17
These two views of *Caninia,* a solitary or horn coral, illustrate the kind of calcareous "house" the coralline animal leaves behind after death. (Photograph by W. J. Sando, U.S. Geological Survey.)

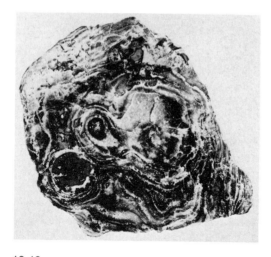

13-18
This polished section of *Stromatopora,* a typical stromatoporoid, illustrates their highly generalized form. The stromatoporoids are a poorly understood group of early and middle Paleozoic reef builders of uncertain biologic kinship. (Photograph by H. L. Cannon, U.S. Geological Survey.)

they included several varieties of corals, and certain sponges, and stromatoporoids (Figure 13-18), colonial animals that were probably related to the corals or sponges.

Trilobites, brachiopods, cephalopods, gastropods, echinoderms, *ostracods* (tiny bean-shaped marine arthropods) (Figure 13-19), and many other organisms continued to prosper throughout the Paleozoic, although the number of trilobites diminished rapidly after the first 200 million years of the Paleozoic. Other animals came along, including the *bryozoa* (Figure 13-20), colonial animals often less than ½ inch (1⅓ centimeter) long that built calcareous homes that superficially resembled coralline reefs, and the *graptolites.* The graptolites are an extinct group of floating, highly advanced but minute colonial animals. Their colonies are worldwide fossils, typically found as carbon films (Figure 13-21) on dark shales; they provide important *index fossils* for correlation of early Paleozoic strata.

Graptolites changed rapidly, spread rap-

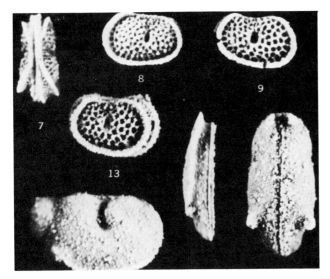

13-19
Ostracods, whose shells are shown
here, are bean-shaped creatures
about ⅛ inch (⅓ centimeter) long.
These are *Chironiptrum,* a fossil
ostracod from rocks whose age is
390 million years. (Photograph by J.
M. Berdan, U.S. Geological Survey.)

idly, occurred frequently, and moved onto
and off of the stage of life quickly. They
make ideal fossils, therefore, from which to
correlate rocks from one area to another.
Such unique, rapidly changing, widespread
abundant fossils are called **index fossils;**
wherever found they precisely date the
rocks that contain them.

Middle Paleozoic Life

By the middle Paleozoic, the trilobites were
in decline; corals and echinoderms, a group
of animals that includes the modern spiny
sea urchins (echinoids) and starfish (Figure
13-22), were becoming supremely important.
Cephalopods had also become plentiful. One

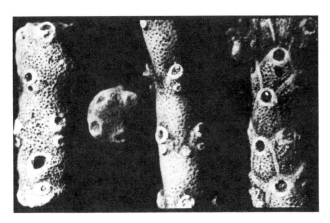

13-20
These are the calcareous "houses"
within which minute animals called
bryozoans once lived as colonial life
forms. Bryozoans are important
fossils both in the Paleozoic and
Cenozoic eras; these are from 55
million-year-old rock. (Photograph by
Alan Cheetham, U.S. Geological
Survey.)

Paleozoic Life   **451**

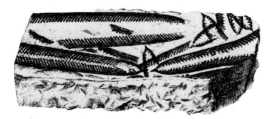

13-21
Graptolites, shown here in a sketch of the surface of a rock slab, are very important index fossils for the early Paleozoic. This is *Didymograptus murchisonii.* (From R. Murchison, 1872, *Silurian System,* courtesy of the History of Science Collections, University of Oklahoma Libraries.)

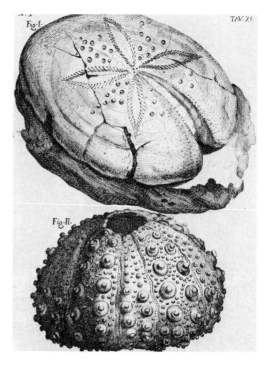

13-22
The echinoids are a group of spiny-skinned marine animals. The upper figure is of a type commonly called a "sand dollar." (From A. Scilla, 1748, *Vain Speculation . . . ,* courtesy of the History of Science Collections, University of Oklahoma Libraries.)

type had a straight, chambered, conical shell and had grown quite large; fossil shells measure up to 5 yards (about 4½ meters) in length. These straight-shelled cephalopods, although abundant as fossils, are only represented today by their coiled cousins of which the modern *Nautilus* is the only surviving example. Graptolites were likewise in rapid decline.

The cause of evolutionary failure is an intriguing question. Why do certain groups of animals go into a fatal decline? The answer is not simple, but certainly predatory pressure must have been part of it. Humans have largely destroyed the large mammal population of North America in less than 50,000 years; it is probable that other animals before us were equally efficient predators.

Another answer may be found in shifting climates and sea levels; the time when the populations of some animals decline coincides with major orogenic events, or major advances and retreats of the ocean across the land. By whatever cause, trilobites, graptolites, and nautiloid cephalopods were

in a steep decline by the middle Paleozoic. From their disappearance we learn that they were unable to adapt to the changes of their time and passed from the scene.

Among the more unique middle Paleozoic animals were the "sea scorpions," or *eurypterids.* Eurypterids look (Figure 13-23) very much like modern air-breathing land scorpions, but they are not closely related. They lived in shallow, brackish waters and must have been terrifying predators; imagine a

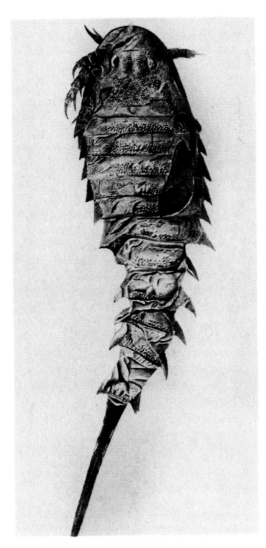

13-23
This eurypterid, known more fully as
Eurypterus mansfieldi, Hall., is about 9 inches
(23 centimeters) long, and inhabited brackish
water about 430 million years ago.
(Photograph by E. B. Hardin, U.S. Geological
Survey.)

scorpionlike animal, 3 yards (2¾ meters) long swimming toward you with a hungry look in its eyes! However, eurypterids failed to survive the Paleozoic era. Members of an allied group, the arachnids, are familiar to us as spiders and ticks.

The most remarkable middle Paleozoic development was the vertebrate fish. Fragmentary remains of armored fish have been found in Lower Paleozoic rocks that date back 510 million years. They apparently had cartilaginous (soft) skeletons like their modern ancestors, the hagfish and lampreys. They also often lacked paired fins and jaws. These bizarre, plated and armored, fishlike animals are called *Agnatha,* which means jawless. With their heavy exterior skeletons, they must have been poor swimmers and were probably filter or deposit feeders that lived on the seafloor.

Whatever their shortcomings, the agnathans represent the first development of a spinal column. The vertebral column, with its enhanced capacity for coordination of nerve impulses over a still larger and longer body, was the key to the development of life on land—the next greatest challenge to life.

The development of the first vertebrate jaw was not long in coming, and the primitive jawed fish, called *placoderms* (armored skin), became streamlined for swimming and predation. The acquistion of hinged jaws, streamlining, and the evolution of powerful swimming muscles probably made the placoderms, which were up to 10 yards (about 9 meters) long, ferocious hunters. Although the placoderms have been extinct at least 230 million years, both the modern shark and the bony fish evolved through them well over 300 million years ago.

Within the bony fish, evolution was rapid; they developed bony *interior* skeletons and traded their exterior armor for scales. The bony fish may include up to 40,000 living species, including many fish familiar to us. The bony fish are split into two divergent groups; nearly all modern bony fish are categorized in, one group, and only six relict species of lungfish and lobe-finned fish are classified in the other.

The lobe-finned fish, long known from fossil remains, were thought to be extinct until a living specimen was caught in 1939 off the east coast of South Africa. Since then, other specimens of this living fossil, called the *coelacanth,* have been caught. As the name suggests, lobe-finned fish have muscular sets of paired fins; in many anatomical details they are truly "living fossils."

During droughts, lobe-finned fish caught in drying lakes and tidal pools might well have used these leglike fins to pull themselves across mud flats to another pond or stream, much like the present-day "walking catfish." Any animal that could manage to survive on land would have a whole new environment open to it, because there was no other animal competition. Although land plants had appeared by 400 million years ago, there was nothing to eat them—yet.

The Continental Foothold

Through selection pressure exerted over several million years, the lobe-finned fish gradually became better adapted (their fins were modified into squat legs) to crawling over land and, for the first time in 4 billion years, the land was colonized by life. The first *amphibians* (animals capable of living in or out of water, but required to return to water to lay their eggs) were, not surprisingly, quite fishlike. They very likely spent

most of their time in water, leaving only occasionally to exploit the empty environmental niche awaiting them.

One of the major problems facing early amphibians was supporting their own weight. Living in water allows water to support much or all of one's own weight, but land life must be self-supporting. By selecting fossils of progressively younger age, we can watch the early amphibians shift their eyes from the sides to the tops of their heads, develop lungs from gill sacs, and greatly strengthen their skeletal systems. Amphibians also had problems with their eggs, which were gelatinous and designed to be laid in water and remain there until they hatched. Amphibians had to solve this problem by returning to the water to lay their eggs, as amphibians do today. This was easy enough if they lived in an area where water was always present, but it limited their use of the rest of the land.

The solution to this problem was finally developed; it was a new type of egg that was encased in shell, and a new type of air-breathing animal that hatched from the egg—the *reptile* (see Chapter Fourteen).

The first invasion of the continents by plants predated the amphibian invasion by about 40 million years. The earliest ancestors of land plants were probably the green algae, but the time of descent from any ancestor to the first land plant is obscure. Land plants had to solve numerous problems, including: (1) withstanding large fluctuations in temperature, moisture, wind, and sunlight; (2) providing fluid, when no longer bathed in fluid; (3) reproducing themselves in an environment nearly devoid of water; (4) respiration of air instead of in water; (5) maintaining a water balance in their tissues by preventing excessive evaporation; and (6) developing a system to transport fluids some distance through tissue while maintaining themselves erect.

Plants met this imposing list of challenges by developing a tough exterior skin to minimize evaporation and to keep themselves erect against wind. They also developed a complex vascular plumbing system to transport nutrient fluids throughout the whole plant system. One type of plant intermediate between the aquatic and land domains is the *mosses;* they lack an efficient system for fluid transport and can live and reproduce only where it is moist. Lacking supportive tissue, their size is also severely limited.

The oldest land plants date from 400 mil-

lion years ago and are known as *psilophytes*. These are simple branching plants (Figure 13-24) that lack leaves and true roots. The *branching stems* in the air carried out photosynthesis; those beneath the soil had primitive structures such as root hairs, which enabled plants to stay in place and draw water and nutrition from the soil. Psilophytes reproduced by the generation of *spores* (an asexual reproductive organ).

Differentiation of the psilopsids (psilophytes) produced three important plant types: *scale trees, horsetails,* and *spore-bearing ferns.* Unlike the psilopsids, the scale trees (Figure 13-25) have true roots and

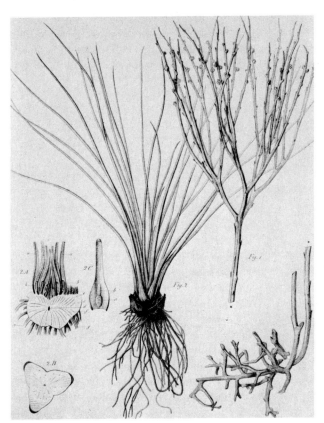

13-24

This is *Psilotum triquetrum,* a living example of one of the most primitive land plants. Psilophytes have neither true roots or leaves; they were the most primitive and earliest land plant to inhabit the continents. (From A. Brongniart, 1857, *Histoire des Vegetaux Fossiles,* courtesy of the History of Science Collections, University of Oklahoma Libraries.)

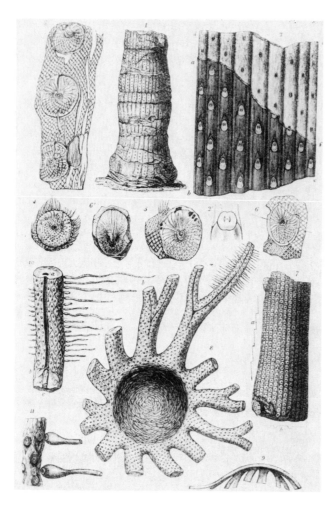

13-25
These sketches are of various kinds of *scale trees,* whose remains are seen as fossils in coal. The scales on the bark were left when the needlelike leaves that once stuck straight out of the bark came loose. Lycopsids like these had both true roots and leaves. (From Reverend William Buckland, 1837, *Geology and Mineralogy Considered . . .,* courtesy of the History of Science Collections, University of Oklahoma Libraries.)

true leaves and ranged up to 30 yards (about 27 meters) or more in height. The leaves grew out from the trunk directly in spiral rows; when the leaves were shed, the trunk was left with leaf scars that looked something like the scales of a reptile skin (hence the name, scale trees).

The horsetails, unlike the scale trees, have a diminutive modern form—the horsetails or scouring rushes found today in moist places.

Modern horsetails are rarely over 1 yard (meter) high and are characterized by smooth, jointed stems; their ancestors 300 million years ago were trees 30 times as tall.

The true ferns are the descendants of these ancient spore-bearing plants and comprise many modern species. They formed both the underbrush and fernlike trees of low to moderate size in the ancient coal swamps of long ago.

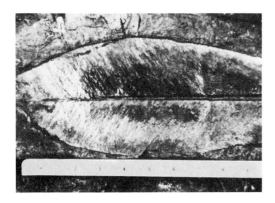

13-26
Photograph of the leaf of a seed fern, *Glossopteris* (compare with Figure 7-4). These were the most primitive seed-bearing plants and are related to the gymnosperms that were to dominate the Mesozoic. (Photograph by D. L. Schmidt, U.S. Geological Survey.)

Late Paleozoic Life

On land the evolution of plants continued, and plants that bore seeds instead of spores developed. One of the seed ferns, *Glossopteris* (Figure 13-26), is an important fossil link in the evidence favoring the theory of the existence of Pangaea at the end of the Paleozoic era (see Chapter Seven). The seed provides enhanced protection for the young embryo plant plus a supply of nutrients, all in a drought-resistant case. The seed plants were to displace slowly the earlier spore-bearing plants, of which only a few survive today.

The seed-bearing plants first appeared as fossil plants about 360 million years ago and gradually became the dominant plant group in late Paleozoic forest. Seed plants include the *seed ferns,* the *cordatids* (a primitive

treelike plant intermediate between conifers and seed ferns), and the *cycads,* primitive palmlike trees. No members of either the seed ferns or the cordatids survive today, but a few members of the cycads, known as sago palms, survive in tropical regions. The *ginkgoes* (Figure 13-27) are another group found fossilized in late Paleozoic rocks that are represented by a single species today.

The best-known group of the seed-bearing trees are, however, the *conifers.* Conifers, evergreen trees that bear their seeds in cones, entered the fossil record 300 million years ago. Their survivors populate modern forests and include cedars, yews, hemlocks, pines, spruces, firs, and larches. The seeds of conifers are borne naked on cones that festoon plants whose leaves are either needles or scales.

All of the seed-bearing plants we have considered so far are known collectively as

13-27
These are leaves from a modern, living ginkgo tree. Ginkgoes are modern living fossils, little changed since the end of the Paleozoic. They are extremely tolerant of adverse environmental conditions. (Specimen courtesy of Velma A. Barnes.)

GYMNOSPERMS, or "naked seed" plants. Gymnosperms gradually dominated the earlier spore-bearing flora, they survive today as cycads, ginkgoes, and a wealth of conifers.

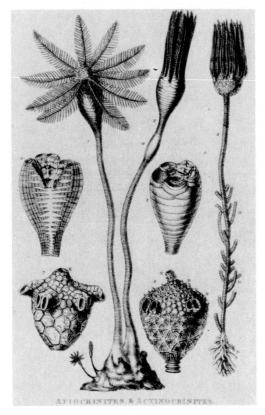

13-28
This view of the complete animal (rarely fossilized in its entirety) suggests why crinoids are usually called "sea lilies." The jointed stems are a common fossil find. The budlike "head" and appendages are far less common fossils. Some crinoids live on in the seas today. (From Reverend William Buckland, 1837, courtesy of the History of Science Collections, University of Oklahoma Libraries.)

Among the invertebrate animals, brachiopods became perhaps the dominant fauna in late Paleozoic rocks, although the whole list of invertebrate life was extraordinarily rich and complex. Pelecypods invaded freshwater environments during the transition to land, and gastropods increased greatly in variety and became air breathers. The coiled cephalopods continued to increase in size and complexity. *Crinoids* and *blastoids,* two types of echinoderms (see Appendix F) that grew rooted to the seafloor (Figure 13-28), became prolific; some late Paloeozoic limestones are composed almost entirely of crinoidal fragments.

One group of unicellular animals that are related to the amoeba learned to secrete hard, calcareous shells around themselves. These tiny animals, called *foraminifera* (pore bearers), first showed up as fossils (Figure 13-29) 500 million years ago, but they became extremely plentiful in late Paleozoic seas. The foraminifera (usually abbreviated to *forams*) may be the main component of many late Paleozoic limestones. One group of large forams have shells about the size and shape of wheat grains; along with their many kin, they are important index fossils in the latest Paleozoic rocks. The *radiolaria,* similar creatures, made their shells out of silica (Figure 13-30); they have been fossil constituents of siliceous rocks since the beginning of Paleozoic time. The *ostracods* (Figure 13-19), miniature arthropods, are in rich supply in both marine and freshwater deposits.

A new class of arthropods, the *insects,* developed during the middle Paleozoic and became a very diverse group in late Paleozoic coal forests. Other small arthropods are ticks, spiders, millipedes, centipedes, scorpions, and cockroaches. Winged insects included dragonflies (Figure 13-31) with wing-

13-29
Here are quite a variety of "forams," a type of single-celled animal that furnishes important index fossils. Their tiny shells may be either siliceous or calcareous. (From Christian G. Ehrenberg, 1854, *Mikrogeologie das Erden und Felsen,* courtesy of the History of Science Collections, University of Oklahoma Libraries.)

For many invertebrates, the end of the Paleozoic was also the end of them. Some forms of corals that were profuse in early and middle Paleozoic seas declined to extinction. The eurypterids and trilobites, certain types of brachiopods, and virtually all of the blastoids also failed to survive the end of the era. Two groups of bryozoa and the two major groups of crinoids became extinct.

13-30
Radiolaria, like the forams, are a group of unicellular animals. They live within a delicate symmetrical framework of opaline silica formed in numerous geometric shapes; their microfossils are incredibly beautiful under the microscope. (From Christian G. Ehrenberg, 1854, courtesy of the History of Science Collections, University of Oklahoma Libraries.)

spans of 2 feet (60 centimeters); they are occasionally preserved in the sediments formed in late Paleozoic coal swamps.

Sponges continued their primitive, solitary existences but became important components of some late Paleozoic reef communities. Bryozoa were abundant; one particular kind of colony of these microscopic animals grew in a spiral network and is a common and easily recognizable fossil in some late Paleozoic marine rocks.

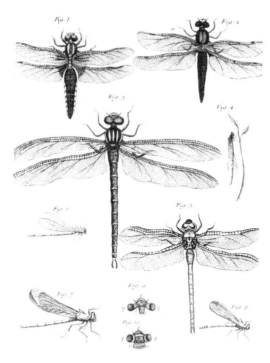

13-31

Dragonflies are preserved in detail in the fine-grained sediments from late Paleozoic swamps. They must have been a common insect in the swamps where the coal was being formed. (From M. DeReamur, 1717, *Memoirs pour Servir a l'Histoire des Insects,* Vol. 6, courtesy of the History of Science Collections, University of Oklahoma Libraries.)

Transitions

The end of the Paleozoic era records one of the greatest wholesale extinctions in the fossil record—and its cause is unknown. The animals that died out were almost exclusively marine and should have been little affected by climate changes. The emergence of the continents at the end of the Paleozoic was substantial; perhaps many of the marine animals were unable to adapt to the increased competition from new forms as the seas crept back to their early marginal positions.

Among the vertebrates, the placoderms had failed to survive much beyond the middle Paleozoic, while both their cartilaginous and bony offspring (Figure 13-32) did very well in late Paleozoic seas and are numerous today. The earliest amphibians, which derived from lobe-finned fish in the middle Paleozoic, were known as *labyrinthodonts*. These and other early amphibians were plentiful in the late Paleozoic and then went into a serious decline. Today only salamanders, frogs, and toads are common descendants of this once great group.

The amphibians had been mostly displaced by the animals they had given birth to—the reptiles. The reptiles evolved during the latter 100 million years of the Paleozoic and were fully terrestrial animals. Amphibians had to stay near water for egg laying and larval development since their thin, moist skins could dry out during droughts.

The reptiles, in contrast, had evolved the **amniotic egg,** which was much like the chicken eggs we enjoy for breakfast. Now the embryo was safely tucked inside its own watery surroundings and could not dry out. The yolk contained food for its growth, and the ''white'' provided a source for its wastes; the shell protected it from harm and allowed gaseous diffusion. The reptiles had also evolved much stronger legs and skeletons and much better lungs.

Present-day reptiles include tuatara, lizardlike creatures found today only on a few islands near New Zealand, turtles, lizards and snakes, and alligators and crocodiles. All living reptiles except alligators and crocodiles seem to have descended from the

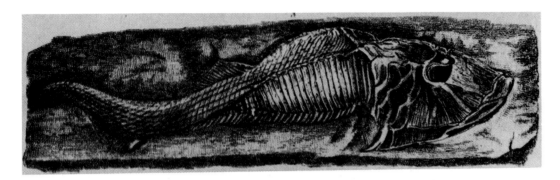

13-32
Here is an example of a middle Paleozoic fish from a sedimentary layer in England. Although odd looking by today's standards, fish of this sort were extremely successful at the time. (From R. Murchison, 1872, courtesy of the History of Science Collections, University of Oklahoma Libraries.)

stem reptiles known as *cotylosaurs*. The cotylosaurs were the source for numerous offspring, including the *pelycosaurs*, the dominant reptiles at the end of the era, which also saw their extinction. These peculiar cold-blooded reptiles were often called fin-back reptiles; their elaborate fins may have been a mechanism of heat exchange in the hot, drying climate. Other lineages include *icthyosaurs, mesosaurs*, and *plesiosaurs*, which returned to the ocean, *therapsids*, which were ancestors of mammals, and *thecodonts*, which were ancestors of crocodilians, birds, *pterosaurs* (flying reptiles), and *dinosaurs*, all of which developed during the following Mesozoic era and will be described in the next chapter.

The end of the Paleozoic was also the end of cotylosaurs, mesosaurs, and pelycosaurs. Therapsids and thecodonts survived the late Paleozoic decimation of invertebrate, amphibian, and reptilian ranks to live on into the next era. They were the source of all modern reptiles, all birds, all mammals, and the dinosaurs, the vast reptilian group that would dominate the Mesozoic era.

SUMMARY   The Paleozoic era, *if* defined as the period of time when multicellular life first became dominant in the sea, began at least 700 million years ago. About 600 million years ago, marine animals and plants gradually acquired the ability to secrete their own skeletons from materials in the ocean water around them. The first skeletons were external and were probably the result of population pressure.

More conventionally, the Paleozoic era began 570 million years ago, a time when many metazoan invertebrates were forming skeletons.

During the first half of this era, life was confined to the sea, but colonized the land first with primitive spore-bearing plants and then with awkward, fishlike creatures that learned to breathe air and waddle across the land. These amphibians sired the reptiles near the end of the era, because reptiles were better adapted to terrestrial life. Reptilians possessed heavy skins, scales, heavy skeletons, better, more powerful legs, and reptilian eggs—safe cradles for their young in a hostile environment.

Once again, life had met a new challenge. Life on land is far more hazardous than life in a watery solution of essentially constant temperature and chemistry. The adaptation to land life led to many awkward evolutionary experiments, many of which failed. Many invertebrate life forms died out at the end of the era, as did many amphibians and a few of the most primitive reptiles.

On the western margin of North America, the complex geosyncline that was eventually to form the Rocky Mountains remained relatively quiet throughout most of Paleozoic time, although there were a few sharp, local bursts of orogenic activity. The eastern geosyncline was progressively deformed by the Taconic, Acadian, and Appalachian orogenies as it changed its character from a passive continental margin to a subduction zone and, finally, to a collision zone that collided first with Europe and then with Africa and South America. The end of the Paleozoic era found the continents locked together in a single landmass. (The basic evidence for this concept was developed in Chapter Seven.)

On the craton, a series of major sequences of marine rocks recorded transgressions across the craton, leaving four major sequences of thin, highly fossiliferous sedimentary rock. The fossils in these rocks record what life was like in the shallow, sunlit seas that alternately covered and uncovered large parts of the center of North America. The cratonic record is thus a series of thin rock units that are separated by numerous intervals of missing, eroded material known as unconformities. The record is far more complete in the marginal geosynclines, which in the last three major periods of uplift produced the Appalachian Mountains as the culminating physical event of the Paleozoic era.

We begin the story of the Mesozoic era in the next chapter. North American rocks record an embrace with Europe, Greenland, and Africa that was soon to be broken. The rocks and fossils within them also suggest that North America was far to the south of its current location and was probably equatorial in location and climate. Everything was right for a new round of continental breakup, accompanied by a burst of evolutionary activity on the land and in the sea and, for the first time, in the air.

The Paleozoic era left us with a rich record (see Appendix F) of the evolution of life on the land and in the sea (Figure 13-33). It also left the Appalachians—a mountain range formed much like the modern Himalayas and probably equally as high. To the west of the Appalachians, the incre-

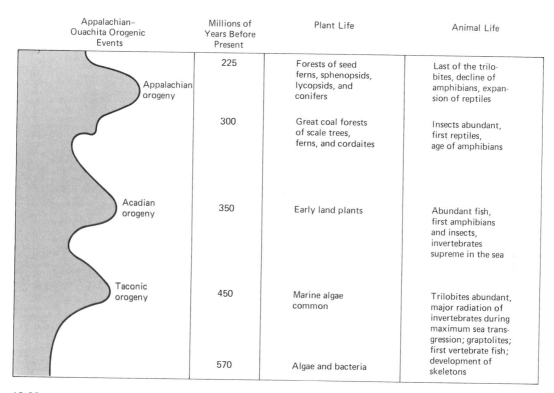

Appalachian–Ouachita Orogenic Events	Millions of Years Before Present	Plant Life	Animal Life
Appalachian orogeny	225	Forests of seed ferns, sphenopsids, lycopsids, and conifers	Last of the trilobites, decline of amphibians, expansion of reptiles
	300	Great coal forests of scale trees, ferns, and cordaites	Insects abundant, first reptiles, age of amphibians
Acadian orogeny	350	Early land plants	Abundant fish, first amphibians and insects, invertebrates supreme in the sea
Taconic orogeny	450	Marine algae common	Trilobites abundant, major radiation of invertebrates during maximum sea transgression; graptolites; first vertebrate fish; development of skeletons
	570	Algae and bacteria	

13-33

A summary of some major events of the Paleozoic era.

dible coal swamps were formed and deformed as eastern North America was tilted upward by the force of intercontinental collision; these coal reserves are one of our greatest Paleozoic economic legacies.

Paleozoic rocks are widely exposed over the United States and are the dominant surface rock over most of the central and eastern United States. Only along the Gulf and Atlantic coasts, where Paleozoic rocks are covered by younger deposits, are Paleozoic rocks obscured from view. In the west, Paleozoic rocks are widely exposed, although exposures are isolated by the complex volcanic and structural events that were to form the west during the Mesozoic and Cenozoic eras.

EXERCISES

1. At the beginning of the Paleozoic era, each year had approximately 408 days and each day had about 21 hours (see Figure 11-1). What

effects, it any, would this "fact of life" have had on oceanic, invertebrate life?

2. It has been noted that with modern oysters, shell thickness is related to the level of wave energy. If early Paleozoic oysterlike fossils had very heavy shells, what inference could we make about tide height?

3. In terms of continental evolution, as discussed in Chapter Twelve, how can the frequent marine invasion of most of North America during the Paleozoic be explained?

4. As described, trilobites have incredibly sophisticated eyes. What, if anything, does this tell us about their habitat and life-style?

5. What kind of evolutionary pressure would select for the amniotic egg?

6. The earliest known vertebrate is a fish named *Anatolepis,* which inhabited marine water 510 million years ago. It had external plates and was probably no longer than 3 inches ($7\frac{1}{2}$ centimeters). What would have been the advantage of having a spinal column to such a small creature?

7. It has been said that *all cells of every living thing* are strictly aquatic organisms. What could this mean?

8. During photosynthesis, the energy of sunlight is used to manufacture sugars and release oxygen as a by product. At night, plants take in oxygen to burn the sugars and release carbon dioxide, just as animals do *at all times.* In what most fundamental way are they different?

SUGGESTED READINGS

Cloud, Preston, 1970, *Adventures in Earth History,* San Francisco, W. H. Freeman, 992 pp.
" . . . *a volume of significant writings from original sources . . . from the time of Nicolaus Steno to the present." Highly recommended.*

Levin, Harold L., 1975, *Life Through Time,* Dubuque, Iowa, William C. Brown, 217 pp.
Brief, well-written review of the history of life.

McAlester, A. Lee, *The History of Life,* 2nd ed., Englewood Cliffs, N.J., Prentice-Hall, 168 pp.
Similar to Levin's book, but superior illustrations.

King, Philip B., 1976, *The Evolution of North America,* rev. ed., Princeton, N.J., Princeton University Press, 198 pp. plus map.
An updated classic. Highly recommended.

King, Philip B., and Beikman, Helen M., 1976, *The Paleozoic and Mesozoic Rocks: A Discussion to Accompany the Geologic Map of the United States,* Washington, D.C., U.S. Government Printing Office, 76 pp. (U.S. Geological Survey Professional Paper 903).
Excellent review, by region, of the United States.

Cratonic events

Four major marine transgressions and regressions; numerous shallow basins and gentle domes; central interior region stable.

Appalachian geosyncline

Taconic, Acadian, and Appalachian orogenies as Europe and Africa collided with the Americas; Ouachita-Marathon belt the southern extension.

Western geosyncline

Remains a passive, trailing continental margin.

Life

Development of skeletons; metazoan life may predate classic Paleozoic lower boundary; abundant marine invertebrate life; vertebrate animals in early Paleozoic seas; amphibians and land plants in middle Paleozoic; end of Paleozoic a time of major dying off.

Pangaea

End product of multiple continental collision in middle to late Paleozoic.

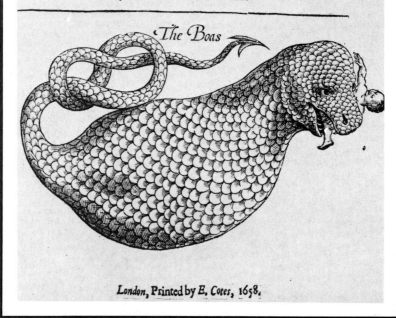

Three centuries later, we know that boa constrictors *do not* swallow children and also that they originated late in the Mesozoic era. These 300 years record the shift from dependence on ancient authority to dependence on experience and reason. (From Edward Topsel, 1658, *The History of Four Footed Beasts and Serpents*, courtesy of the History of Science Collections, University of Oklahoma Libraries.)

Chapter Fourteen

MIDDAY

the mesozoic

"More individuals are born than can possibly survive. A grain in the balance can determine which individuals shall live and which shall die."
Charles Darwin

The Mezozoic era began about 225 million years ago and terminated 65 million years ago. Within that 160 million-year span there was a major advance and retreat of a shallow inland sea, the breakup of Pangaea, volcanism and intrusion of plutons in the developing western United States, which culminated in the beginning of formation of the Rocky Mountains, and the rise and fall of reptiles as the dominant life form on the land, in the sea, and in the air.

No single story so captures our imagination as the story of the dinosaurs, a few of which were the largest animals ever to inhabit the land. Reptiles dominated this middle era so thoroughly that the mammals, even though they appeared early in the Mesozoic era, were a small, unimportant Mesozoic group. The decline of the dinosaurs and other reptiles at the end of this era finally gave them ecological niches to exploit in the Cenozoic era. The passing of the dinosaurs at the end of the Mesozoic era is one of the many unsolved mysteries in the history of life.

The story of continental fragmentation is recorded in Mesozoic rocks; rocks along the Atlantic coast record this breakup and separation along a newly formed zone of seafloor spreading—the modern Atlantic ridge. Along the developing west coast of the United States, the relatively passive United States began to override the Pacific Ocean Basin, and the area became a consumptive margin.

Mesozoic rocks are widely exposed over much of the United States, particularly in the west, and form the backdrop for many of our national parks and monuments. There is another enormous reservoir of coal within the western rocks. This coal, like the eastern Paleozoic coals, was produced as a rising mountain range blocked western drainages and turned much of the west into a gigantic swamp. Let us examine each of these Mesozoic stories in more detail.

PHYSICAL EVENTS

The physical events of the Mesozoic are dominated by the breakup of the giant supercontinent, *Pangaea*. What kinds of evidence allow us to interpret the opening and closing of ocean basins?

The opening of the Atlantic Ocean must have taken place as a spreading center split the old Pangaean landmass down a line of rifting that was roughly parallel to the modern shorelines of the Americas, Europe, and Africa. This would be similar to what is happening in east Africa today; the eastern one-third of the African continent is being split into two continental fragments (see Figure 7-13). An example of a slightly more advanced stage is furnished by the opening of the Red Sea (Figure 7-12) as Arabia and Africa part company. Rifting is accompanied by a great deal of tension; continental rocks are horizontally pulled apart, and the continental margins founder. We might well expect massive intrusions of diabase (medium-grained basalt) and extrusions of basalt to mark the formation of the first ridge and the injection of basaltic upper mantle material into the continental rifted margin. As the continents begin to be shoved apart, deeper water sediments should suddenly overlie shallow water sediments; eugeosynclinal sediments should replace the miogeosynclinal sediments that are resting on cratonic rock. The following pages will tell us if these predictions are accurate.

The Appalachian East

The elevated Appalachian range dominated the eastern part of the United States while, to the south, the Ouachita and Marathon ranges were similarly high mountains. These ranges shed continental sediments that are rarely seen throughout much of the east because of later erosion. Early Mesozoic sedimentation throughout the east was trapped in a series of fault-bounded (breaks along which rocks move) troughs; the resulting reddish sedimentary rocks form a discontinuous record (Figure 14-1) of the foundering and rifting of the eastern margin.

Within these generally reddish sediments, which are bounded by faults, are numerous diabasic and basaltic dikes and flows and the imprint of dinosaur tracks. Many of these downfaulted troughs were themselves tilted and penetrated by numerous basaltic sills. The Palisades of the Hudson River (a series of cliffs) is the eroded edge of a thick sill that intruded at this early Mesozoic time.

The eastern area thus clearly documents the beginning of the breakup that was to separate Europe from America. Fossils in the deep sea sediment shed from the eastern continental margins date the complete separation of Europe from America about 180 million years ago; radiometric dates from the ocean floor basalts formed along our eastern coast are consistent with this age dating.

Greenland remained attached to North America until approximately 80 million years ago, when it finally separated, producing the Davis Strait and a series of submarine volcanoes that date the rifting of the seafloor. The breakaway of Greenland from Europe occurred still later, near the beginning of the Cenozoic era. Thus North America—including Greenland—and Europe did

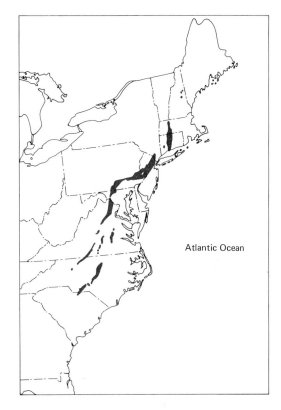

14-1
The colored areas are early Mesozoic sedimentary rocks, exposed in the eastern United States. (From P. B. King and H. M. Beikman, 1976, U.S. Geological Survey Professional Paper 903.)

not come unstuck all at once, much as the more recent geologic separation of Africa, east Africa, and the Arabian Peninsula.

Throughout the remainder of the Mesozoic era, the central and eastern parts of the United States remained mostly emergent while they shed their debris onto the passive continental shelves facing a rift ocean. The north-central and eastern United States thus became a *sediment source* throughout the remainder of Mesozoic and Cenozoic times. The later sedimentary record of the present continent was therefore to be written primarily in the west, partly by deposits stripped from the heartland of North America. The Appalachians shed part of their sedimentary load to the east, forming the Atlantic coastal plain. These plains consist of miogeosynclinal sediments deposited on cratonic rock whose age is partially Paleozoic. Deep drilling off the east coast reveals a series of typical miogeosynclinal rock wedges whose oldest rocks are nearly 180 million years old; the youngest rocks are being formed today. To the south, the southern margin of the continent was to witness one of the most extensive invasions of the shallow continental seas since the early Paleozoic, three hundred fifty million years before.

The Gulf Coast

By 170 million years ago, our current Gulf of Mexico area was a gigantic evaporitic basin, its salt now an important resource throughout the south and west. The equator trended slightly north of east through the southern portion of the Gulf; conditions were like those of the modern Persian Gulf. North America was now heading slowly northwest but, overall, its climate remained tropical and warm.

A major advance of the sea across the land began 140 million years ago that mostly covered the southern Ouachita and Marathon mountains and invaded nearly the entire western and south-central United States. Younger and younger marine rocks were deposited toward the center of the craton. By 100 million years ago, late Mesozoic seas covered all of the United States except for the Appalachian region, the north-central United States, and a rising mountainous mass in the west that would soon be the Rocky Mountains (Figure 14-2).

A Speculative Idea

What could have caused such a massive marine transgression? We have touched on the idea before; let us develop one of several competing ideas that might apply to the Mesozoic world.

We know that the oceanic ridge system of the world constitutes the world's greatest single mountain chain, but one that is only rarely visible, since almost all the volcanic mountains are submarine. As lithosphere is formed at a spreading center, it is hot and, therefore, forms an elevated mass. As the mass slowly cools, it subsides—and occupies less volume. During periods of time when the spreading rate is high, large volumes of magma are being injected into the ridge system, which becomes quite high and broad. The *volume* of the ridge is, then, a function of spreading rate. As the volume of the worldwide ridge system is increased, the volume of the ocean basin is diminished. The water in the ocean basins must go somewhere; the answer is, of course, that it spreads across edges of the continents.

Note that the concept proposed here should call for *worldwide* changes in sea level, because increases in the total volume of the ridge system, due to a high spreading rate, should be reflected in worldwide, simultaneous transgression of the sea onto the land. Can such worldwide changes in sea level be recognized? Can similar cratonic sequences of marine rocks be recognized on every continent?

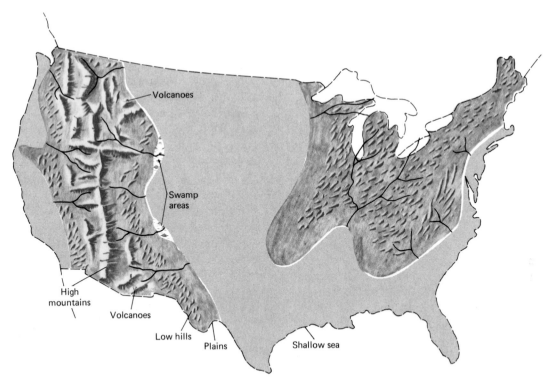

14-2
A map of the probable geography of the United States 100 million years ago.
(Map from U.S. Geological Survey.)

Many, but by no means all, geologists believe that the unconformities marking worldwide regressions of the sea from continental cratons can readily be recognized and are an important basis for *intercontinental* correlations. Similarly, many geologists point out that worldwide rise in sea level can also be recognized in the form of transgressive marine rocks of similar ages on every continent. Around the world, one such time is the end of the Mesozoic era; the continents of the world all record very substantial marine invasions over their cratons at this time. Similarly, the end of the Paleozoic and the beginning of the Mesozoic was a widespread

time of continental *emergence;* erosional intervals and continental sedimentation are the usual kinds of sedimentary records on most of the world's continents from 200 to 250 million years ago.

Such apparent worldwide periodicity in the rise and fall of the sea *could* be related to spreading rates but, if it is, worldwide times of maximum transgression also should coincide with *broad* belts of magnetically polarized rocks (see Chapter Seven) on the seafloor. The science of paleomagnetism allows us to reconstruct these spreading rates. Briefly, careful calculation of the variation in the spreading rate shows a strong correlation between spreading rates, continental fragmentation, and marine transgressions over continents.

We can take our model one step further. A brief consideration of the effect of widespread seas covering most of the continent (maximum *transgression*) versus a time of highly emergent shelves (maximum *regression*) will suggest that times of *maximum transgression should be times of mild, moderate climates*. As we reflected earlier (see Chapter 12), seawater is difficult to heat *or* cool; its presence moderates climate and buffers any rapid climatic changes.

Furthermore, as the extent of epicontinental seas grows, an enormous diversity of habitats are produced under a highly moderated climate. Biologists predict that in such a climate, the diversity of both plant and animal life should increase.

In contrast, as sea level falls, marine life is restricted to a diminishing area, a diminishing food supply, and increased extremes in climate. Biologic diversity should diminish.

When a supercontinent is fragmented, the spreading centers stand higher than the subduction zones that will eventually consume their basaltic product; that fact, plus accelerated spreading rates, *should* produce marine transgressions. Thus it is that *sea transgressions often follow continental breakup;* we have seen the results most vividly as the Atlantic Ocean Basin continued to grow in width throughout the late Mesozoic.

In the same way, as continents are carried toward one another, their relative motions must be slowed or cease, and the spreading rates responsible for their motion must also decrease or cease. *Continental reassembly thus should lead to marine regression;* we have seen that effect at work at the end of the Paleozoic; all land joined together as Pangaea and, worldwide, the continents became strongly emergent. The compressional uplift of mountain chains as a result of these collisions, of course, tends to reinforce this principle.

The tie, however tenuous, between spreading rates, fossil diversities, ancient climates, and worldwide oscillations in sea level is one of the more interesting speculative hypotheses being considered by geologists just now, but is it truth?

Not all geologists agree that fluctuations of sea level are episodic on a worldwide basis. Some geologists have pointed out, quite correctly, that in many cratonic sequences, there are numerous unconformities. Pick just the "right" one, and worldwide unconformities can be demonstrated; pick a different one, and each continent, or fragment of a continent, has its own unique record. Nor is our timekeeping sufficiently accurate to allow us to date many unconformities with real precision; the hours and minutes are often not a problem, but our geologic timepieces usually lack a sweep-second hand. We simply cannot date many unconformities more closely than, perhaps, 10 million years; worldwide correlation with those limits of accuracy must be regarded with some suspicion.

The recent return by many geologists to viewing the earth as a body whose continents are occasionally recipients of cyclic, synchronous marine invasion is in many ways a step back into the history of geology. Two centuries ago, scientists, including Cuvier, explained breaks in the fossil record as catastrophes occasioned by the worldwide fall and rise of the sea (see Chapter Five). Such changes in the level of the sea (including the latest, the Noachian flood) were then viewed as catastrophic and as the source of all change in the character of life. A century ago, the more gentle rise and fall of a world-wide sea across static continent and identical ocean floor was accepted geologic truth.

How interesting that modern geologists are returning to a similar concept; the rise and fall of sea level, occasioned by *changes* in the submarine ridge system, is once again being seen as largely responsible for periods of rapid change in the history of life. It does seem that the world is somewhat more episodic than some might have thought; the character of life is often profoundly affected by major periods of transgression and regression of the sea.

We cannot picture marine transgression as a thundering wave roaring across the land; by dating the position and age of rocks in many transgressive sequences, we can show that transgression occurs at the rate of a few tens of miles (kilometers) across the land during 1 million years. It seems not to be the suddenness of transgression and regression that causes many life forms to disappear from the scene but, instead, their inability to adapt to the changed environmental conditions that accompanied major transgressions and regressions.

Our ideas on the origin of changes in sea level and its consequences on life are quite new, having been largely developed within the last 10 or 20 years. But the basic model of rising and falling seas across the land, with its profound (once envisioned as catastrophic) effect on life, predates the beginning of modern geology nearly 200 years ago. Is any idea really new?

The Western Margin

During the early Mesozoic, much of the western part of the North American craton was receiving reddish continental and marine sediments, intermingled with lake and river deposits, from the north and east. The Petrified Forest and Painted Desert of Arizona are among the many examples of the rocks left from this early Mesozoic environment. Still further west, this area of continental sediments grade into typical miogeosynclinal and eugeosynclinal rocks deposited along the continental margin.

By about 180 million years ago, vast deposits of sand covered the western cratonic margin. The source of these sands was from the north, based on the direction of cross-bedding within the sand, and they apparently were deposited by the wind as massive sand dune fields, similar to those of southwestern Africa today. We can see these sands today as the massive cross-bedded sandstones in Zion National Park (see Figure 5-4). To the west of Zion was a newly risen highland area, the *Mesocordilleran highland,* which was to divide the western geosyncline from the cratonic east.

In time, the western interior was inundated by the same transgressive sea that had previously buried the evaporites of the Gulf of Mexico. The Gulf of Mexico had formed as North America broke free from Africa and South America, and it had become a new geosynclinal site along our passive southern border, as the western border became a consumptive margin. To the far west, volcanism had been common since the beginning of the Mesozoic era, and the intrusion of gigantic masses of plutonic igneous rock (Figure 14-3) occurred near the end of the era. We know these masses of rock today as the Sierra Nevada of California, the Sawtooth Range of Idaho, and the granitic mountains of westernmost British Columbia.

By 150 million years ago, a vast alluvial

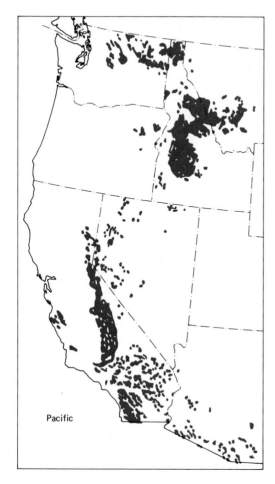

14-3
Late Mesozoic intrusive bodies in the western United States. (From P. B. King and H. M. Beikman, 1976, U.S. Geological Survey Professional Paper 903.)

Pacific

(water-laid) plain, covering nearly 800,000 square miles (2 million square kilometers), had spread eastward from the Mesocordilleran highland. These vast deposits of continental origin, known as the Morrison *Formation* (a formation is a recognizable unit of rocks that can be displayed on a geologic map), were spread eastward by rivers from the Mesocordilleran highland. Within the Morrison are two treasures: extensive uranium deposits and abundant dinosaur remains.

By the end of the Mesozoic era, the sea had encroached across all of western North America except for the Mesocordilleran highlands, which must have stood above these seas as islands. The coastline along the highland was warm, poorly drained, and an ideal site for coal deposition, and oscillating sea levels left successive layers of dark, marine shales, tan sands, and immense deposits of coal.

Like the eastern coal, the western coals (Figure 14-4) were deposited in swamps adjacent to highlands as sea levels rose and fell during this greatest marine invasion of the Mesozoic. This worldwide invasion covered approximately one-third of the earth's present land area.

Still further west, enormous quantities of sand and mud poured into deep water, mostly as turbidites, and formed the interbedded clastic rocks and deep water radiolarian (Figure 13-30) cherts collectively known as the Franciscan Group of western California and Oregon. These western rocks were intensively deformed by orogenic events coincident with the large plutonic intrusions previously mentioned; this western orogeny is called the **Nevadan orogeny.** These events were extremely complex and difficult to generalize, but it is likely that the western margin of North America looked at this time (150 million years ago) much like the modern west coast of South America.

To the east, an enormous volume of sediments, whose ages range from 50 to 100 million years old, was shed from a now vastly

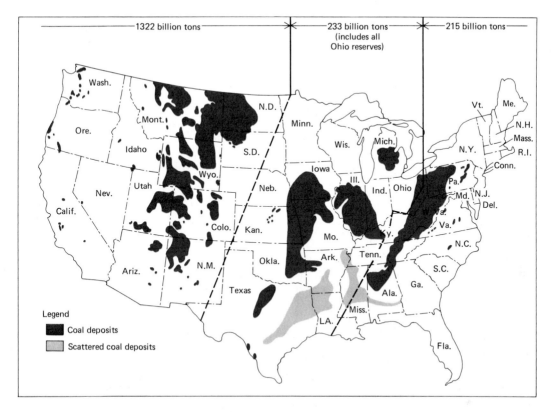

14-4
Major coal reserves in the United States; western coal of Mesozoic age accounts for three-quarters of the total reserve. (Map from Environmental Protection Agency, 1977.)

The Rocky Mountains

enlarged Cordilleran highland area. The Rocky Mountains had come to claim their space in the sky.

We have seen that the Morrison Formation was a middle Mesozoic clastic wedge (an accumulation of sediment that, in cross section, is wedge shaped) from the Mesocordil-

leran highland that forced the sea to retreat (regress) temporarily before the onslaught of sediment. Much further west, batholithic intrusions had occurred coincident with the western movement of North America over the Pacific Ocean. This movement, which began as North America was carried northwestward away from Europe and Africa, resulted in intensive volcanism from island arcs along our western coast. Additionally, ophiolites, blueschists, and typical consumptive plate margins (deep water sediments) were contorted and strongly metamorphosed as they were jammed onto the land.

Thus areas that are now parts of Washington, Oregon, and California were added to the United States during a complex series of early and middle Mesozoic events. It was essentially a western duplication of the Taconic orogeny, 300 million years earlier. But what does all this activity have to do with the Rocky Mountains?

The Rockies now split the United States into a western one-third and an eastern two-thirds; they extend from Alaska to the Antarctic continent as an enormous, mountainous spine, sometimes called the "backbone of the Americas." While all the sound and fury was going on along our modern western coast, what was happening in Montana, Wyoming, Colorado, and New Mexico? The Rockies are far to the east of the events along our western margin.

The Rocky Mountains reflect a generally younger series of orogenic events, sometimes called the **Laramide orogeny,** as the sequence of mountain-building events rippled from west to east throughout most of Mesozoic time. The documentation of the rise of the Rockies comes from two dissimilar sources of evidence that are of related origin: (1) vast deposits of debris were shed from the rising Rocky Mountains between 60 and 100 million years ago, and (2) rapid subsidence of the western cratonic margin began as the Rockies formed. No other mountain system had ever directly involved the craton, but the subsiding eastern margin of the miogeosyncline played a major role in the accumulation of sediment at the very end of the Mesozoic era. This accumulated sediment was later crushed eastward against the new cratonic margin as the sediments filling in the eastern part of the western geosyncline were crushed, crumpled, metamorphosed, and thrust up onto the craton.

Rocks from the west were carried far to the east, an event duplicating still older events in the west several times. The thrusting and eastward compression of the western geosyncline to make the Rocky Mountains was largely an event of the early Cenozoic era; it is referred to here to complete partially the story of the Rocky Mountains.

The story of the origin and development of the Rocky Mountains is, of course, written in the rocks. Figure 14-5 is a simplified columnar section of the total series of rocks exposed in the Philmont Scout Ranch area of east-central New Mexico. As only one example of the kinds of evidence available to curious earth scientists, the rocks of this region portray the story of the origin of the Rocky Mountains as seen in New Mexico.

Within that column of rocks is, of course, a rich history of life, and it is the story of Mesozoic life that we will now study. The term Mesozoic means "middle life" and includes an amazing tale of oceanic and continental development of it.

MESOZOIC LIFE

Both the beginning and the end of the Mesozoic were marked by widespread extinction of preexisting faunas. The causes of decline in fossil faunal diversity can never be fully known; the causes of *modern* extinction are still a subject of lively debate among biologists. But it is clear that the late Paleozoic was marked by climatic extremes. In the southern continental cluster, glacia-

Age in million years

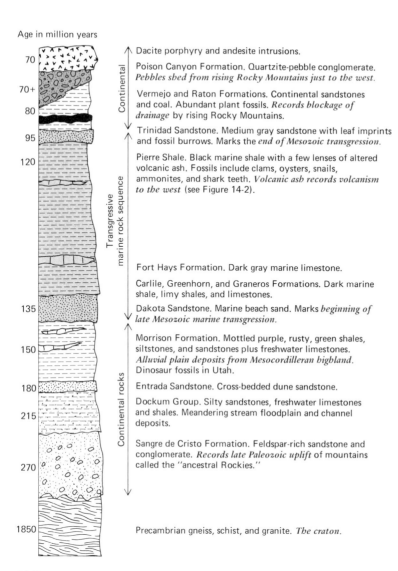

Dacite porphyry and andesite intrusions.

Poison Canyon Formation. Quartzite-pebble conglomerate. *Pebbles shed from rising Rocky Mountains just to the west.*

Vermejo and Raton Formations. Continental sandstones and coal. Abundant plant fossils. *Records blockage of drainage* by rising Rocky Mountains.

Trinidad Sandstone. Medium gray sandstone with leaf imprints and fossil burrows. Marks the *end of Mesozoic transgression.*

Pierre Shale. Black marine shale with a few lenses of altered volcanic ash. Fossils include clams, oysters, snails, ammonites, and shark teeth. *Volcanic ash records volcanism to the west* (see Figure 14-2).

Fort Hays Formation. Dark gray marine limestone.

Carlile, Greenhorn, and Graneros Formations. Dark marine shale, limy shales, and limestones.

Dakota Sandstone. Marine beach sand. Marks *beginning of late Mesozoic marine transgression.*

Morrison Formation. Mottled purple, rusty, green shales, siltstones, and sandstones plus freshwater limestones. *Alluvial plain deposits from Mesocordilleran highland.* Dinosaur fossils in Utah.

Entrada Sandstone. Cross-bedded dune sandstone.

Dockum Group. Silty sandstones, freshwater limestones and shales. Meandering stream floodplain and channel deposits.

Sangre de Cristo Formation. Feldspar-rich sandstone and conglomerate. *Records late Paleozoic uplift of mountains* called the "ancestral Rockies."

Precambrian gneiss, schist, and granite. *The craton.*

14-5
Schematic column of sedimentary rocks exposed in the Philmont Scout Ranch region of north-central New Mexico. Within these rocks is the story of the origin of the Rocky Mountains. Events of the Cenozoic era are omitted. (Simplified from G. D. Robinson, et al., 1964, U.S. Geological Survey Professional Paper 505.)

tion was widespread; in the northern continental cluster, the end of the Paleozoic was a time of widespread sea retreat and development of reddish sediments, mostly of continental origin.

As predicted, times of continental agglomeration were also times of widespread marine regression, enhanced in this case by widespread southern glaciation. By analogy, within the last few million years essentially modern glaciation dropped worldwide sea levels several hundred feet (60 to 100 meters), exposing large areas of the continental shelves to continental conditions and erosion. Even the end of the Precambrian had been marked by a similar widespread glaciation; many latest Precambrian sedimentary sequences around the world are marked by unique gravel layers that have been interpreted as glacial deposits.

And yet glacial climate can hardly be called on to explain the reduction in faunal diversity entirely; radical changes in climate should affect continental life even more than marine life, and it was usually the marine faunas (animal groups) that exhibited substantial change at the end of the Paleozoic.

A similar wave of wholesale extinction was to occupy the end of the Mesozoic as the broadly transgressive seas began a retreat to their present shoreline. The Mesozoic extinction was to involve not only marine fauna, but also wholesale extinction of the dominant reptilian fauna, accompanied by the rise of warm-blooded mammals, a resurgence of insects, and the development of flowering and fruiting plants.

Invertebrates

The marine life of the Mesozoic period is so different from its Paleozoic ancestry that at first glance the Mesozoic seems to be a different world. Beginning with a time of continental emergence, the marine record of earliest Mesozoic is extremely sparse. Crinoids and brachiopods became far less numerous, and corals nearly became extinct. Bryozoa and foraminifera also became practically extinct, but they later flowered in late Mesozoic and Cenozoic seas. Several types of corals did disappear, but were replaced later in the Mesozoic by newer types, which

14-6
A variety of coiled cephalopods. The patterns on the exteriors of most of the shells are caused by the intersection of numerous interior walls with the exterior of the shell. The intricate folding was perhaps an adaptation for greater strength. (From G. W. Leibniz, 1749, *Protogaea,* courtesy of the History of Science Collections, University of Oklahoma Libraries.)

once again constructed reefs. Many echinoderms, notably the blastoids, and all but a small group of crinoids disappeared.

Only the mollusks seemed to have weathered the entry into the Mesozoic. Gastropods, some of which had adapted to continental life in the late Paleozoic, became an increasingly important part of both land and marine life, and the clams and oysters became supremely abundant—so much so that many late Mesozoic limestones are essentially deposits of oyster shells.

More than any one other single group, the oceans were dominated by the cephalopods. Coiled cephalopods were the ancestors of successively larger squidlike creatures that built larger chambers for themselves as they grew. Some of these coiled cephalopods approached 1 yard (about 1 meter) or more in diameter, and their filled fossil shells are so heavy that it takes several persons to pick them up. One variety of coiled cephalopod, the *ammonite* (Figure 14-6), has been used worldwide as an important fossil for correlation of marine Mesozoic rocks.

One cephalopod grew around long, internal conical straight skeletons; these fossils have been called "fossil cigars" (Figure 14-7). The cephalopods are a remarkably advanced group, well adapted for life in the sea. They are predaceous, able to move rapidly, have a large, complex nervous system and brain, a cartilagenous skeleton, and eyes that work very much like those of humans.

If there is one thing Mesozoic marine faunas tell us, it is that evolutionary success belongs to those who can *move*. In a general way, rooted, attached life did not compete well in the Mesozoic seas; the agile and those with adaptations for predation, including strong grasping appendages, sharp teeth and bills, and swift speed, evolved. Thus the place of the trilobite was taken by the crus-

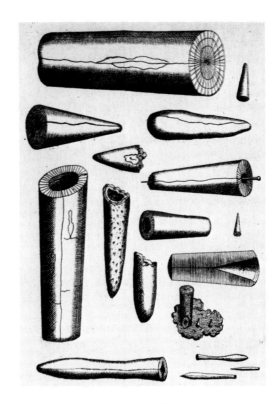

14-7
The fossil remains of straight cephalopods. In life, the creature surrounded the internal skeletons shown here. (From G. W. Leibniz, 1749, courtesy of the History of Science Collections, University of Oklahoma Libraries.)

taceans, better adapted to prey on one another. Shrimps, lobsters, barnacles (see Appendix F), and crabs appeared in the Mesozoic seas, as did starfish and spiny sea urchins (echinoids).

On land, freshwater and air-breathing snails were abundant, as were clams, ostracods, and freshwater sponges. The dominant land invertebrates, however, were the insects, and the most important of these were bees and butterflies. Rising in abundance, parallel with the insects, was a new kind of plant capable of producing a flower or fruit that *shielded its seeds;* that flower needed to be pollinated (fertilized) by insects. A mutually beneficial relation developed between insects and the flowering and fruit-bearing plants, the **angiosperms,** that continues to this day. The angiosperms furnish food for bees, and bees inadvertently fertilize the plants, thus ensuring that they produce seeds and reproduce themselves.

Plants

The Paleozoic plant world had been the world of psilopsids, scale trees, horsetails, ferns, seed ferns, ginkgoes, cycads, cordaites, and conifers. Of this diverse group, a few remnants of the psilopsids, scale trees, and horsetails survive today; the seed ferns and cordaites died out. By the middle Mesozoic, only the cycads, ginkgoes, and conifers remained to complete the plant scene. The cycads and conifers are classic **gymnosperms** (naked-seed plants) and were the dominant plant components of the Mesozoic flora until almost the end of the era.

Near the end of the Mesozoic, angiosperms became the dominant plants, as they are today. While the reproductive structures of gymnosperms are cones with naked seeds, the angiosperms enclose their reproductive structures in flowers; the flowers pollinated by insects and other animals are usually quite showy. The ovarian part of the flower, once pollinated, may develop into a fruit that totally encloses the seed. The fruit protects the seeds from drying and helps disperse them; animals eat the fruit and then release the seeds unharmed, coated with the rich natural fertilizer of their excrement. An-

giosperms include a tremendous variety of plants that are familiar to us including willows, grasses, roses, corn, oaks, tomatoes, beans, wheat, lilies, and dandelions.

The worldwide explosive growth in angiosperms has long been a puzzle to *paleobotanists,* scientists who study ancient plant life. No doubt the growth of angiosperms was assisted by the rise of pollinating insects, whose numbers grew at the same time. It is well known that the middle and late Mesozoic climate was universally mild as a result of the marine transgression previously described. In such a moderate climate, continental life prospers under ideal conditions.

Reptiles

The Mesozoic is often called the "age of reptiles"; they dominated the land, sea, and air as no other animal group had before them. But what of the vertebrate ancestors that had preceded them?

In the Mesozoic seas, fish prospered. Both the cartilaginous- and bony-skeleton fish entered a golden age and filled essentially every marine environment available to them. The lungfish and lobe-finned fish remained unimportant, sparse members of the marine community, as they do today. The late Paleozoic decline of the amphibians continued, and only the frogs and salamanders remain as inconspicuous survivors today. From the line of descent stretching from lobe-finned fish through the amphibians to the cotylosaurs, the differentiation of formerly marine life to reptilian life, with their very special amniotic egg, was complete as the Mesozoic era began.

Early Mesozoic reptiles include two major groups. The *therapsids* were mamallike reptiles, originating near the end of the Paleozoic. They had all four legs directly under their bodies and walked on all fours. Although regarded as reptiles, they *may* have been warm-blooded and perhaps even had hair. Their teeth, skeletal arrangements, and probable heart divisions were also very much like those of modern mammals. The therapsids seem to have been the ancestors of modern mammals (including humans).

The *thecodonts* were the ancestors of all the reptiles popularly called the dinosaurs, plus birds and pterosaurs. The thecodonts, which were about the size of a large dog, were reptiles that ran on their two hind feet. Because the weight of their bodies, while running, was supported from the hips, their pelvic structures were extensively modified to support their weight. Two modifications appeared. The early modification was a typical lizard-style hip, like that of the thecodonts; the later modification resulted in a pelvic structure more like that of birds. Both lizard-hipped and bird-hipped dinosaurs existed together throughout the Mesozoic, although the bird-hipped variety entered the scene 40 million years late. All bird-hipped dinosaurs were plant eaters; unfortunately for them, many of their lizard-hipped cousins were not.

Lizard-Hipped Dinosaurs. The earliest lizard-hipped dinosaurs were direct descendants of the thecodonts and were equally small. These animals were *carnivores* (meat eaters), and they ran on their two hind legs. Throughout the Mesozoic era their maximum size increased. *Allosaurus* and *Tyrannosaurus* are two of the best examples of a late stage in development of these carniverous monsters. The head of the *Tyrannosaurus* was 20 feet (6 meters) above the ground;

14-8
The fossilized head of *Tyranosaurus rex* suggests how well adapted this creature was for a carniverous lifestyle. The teeth in this 100 million-year-old specimen remain awesome. (Photograph by W. T. Lee, U.S. Geological Survey.)

individual teeth were the size of a modern flashlight (Figure 14-8). Weighing 6 tons (5½ metric tons), these were the largest meat eaters that ever lived.

By the middle Mesozoic, herbivorous (plant-eating) lizard-hipped dinosaurs had become the largest land animals ever known and included animals such as the *Brontosaurus* and *Apatosaurus* (Figure 14-9). These animals had massive legs to support their enormous weight [up to 40 tons (36 metric tons)], walked on all fours, and had necks 18 feet (5½ meters) long and blunt peglike teeth, adapted for grazing on vegetation. Their size was extraordinary—one middle Mesozoic variety was about 80 percent the length of a football field.

The value of such enormous size has long been debated. If, as many geologists believe, these dinosaurs were cold-blooded, like modern lizards, turtles, crocodiles, and

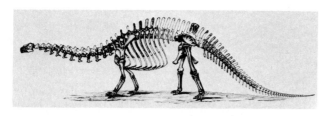

14-9
Modern scholarship indicates this reconstruction has the wrong head (of a *different* dinosaur) mounted on the correct skeleton. With an 18-foot (5½-meter) neck, *Brontosaurus* must have been well adapted for grazing in high trees, much like modern giraffes. They were an ultimate expression of the tendency for animals to grow larger through time. (From O. C. Marsh, 1896, *The Dinosaurs of North America*, 16th Ann. Rpt., U.S. Geological Survey, *courtesy of the History of Science Collections, University of Oklahoma Libraries.)*

other reptiles, it would have been possible to maintain their enormous bulk (equal to 750 average humans) with relatively little food. The sun kept them warm, and wading in water kept them cool. It is quite probable that these monsters spent some of their time in water, which would have helped support their weight while keeping their carniverous cousins at a respectable distance.

Recently, some geologists have suggested that many, if not all, dinosaurs were warm-blooded. If this is true, they kept their body temperature constant. The ensuing debate is a lively one, and we will touch on it again. For now, note that *if* these monsters were warm-blooded, they must have packed away an *incredible* quantity of food on an average day.

Bird-Hipped Dinosaurs. These dinosaurs had no teeth, like modern birds but, instead, had ducklike bills and birdlike beaks with which to chew away at their vegetative diet. They never grew as large as their lizard-hipped kindred and were entirely herbivorous. As smaller, plant-eating dinosaurs, they would have furnished a tasty dish for their meat-eating kin; their response was to develop some of the most elaborate and bizzare defensive features in the history of life.

The *Stegosaurus* is one example of extreme defensive adaptations. This four-footed plant eater had a row of huge plates along its spine (Figure 14-10) and a tail capped with several bony spikes. The spinal plates may have been used as heat regulators, much like the plates in a car radiator, but certainly would have been an unpleasant mouthful. The spiny tail also would have been an awesome weapon. One of the many remarkable things about this animal was that it had two sets of "brains"—a quite small one in the head and another nerve concentration at the end of the spine. As one wag said long ago "no problem bothered him a bit; he made both head and tail of it. . . . He though twice before he spoke, and thus had no judgement to revoke." In reality, *Stegosaurus,* with its tiny forward brain, must have been a remarkably stupid creature, and it, too, became extinct.

The *Ankylosaurus* is a later example of a similar defense; its back consisted of armored plates, like turtles, from which large, pointed spines projected. The tail ended in a great, spiked club. Other dinosaurs, of which the best known is *Triceratops*, looked (Figure 14-11) something like the modern rhinoceros. The neck and head were covered with a massive, bony plate from which three large bony spines projected. Attacked

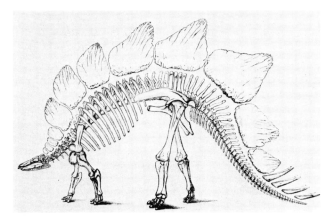

14-10

Stegosaurus was one of many bizarre adaptations among the dinosaurs. The great bony plates along its spine have been suggested as both defensive armor and heat-dissipating fins. (From O. C. Marsh, 1896, courtesy of the History of Science Collections, University of Oklahoma Libraries.)

from the front, they would have been hazardous to the health of *Tyrannosaurus* and other carnivores.

Dinosaur Extinction. Both the lizard- and bird-hipped dinosaurs are abundant fossils in latest Mesozoic rocks, but they are absent from Cenozoic rocks. In the span of perhaps 10 million years, a large, diverse group disappeared completely. Only turtles, the lizards, the isolated tuataras of New Zealand, the snakes, and the crocodiles, plus the birds and mammals, survived this era. A vast group of reptiles that conquered the land, sea, and air were *gone*. What happened?

There have been many suggestions. Perhaps a great plague—a disease so virulent that they could not resist it—over took them all. Perhaps as the seas withdrew from the land at the very end of the Mesozoic, these primarily cold-blooded creatures could not withstand the colder, continental climates that were to come. Perhaps the small mammals underfoot had discovered what a marvelous meal a basketball-sized dinosaur egg was, and were such ruthless egg hunters that dinosaurs were literally eaten into extinction.

Speculations as to the demise of the dinosaurs are endless, and they again highlight the fact that we simply do not know enough about the intricate web of life to understand what causes extinction. Perhaps some nec-

14-11

The third horn is somewhat hidden in this view of the massive skull of *Triceratops.* The neck muscles required to support this weight must have been quite large. A near relative is *Pentaceratops,* which had five horns. (From O. C. Marsh, 1896, courtesy of the History of Science Collections, University of Oklahoma Libraries.)

essary creature in the total food chain leading up to dinosaurs disappeared, and the entire ecosystem broke down. But why should a diverse group of land, water, and air dwellers all disappear at once? While 10 million years is hardly "at once," they were still gone, and we do not yet know why.

Reptiles at Sea. One of the surprises in any evolutionary trend is that it is seldom unidirectional. Once the benefits of marine life had been abandoned by primitive amphibians in the latest Paleozoic, several groups promptly returned to the sea—but with lungs, legs, and eggs. Readaptation occurred as legs were modified back to flippers and breathing was restricted to time spent at the air-water interface.

Among this group were the *mososaurs,*

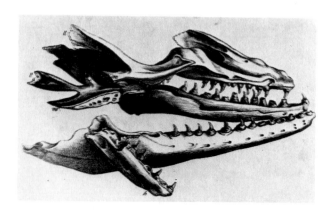

14-12
When these jaws were found in a chalk quarry in 1770, they caused a sensation; no one could imagine that such an immense "lizard" had ever lived, much less that it could be marine! (From Reverend William Buckland, 1837, courtesy of the History of Science Collections, University of Oklahoma Libraries.)

essentially marine lizards with streamlined, fishlike bodies, a powerful, paddling tail, and a head whose elongated jaw was full of wicked teeth (Figure 14-12). The mosasaur called *Tylosaurus* grew up to 30 feet (9 meters) long, and must have been the terror of late Mesozoic seas. The *plesiosaurs* looked more like turtles without shells; their legs were modified into paddles, and their necks were somewhat elongated. The *icthyosaurs* looked much like modern sharks or swordfish and were eminently adapted for aquatic life. The largest icthyosaurs were as big as mosasaurs, although most were much smaller (Figure 14-13).

All of these swimming reptiles, adapted so well to marine existence, disappeared by the end of the Mesozoic era. Only their modern relatives, the crocodiles, turtles, and some of the snakes, remain adapted to a partly aquatic existence.

Reptiles in the Air. By the middle Mesozoic, two different groups of reptiles, descended from thecodonts, had taken to the air. One group is the *pterosaurs,* creatures whose toe was enormously extended and covered with wing membranes, similarly to modern bats. The pterosaurs were probably fish eaters, although the air must have also been full of insects.

Pterosaurs (Figure 14-14), including a group called *pterodactyls,* equipped with batlike leathery wings, powerful necks, and pelicanlike jaws full of teeth, must have been fierce competitors for food from any source. One recent find was a pterosaur fossil with a wingspan of more than 40 feet (12 meters), which makes it the largest flying creature ever known. From the tip of one wing to the tip of the other would be the height of an average six-story building; that pterosaur

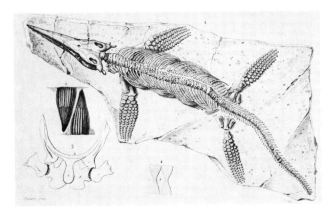

14-13
The *ichthyosaurus* must have been a creature one would not want to meet on a casual swim; the triangular objects shown beneath its skull are two of its teeth. Notice the bony flippers. (From Alcide D'Orbigny, 1849, *Dictionaire Universelle . . . ,* courtesy of the History of Science Collections, University of Oklahoma Libraries.)

would have been a flying reptile who got no arguments.

Like their fellow reptiles, pterosaurs also failed to survive the Mesozoic era and also faded into oblivion. They raise interesting questions. Where did their enormous energy come from in order to fly? Were some of these reptiles warm-blooded? If so, their high metabolism, typical of modern birds, would be all the energy they needed. *If* they were cold-blooded, there is every reason to doubt that they could have sustained the en-

ergy requirements necessary for flight, and yet it seems obvious that they flew. Before we reexamine this interesting and highly controversial question, let us first discuss birds.

Another lineage of flying reptiles developed quite a different design than the pterosaurs. This group developed *feathers,* derived from scales, that were attached to highly modified front limbs that we call wings. The oldest known fossil bird is *Archaeopteryx* (Figure 14-15), from middle

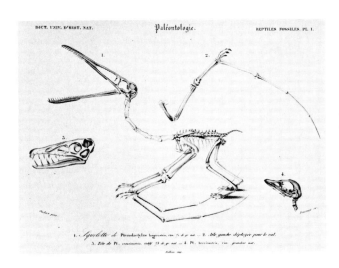

14-14
This skeleton of a *pterodactyl* illustrates its ferocious teeth (remember that true birds have *no* teeth) and the modification of its arm into an immense wing, complete with vestiges of a claw "midwing." (From Alcide D'Orbigny, 1849, courtesy of the History of Science Collections, University of Oklahoma Libraries.)

Mesozoic rocks in southern Europe whose fine grain size allowed preservation of impressions of feathers; if the feather impressions had not been preserved, *Archaeopteryx* would have been called a dinosaur, because it had both teeth and a jointed tail, which are reptilian characteristics.

By an accident of lucky preservation, we have a missing link—Archaeopteryx, a fossil intermediate between reptiles and one of their offspring, birds. Birds have a number of adaptations to aerial life: (1) highly efficient, four-chambered hearts; (2) modification of all scales, except those on the feet, as feathers, which provide lightweight insulation against heat loss; (3) hollow bones; (4) extensive air sacs surrounding the lungs; (5) keen vision and a sense of equilibrium; and (6) warm-bloodedness.

Warm-Bloodedness. In cold-blooded animals such as the crocodile, cellular respiration captures about one-half the energy released from the oxidation of food. The rest is released as waste heat; one-half the energy consumed is wasted. Their body temperature is simply the same as the surrounding medium. But metabolic rate—the rate at which internal chemical reactions break down food—is controlled by temperature, which approximately doubles for every 10 degrees Celsius rise in temperature. It is thus to the animal's advantage to maintain a temperature that will keep its body processes working within a fairly narrow temperature range. There is a critical temperature below which death occurs because metabolic processes become too slow and another critical temperature above which metabolic rates become too high, and the animal dies of exhaustion. A cold-blooded animal is at the mercy of its environment; not surprisingly, cold-blooded animals, like reptiles, either live in the tropics or develop elaborate mechanisms for modifying the environment.

Warm-blooded animals, in contrast, put the "waste" heat of metabolism to work and maintain temperatures approximately 40 degrees Celsius higher than their surroundings. The heat can be retained by effective insulation—fur or fat—and can be increased by shivering, an involuntary muscular activity that stimulates more heat production.

14-15
This drawing by Richard Owen, a brilliant British paleontologist of the last century who never accepted the evolutionary origin of species, is of an *Archaeopteryx*. Notice the impressions of feathers on the two "arms" and the well-preserved feathers on the jointed tail. (From Richard Owen, 1863, *On the Archaeopteryx of Von Meyer*, Phil. Trans. Royal Soc. of London, courtesy of the History of Science Collections, University of Oklahoma Libraries.)

Warm-bloodedness has several advantages; metabolism now converts nearly all the energy of food into useful work, and warm-blooded animals have no difficulty maintaining a body temperature that is ideal for continuing metabolism. Only one environment is potentially fatal to warm-blooded animals, and that is an environment more than a few degrees *above* their normal body temperatures.

Human bodies are highly efficient furnaces, and we are well insulated, but we do not possess very efficient cooling devices. We can counteract cold, but we cannot stand much heat—hence the universal rise in the use of air conditioning in climates that only 30 years ago were singularly unattractive places to live.

For all animals, cold-blooded or hot-blooded, the metabolic rate is inversely related to body size. For small animals such as shrews, their surface area-to-volume ratio is high; the great heat loss from the surface requires that a shrew eat nearly its weight in food *every day*. Some small animals such as hummingbirds are so small that they hibernate every night to conserve energy. For elephants, or even humans, only a small daily fraction of one's own body weight in food is required.

With that background, what can be said about the current debate over the status of dinosaurs—were they warm-blooded or were they not?

Warm-blooded Dinosaurs?

The first question that comes to mind is how one would recognize warm-bloodedness in fossil animals. Four answers are surprisingly clear. FIRST, warm-blooded animals require far more food per unit of body weight; therefore the ratio of predator to prey in carni-

vores is quite low. SECOND, the bones of warm-blooded animals are much richer in blood passages than those of cold-blooded animals, because *much* more blood must be circulated to maintain uniform body heat. THIRD, warm-blooded animals can successfully live in cold climates, while cold-blooded animals are usually found only in temperate to tropical climates. Since both rocks and fossils allow us to reconstruct past climates, if we found dinosaur fossils among rocks indicative of severe climates, the dinosaurs must have been warm-blooded. FOURTH, fossil dinosaur tracks suggest that they walked *upright,* a characteristic associated with warm-bloodedness, as contrasted with the sprawling lizard in the sun.

In one respect, the success of allegedly cold-blooded dinosaurs over their warm-blooded contemporaries—the early mammals—has always been a puzzle. For 140 million years, mammals coexisted with dinosaurs but remained small, insignificant, and sparse; the mammals only blossomed after the dinosaurs were gone. How could a cold-blooded reptile monopolize the environment when it had warm-blooded mammalian competitors that possessed all the advantages of warm-bloodedness?

To at least a few geologists, the answer to this is simple. From what can be reconstructed from predator-to-prey ratios, the distribution of fossil dinosaurs in areas of once-severe climate, the nature of dinosaur footprints, and the examiniation of well-preserved dinosaur bones, the majority of Mesozoic dinosaurs *were* warm-blooded animals; one group (arboreal thecodonts) of them evolved into *their successors, the birds,* at the end of the Mesozoic era.

The evidence *for* partial warm-bloodedness in some groups of dinosaurs has been long known. The ancestors to *Archaeopteryx* may well have been warm-blooded, since the feathery insulation of that group was probably insulation much like that of warm-blooded birds today. The pterosaurs, with their ability to fly, have long been thought to be at least partially warm-blooded. It is probable that many large dinosaurs had four-chambered hearts, a complex heart development more typical of warm-blooded animals; the high blood pressure needed for their size is only possible with a four-chambered heart.

On the other hand, most dinosaurs—except for the pterosaurs and coelurosaurs with primitive feathers—had quite small brains, and *that* feature is associated with cold-bloodedness. The indirect descendants of dinosaurs, the crocodiles, are also cold-blooded. Even though the fossil bones of many dinosaurs are rich with fossil blood vessels, some geologists argue that very large vertebrates maintain nearly constant temperatures because of their sheer bulk, and this might have influenced the development of their bone.

The evidence that many middle and late Mesozoic dinosaurs did survive in the northern latitudes can be interpreted two ways: (1) the climate in the middle and late Mesozoic was remarkably equable, so that cold-blooded dinosaurs could have survived, even though the climate was rather vigorous; or (2) northern latitudes even in the late Mesozoic were undergoing a vigorous climate with quite cold winters, so the smaller dinosaur fossils found in these areas indicate that the majority, if not all, of dinosaurs were warm-blooded. The predator-to-prey ratios, while easily obtained from modern life, became more and more susceptible to interpretation when one deals with more ancient, fossilized life. How does one know predator-to-prey ratios when the prey has long ago been eaten?

The evidence for warm-bloodedness in dinosaurs is regarded as scanty by the majority of geologists, but it is another new idea that challenges 100 years or more of firmly held beliefs that dinosaurs are reptiles, which are, by definition, cold-blooded.

The controversy also illuminates the transitional nature of our classification boundaries between natural phenomena. What can we make of a birdlike creature that is covered with feathers but has teeth and a skeletal development exactly like certain small dinosaurs? Is it a reptile, a bird, or something in between? And what of the therapsids? They, too, were one-half mammal and one-half reptile, and *they* may have been warm-blooded. The controversy continues.

SUMMARY   Mesozoic rocks occur in excellent exposures over most of the western one-half of the United States and in a broad band that parallels the great marine invasion of our southern and eastern coastline near the end of the Mesozoic era (Figure 14-2). Early Mesozoic rocks contain a largely nonmarine record, because the mostly emergent North American continents spanned the Paleozoic-Mesozoic boundary.

This boundary marks a substantial change in the character of life. With the exception of the mollusks, Paleozoic invertebrate life faltered and declined, bringing many groups to extinction or near extinction. As the seas began their persistent transgression in the middle Mesozoic, the diversity of marine life again swelled, and the molluscan faunas becoming the dominant marine invertebrate group. Fish continued as an important marine life form and were joined in the middle Mesozoic by a variety of swimming reptiles that became highly adapted to a marine existence, but then died out near the end of the Mesozoic as the seas again withdrew. Reptiles also took to the air and dominated the land, forcing the amphibians to play a minor role, along with the mammals, our own ancestors.

A prolonged episode of batholithic intrusion, volcanic eruption, and deep sea sedimentation marked the western movement of North America as it rifted loose from Europe about 180 million years ago and began to subduct and consume the Pacific Ocean floor. Orogenic events in the west were extraordinarily complex and were superimposed on several earlier episodes of Paleozoic activity throughout the west. *In general, orogenic activity in the western United States migrated eastward through time,* passing from earlier volcanic to batholithic phases to later crushing of the complex miogeosyncline against a downbuckled western cratonic margin.

The results of all this activity can be seen throughout the west, which includes scenery that makes the western United States unique. Most of all, the activity culminated in the uplift of the Rocky Mountains, which stretch from Alaska to the Antarctic as a complex, sinuous chain of distorted, crumpled, faulted sedimentary rocks. The crumpling and uplift of the Rocky Mountains was to span the Meso-Cenozoic boundary and continue well into the middle of the Cenozoic era.

By the end of the Mesozoic, the present geography of the United States was reasonably complete. The Appalachians were still an imposing mountain range to the east, shedding Mesozoic and Cenozoic sediments to the rifted eastern margin to make up the Atlantic coastal plain. To the south, the widespread advance of the seas brought them as far north (Figure 14-2) as southernmost Illinois; the seas were to retreat to their modern position over the next 70 million years of the Cenozoic era.

To the west, the bright reddish rocks of the early Mesozoic give way to marine rocks in the middle and late Mesozoic; interbedded continental rocks contain very large supplies of low-sulphur coal, a major energy resource. Along the western coastal states, Mesozoic rocks include the granitic rocks of the Sierra Nevada, Idaho, and Coast Range batholiths and a complex series of eugeosynclinal and ophiolitic rocks that now mark the former western continental edge. The western coastal states were added during a series of orogenic events that culminated in the development of the Rocky Mountain chain much further to the east, but our western coast continues to be an area of major geologic activity as complex interactions occur between the northwestern-moving American plate and the overridden Pacific plate.

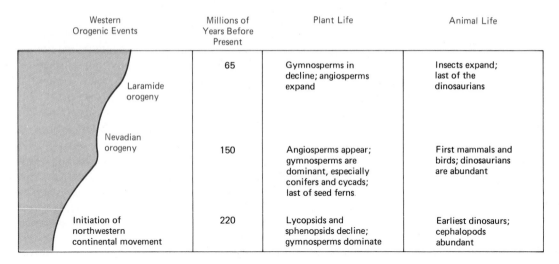

Western Orogenic Events	Millions of Years Before Present	Plant Life	Animal Life
Laramide orogeny	65	Gymnosperms in decline; angiosperms expand	Insects expand; last of the dinosaurians
Nevadian orogeny	150	Angiosperms appear; gymnosperms are dominant, especially conifers and cycads; last of seed ferns.	First mammals and birds; dinosaurians are abundant
Initiation of northwestern continental movement	220	Lycopsids and sphenopsids decline; gymnosperms dominate	Earliest dinosaurs; cephalopods abundant

14-16
A summary of some major events of the Mesozoic era.

The Mesozoic—the age of middle life—was the period of the growth and development of the American west (Figure 14-16). It was also the period when life completed its assault on the land; reptiles had developed the amniotic egg and may have developed a primarily warm-blooded character. Among the reptiles, we always think of the dinosaurs first; they were among the largest and most bizarre creatures ever to inhabit the continents, the oceans, and the air. Both the lizard- and bird-hipped dinosaurs disappeared from land, sea, and air at the end of the Mesozoic; their disappearance over a period of perhaps 10 million years is one of many mysteries in the history of life—a history that was to lead to the development of humanity about 55 million years later.

EXERCISES

1. The five groups of herbivorous (plant-eating) dinosarus developed three major lines of defense against the meat eaters. Some became immense and apparently lived mostly in water; others developed both armor and defensive weapons, and still others became very rapid runners. How, from evidence from fossils, could these modes of defense be ascertained?
2. In what ways can birds be considered "feathered reptiles?"
3. Since the skeletons are all that is commonly preserved, how could a

slow-moving, ponderous, cold-blooded animal be separated from a swift, agile, warm-blooded animal?

4. In terms of fossil evidence, lizards came before snakes, whose earliest fossils are in late Mesozoic rocks. Since snakes seem to be evolutionary offshoots of lizards, what lizardlike characteristics do snakes still retain?

5. In a general way, the western eugeosyncline was first deformed and intruded by igneous batholiths, and later the miogeosyncline was deformed in an orogenic sequence that moved generally from marginal sea toward the cration through time. What similarities are there between the western sequence and events in the Appalachians, if any?

6. What similarities might one expect to see between early Mesozoic rocks in the east and rocks forming along the Red Sea today? Why the similarities?

SUGGESTED READINGS

Stearn, Colin W., Carroll, Robert L., and Clark, Thomas H. 1979, *Geological Evolution of North America,* 3rd ed., New York, Wiley, 566 pp.
  An outstanding text in earth history, newly updated.

Dott, Robert H., Jr., and Batten, Roger L., 1976, *Evolution of the Earth,* 2nd ed., New York, McGraw Hill, 504 pp.
  Another fine text, integrative, with worldwide examples.

Desmond, Adrian J., 1976, *The Hot-Blooded Dinosaurs,* New York, Dial Press, 238 pp.
  Delightful reading on the dinosaur controversy marred by some inaccurate paleontology now and then.

Rudwick, Martin J. S., 1976, *The Meaning of Fossils,* 2nd ed., New York, Neal Watson Academic Publications, (Science History Publications, USA), 287 pp.
  Delightful scholarship on the history of human thought about fossils. Highly recommended.

KEY CONCEPTS

Physical Events

Major marine regression at beginning of era, followed by major transgression throughout era; regression leads to reduced diversity and transgression to increased diversity according to a speculative model; western area deformed by a series of events that are best characterized as orogenic events migrating easterly throughout the Mesozoic.

Biologic events

Major changes in Paleozoic fauna and flora under moderating, transgressive environments.

Rise of cephalopods, end of trilobites and blastoids; rise of angiosperms, decline of gymnosperms near the end of the era; rise and decline of reptiles on land, sea, and air; are dinosaurs reptiles or birds?

Western coals the major fossil fuel energy source for the United States.

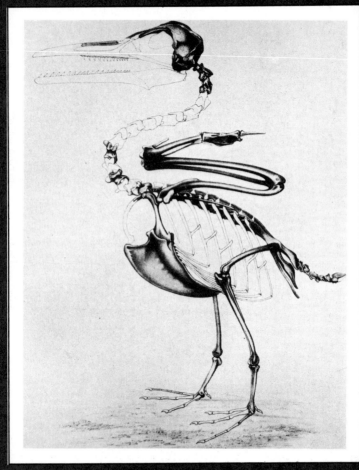

This figure illustrates the techniques of restoration possible when skilled paleontologists have a little less than one-half the fossil bones preserved. Through a knowledge of detailed comparative anatomy, the shape and location of the missing bones can be filled in to yield a fairly complete restoration. (From O. C. Marsh, 1880, *Odontornithes*, Mem. Peabody Mus., Vol. 1, courtesy of the History of Science Collections, University of Oklahoma Libraries.)

Chapter Fifteen
AN AFTERNOON
the cenozoic

"The season of storms and cold . . . came and went, blown away by the big winds of the awakening earth."
A Wintu story, translated by Theodora Kroeber

The Cenozoic era began 65 million years ago and still continues. The span of time we call Cenozoic covers slightly more than 1 percent of the earth's total history, but this last interval of time has left the least disrupted record.

Within this last fragment of time the North American continent was brought to its current state, the Rocky Mountains culminated their development, and the dominant form of life became the mammal. Human beings appeared as fossils a few million years ago and began their climb to ascendancy.

The rocks of the Cenozoic era are subdivided into seven epochs of time according to a subdivision originally proposed by Charles Lyell. Lyell had recognized in his travels through Italy and France that older Cenozoic rocks contained a high percentage of fossil species no longer alive, but a small percentage of species occurring as fossils, which also still lived. In younger Cenozoic rocks, the ratio of still-living species to extinct ones in a fossil assemblage increased. He then proposed that rocks of the Cenozoic era be subdivided (Appendix D, Figure D-3) based on the percentage of still-living species preserved as fossils. With some modifications and additions, Lyell's system remains today the standard method of subdivision of Cenozoic time.

The older 63 million years of Cenozoic time is known as the **Tertiary period,** a name that is a holdover from 100 years before, when the term Tertiary (meaning third period) was adopted to include nearly all loosely consolidated rocks on the earth's surface. The last 2 million years of Cenozoic time are called the **Quaternary period,** again a throwback to the time when Quaternary (fourth period) rocks were believed to be the youngest rocks formed since the deluge. Rocks of the Tertiary period are subdivided

into five epochs; those of the Quaternary period are subdivided into two epochs.

To many geologists, the Cenozoic rocks and fossils are the most absorbing of all, because the evidence they present is relatively fresh and complete. Therefore the last 1 percent of geologic time is the most clearly understood interval. Whatever one's geologic disposition, these young rocks record a remarkable record of the culmination of the North American continent and the culmination of life—in the development of humans.

PHYSICAL EVENTS

The physical events of this brief era can be readily divided into innumerable detailed stories, because the Cenozoic record is a remarkably complete story. We will be discussing the physical events of the Cenozoic in a number of different areas: (1) the coastal plains, from New England to the Yucatan; (2) the area east of the Rocky Mountains; (3) the intramontane basins of the Rockies; (4) the Colorado Plateau and Basin and Range; (5) the Snake River-Columbia basaltic fields; and (6) events along the Pacific margin. As the final event in the era, we will briefly discuss the events connected with continental and Alpine glaciation, which so profoundly influenced both the scenery and the life forms of North America. Each of these are also intended to suggest how geologists extract history from rocks—the basic evidence left behind by a restless earth.

The Coastal Plains

Throughout the Atlantic and Gulf coastal plains, the Cenozoic history of our southern and eastern margin records discontinuous regression of the seas from the land throughout most of this era. As the Appalachian Mountains were worn down, sediments deposited on the Atlantic coastal plain become an inverted record of Appalachian history; the youngest sediments are largely eroded from the recently exposed core of the oldest Appalachian rocks. The climate throughout the Gulf coastal plain remained warm and tropical throughout the Cenozoic era. In Arkansas, the weathering of aluminum-rich igneous rocks to form *bauxite,* the ore of aluminum, could have only taken place in a tropical environment. Similarly, in the area around modern Florida, which has no muddy rivers draining to the sea, the clear, sunlit waters of the Gulf enabled a rich, diverse group of reef-building animals to exist; limestone deposition continues today along the west coast of Florida and a part of its eastern coast.

From salt layers in Mesozoic rocks, buried under as much as 24,000 feet (7300 meters) of younger rock and recent sediments, plumes of low-density salt (Figure 5-21) arose and pushed upward through the overlying sediment, much like igneous intrusions. Salt is generally less dense than the overlying materials and rises for the same reason that a wooden ball will not stay submerged under water. Oil and natural gas may accumulate in the flanking uparched and broken rocks, where they are truncated (cut) by impermeable salt; many of the major oil fields of the Gulf coast are found adjacent to such salt domes. Similar domes occur in Iran and in Ethiopia, which are places where the sutures joining continental masses have recently split.

Throughout the coastal plains, the sands, silt, mud, and lime rest on a basement of Paleozoic and Mesozoic rock. Further out at sea, similar sedimentary accumulations rest on ocean floor basalts. As sediment continues to accumulate on these passive shelves, they seem in many respects to be modern geosynclines.

The huge embayment of sediments and sedimentary rock that covers our Gulf coast has covered a particularly interesting Paleozoic problem. As far south as the Appalachian Mountains can be traced and as far east as the Ouachita-Marathon mountains (Figure 15-1) can be traced by deep oil wells, the rocks of these two major mountain systems of similar age and origin approach each other at right angles. The area of intersection has yet to be penetrated by deep oil well drilling; the nature of the junction between these two mountain ranges remains unknown.

The High Plains

Stretching eastward from the Rocky Mountains is an immense alluvial fan of Cenozoic sedimentary rocks. In terms of association and position, these rocks are somewhat akin to the Queenston and Catskill rocks shed from the rising Appalachians. They form a topographically high, flat tableland to the east of the Rocky Mountains, which also acts as a major moisture barrier. This part of the western United States is generally a region of lonely, nearly empty, country. Irrigated and dry-land agriculture are practiced; ranching and grazing are other profitable activities over this vast region known as *the High Plains.* To the east of the High Plains are the lower plains, which receive more moisture and originally supported tall prairie grass, but now supply much of our wheat and corn.

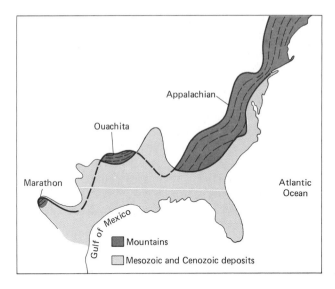

15-1
The trend of buried folded rocks is shown as a single dashed line where these rocks are buried under the rocks and sediments deposited during the Mesozoic transgression and the Cenozoic regression. (Simplified from P. B. King and G. J. Edmonston, 1972, *Generalized Tectonic Map of North America,* U.S. Geological Survey.)

The High Plains are very approximately bounded by the hundredth and one hundred and fifth meridian of longitude (Figure 15-2), and are the result of sedimentation throughout the middle and late Tertiary period. Their eastern margin—locally called the break in the "cap rock"—is the junction formed by eastward-draining streams eroding back into these alluvial fan deposits shed from the rising Rocky Mountains. The eastern margin is also commonly a sharp topographic break and corresponds approximately with the hundredth meridian of longitude (see Appendix D).

In this way rising mountains make themselves known in the record of the rocks. The tablelands of the High Plains are nothing more than gigantic coalescing alluvial fans, composed mostly of silt, minor volcanic ash, and local freshwater limestone. The sediments aggregate a few hundred yards (meters) in thickness and cover parts of seven states (Figure 15-2).

Basins in the Rocky Mountains

The development of the Rocky Mountains throughout the Tertiary period should not be thought of as the rising of a single homogeneous mass. Instead, parts of the marginal cratonic basin were lifted up here and there, only to be eroded back down again. Between these rising segments, numerous shallow basins received the sediment load flowing from the uplifted nearby highlands.

Coal was deposited in some of these basins throughout the entire Tertiary period, and it forms a major economic resource for the northern Great Plains and the northern Rocky Mountains. Along with coal came volumes of silt, freshwater limestone, volcanic ash, and well-preserved fossils of freshwater fish and air-breathing life. Some of these freshwater basins were undoubtedly giant lakes for a time, and the abundance of animal and plant life in them left the lake sediments richly endowed with organic de-

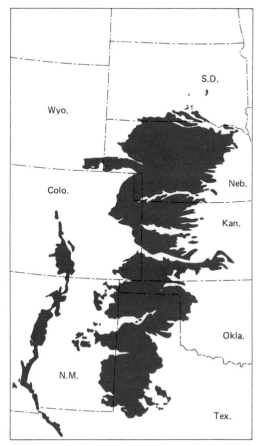

15-2

Surface distribution of late Cenozoic rocks adjacent to the Rocky Mountains. (After P. B. King and H. M. Beikman, 1978, U.S. Geological Survey Professional Paper 904.)

bris; some of these sediments are oil shales (see Chapter Nine).

The basin-fill deposits of the Rocky Mountain region are widespread over the west (Figure 15-3) and, in addition to providing a rich source for coal and oil shale, they are readily eroded into picturesque land-

forms and badland topography. Many of the park areas of the west, such as Bryce Canyon, Badlands, and Cedar Breaks, display these uplifted and eroded continental sedimentary rocks with their delicate hues of pink, orange, gold, yellow, and lavender.

The last major push in the long story of the development of the Rocky Mountains occurred about 40 million years ago. Older Tertiary rocks were tilted and beveled (cut off) to form a platform for younger Tertiary sediments throughout much of the Rocky Mountain region. The rocks trapped within

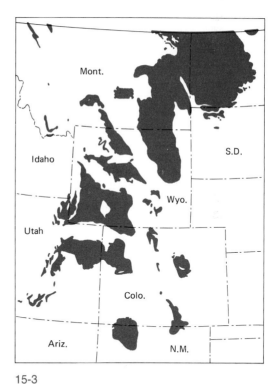

15-3

Surface distribution of early Cenozoic rocks *within* the Rocky Mountain area. (After Philip B. King and Helen M. Beikman, 1978, U.S. Geological Survey Professional Paper 904.)

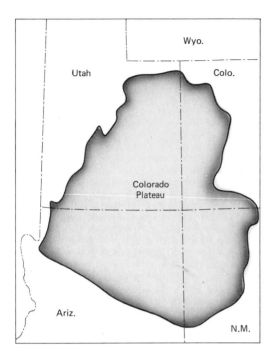

15-4
The Colorado Plateau is an area of stable cratonic rock, covered with a thin veneer of sediments. The plateau has recently been uplifted many thousands of feet (several hundred meters) above its middle Cenozoic elevation.

Cenozoic era. This area, known as the *Colorado Plateau*, rose nearly 1 mile (1⁶⁄₁₀ kilometer) within the last 10 million years.

The Colorado Plateau

The Colorado Plateau is a region centered around the point where Arizona, Utah, Colorado, and New Mexico share a common corner (Figure 15-4). The surface rock over the plateau includes sedimentary rocks from each of the eras since the Precambrian, resting on cratonic basement of Precambrian age. Throughout the plateau the sedimentary layers are flat but are interrupted by steep folds (Figure 15-5) and by the development of large, broad basins, domes, and sharp uplifts.

15-5
This aerial photograph of an area near the Grand Canyon, known locally as Gray Mountain, displays an area that has been strongly folded and faulted by a typical Laramide uplift. (Photograph by Michael Collier.)

middle and late Cenozoic basins also suggest a general drying trend, as the rising Rocky Mountains cut off the flow of humid air from the west.

The latest event within the Rockies was a general broad uplift of the entire area, raising old basin-fill deposits perhaps ½ mile (⁴⁄₅ kilometer) or more above the elevation at which they were originally deposited. Coincident with this broad uplift, a large, roughly circular mass of the craton west of the Rockies also began to rise near the end of the

500   *Afternoon—the Cenozoic*

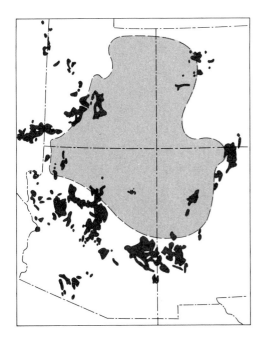

15-6
Surface distribution of volcanic rocks yielding readiometric age dates between 4 to 10 million years ago. The boundaries of the Colorado Plateau, as shown in Figure 15-4, have been superimposed to illustrate the striking geographic relation between Colorado Plateau boundaries and volcanic areas. (Adapted from Philip B. King and Helen M. Beikman, 1978, U.S. Geological Survey Professional Paper 904.)

Around the margin of the plateau, Tertiary and Quaternary volcanism has left a substantial record (Figure 15-6). The changing character of plant fossils from the margins of the plateau also suggest an extensive change in elevation beginning about 10 million years ago. As the plateau rose less than 1 mile (1⁶/₁₀ kilometer) into the air, the rivers that flowed across the plateau gained renewed cutting power—power even to cut through the hardest rocks in the highest places. No one example of the power of a newly elevated river to carve deeply into its own bed is better known than the Grand Canyon (Figure 15-7). All over the plateau, other rivers cut deeply; the result is an area of high tablelands, deeply incised (cut into) by vigorous streams in a generally semiarid climate.

Superb scenery was also developed (Figure 15-8); the semiarid climate leaves rocks standing in bare, rugged relief, and the intricate stream erosion of multicolored, layered rocks of the plateau country has attracted many of America's most famous geologists for more than 100 years.

The Basin and Range

Surrounding the Colorado Plateau, except along its eastern margin, is a region of faulted sedimentary rocks that generally forms a series of uplifted, faulted, and tilted sedimentary blocks (the ranges) separated by intervening depressions (the basins) filled with sediment from the surrounding ranges (Figure 8-19). This lovely country has a desert climate and contains some of the most splendid examples of volcanism known.

This large area seems to have been stretched and thinned during the middle of the Cenozoic era, much like the Atlantic coast of North America must have been as it pulled away from Europe in the middle Mesozoic. Faulting and subsidence of crusted blocks were very common, as was extensive volcanism. The cause for this extension and rifting of the western interior of North America remains an elusive question, although many geologists believe it was coincident with North America overriding the Pacific spreading center.

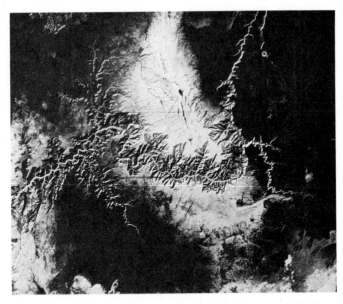

15-7

The Grand Canyon, here seen in an image taken 600 miles (1000 kilometers) above it, has been carved across the Colorado Plateau as it rose by the Colorado River. The canyon cut by the river is not quite 1 mile (½ kilometer) deep, averages 8 miles (13 kilometers) wide, and is 280 miles (450 kilometers) long. (LANDSAT image, reformulated to negative mode, courtesy of Geospace Corporation and Cities Service Company, used by permission.)

15-8

In the foreground is the gorge of the Little Colorado River, in the middleground is a large fold, and in the distance are the San Francisco Mountains, a series of stratovolcanoes whose peaks reach nearly 13,000 feet (400 meters) elevation and are snowcapped much of the year. The *relief* (total elevation difference) within this photo is 2 miles (3 kilometers); the horizontal distance is about 80 miles (130 kilometers). The area is in north-central Arizona on the southern margin of the Colorado Plateau. (Photograph by Michael Collier.)

The Columbia Plateau

During the Cenozoic era, one of the greatest outpourings of continental volcanic rocks known occurred as a repetitive sequence of basaltic lava flows from numerous eruptive centers. The total series of flows covers large parts of three states (Figure 15-9). The total amount of lava, which flowed out in a series of several dozen eruptions during the Cenozoic, has an estimated volume four times that of the entire island of Hawaii.

Again, such imposing flows of volcanic rock signal a continent being rifted apart, with basaltic lava from the mantle accumulating to heal the rift. The cause of rifting remains something of an enigma, even though basaltic lava flows did start at approximately the same time as the Basin and Range began to come apart. Perhaps as we look still further west, we can find several answers to the persistent events of the Cenozoic that so disturbed the western part of the United States.

The Pacific Rim

Along the California Pacific rim, sedimentation from the Rocky Mountains far to the east filled the shelf and trench off the western coast throughout the early Cenozoic era; the Sierra Nevada mountains, Cascade volcanoes, and California Coast Ranges had not yet formed, or they would have interrupted the westward flow of rivers from the Rockies. The sediments that date from this time are largely turbidites, suggesting deep water deposition on the continental rise. Along the northern Pacific rim, where the modern states of Washington and Oregon stand, early Cenozoic sedimentation is volcanic, suggesting that the crustal unrest that was to dominate the entire Pacific rim throughout its Cenozoic history had already begun.

By middle Cenozoic time, the San Andreas Fault system had begun to be active as westernmost North America began to override the Pacific plate's spreading system (see Figure 7-15). The result was that the spreading motion of the ridge was transformed into horizontal motion approximately perpendicular to the buried ridge axis. This large transform fault system we know today as the *San Andreas Fault*. By matching up offset, distinctive rocks, now sheared and separated by the transform fault, geologists are able to suggest that the fault may have first begun to move about 40 million years ago and has had

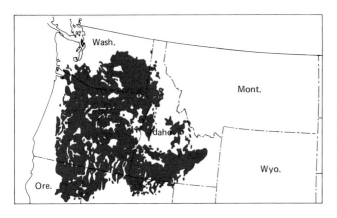

15-9

Distribution of Cenozoic volcanic rocks in the Columbia Plateau region of Idaho, Washington, and Oregon. (After King, Philip B., and Beikman, Helen M., 1978, U.S. Geological Survey Professional Paper 904.)

a total horizontal shift of over 120 miles (200 kilometers) since that time.

At about this same time, the Sierra Nevada granitic rocks, formed during the early Mesozoic as a gigantic, composite batholithic mass deep beneath the surface of the earth, began to move upward. As these granitic rocks rose and were exposed by erosion, a change in the character of sediments deposited along the southwestern margin of what was to be California became apparent. This uplift was largely accomplished along a fault system that stretches along the east face of the Sierras for 450 miles (700 kilometers). The Sierras were eventually to move upward several miles (kilometers) and to be intensely glaciated in the latest Cenozoic to form the Sierra Nevada mountains (Figure 8-36). To the west the uplift of the Sierras was accompanied by the development of the immense depression known as the Sacramento and San Joaquin valleys. Within these depressions are nearly 6 miles (10 kilometers) of sediment derived from the Sierras, recording continuing uplift of the Sierras and structural disturbance throughout the middle and late Cenozoic era.

Still further north, a chain of beautiful stratovolcanoes or composite cones (Figure 3-28) were a late Cenozoic addition to an area that had been structurally unstable thoughout the Cenozoic. The Cascade volcanoes were a new island arc, superimposed across older metamorphic and granitic rocks capped with Tertiary lavas. The western coast of northern California, Oregon, and Washington must have looked something like the modern west coast of South America thoughout much of Mesozoic and early Cenozoic time, since volcanism and dark, deep water volcanic sediments were the rule throughout this time.

The collision of the North American continental plate with the Pacific Ocean spreading center may well have been the cause for the thinning and rifting of the Basin and Range. The collision may have been accompanied only a few million years ago by the formation of the Gulf of California as new seafloor formed along the East Pacific rise (Figure 7-15). The rise of the Sierra Nevada dates from a similar time, as does the formation of the Columbia Plateau basalts and synchronous volcanism in the Pacific Northwest. At about the same time (around 40 million years ago), the San Andreas transform fault system originated and began to slice across southwestern California, and a small part of the North American continent became a part of the Pacific plate.

This middle Cenozoic event affected, in rather different ways, the whole of the western United States and continues to affect the California Coast Ranges today—for events along the California Coast Ranges and the Gulf of California are examples of continuing continental fragmentation and orogeny. By whatever name or names we call the variety of interrelated events throughout the west and far west, the middle and late Cenozoic were times of substantial unrest. What of the Pacific Basin itself?

The motion of the Pacific plate can be read from two different sources of information. Stretching northwestward from the island of Hawaii are a series of volcanic islands and submerged volcanoes whose rocks yield progressively older dates northwestward almost to Japan (Figure 15-10). The abrupt northward bend in the line of submerged volcanoes older than 40 million years has been interpreted in terms of the concept of *mantle plumes,* "hot spots" of upwelling magma from the earth's mantle.

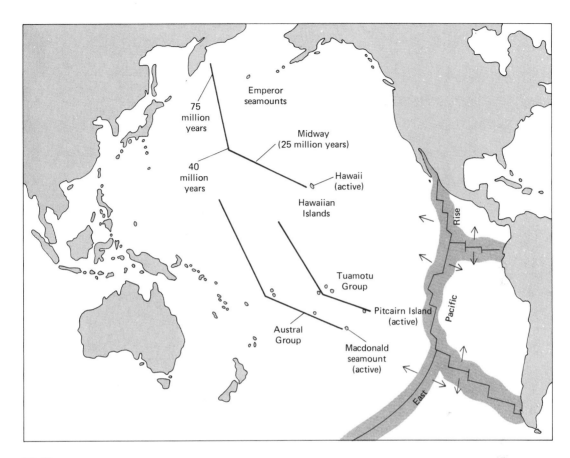

15-10

In 1838, James Dwight Dana, an American geologist, recognized, based on the extent of erosion of each island, that the islands in the Hawaiian Island chain were progressively older to the northwest. Nearly 150 years later, Dana's shrewd observation can be explained. The Hawaiian, Tuamotu, and Austral islands all exhibit the same trend. All three chains, including their older submerged continuations, exhibit radiometric ages (Chapter 11) that suggest that they formed by northerly and then northwesterly movement of the seafloor over *stationary* hot spots. (Map modified from "Hot Spots on the Earth's Surface," Kevin C. Burke and J. Tuzo Wilson. Copyright © 1976 by Scientific American, Inc. All rights reserved. Adapted with permission.)

Scattered over the earth's surface are a number of isolated regions where basaltic volcanism from the mantle seems to be continuous; these sites have been called hot spots and are interpreted as zones of hot material rising steadily from the upper mantle as convective plumes. These hot spots seem to remain stationary in space throughout time; when an oceanic plate rides over the hot spot, volcanoes occur as the molten material is vented, and a string of extinct volcanoes extends away from the hot spots *in the direction of plate motion*.

The string of volcanoes across the northwest Pacific floor thus is interpreted as recording the direction of movement of the Pacific plate for the last 100 million years or so. Forty million years ago, if the model is correct, the movement changed from northerly to northwesterly. Zones of seafloor sediments, rich in fossil microscopic animals that live only near the equator, support this interpretation; progressively older deposits of these equatorial fossils are found in progressively more northerly deep-sea drilling sites.

Summing up these lines of evidence, it seems that the Pacific plate has moved north and then northwest 2000 miles (3200 kilometers) since the late Mesozoic, with a distinct change in direction about 40 million years ago—*at about the same time the American plate rode up over the inferred Pacific spreading center*.

The Ice Age

Within the last several million years, continental ice sheets have invaded part of North America and Europe at least four times, dramatically altering the scenery throughout very large areas of the United States. As described in Chapter Eight, continental glaciers spread southward to a limit approximately coincident with the modern Missouri and Ohio rivers in the midwest and Long Island in the northeast (Figure 15-11). The Finger Lakes region of New York State were carved out as the glaciers flowed out radially from their twin source areas in central Canada (Figure 15-12).

The Great Lakes, too, were a product of this period of multiple ice advance and retreat. No fewer than seven separate glacial substages have been recognized throughout the Great Lakes region, and the recency of the events allows the record to be read in great detail. The record of superimposed lake deposits, beach ridges, stream channels, moraines, and may kinds of glacial deposits has been carefully worked out by many geologists to produce a surprisingly intricate history.

The Great Lakes are the largest single source of fresh water in the world, and they are also the world's largest inland river system (Figure 15-13). As Figure 15-13 suggests, the connected lakes are essentially a river system draining eastward into the Saint Lawrence River, although the elevation drop between shallow Lake Erie and deep Lake Ontario is primarily accommodated by Niagara Falls. As erosion is intensified at the falls, the location of the falls moves westward at the rate of 1 or 2 yards (meters) a year; in about 25,000 years the falls will reach Lake Erie and completely drain it.

The Great Lakes developed from glacial erosion of a river system that must have originally flowed south to the Gulf of Mexico. The major glacial event recognized occurred about 15,000 years ago, when the youngest of the glacial invasions from Can-

15-11
North America during the maximum extent of glacial advance during the Ice Ages. The colored arrows display inferred direction of glacial motion. The black areas in the west, south of the glacial margin, are inland lakes, formed by the higher rainfall and lower evaporation typical of the very cool temperate climate near a glacial margin. (Modified slightly from map by the U.S. Geological Survey.)

ada began its retreat. Glacial-margin lakes formed in the scoured river valleys and spilled south out of successively more northerly and lower outlets as the glacier generally retreated—but with numerous small advances in between. Finally, only a few thousand years ago, the ice melted far back and the Saint Lawrence River became the lowest drainageway for the Great Lakes; it is now a major shipping seaway.

Further west, the effect of glacial climates was to bring the higher moutain regions under intense alpine glaciation, carving and sharpening ridgelines, and sculpting the high peaks of the Sierras, the Rockies, and numerous other higher peaks into rugged, ele-

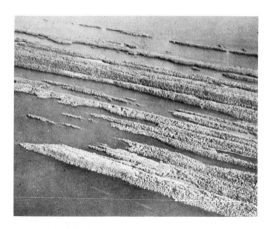

15-12
This aerial photograph illustrates the kind of large-scale grooving of the land surface produced by passage of a large continental glacier. The fingerlike promontories, surrounded by lake water, are in Isle Royale National Park, Michigan. (Photograph by N. K. Huber, U.S. Geological Survey.)

gant scenery (Figure 15-14). At lower elevations, perennial snow was not possible, but the colder climate also produced a wetter climate as evaporation was greatly retarded.

Because of this, inland lakes formed; among them, Agassiz, Missoula, Lahontan, and Bonneville (Figure 8-42) were the largest. The catastrophic landscape created by the sudden break in the ice dam that created Lake Missoula has already been referred to in Chapter Eight. Consider instead the scenery produced by another lake developed during the cool, rainy climate typical of the glacial period—Lake Bonneville.

The modern remnant of Lake Bonneville is known as the Great Salt Lake in Utah, but evidence from abandoned former beaches, deltas (Figure 15-15), and other shoreline features shows that Bonneville at one time covered perhaps 20,000 square miles (52,000 square kilometers) and was several hundred

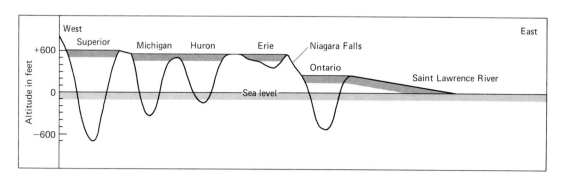

15-13
Diagrammatic profile of the Great Lakes from west to east. Notice that, except for Niagara Falls, the interconnected lakes form a large river system whose valley bottoms are carved well below sea level by past glacial erosion.
(Adapted from Jack L. Hough, 1958, *Geology of the Great Lakes,* copyright ©
1958, University of Illinois Press. All rights reserved. Used with permission.)

15-14
This photograph, taken in 1899, illustrates what the Rocky Mountains probably looked like 12,000 years ago. The glaciers are almost gone from the Rockies, and we are left with ice-sculptured peaks like these. This is the Skolai Glacier, Alaska, where the Ice Age continues. (Photograph by S. R. Capps, U.S. Geological Survey.)

yards (meters) deep. This ancient lake had its outlet in an area of southeastern Idaho known today as Red Rock Pass and spilled into the Snake River as its former normal outlet. As the climate was warmed at the end of the Ice Age, the great inland lake shrank until it had no outlet, and its salty remnant is now near Salt Lake City, Utah.

The water level in Ice Age Lake Bonneville fluctuated many times throughout its existence as a function of the climate; the periods between ice advance were relatively warm, much like the periods between present-day ice advances. Because of the fluctuation, shoreline features moved up and down the mountain slopes that ringed the lake; in some areas the cyclic shorelines are extremely well preserved (Figure 15-15).

The filling and emptying of these large western lakes caused the continental crust to be depressed under the weight of water and then rebound as the lake gradually lost its great volume of water. Precise measurement of the fossil shorelines of known radiometric age allow the rate and location of isostatic rebound to be accurately measured, once again telling us something about the fluid nature of the upper mantle and asthenosphere tucked so invisibly beneath our continental crust.

Further evidence of the Ice Age glaciation of North America within the last few million years comes from examination of our continental shelf. During periods of major ice advance, when a larger percentage of the world's water was tied up in solid ice, sea levels around the world fell by more than 300 feet (100 meters). Today we find fossils of continental animals in water over 100 yards (about 90 meters) deep, and anthropologists are able to recognize the remains of human dwellings—even camp fires—on what is now the flooded continental shelf. As worldwide sea level fell, the rivers on the continent had their erosive power enhanced, not only because baselevel fell, but also because they generally received more precipitation in a cooler climate.

Stream erosion continued many miles (kilometers) out onto the emergent continental shelf; streams cut quite large canyons in the shelf while dumping huge volumes of coarse sediment into the deeper water covering the continental slopes and rises. Sediment that would have been trapped on the shelf was washed by streams right across it and out to deep sea; the large canyons left behind now form an impressive group of submarine canyons across the continental shelf.

It seems that among the glacial advances

THE ANCIENT DELTAS OF LOGAN RIVER, AS SEEN FROM THE TEMPLE.

15-15
Rivers flowing out of the mountains into former Lake Bonneville formed
deltas at the point of their entry into the lake. As the lake level changed, so
did the level of each delta. What is left behind is a series of nearly flat
surfaces. The town of Logan, Utah, is built on several of these surfaces. This
view, drawn in 1890, is looking east from Logan, Utah. (From Grove Karl
Gilbert, 1890, *Lake Bonneville*, U.S. Geological Survey Monograph 1, Pl. 27.)

and retreats recorded by the lake basins, moraines, and life of the Ice Age (sometimes called the Pleistocene epoch) the most severe climate was experienced by North America during its *last* major ice advance, 15,000 years ago, before the time of most intense cold. We might well ask what the effect of glacial cold, changing shorelines, and oscillating climate had on human life.

There had been only two major intervals of continental glaciation before: the first spanned the late Precambrian-early Paleozoic boundary, while the second spanned the late Paleozoic-early Mesozoic boundary among what are now the southern continents, plus part of India. Each of these past periods of glacial climate had been associated with substantial continental emergence, increased erosional rates, and dramatic changes in the overall complexity of life. Did

the latest Cenozoic glaciation also produce rapid changes in life? How did glacial climates affect life? What was the history of life for the last 1 percent of geologic time?

CENOZOIC LIFE

The Cenozoic era is called the "age of mammals," because this diverse group has dominated the land, sea, and air during all of Cenozoic time. Before we discuss the place of mammals in the last fragment of earth history, we briefly review the status of the other animal and plant groups that survived from earlier times.

Cenozoic Plants

Among the plants, remnants of the horsetails, mosses, psilopsids, cycads, and ginkgoes exist today, but modern plant communities are dominated by the true ferns, the conifers, and the enormous group we call the angiosperms. The angiosperms, including the *critically* important food group, the grasses, spread from their middle Mesozoic beginning to an almost explosive Cenozoic evolution that was coincident with the rise of insects; they form the dominant floral regime in temperate and tropical regimes today.

In subarctic, high-latitude areas, by contrast, plant diversity is immensely diminished, and only the simpler, more primitive plants survive in an area that is still very much in the grip of the ice age. The ice age that we associate with the last 2 or 3 million years in the United States began in the Antarctic about 40 million years ago and still continues. On that giant continent, the history of plants is far different than in midlatitudinal zones. Even the insects are quite different; the largest ones are smaller than a human fingernail, and most are much smaller than that.

Invertebrates

Among unicellular life, the *foraminifera* have become an important part of marine planktonic communities; their calcereous shells form a major part of the ocean floor sediment in some areas. Their siliceous cousins—the *radiolaria*—also are an important part of the marine scene. The sponges maintain their solitary ways, as do two major groups of the corals. The bryozoa likewise maintain themselves, but the brachiopods continue much diminished from the Mesozoic.

The shelled cephalopods are represented only by the nautiloids; their belemnoid and ammonoid kindred did not survive the Mesozoic seas they dominated. The clams and snails continue their steady course, as do the crinoids and echinoids. Among the arthropods, the insects became dominant. These creatures occupy every conceivable ecological niche on the continents; there are more species of insects than all of the other animal groups of the world put together. Their equivalents in the sea are the crustaceans, another group of diverse arthropods whose geologic history predates the Cenozoic. The minute, bivalved ostracods, another group of geologically important arthropods dating from early Paleozoic times, remain an important component of the invertebrate freshwater and seawater faunas today.

Vertebrates Other Than Mammals

Among the fish, lungfish and lobe-finned fish are still minor components, but the cartilaginous fish and the bony-skeleton fish are dominant in the sea today. The amphibians occupy a minor portion of the scene today— a half-water and half-land existence shared with the reptilian turtles, marine iguanas, and crocodiles. On land, only the lizards, the tuatara, and the snakes—some of which have partially or wholly returned to the water—remain as remnants of the reptilian group that dominated every environment of the Mesozoic era.

The birds, which differed from reptiles in the middle Mesozoic, became an important part of the Cenozoic era; not surprisingly, they are rarely preserved as fossils. The birds dominate the air and, with their mammalian counterparts, the bats, are important aerial predators and scavengers. The birds, including a few flightless birds of the past and present, share scales on their legs and egg-laying reproduction with their reptilian ancestry, but they share a far more elaborate circulatory system and warm-bloodedness with mammals.

Mammals

Mammals seem to have arisen from the *therapsids;* they slowly evolved more and more mammalian characteristics throughout the Mesozoic era. There was no sudden transformation of reptile to mammal; instead mammalian characteristics simply became more prevalent in time through the Mesozoic in small, unimportant Mesozoic mammals that probably ate insects and tried desperately to stay out of the way of carnivorous dinosaurs. The earliest mammals were quite small and much like modern moles and shrews.

One curious group of modern mammals—the duck-billed platypus and the spiny echidna—is a combination of mammalian and reptilian characteristics. The creatures lay eggs (a reptilian characteristic) and yet secrete milk from mammary glands for their young (a mammalian trait). Another odd group of mammals is the *marsupials,* such as the opossum or kangaroo, which give birth to very immature live young that must finish their embryonic life attached to a nipple in their mother's pouch.

In a general way, it seems that the duck-billed platypus and the spiny echidna are among the most primitive living mammals; they are sometimes called "living therapsids." The marsupial mammals such as opossum and kangaroo are somewhat less primitive and are mostly confined to the southern continents, which were isolated throughout much of the Cenozoic era. Australia is the finest example of this phenome-

non; only in historic times did dogs, rabbits, and humans arrive to threaten an otherwise largely marsupial fauna. The earliest marsupial mammals are found as fossils from the middle Mesozoic and look very much like the modern opossum.

Australia and South America both share the distinction of having been geologically isolated through the Cenozoic era (except that South America did join North America in the late Mesozoic), and their primarily marsupial fauna underwent evolution isolated from the rest of the world. The *placental* mammals (those that give birth to fully developed young) were likewise developing in Africa, free from marsupial interference. In Eurasia and North America, connected by Greenland for the first one-half of the era, placental mammals were also widespread but did eventually have some contact with marsupial mammals as well.

All the rest of the mammals give birth to live, fully developed young and have other distinguishing characteristics. All mammals are warm-blooded, having hairy skins and fat layers for insulation. The lower jaw in mammals is a single, movable bone with teeth that are strikingly differentiated for specific purposes. The mammalian brain is quite large; mammals can learn from experience. No eggs are laid; the young are born alive from their mother's uterus and suckle milk from modified sweat glands called mammary glands. Mammals have an efficient four-chambered heart; oxygenated and unoxygenated blood are kept in separate circulatory systems. Their respiration is assisted by a thoracic (chest) diaphragm, and the palate separates breathing from eating functions.

Among the other characteristics of mammals that were to be critical in their future development was the enlarging brain-to-body ratio of mammals with time. Hair, breasts, warm-bloodedness, and live birth are important mammalian characteristics, but perhaps no other feature has been so important in human development as the enlargement of the brain.

If brain size is an approximate indication of intelligence—and it seems to be—even the smallest-brained mammal is a mental giant compared to its reptilian ancestry. As the mammals first competed with reptiles and then later with themselves, the quick-witted survived; the development of complex, large brains is an evolutionary development that was to reach its late Cenozoic culmination in the formation of a primitive human.

The mammals of today (see Appendix F) include flying mammals (bats) and swimming mammals (walrus, otters, whales, and dolphins). On land, mammals include the pigs, deer, horses, zebras, camels, opossums, moles, shrews, lemurs, monkeys, apes, elephants, armadillos, sloths, rabbits, cats, dogs, bears, rats, mice, cattle, squirrels, beavers, porcupines, *human beings*— and many, many others.

North American continental deposits, mostly in the west, provide a rich record of the development of mammals in North America. Geologists have been studying the Cenozoic marine and continental sediments of North America for 100 years; it is to that record that we now turn.

Insectivores. Insectivores are small mammals such as shrews and moles. They are among the earliest mammals and today maintain a primitive generalized form. They seem to be among the oldest of true mammals and have survived by virtue of small size, secretiveness, and nocturnal habits.

We have referred to shrews before; their tiny size requires that their life be a frantic race for food in order to maintain their metabolism. Not surprisingly, shrews are extremely nervous creatures; they *must* locate their weight in food each day.

Carnivores. The oldest carnivores were creodonts of remarkably small brain size and unspecialized skeletal structure. They would not be successful carnivores today, because they lacked the highly specialized teeth, quick-wittedness, running speed, and musculature that distinguish modern meat eaters. The creodonts became extinct by the middle Cenozoic.

Plant-eating animals have always had the best of worlds in many ways. Their food is all around them, and they can eat it at leisure because it cannot run away. The teeth of plant eaters, or herbivores, are always short, flat, and suited for crushing and grinding; the incisors are modified for nipping. Teeth must be tough and capable of surviving a great deal of abrasion without being worn down. The disadvantage of being a herbivore is that the protein content of plants is generally lower than that of meat, so more food must be eaten in order to get the same nourishment.

Carnivores have the opposite predicament. Their food comes in a highly nutritious form that is rich in protein and still contains up to one-quarter of all the food energy the prey has eaten, *but the food runs away or hides*. Alternately, the food will protect its life with a variety of vicious defenses, including antlers, horns, spikes, armored skins, unpleasant smells, stinging fluids, and the like. Carnivores overcome these problems by being fleet of foot and possessing vicious, sharp-pointed teeth and pointed claws for tearing and grasping and great flat teeth for tearing and grinding bone and flesh. Many carnivores hunt in packs and have a complex social order.

Among the most interesting of carnivores are modern dogs and cats. Dogs make their fossil appearance 40 million years ago; they had long limbs and large brains and were well-adapted for high-speed chase. Cats appear at the same time as dogs and have changed little since that time. Among the most interesting of all cats is the saber-toothed cat, which died out in North America only a few thousand years ago. The most famous representative is *Smilodon* (Figure 15-16), whose great teeth must have been used in stabbing their luckless victims to death. Numerous complete fossils of *Smilodon* and their kindred have been recovered from the famous La Brea tar areas in Los Angeles; they must have ventured into the

sticky tar in search of stranded meals, only to become part of the fossil record instead.

The social life typical of most members of the dog family contrasts sharply with the independence and stealth that are characteristic of members of the cat family. These traits are still apparent in domesticated dogs and cats. As Luther Burbank, prominent plant geneticist of the past, said so well "Heredity is nothing but stored environment."

Bears are another carnivore that fascinate us. They are present in the fossil record 15 million years ago and share a common ancestry with dogs. Bears are *omnivores;* they eat anything, and their teeth reflect the modification away from the slicing, slashing teeth of true carnivores.

Other carnivores, including walrus, seals, and sea lions, live at sea and have done so since at least 20 million years ago. Paws have been modified into paddles, which can also be used for a type of walking on land by all but the seals. The huge canine teeth or tusks of walrus are, of course, their most characteristic trademark, but other teeth are modified for crushing and grinding shelled mollusks.

15-16

Smilodon, the saber-toothed cat, must have been a fierce Ice Age predator. This painting is a restoration of a South American cat. (Photograph from American Museum of Natural History. Used with permission.)

Bats. Bats are among the most fascinating of mammals, because they are the only true mammals that fly. Since they fly mostly at dusk and at night, they may be essentially blind, but they have an extremely well-developed radar, complete with highly sophisticated stereophonic receivers (ears) that allow them to find food and miss obstructions as they fly in the dark.

Most people shudder when they think of bats, no doubt having heard too many stories about vampire bats. However, the vast majority of bats make their diet from insects, although herbivorous and "vampire" bats are also known. They date from 50 million years ago as fossils, but they are usually poorly preserved in the geologic record.

Cetaceans. Another group of swimming mammals, apparently descended from carnivores, include the dolphins, killer whales, and great whales. The fossil record for this group is quite scanty, but it dates back to about 50 million years.

Edentates. The term edentate means "without teeth" and includes a group of obscure modern animals—armadillos, anteaters, and sloths. Armadillos live in warm climates and seem to be sensitive indicators of climate, because they migrate to the south in colder weather. Their ancestors in the middle to late Cenozoic were the *Glyptodonts*, upright, bizarre, armored turtles with spiny knobs on their tails—something like an updated *Ankylosaurus*. The Glyptodonts were walking fortresses; when threatened, they could roll up in balls like modern armadillos and wield their spiked tails as fierce weapons for defense.

Sloths are most popular modern edentate; they are great hairy apparitions covered with green algae that hang down from tropical trees. During the Ice Age, their ancestors were animals such as *Megatherium* (Figure 15-17), giant ground sloths that were the size of modern elephants. Like all sloths, these animals walked on the knuckles of their front paws and the sides of their back paws; their gait was hardly graceful. *Megatherium* was a contemporary of early humans on this continent; they died out only a few thousand years ago, at the very end of the Ice Age, probably hunted to extinction by humans.

Rodents. The rodents are, in some ways, the most successful of mammals. They have invaded every available land area on our earth. They also outnumber all other mammals combined. We are perhaps most familiar with rats as typical rodents. They steal our food, make us sick, invade our homes, and follow us wherever we go.

Other rodents include hamsters, (which are excellent pets) chipmunks, squirrels, porcupines, mice, rabbits, and beavers. All rodents have prominent canine teeth—long,

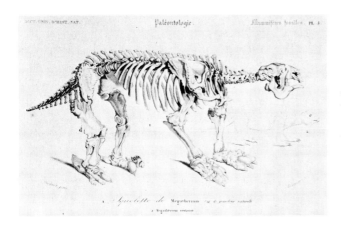

15-17
This skeleton of *Megatherium* illustrates the skeleton available for a total reconstruction of a beast that must have looked a bit like the modern polar bear. (From A. D'Orbigny, 1849, courtesy of the History of Science Collections, University of Oklahoma Libraries.)

Cenozoic Life   **515**

sharpened teeth that grow continuously and are sharpened by gnawing on hard material. Further back in the mouth are flatter teeth that are suitable for grinding and shredding. Rodents are among the oldest mammal fossils known, going back to the earliest Cenozoic rocks. Since most rodents are fairly small, their tiny bone and teeth fossils are not common, and, where found, must be sieved from loose sediment.

One of the stranger rodents of the past is *Epigaulus,* small, burrowing creatures similar to modern prairie dogs. The one distinction of *Epigaulus,* however, is a tiny set of horns. Giant beavers as large as modern buffalo and with tails over 1 yard (meter) long were also Ice Age rodents.

Ungulates. Ungulates are hoofed animals and are among the most successful mammals. Ungulates are either herbivorous or omnivorous; none are wholly carnivorous. Among the earliest ungulates were the *condylarths* and *pantodonts; Uintatherium* is an example of a bulky, stupid pantodont from 50 million years ago. Both condylarths and pantodonts must have made tasty meals for creodonts, since they disappeared before the middle Cenozoic.

By convention, ungulates are divided into two subgroups: (1) odd-toed ungulates, including horses, tapirs, zebras, and rhinoceroses, and (2) even-toed ungulates, including cattle, camels, pigs, hippopotamuses, deer, and giraffes. In a general sense, odd-toed ungulates have been less successful (they have poor digestive systems) than their even-toed kin, which are the dominant large land mammals of the world.

All ungulates share one common feature. They walk or run (like sprinters) on their enlarged toes, which are diminished in number from the primitive five. Modern horses are a good example; they, of course, have only one hoof per foot. The history of most ungulates has shown a decrease in number of toes and an increase in overall body size.

Titanotheres and *chalicotheres* were two groups of odd-toed ungulates that failed to survive the Cenozoic era. Titanotheres are well represented by the ponderous *Titanotherium,* an extremely common fossil find (Figure 15-18) in 30 million-year-old sediments in the South Dakota badlands. Titanotheres had become extinct by the middle Mesozoic; chalicotheres followed them into extinction after the Ice Age.

Rhinoceroses are also odd-toed ungulates that seem headed for extinction; they may become one of the more than 400 species humanity has forced into extinction in the recent past. Rhinoceroses first appear in the fossil record about 50 million years ago. The best-known fossil rhinoceros is *Baluchiterium.* With a height over 5 yards (4½ meters), *Baluchiterium* was the largest land mammal known.

The first horses appear as fossils 60 million years ago, as the Cenozoic was just beginning. Known as "dawn horses" or *Eohippus* (or, more properly, as *Hydracotherium*), and found in western North America, the earliest horses were the size of small dogs. They had three-toed hind feet and four-toed front feet. By 30 million years ago, *Mesohippus,* about 2 feet (60 centimeters) tall, looked much like tiny horses but had three toes on each foot. As grass became the dominant angiosperm in the middle Cenozoic, the horse family took to the plains and to the woodlands.

By 15 million years ago, the horse family had become quite diverse. *Merychippus,*

15-18
This painting of a *Titanotherium* illustrates the rhinoceroslike appearance of this ancient mammal. (Photograph from American Museum of Natural History. Used with permission.)

now about 1 yard (1 meter) tall, had a single, functional middle toe and reduced lateral toes and resembled modern small ponies; they were one among many different kinds of horse. By 4 million years ago, *Pliohippus* was in the mainstream of evolution; only vestiges of the lateral toe were left, and *Pliohippus* gave rise to *Equus,* the modern horse (Figure 11-11).

The evolution of horses, faithfully recorded in continental sediments from North America, is a nearly classic example of the changes in odd-toed ungulates; it involved increase in overall size, lengthening of limbs, increase in brain size, loss of lateral toes, straightening of the back, and substantial increases in the complexity and differentiation of the teeth in a longer and deeper jaw.

The bones of *Equus* litter Ice Age deposits around the world and then suddenly, about 10,000 years ago in both North and South America, horses completely disappeared from the New World. Horses, which developed here, had to be reintroduced from Europe by sixteenth-century Spanish explorers of the New World.

What could have caused such a dramatic extinction of a creature native to this continent that survived the worst in climate the Ice Age had to offer? We will see similar events repeated for many other large animals, including the imperial, columbian, and wooly mammoths, the ground sloths, the mastodons, the dire wolves, and the giant bison. All of these large animals disappeared just as the Ice Age was *loosening* its grip on North America 10,000 years ago. What happened to these successful mammals, including the native horses?

We will probably never know, but many anthropologists note that the decline of these large mammals is parallel with the time of growing paleo-Indian civilizations, which must have found an important addition to their diet in large mammals. We know that humans have been ruthless hunters; the hordes of buffalo that numbered in the millions 100 years ago were reduced to a few hundred before finally being protected.

Could our Ice Age ancestors have been the villains? The answers will never be sure, but the question is a sobering one for a civilization that presently drives an average of one species to extinction every 2 years.

The even-toed ungulates are apparent descendants of the condylarths; they arrived 50 million years ago and became the dominant grazers throughout middle and late Cenozoic history. To make humans even toed, we would have to remove our big toes and walk on either four or two toes. The earlier even-toed ungulates included *oreodonts,* common fossils among the lakebeds of South Dakota's badlands.

Camels and llamas began their evolution in North America 50 million years ago. One form from 8 million years ago, *Alticamelus,* is a giraffelike form adapted to browsing in trees. Camels and llamas are both common fossils in North America during the Ice Age. Later they migrated to South America, where llamas became dominant, and to Eurasia, where camels became important in the deserts of Asia and Africa. Curiously, these creatures, native to North America, became extinct here at the end of the Ice Age.

Deer, another example of a successful even-toed ungulate, occur as fossils 40 million years ago. Antlers are, of course, the trademark of deer and elks. *Megaloceras* (Figure 15-19) had antlers almost 12 feet (3½ meters) long from tip to tip. The first cattle date from only 12 million years ago; they replaced antlers, which they shed every year, with permanent horns. The ancestry of pigs can be traced back 30 million years, and they have become mainstays of domestic mammals. Pigs occur as fossils as large as modern rhinoceroses. Hippotamuses, which are found as fossils only since 7 million years ago, are related to pigs. Hippopotamuses are the only amphibious ungulates.

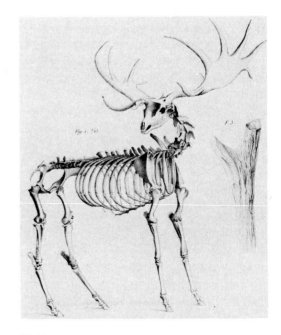

15-19
This sketch of *Megaloceras,* often called the Irish "elk," is representative of this extravagant deer. It is a common Ice Age fossil in Irish peat bogs; many complete skeletons are known. (From G. Cuvier, 1836, *Recherches sur les Ossemens Fossiles,* courtesy of the History of Science Collections, University of Oklahoma Libraries.)

Proboscidea. As the name suggests, proboscideans are animals that have elongated noses or trunks. The oldest animals of this sort come from 50 million-year-old sediments in Africa. Younger proboscideans include *Dinotherium* (Figure 15-20).

Mastodons include 30 million-year-old animals such as *Palaeomastodon,* which have short trunks and small tusks. The variety among the mastodons approached the bizarre; *Amebelodon* is an 8 million-year-old mastodon whose shovel-shaped tusks were probably used to scoop up vegetation. By

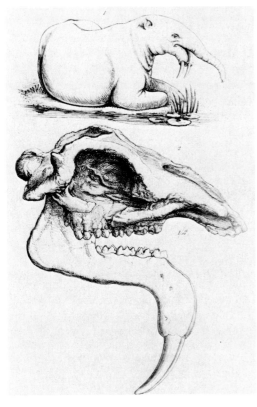

15-20
This reconstruction of an early pachyderm, *Dinotherium,* illustrates the elephantlike character of this fossil mammal. Notice the teeth, adapted for grinding vegetable matter. (From Reverend William Buckland, 1837, courtesy of the History of Science Collections, University of Oklahoma Libraries.)

the Ice Age, mastodons were abundant throughout North America and were probably the favorite game of early people. One example is shown in Figure 15-21. Like most mastodons, the jaws were somewhat elongated and contained heavy, pointed teeth well adapted for browsing. The mastodons roamed North America until only 6000 to 8000 years ago, and then they, too, became extinct.

True elephants separated from the mastodon lineage about 15 million years ago and developed shorter jaws and large, flat teeth (Figure 15-22) with heavy enamel that were well suited for grazing. The early elephants, also called *mammoths,* were an important part of the late Cenozoic in North America, and they became spectacular during the Ice Age. Wooly mammoths disappeared from the American scene only 10,000 years ago; drawings of wooly mammoths festoon the caves of our Ice Age ancestors who knew the beasts as fair game. Imperial mammoths reached 12 feet (3½ meters) high *at the shoulders* (Figure 15-23) and had tusks of equal length. Columbian elephants (or mammoths) had enormous spiral tusks that crossed at their tips; they disappeared from North America less than 8000 years ago. Ice Age elephants have also recently been found as frozen carcasses in Siberia; detailed information as to their eating habits were gleaned from undigested food in their stomachs.

Ice Age North America contained an animal fauna comparable in many ways with the life of central Africa today. If we could have only lived in North America 20,000 years ago, we would have known the mastodons, elephants, saber-toothed cats, ground sloths, hunting dogs, wild horses, large camels, large pigs, and other species now found only in central Africa. The decline of large mammals, leading to their almost total extinction in North America by the time of the rise of early old-world civilizations in the Mediterranean area, is one of the most puzzling stories of the last instant in time.

One animal group among the mammals has yet to be considered—the *primates.* No other animal learned to grasp like the pri-

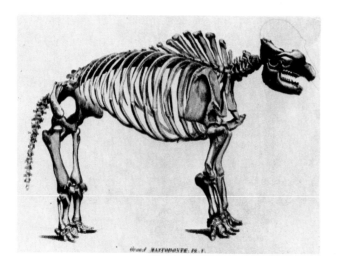

15-21
Like *Dinotherium*, the mastodon was adapted for browsing; it had pointed, sturdy teeth. The massive bone structure is typical of large mammals. (From G. Cuvier, 1836, courtesy of the History of Science Collections, University of Oklahoma Libraries.)

mates with their unique hands and feet. Primates could not run fast, but they could construct tools and hunting implements against which the speed of most of the other mammals was of little value.

Primates. People are primates, so we acquire a special interest in looking into our own past. Primates apparently came from the early insectivores early in the Cenozoic and adopted several traits that have distinguished them throughout the Cenozoic era. The feet and hands each have five mobile fingers with flattened nails. The thumbs and big toes are capable of *clasping*. The brain has *expanded*, particularly the cerebral cortex, which controls highly complex nervous system coordination functions. Vision is binocular, color-sensitive, and stereoscopic. Primates can perceive depth quite accurately; this is important if one is to jump from limb to limb or drive a car. The arms and legs are highly mobile, with considerable mobility at shoulders, elbows, fingers,

knees, hips, and ankle joints including a limited mobility to swing one's arms and legs to the side as well as back and forth. All of the preceding characteristics were necessary for life in the trees, where one's only defense was to run.

If we compare humans to primates, we find that we are more like monkeys and apes than lemurs and tarsiers; the latter two are called *prosimians*, or premonkeys, by biologists. The monkeys diverged from prosimian ancestors 30 million years ago, and the apes separated from the same line slightly later. Monkeys, however, have tails and small brains, and so we are more apelike than monkeylike.

Apes include gibbons, orangutangs, gorillas, and chimpanzees. They all lack tails, walk upright, have very long arms, and have large skulls with sizable brains. Overall, chimpanzees are the most humanlike of all the apes. They are able to open doors and manipulate tools, and several fine specimens have recently been taught to communicate effectively by psychologists.

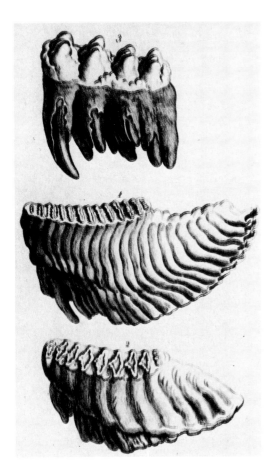

15-22

The upper teeth are those of a *mastodon,* with rounded cusps for crushing plant material. The middle tooth is that of a modern *elephant,* while the lower tooth is from a *mammoth* found in Ohio. Mammoth or elephant teeth have numerous infolds that strengthen the tooth for grazing and crushing plant material. (From Bartholomew Faujas de Saint-Fond, 1809, *Essai di Geologie,* Vol. 1, courtesy of the History of Science Collections, University of Oklahoma Libraries.)

Recent biochemical, dental, and detailed blood tests and paleontological evidence indicate that humans are most like gorillas and chimpanzees—but that neither gorillas or chimpanzees are human. How are we different?

Our jaws are smaller, with smaller teeth, and our spines sit directly under the centers of our heads. Our brains are larger, and we have large vertical foreheads. Our noses are more prominent, our big toes are not capable of fully touching the other toes in grasping motion, and our feet are flattened with arches.

If we search back in time, we find that human skeletal material grades imperceptibly into apelike creatures that are intermediate among the differences just described. These apelike creatures are placed in the family *Hominidae* in biological classification; the hominids include all humans, and we are the only living species. The oldest fossils assigned to this family are extremely incomplete specimens of *Ramapithecus* from about 11 million years ago. *Ramapithecus* are intermediate apelike animals that may be sufficiently, although subtly, advanced to be called hominids. There is *no* evidence that they walked upright; their place in hominid evolution is probably overstated.

Primates had essentially left North America by 40 million years ago, so the evolution of all hominids took place in the Old World. Eastern Africa, Java, China, and Israel have been particularly productive hunting grounds for fossils. Hunting in these latter areas has recovered numerous remains of much more humanlike creatures called *Australopithicus,* found in sediments more than 2 million years old.

Australopithecines were quite humanlike;

15-23
This mammoth, found in Siberia in 1799, is one of several found frozen in the ice within the last few centuries. Many of these beasts must have met their death as they walked on ice-covered lakes and crashed through the ice. (From R. Owen, 1846, *A History of British Fossil Mammals and Birds,* courtesy of the History of Science Collections, University of Oklahoma Libraries.)

Mammoth found in Siberia, 1799.

they apparently usually ran on their two rear legs and had brain capacities greater than those of chimpanzees, although only one-half that of modern people. They also had large jaws and low foreheads—both apelike characteristics. There are two groups of australopithicines; they vary in overall size and tooth type. These early humanlike creatures stood about 1 yard (meter) high, the size of an average 4-year-old today.

The next step in human evolution is *Homo erectus,* which appeared about 600,-000 years ago. The facial features of *Homo erectus* remain apelike, but brain size was now two-thirds that of modern humans. *Homo erectus* used stone tools, learned to use fire, made shelters of wood and stone, and lived in groups with others. The interior of the skull suggests that the speech areas of the brain were developed.

Modern humans are called *Homo sapiens,* meaning "wise persons." The earliest undoubted members of this group are the *Neanderthals;* their brain size was nearly equal to that of modern humans. The oldest

H. sapiens are found in sediments 300,000 years old, and they are about 4 feet (1⅓ meters) tall. Neanderthals were tool users, and they made complex burial sites; this was the first indication that *Homo* was capable of abstract, religious thought.

With the advent of the *Cro-Magnons* 30,-000 to 50,000 years ago, modern humans had arrived. By 40,000 years ago, native Americans had arrived in North America; their trek from the Old World must have brought them across a land bridge spanning the Bering Strait during glacial times, with its lowered sea level. The presence of native Americans is documented by the occasional fossil finds of partial or intact skeletons, by living and burial sites, and by spear points and arrow points in the bones of large mammals such as bison. Native Americans had arrived to take up their inheritance and to await a new wave of European immigrants who were to "discover" their land again 40,000 years later.

Most of the evolution of modern humans took place during the last several million years—a period of time coincident with the Ice Age. Our distant ancestors knew the cold and felt the glacial chill. They left pictures in caves in southern Spain of a culture like that of the modern Eskimo. They endured, and, in the last brief flicker of time, began to create communities and societies. Within the last 200 years we have wrested their history and the history of all life from the long-silent rocks.

The Ice Age is in our past and, perhaps, in our future. As we try to look back to distant times, mentally watching our Neanderthal kin bury a loved one, and reaching for the mystery of life, we are watching ourselves.

SUMMARY   The past 65 million years that we call the Cenozoic era include the modern development of the continent (Figure 15-24). In the far west, late Cenozoic events were largely the result of the American plate overriding the Pacific

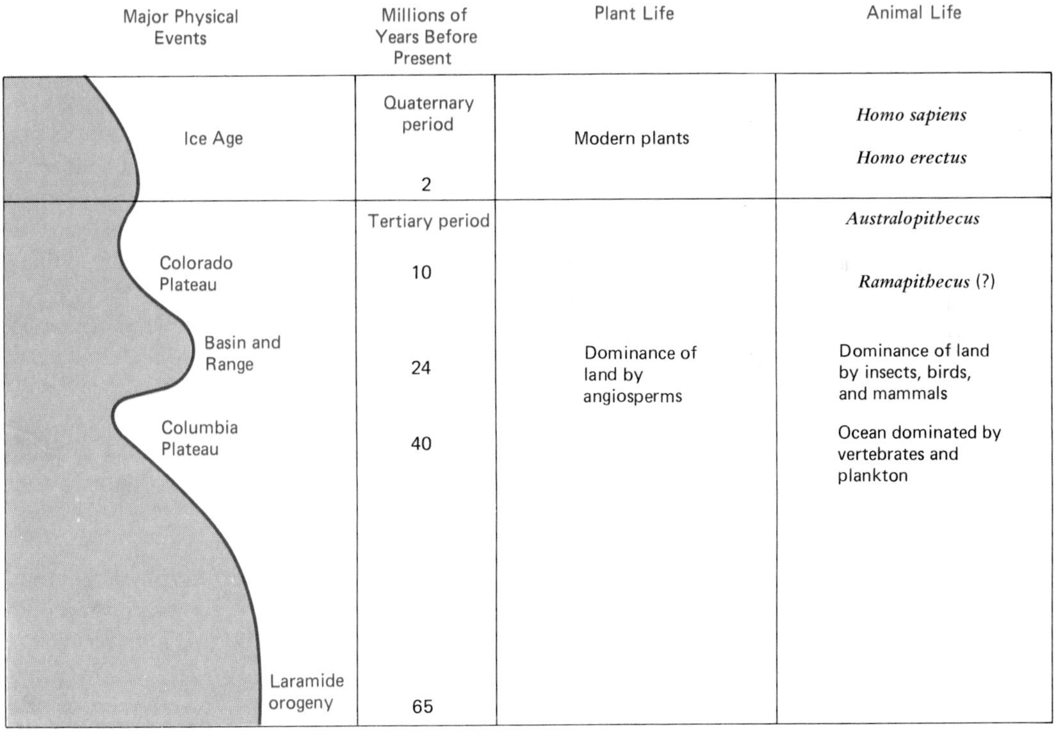

Major Physical Events	Millions of Years Before Present	Plant Life	Animal Life
Ice Age	Quaternary period 2	Modern plants	*Homo sapiens* *Homo erectus*
	Tertiary period		*Australopithecus*
Colorado Plateau	10		*Ramapithecus* (?)
Basin and Range	24	Dominance of land by angiosperms	Dominance of land by insects, birds, and mammals
Columbia Plateau	40		Ocean dominated by vertebrates and plankton
Laramide orogeny	65		

15-24
A summary of some of the major events during the Cenozoic era.

oceanic rise. Within the last 10 million years the uplift of the Sierra Nevada batholith, the formation of the Cascade stratovolcanoes, the rifting of the Basin and Range, and the uplift of the Colorado Plateau were events that were probably tied in with the transformed convergent motion of these two plates.

Further east, widespread compression culminated in the crumpling of the Rocky Mountains and later continued uplift. The uplift of the Rockies is documented by the formation of the High Plains. This is a broad table-land covering parts of seven states; it formed as an alluvial fan. Other evidence includes a host of freshwater basins within the Rocky Mountain region filled with sediments from nearby uplifts.

Among those basin-fill deposits are widespread deposits of Tertiary coal, an important resource within the north-central plains. Oil produced from Cenozoic basins both onshore and offshore is the major economic resource from this time; three-quarters of the world's oil is found in Cenozoic rocks and sediments.

The Gulf Coast records a discontinuously regressive sea, with a shoreline moving south through time as the latest Mesozoic sea slowly withdrew. This advance covered with sediment much of the evidence for the Appalachian orogeny of late Paleozoic time, but formed a deposit of miogeosynclinal sediments over 6 miles (10 kilometers) thick. Abundant oil and major intrusions of low-density Mesozoic salt, mobilized in the latest Cenozoic by the mass of denser sediments placed above them, are within these sediments. The salt from these intrusions is another important Cenozoic resource, and rocks intruded by the salt domes of the Gulf coast have been major traps for petroleum accumulation.

Along the Atlantic coast, the Appalachians continued to be subdued by erosion, and the resulting Cenozoic sediments helped to form the Atlantic coastal plain. On the western, Atlantic, and Gulf coastal plains, large submarine canyons formed within the last few million years as worldwide sea level dropped several times during the Ice Age. Large areas of modern continental shelves were emergent as the seas regressed to their lowest level since the latest Paleozoic.

Among the life of the Cenozoic, angiosperms and conifers dominate the plant community, and grasses become the most important plant resource for life. As mammals gained dominance over their largely extinct reptilian ancestors, the plains, with their rich harvest of short and tall grasses, allowed many new species of herbivores (their teeth now adapted for grazing) to thrive. Among the herbivores, the ungulates were numberous and still are. Edentates, proboscids, primates, insectivores, and rodents arose to eat the new burst of plant life, while carnivores developed to eat the herbivores. Insects pollinated many of the angiosperms and were in turn eaten by bats and true birds. In the sea, the dwindling invertebrate fauna—

composed of forams, radiolaria, sponges, corals, bryozoa, clams, snails, crinoids, and echinoids—continued, while shelled cephalopods and brachiopods were vastly diminished.

Joining them in the sea were marine reptiles of both carnivorous and herbivorous habit, including whales, dolphins, walrus, sea lions, and seals. On land, the remnants of the amphibian and reptilian faunas continued, much diminished, while their vertebrate ancestors, the bony and cartilaginous fish, became abundant in both fresh water and saltwalter.

Among the primates, which trace their ancestry to early Cenozoic insectivores, evolution among one line of the apes led to upright humanlike animals by 4 million years ago; this, our oldest known ancestor, is *Australopithecus*. Through a series of anthropological finds from the Old World, increasingly human hominids can be traced to our common ancestors, the Neanderthals, creatures of the last major advance of the ice.

For Neanderthals, life must have been an awesome struggle against the giant mammals that were both their food and their predator. More and more sophisticated use of tools, language, and social systems allowed primitive humans to triumph over mammals many times their size in a climate that must have been similar to that of northern Alaska today.

Using our brains, our marvelously mobile limbs and grasping hands, and our superb vision, we humans dominate the physical and biological world. Like all dominant creatures, our arrival has signaled the departure of others that could not compete against our prowess. Our danger no longer comes from saber-toothed cats or rampaging mammoths.

Instead, we endanger one another, because we have forgotten that we, too, are a part of the earth. As we have come to dominate the earth and begin to understand it, we have ceased to revere it and care for it and for one another. Nature's increasing restraints on our vision of an ever more affluent life remind us that there are no free lunches—and there never were.

EXERCISES

1. Recently scientist Jacob Bronowski commented that the power that people have over nature lies in our command of imaginary experience; the symbol is the tool that separates humans from all other animals. To imagine is to create images and move them inside our heads into new arrangements; only humans can work with symbolic images. Comment on this.

2. Science has been called experience rationally organized. Comment on this.

3. Suppose we obtained two radiometric age dates from minerals in

granite from the Sierra Nevada batholith. From a mineral that we know should form early in Bowen's reaction series, we obtain several dates that are 1.6 million years older than dates obtained from a mineral that should have formed late. What information do we now have?

4. Concentrations of mammalian fossil bones are often found associated with rocks marginal to freshwater lake sediments. How could this association be explained?

5. Suppose that pollen from older sediments in a freshwater lake are mostly spruce-fir pollen, yet the modern lake is in a warm, low-elevation, semiarid climate. There are several ways to explain the evidence. Name two.

6. Recently discovered tracks of fossil hominids have allowed scientists studying only the tracks to estimate that the creatures were 4 feet (1⅓ meters) tall. What assumptions underlie that kind of prediction?

7. In northern Minnesota, a small forest of spruce logs yielding radiometric age dates near 10,000 years has been uncovered. The relatively little-changed trees lie flat under a thick deposit of very coarse gravel. How could that be explained? What other evidence would you look for to support or deny your hypothesis?

8. Some fossil elm leaves, rapidly buried under volcanic ash, were recently discovered. The leaves are still bright green. What information would you want to obtain if these leaves would be available to you for experiment. What should you want to know?

9. If the Rocky Mountains had been totally eroded away, what information within the poorly consolidated sedimentary rocks of the High Plains would still tell the direction and timing of the Rocky Mountain uplift?

10. The basalts that form the Columbia Plateau erupted from fissures, not from volcanic hills, and spread out in relatively uniform, sheetlike flows, one on top of another. They presumably formed in a tensional environment. Why can one make this assumption?

SUGGESTED READINGS

Flint, R. F., 1971, *Glacial and Pleistocene Geology,* New York, Wiley, 436 pp.
   Basic reference on events of the ice ages.
National Geographic Society, 1976, *Our Continent, a Natural History of North America,* Washington, D.C., National Geographic Society, 398 pp.
   Elegantly illustrated, full of information, and a joy to own.

King, Philip B., and Beikman, Helen M., 1978, *The Cenozoic Rocks; a Discussion to Accompany the Geology Map of the United States,* U.S. Geological Survey Professional Paper 904, Washington, D.C., U.S. Government Printing Office, 82 pp.

Thorough review of the evidence for major Cenozoic events in different regions of the United States.

KEY
CONCEPTS

Physical events

Regression on the eastern and Gulf coastal plains; deposition of coalescing alluvial fan from the Rocky Mountains, forming the High Plains; deposition in intermontane basins in the Rockies; extension of the Basin and Range; uplift of the Colorado Plateau; volcanism on the Columbia Plateau; Pacific rim overriding Pacific spreading center; last 2 million years, the Ice Age.

Biologic events

Dominance of angiosperms; radiation of mammals and insects into every imaginable ecologic niche; development of birds; development of hominids; rise of civilization.

View over Big Sur country of California.
(Photograph by Michael Collier.)

Epilogue

"Truth is that which changes most in time."
L. Durrell

The story of the earth, briefly outlined in the past chapters, tells us something about the nature of the earth, its history, and its life. But what are the lessons that come from the earth? Is is a question I often ask myself, and one that I am often asked in subtly different ways. What, overall, does the study of geology have to say to those who do not intend to follow it as a profession?

For most people, the central value in a geology course is the appreciation of the immense variety of geologic experience and the knowledge that the earth is always changing in predictable ways. Long after this book is laid aside, your understanding of geologic knowledge will make a walk, a car ride, or an airplane trip a much more meaningful experience. Finding beautiful rocks and ancient fossils is certainly a part of the lifetime enjoyment of an expanded understanding of the earth.

There are subtler values as well. We learn that in a modern view of the earth, humanity is a latecomer—an invited guest preceded by 40 million centuries of ancestors. We seem insignificant and unimportant, an ego-flattening experience produced by our own knowledge. Yet that same level of knowledge allows us to dominate the earth, alter our surroundings, and seize prize after prize from the earth.

We have learned that science is simply an extension of human rational thought—an insistence that time flows, that effect is the child of cause—and that scientific understanding moves in turbulent streams of human history. Long periods of time, during which the prevailing notion of how things are is little challenged, are then suddenly attacked by the brilliant insights of a Copernicus, a Newton, a Hutton, a Darwin, or a Wegener. Such attacks are met with all the objectivity of a kangaroo court but, in time, good ideas may prevail and become no longer heresy, but dogma.

Perhaps the greatest single lesson that geology and other sciences can offer is the observation that nothing material is permanent. Life, planetary systems, chemical elements, and the earth all evolve; even time changes, and probably the same is true for many other physical "constants." Science can only seek to understand the material world, and the basic lesson is that nothing ever remains the same.

The scientific world can only offer us a view of a world in motion, but not a world of perpetual, cyclic motion; all the motion goes somewhere, and no cycle is truly endless. Samuel Butler, English man of letters, once suggested that "A hen is only an egg's way of making another egg." We do not understand the hen in quite that way today, for a hen is an egg's way of making a slightly different egg.

If science cannot give us a vision of anything permanent, what, then, *is* permanent?

That question has haunted us all. It must have plagued anguished Neanderthal families as they laid their now-cold children in ancient graves. It continues as the fundamental question for us all. We learn from experience that life is not entirely bounded by the world of the senses and the world of reason. There are realities beyond these two, and they draw us toward what cannot be seen, touched, or proved.

All of us can now look backward, and mentally watch the Appalachians rise, examine a tiny speck of Precambrian life as it struggles for life in a lifeless world, and know that life succeeds only when it grows, when it struggles, when it has a purpose, and when it BELONGS.

We cannot live in isolation from the earth or from one another. We come from the earth, and we will return to it. We are both product and observer of billions of years of change. From that vantage point, we all briefly share in the human experience.

Appendix A
Identification of Common Minerals

The determinative tables are *organized* to help you identify minerals through a simple process of elimination. FIRST, determine whether the luster is metallic/submetallic (reflects light like a metallic object) or nonmetallic (anything else).

If the mineral's luster is metallic/submetallic, proceed to the first part of the identification tables, which are for all minerals with a metallic to submetallic luster. If the luster is nonmetallic, proceed to the second part of the tables, which list all other minerals whose luster is nonmetallic. (If a mineral commonly exhibits either metallic or nonmetallic luster, it is shown in both parts of the tables.)

SECOND, determine the mineral's hardness on the Mohs scale. Within each table, minerals are arranged in groups of increasing hardness.

Once you have determined the luster and the hardness, you should have anywhere from one to eight minerals left from which to choose. Examination of other physical properties should help you to make the correct

choice from those remaining.

THIRD, for some minerals you will have to determine the mineral's streak using a porcelain streak plate.

The identification tables in this appendix are organized as follows.

LUSTER: METALLIC OR
           SUBMETALLIC
           Hardness: less than $2\frac{1}{2}$
           Hardness: between $2\frac{1}{2}$ and 5
           Hardness: greater than 5
LUSTER: NONMETALLIC
  Streak: definitely colored
  Streak: colorless
           Hardness: less than $2\frac{1}{2}$
           Hardness: between $2\frac{1}{2}$ and 5
           Hardness: between 5 and 7
           Hardness: greater than 7

Note that within the nonmetallic group, minerals that yield a distinctively colored streak are separated into their own small group and are not subdivided by hardness: other properties allow rapid distinction among the members of this group.

For every mineral its specific gravity (G.),

color, streak (if any), chemical composition (see Appendix B), crystal system, and remarks about distinctive identifying properties are also given.

You will need a set of minerals of known hardness, a magnet, a glass plate, a copper penny, a common nail, dilute 10 percent hydrochloric acid, and a magnifying glass in order to complete all the tests used to identify minerals.

Mineral Identification Chart

Luster: Metallic or Submetallic
Hardness: Less Than 2½

Streak	Color	G.	H.	Remarks	Name, Composition, Crystal System
Black	Gray to iron black	2.3	1–1½	One direction perfect cleavage, greasy feel	Graphite, C, hexagonal
Black, slightly greenish	Blue black	4.7	1–1½	One direction perfect cleavage, greasy feel	Molybdenite, MoS_2, hexagonal
Gray black	Black to lead gray	7.6	2½	Perfect cubic cleavage; in cubic crystals, massive, granular	Galena, PbS, isometric
	Blue black to lead gray	4.5	2	One direction perfect cleavage, bladed with cross striations	Stibnite, Sb_2S_3, orthorhombic
Bright red	Red to vermilion	8.1	2–2½	One direction perfect cleavage. Usually granular massive	Cinnabar, HgS, hexagonal (R)[a]
Red brown	Red to vermilion	5.3	1+	Earthy. Crystalline hermatite is harder and black	Hematite, Fe_2O_3, hexagonal (R)[a]

Hardness: Greater Than 2½, Less Than 5

Streak	Color	G.	H.	Remarks	Name, Composition, Crystal System
Black	Iron black	4.7	2½+	Usually splintery or in radiating fibrous aggregates; sometimes softer	Pyrolusite, MnO_2 tetragonal
Gray black	Steel gray to black on exposure	5.7	2½–3	Usually compact massive; associated with other copper minerals	Chalcocite Cu_2S Orthorhombic
Black	Fresh surface, brownish bronze, purple tarnish	5.1	3	Usually massive, associated with other copper minerals	Bornite, Cu_5FeS_4, isometric

[a](R) refers to the rhombohedral subdivision of the hexagonal system.
[b]Luster can be considered as vitreous unless specified otherwise.

Streak	Color	G.	H.	Remarks	Name, Composition, Crystal System
	Brass yellow	4.2	$3\frac{1}{2}$–4	Usually massive, may occur as tarnished crystals resembling tetrahedrons, associated with other copper minerals, darker than pryite	Chalcopyrite, $CuFeS_2$, tetragonal
Light to dark brown	Dark to yellowish brown	4.0	$3\frac{1}{2}$–4	Six directions perfect cleavage, tetrahedral crystals, streak lighter than specimen	Sphalerite, ZnS, isometric
Copper red	Copper red, tarnish black	8.9	$2\frac{1}{2}$–3	Malleable; usually in irregular grains	Copper, Cu, isometric
Silver white	Silver white, tarnish black	10.5	$2\frac{1}{2}$–3	Malleable; usually in irregular grains	Silver, Ag, isometric
Gold yellow	Gold yellow	15.0 to 19.3	$2\frac{1}{2}$–3	Malleable; usually as irregular grains, nuggets. density varies with silver content	Gold, Au, Isometric

Hardness: Greater Than 5

Black	Pale brass yellow	5.0	6–$6\frac{1}{2}$	Often in striated cubes. Massive, granular; it's the most common sulfide mineral	Pyrite, FeS_2, isometric
	Black	5.2	6	Granular; strongly magnetic (attracted to magnets)	Magnetite, Fe_3O_4, isometric
Red brown	Dark brown red to black	5.0	$5\frac{1}{2}$–$6\frac{1}{2}$	Massive, radiating, sometimes micaceous (specular hematite). Earthy or metallic luster	Hematite, Fe_2O_3, hexagonal (R)[a]

Luster: Nonmetallic[b]
Streak: Definitely Colored

Yellow brown	Yellow to dark brown	3.3+	1–2	Dull luster, massive, earthy. Also called goethite	Limonite, hydrous iron oxides, orthorhombic (?)
Pale yellow	Pale yellow	2.1	$1\frac{1}{2}$–$2\frac{1}{2}$	Granular to earthy	Sulfur, S, orthorhombic
Yellow brown	Light to dark brown	4.0	$3\frac{1}{2}$–4	Six directions perfect cleavage; tetrahedral crystals, streak lighter than specimen. Luster is resinous	Sphalerite, ZnS, isometric

Mineral Identification Chart (*Continued*)

Streak	Color	G.	H.	Remarks	Name, Composition, Crystal System
Brown	Light to dark brown	3.8	$3\frac{1}{2}$–4	Three directions (rhombohedral) cleavage, not at right angles, magnetic when heated in a candle flame	Siderite, $FeCO_3$, hexagonal (R)[a]
Red brown	Dark brown red to black	5.0	$5\frac{1}{2}$–$6\frac{1}{2}$	Massive, radiating, sometimes micaeous (specular hematite)	Hematite, Fe_2O_3, hexagonal (R)[a]
Light green	Bright green	4.0	$3\frac{1}{2}$–4	Radiating fibrous crystals; associated with azurite. Effervesces in cold hydrochloric acid	Malachite, $Cu_2CO_3(OH)_2$, monoclinic
Light blue	Intense azure blue	3.8	$3\frac{1}{2}$–4	Radiating fibrous, small crystals; associated with malachite. Effervesces in cold hydrochloric acid	Azurite, $Cu_3(CO_3)_2(OH)_2$, monoclinic
Very light blue	Light green to turquoise blue	2.2	2–4	Massive, compact; associated with oxidized copper minerals. Sticks to tongue	Chrysocolla, hydrous Cu silicate, amorphous

Luster: Nonmetallic[b]
Streak: Colorless
Hardness: Less Than $2\frac{1}{2}$

Cleavage

Cleavage	Color	G.	H.	Remarks	Name, Composition, Crystal System
One direction, perfect cleavage	White, gray, apple green	2.7	1	Greasy feel. Often distinctly foliated or micaeous	Talc, $Mg_3(Si_4O_{10})(OH)_2$, monoclinic
	White	2.8	2–$2\frac{1}{2}$	In foliated masses and scales. Cleavage flakes are elastic	Muscovite, $KAl_2(AlSi_3O_{10})(OH)_2$, monoclinic
	Dark brown, black	3.0	$2\frac{1}{2}$–3	Usually in irregular foliated masses. Cleavage flakes are elastic	Biotite, $K(Mg,Fe)_3(AlSi_3O_{10})(OH)_2$, monoclinic
	Green	2.8	2–$2\frac{1}{2}$	Usually in irregular foliated masses	Chlorite, complex Fe-Mg silicate, monoclinic
One direction, perfect cleavage, seldom seen	White, gray	2.6	2–$2\frac{1}{2}$	Compact, earthy; adheres to dry tongue	Kaolinite, $Al_4(Si_4O_{10})(OH)_8$, monoclinic

Cleavage	Color	G.	H.	Remarks	Name, Composition, Crystal System
One direction perfect; two directions, good; fourth direction, fair	White	2.3	2	Occurs as crystals and compact cleavable masses; also fibrous	Gypsum, $CaSO_4 \cdot 2H_2O$, monoclinic
Fracture is uneven	Pale yellow	2.1	$1\frac{1}{2}$–$2\frac{1}{2}$	Granular to earthy; luster dull to resinous	Sulfur, S, orthorhombic
	Gray, yellow, brown	2.0 to 2.5	1–3	In rounded grains, often earthy and claylike. Often harder than $2\frac{1}{2}$	Bauxite, hydroxides of Al, amorphous

Luster: Nonmetallic[b]
Streak: Colorless
Hardness: Greater Than $2\frac{1}{2}$, Less Than 5

Cleavage	Color	G.	H.	Remarks	Name, Composition, Crystal System
Perfect cubic cleavage	Colorless, white, red blue	2.2	$2\frac{1}{2}$	Common salt. Soluble in water, salty taste. In granular masses or cubic crystals	Halite, NaCl, isometric
Three directions, not at right angles (rhombohedral)	Colorless, white, blue, varied	2.7	3	Effervesces rapidly in cold hydrochloric acid.	Calcite, $CaCO_3$, hexagonal (R)[a]
	Colorless, white, pink	2.8	$3\frac{1}{2}$–4	Powdered mineral will slowly effervesce in cold acid. Usually harder than 3	Dolomite, $CaMg(CO_3)_2$, hexagonal (R)[a]
	Light to dark brown	3.8	$3\frac{1}{2}$–4	Becomes magnetic when heated in a candle flame	Siderite, $FeCO_3$, hexagonal (R)[a]
One direction	Colorless, yellow, pink bluish	3.5	8	Usually as prismatic crystals; found in pegmatites (coarse-grained granite)	Topaz, $Al_2SiO_4(OH,F)_2$, Orthorhombic
Four directions	Colorless, yellow, red, blue, black	3.5	10	Adamantine (brilliant) luster. Often as octahedral crystals	Diamond, C, isometric

Cleavage	Color	G.	H.	Remarks	Name, Composition, Crystal System
	Pink, rose red	3.5	$3\frac{1}{2}$–$4\frac{1}{2}$	Characterized by rhombic cleavage and color	Rhodochrosite, $MnCO_3$, hexagonal (R)[a]
Three directions, two at right angles to third, unequal quality	Colorless, white, blue, yellow, red	4.5	3–$3\frac{1}{2}$	Aggregates of platy crystals. Characterized by high density for a nonmetallic mineral	Barite, $BaSO_4$, orthorhombic
Four directions, equal quality	Colorless, pink, green, purple, etc.	3.2	4	In cubic crystals, characterized by cleavage	Fluorite, CaF_2, isometric
Six directions, equal quality	Dark yellow brown	4.0	$3\frac{1}{2}$–4	Luster resinous. Usually in cleavable masses, sometimes as tetrahedrons	Sphalerite, ZnS, isometric
Cleavage not prominent	Olive to blackish green	2.2	2–5	Massive; fibrous in the asbestos variety. Frequently mottled green in the massive variety	Serpentine, $Mg_6Si_4O_{10}(OH)_8$, monoclinic
	Colorless, white, blue, varied	2.7	3	May be fibrous, fine-granular, banded as in Mexican onyx. Effervesces in cold acid	Calcite, $CaCO_3$, hexagonal (R)[a]
	Yellow, red, orange	6.8	3	Luster is adamantine. Usually in square tabular crystals. Color and high density are characteristic	Wulfenite, $PbMoO_4$, tetragonal

Luster: Nonmetallic[b]
Streak: Colorless
Hardness: Greater Than 5, Less Than 7

Cleavage	Color	G.	H.	Remarks	Name, Composition, Crystal System
One direction	Blue to gray blue	3.6	5–7	In bladed aggregates with cleavage parallel to length. H5 parallel to length, H7 across length. In metamorphic rocks	Kyanite, Al_2SiO_5, triclinic
	Hair brown to grayish	3.2	6–7	As long prismatic tiny crystals, may be in parallel groups. Looks like fine hair or slender crystals. In metamorphic rocks	Sillimanite, Al_2SiO_5, orthorhombic
	Yellowish blackish green	3.4	6–7	As short prismatic crystals striated parallel to length	Epidote, complex Fe-Mg silicate, monoclinic

Cleavage	Color	G.	H.	Remarks	Name, Composition, Crystal System
Two directions, unequal quality	Colorless, white, gray	2.8	5–5½	Usually cleavable; massive to fibrous	Wollastonite, $CaSiO_3$, triclinic
Two directions, equal quality	Colorless, white, pink, gray	2.5	6	In cleavable masses or as irregular grains in rocks. *Cleavage directions are perpendicular*	Orthoclase, $KAlSi_3O_8$, monoclinic
	Colorless, white, gray, bluish	2.7	6	Same as for orthoclase. Also often exhibits a play of colors. Parallel twinning striations seen on one of two cleavages	Plagioclase, $NaAlSi_3O_8$ to $CaAl_2Si_2O_8$, triclinic
	Green, black	3.1 to 3.5	5–6	In stout prisms with rectangular cross sections. Cleavage angles of 87 and 93 degrees are characteristic	Pyroxene group, complex Ca,Mg silicates, monoclinic
	Green, black	3.0 to 3.3	5–6	Crystal are slender prisms. Characterized by cleavage angles of 56 and 124 degrees	Amphibole group, complex Ca, Mg, Fe, silicates, monoclinic
Cleavage not prominent	Yellow, blue, green, brown varied	3.2	5	Usually in hexagonal prisms; also massive, vitreous luster	Apatite, $Ca_5(PO_4)(F,Cl,OH)$, hexagonal
	Colorless, red, brown, gray, yellow, blue	2.0	5–6	Conchoidal fracture. Hardness and density less than quartz. Precious opal shows play of colors (irridescence)	Opal, $SiO_2 \cdot nH_2O$, amorphous
	Yellow, brown	3.5	5–5½	Luster is brilliant to resinous, as wedge-shaped crystals in rocks	Sphene, $CaTiSiO_5$, monoclinic
	Blue, green, bluish green	2.7	6	Usually appears as amorphous masses	Turquoise, $CuAl_5(PO_4)_4(OH)_8 \cdot 4H_2O$, triclinic
	Colorless, white, varied	2.7	7	Crystals usually show horizontally striated hexagonal prisms. Conchoidal fracture; striations parallel one another	Quartz, SiO_2, hexagonal (R)[a]
	Light brown, yellow, red, green	2.7	7	Luster is waxy to dull. May be banded or lining cavities	Chalcedony, SiO_2 cryptocrystalline quartz
	Olive to grayish green, brown green	3.3	6½–7	As rounded disseminated grains in rocks. May be massive granular	Olivine, $(Mg,Fe)_2SiO_4$, orthorhombic

Mineral Identification Chart (*Continued*)

Luster: Nonmetallic[b]
Streak: Colorless
Hardness: Greater Than 7

Cleavage	Color	G.	H.	Remarks	Name, Composition, Crystal System
Cleavage not prominent	Green, red blue, pink, black	3.2	$7–7\frac{1}{2}$	In slender prismatic crystals with rounded triangular cross section. Found in pegmatites, usually black	Tourmaline, complex silicates, hexagonal (R)[a]
	Brown to brownish black	3.7	$7–7\frac{1}{2}$	In prismatic crystals; commonly cross shaped. Alteration on surface causes reduced hardness	Staurolite, $Fe_2Al_9O_6(SiO_4)_4(O,OH)_2$, orthorhombic
	Reddish brown to olive green	3.2	$7\frac{1}{2}$	Prismatic crystals with nearly square cross sections. May show central black cross (chiastolite)	Andalusite, AI_2SiO_5, orthorhombic
	Brown to red, green, black	3.5 to 4.3	$6\frac{1}{2}–7\frac{1}{2}$	Usually in crystals showing dodecahedrons, well formed. Common in metamorphic rocks.	Garnet, complex silicate, isometric
	Bluish green, yellow, pink colorless	2.8	$7\frac{1}{2}–8$	Commonly as hexagonal prisms; often found in pegmatites	Beryl, $Be_3Al_2Si_6O_{18}$, hexagonal
	Bluish gray, varied	4.0	9	Luster is vitreous. Crystals are rounded hexagonal prisms	Corundum, Al_2O_3, hexagonal (R)[a]

Appendix B
Chemical Principles in Geology

Since this book assumes an acquaintance with some chemical principles, some fundamental chemical ideas are included here for your convenience in review and reference.

THE COMPOSITION OF MATTER

Elements are the fundamental chemical entity. They are composed of still smaller units and may link together to form still larger chemical units. *Atoms* are the smallest electrically neutral units that still have the chemical properties of the element.

An atom contains a nucleus; a nucleus consists of densely packed *protons,* which are particles of positive charge, and *neutrons,* which are particles with no electrical charge. The protons and neutrons comprise essentially all of the mass of the atom. The number of protons in an atom is called the *atomic number.*

The tightly packed nucleus contains essentially all of the mass, but most of the volume of an atom is composed of empty space in which tiny *electrons,* particles of negative electrical charge, orbit the nucleus in concentric shells. Since an atom is electrically neutral, the number of electrons and protons in an atom are the same, thereby providing a balanced overall charge. Thus the atomic number not only specifies the number of protons, but also the number of electrons in an atom.

The number of protons and electrons in an atom distinguishes one element from another. There are approximately 88 naturally occurring elements; each is distinguished from all the others by its atomic number.

Variations within one element arise because the number of protons is not always accompanied by the same number of neutrons. Variations of the same element, all having the same number of protons (and electrons) but different numbers of neutrons in their nucleus, are known as *isotopes* of that element. The *mass number* of an element is the number of neutrons plus the number of protons. Thus all isotopes have the same atomic number but different mass numbers.

In the same way, different isotopes of unlike elements have the same mass number, usually written as a raised subscript. N^{14} is an isotope of nitrogen, whose nucleus contains 7 protons and 7 neutrons; C^{14} is an isotope of carbon, whose nucleus contains 6 protons and 8 neutrons. The atomic number of nitrogen is 7, and the atomic number of carbon is 6, but isotopes of each may have the common mass number 14.

Both the particles in the nucleus and the electrons that orbit the nucleus are thought to be arranged in concentric shells. If all the available sites in a shell are filled, the resulting atom is quite stable. As the number of shells increases, the overall size of the atom increases.

If an atom, an electrically neutral particle, gains or loses electrons from its shells, it becomes an *ion* and possesses an electric charge. If the atom gains one or more electrons, it has an excess negative charge and is called a negatively charged ion, or *anion*. Oxygen is one example; it readily acquires two excess electrons and becomes an anion with an overall charge of -2. Silicon may readily lose 4 electrons and thus become a positively charged *cation* with an overall charge of $+4$ (having lost 4 electrons).

Molecules

If two oxygen anions (having a *combined charge* of -4) join with a single silicon cation (having a charge of $+4$), a new entity is formed that is *electrically neutral* and therefore stable. The resulting *molecule,* the fundamental chemical unit of compounds, is composed of 1 ion of silicon, contributing 4 positive charges, and $1 + 1$ ions of oxygen, contributing a combined charge of four negative charges.

Such a molecule is written in chemical shorthand as SiO_2, meaning that 1 ion of silicon is joined with 2 ions of oxygen. The resulting unit is a molecule of *silicon dioxide,* a *chemical compound* formed when 1 silicon cation and 2 oxygen anions share their electrons to create an electrically neutral unit.

A chemical compound is formed when two or more elements join together to form a new substance. A compound is distinguished from a mixture (for example, a mixture of iron filings and powdered sulfur) by being a single chemical unit that requires the expenditure of energy to reseparate into its components and whose components are locked together in *constant, fixed proportions*. Thus FeS_2 is iron sulfide, a chemical compound, but a mixture of powdered iron and powdered sulfur is just that, a mechanical mixture, easily separated with a magnet.

There are only 24 or more elements of interest in most geologic environments; the following table lists them along with their atomic numbers and shorthand symbols:

Radioactivity

Radioactivity is the result of spontaneous changes in the atomic nucleus, involving both the emission of detectable particles of many kinds and the emission of varieties of electromagnetic radiation, mainly heat.

One particle emitted is called the *alpha* (α) particle, which is identical with a helium

Atomic Number	Element Name	Chemical Symbol
1	Hydrogen	H
6	Carbon	C
7	Nitrogen	N
8	Oxygen	O
9	Fluorine	F
11	Sodium	Na
12	Magnesium	Mg
13	Aluminum	Al
14	Silicon	Si
15	Phosphorous	P
16	Sulfur	S
17	Chlorine	Cl
19	Potassium	K
20	Calcium	Ca
22	Titanium	Ti
25	Manganese	Mn
26	Iron	Fe
28	Nickel	Ni
29	Copper	Cu
37	Rubidium	Rb
38	Strontium	Sr
79	Gold	Au
80	Mercury	Hg
82	Lead	Pb
86	Radon	Rn
88	Radium	Ra
92	Uranium	U

nucleus, which consists of 2 protons and 2 neutrons (He^4).

Another particle emitted in addition to alpha particles may be a *beta* (β) particle. Beta particles include particles of the same mass as electrons but of opposite (positive) charge, called *positrons,* and electrons.

Emission of alpha or beta particles may also be accompanied by the emission of *gamma* rays (γ), a type of electromagnetic radiation that partially overlaps X rays in the total spectrum of electromagnetic radiation.

If an unstable element emits an alpha par-

ticle, its mass number decreases by 4 and its atomic number decreases by 2. Since the atomic number decreases, a new element is left behind—one whose atomic number is 2 less than its parent element. Thus radium (atomic number 88), becomes radon (atomic number 86) by emitting an alpha particle.

Emission of beta particles is a complex field; the particles emitted are presumably in the nucleus and include four types of particles. When the element gains an electron, a proton becomes a neutron; when an electron is lost, a neutron becomes a proton. Thus beta particle emission is characterized by no change in the mass number, but a change in the atomic number. For example, C^{14} becomes N^{14} by losing a beta particle, while K^{40} becomes Ar^{40} by gaining an electron or Ca^{40} by losing a beta particle. The isotopes of nitrogen and carbon share a common mass number (14) and the isotopes of calcium, argon, and potassium also share a common mass number (40).

Radioactivity is the result of spontaneous change and may be detected by a variety of chemical and photographic methods that allow recognition of emission of the particles and energy associated with radioactive decay.

Appendix C
Rock Identification Charts

Chapters Three and Five both contain rock identification charts, and additional information and charts are presented here.

If you know absolutely nothing about a rock specimen given to you for identification, you must first decide whether it is of igneous, sedimentary, or metamorphic origin. For some rocks, even this broad distinction is remarkably difficult to make. Several hints of what to look for follow.

ROCK NONCRYSTALLINE: composed of fragments

1. If fragments are glassy or volcanic, rock is pyroclastic.
2. If fragments are plant fragments, rock is a low-grade coal.
3. If fragments are bits of shell and bone, rock is a clastic limestone.
4. If fragments are in regular layers and are cemented together, rock is sedimentary.

ROCK CRYSTALLINE: crystals are aligned and layered

1. Rock is most likely metamorphic, although flowage in cooling magma or lava may align some minerals in an igneous rock.

ROCK CRYSTALLINE: crystals not aligned

1. Rock may be igneous. Should contain minerals characteristic of igneous rocks.
2. Rock may be a nonfoliated metamorphic rock. If so, should be dense and composed of quartz crystals (quartzite), calcite crystals (marble), or metamorphic minerals.
3. Rock may be a chemical sedimentary rock. If so, should *not* be dense, and test should be made for gypsum, salt, dolomite, calcite (acid test) and similar minerals.

C-1

Identification of Common Igneous Rocks

Mineral Composition		Texture				
Dominant Feldspar	Dominant Ferromagnesian	Super Coarse 2 centimeters	Coarse Grained visible crystals	Fine Grained invisible crystals	Glassy	Fragmental[b]
Absent			Peridotite	Unknown		
Ca-plagioclase	Olivine Pyroxene		Gabbro	Basalt (scoria if frothy)		Agglomerate (large, rounded fragments)
Na-plagioclase			Diorite	Andesite		Breccia (large angular fragments)
Plagioclase = orthoclase	Hornblende		Quartz monzonite[a]	Dacite[a]		Tuff breccia (mixture of small and large fragments)
Orthoclase	Biotite	Pegmatite[a]	Granite[a]	Rhyolite[a]	Obsidian (massive) or Pumice (frothy)	Tuff (small fragments)

[a]Contain quartz.
[b]Rock composition may range from basalt to rhyolite.

ROCK GLASSY OR POROUS
1. Probably a volcanic rock.
2. May be a poorly cemented breccia or a poorly cemented travertine or similar freshwater limestone. Test for calcite with dilute hydrochloric acid.

These tests outlined will not guarantee placement of any rock in the correct category, but they should help. Rock identification is an art as much as a science; the more rocks you can identify, the better you will become at it. Tables C-1 to C-3 for rock identification provide a systematic means to rock identification.

Table C-1 depends on your being able to identify the dominant feldspar type if the rock is plutonic (coarse grained) and on your being able to identify the dominant ferromagnesian minerals (the compounds of iron or magnesium that form dark-colored minerals). If the rock is fine grained and, hence, volcanic, unless there are feldspar phenocrysts, identification must be made on the basis of color, with darker rocks at the top of the chart. If the rock is glassy, obsidian is often a dark, volcanic glass; and pumice is usually a light-colored, frothy glass. Fragmental or pyroclastic rocks are classified by dominant grain size.

Table C-2 separates clastic rocks, which

C-2

Identification of Sedimentary Rocks

Clastic or Fragmental Sedimentary Rocks		
Rock	Original Unconsolidated Debris	Average Diameter of Fragments
Conglomerate	Rounded pebbles of quartz, rock fragments, etc.	Larger than 2 millimeters (gravel)
Sandstone	Sand-sized fragments of quartz, feldspar, rock fragments	$1/16$–2 millimeters (sand) (pinhead to invisible)
Siltstone	Silt-sized fragments of quartz, feldspar, etc.	$1/256$–$1/16$ millimeter (silt) (invisible, but gritty)
Shale and mudstone	Clay minerals, very fine quartz. (Shale splits easily along the bedding. Mudstone breaks into angular blocks)	Smaller than $1/256$ millimeter (clay) (smooth to touch)

Chemical and Organic Sedimentary Rocks

Rock		Original Unconsolidated Material	Comments
Limestone	Sparry limestone	Interlocking crystals	Composed of the mineral calcite; "fizzes" with dilute HCl acid
	Coquina	Skeletal fragments	
	Skeletal micrite	Lime mud plus skeletal fragments	
	Micrite	Lime mud and silt	
	Dolostone	Limestone or calcareous ooze altered to dolostone by solution	Composed of mineral dolomite; must be powdered to "fizz" in HCl
	Chert	Silicous parts of animals (sponges) and plants (diatoms). Replacement of organic tissue by solutions. Inorganic precipitation around submarine hot springs.	Cannot be scratched with knife
Evaporite	Gypsum	Gypsum	Scratched with fingernail
	Salt	Halite	Salty taste

generally feel "gritty" to the touch and are well layered, from crystalline rocks. Clastic rocks are classified on the basis of dominant grain size, chemical rocks on the basis of composition.

Like igneous rocks, metamorphic rocks are classified based on both their composition and texture (Table C-3).

Classification of fine-grained rocks is always tenuous for any rock. Here the separation depends on being able to recognize slaty cleavage, or its absence.

C-3

Identification of Metamorphic Rocks

Common Minerals	Texture		
	Nonfoliated	Foliated or Schistose	Banded or Gneissose
Quartz	Quartzite		
Calcite, dolomite	Marble		
Mica, chlorite + quartz, feldspar		Fine-grained slate	
Mica, chlorite + quartz, feldspar	Coarse-grained Granofels	medium-grained phyllite	
Mica, chlorite, garnet, amphibole + quartz, feldspar, pyroxene		Coarse-grained schist	Coarse-grained gneiss
Garnet, wollastonite pyroxene, calcite + amphibole, plagioclase	Coarse-grained skarn		
Amphibole, plagioclase	Coarse-grained amphibolite	Coarse-grained amphibolite	

Appendix D
Topographic and Geologic Maps

Any map is a representation of some property of the earth. If the map displays the shape of the earth's surface and the location of specific features, it is a *topographic* map. The term topographic literally translates as a "place drawing." A *geologic* map is often overprinted onto a topographic map; it shows the configuration of the earth's surface and its surface features and the geologist's interpretation of the kinds and attitudes of rock, or other geologic features, within the mapped area.

TOPOGRAPHIC MAPS

All maps, printed on flat paper, inevitably involve some distortion of the earth's shape, which is essentially a sphere. Maps of small areas involve minimal distortion, while maps of entire continents, or of the whole world, involve more and more sophisticated methods of projecting the earth's curved surface onto a flat plane in order to minimize the distortion.

The amount of area that can be covered depends on the ratio of map distance (the distance between two points on the map) to true distance (the distance between two points on the earth). Most commonly the *scale* of a map is stated as a ratio of these two distances. For many topographic maps, common scales are 1:24,000, 1:62,500, and 1:250,000. The scale of 1:62,500 implies that one unit of anything (inches, centimeters, feet, pencil lengths) equals 62,500 of the same unit on the earth. By design, the scale of 1:62,500 is also approximately the scale of 1 inch on the map equal to 1 mile on the earth. Many maps also include a bar scale as another device for showing the relation between map distance and true distance.

Topographic maps are the only maps that attempt to show the configuration of the earth's surface, plus all drainage features, vegetation, buildings, highways, bridges, dams, and cities—anything constructed by human beings. On most topographic maps, five different colors are used to sort out the kinds of features displayed.

1. *Brown.* Landforms of the area are displayed by means of thin brown lines, some of which have elevations printed on them. These lines are called *contour lines;* they connect all points on a map of equal elevation above sea level (Figure D-1). The contour interval (C.I.) is stated on the map and is the elevation difference between adjacent lines.

2. *Green.* An optional overprint that indicates areas of substantial vegetative cover.

3. *Blue.* All bodies of water, including lakes, rivers, streams, and glaciers. Intermittent streams, which flow only part of a year, are shown as alternate dashes and three dots. Perennial streams, which flow year around, are shown as solid blue lines.

4. *Red.* On more modern maps, highways, location information, and some metropolitan areas are shown in red and light red.

5. *Black.* All objects made by humans, including constructed objects and geographic names and boundaries, plus some information on position, including latitude and longitude information. Township-range information on older maps is in black, on more modern maps is in red.

Location of an object on a map is usually given in at least two complementary systems. The system of latitude and longitude are familiar systems, wherein objects north

D-1
Contour lines suggest the contours of the face and body of a former superintendent of the U.S. Geological Survey's Topographic Division. (Courtesy of the U.S. Geological Survey.)

and south of the equator are described in terms of their *latitude* (degrees north or south of equator) and objects east and west of the prime meridian, running north-south through Greenwich, England, are described in terms of their longitude (degrees east or west of Greenwich).

The township-range system numbers *township* strips of 36 square miles (93 square kilometers) north and south of some arbitrary line and *ranges* east and west of some arbitrary line. The grid of township-range lines produces blocks of land containing ap-

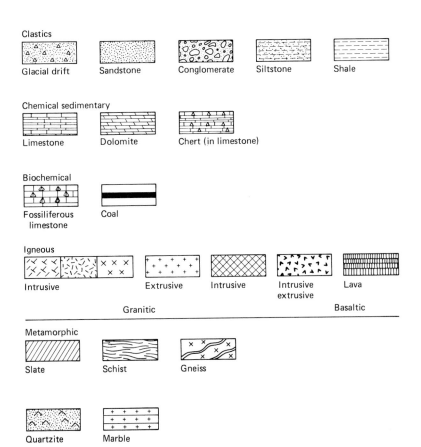

Clastics

Glacial drift Sandstone Conglomerate Siltstone Shale

Chemical sedimentary

Limestone Dolomite Chert (in limestone)

Biochemical

Fossiliferous Coal
limestone

Igneous

Intrusive Extrusive Intrusive Intrusive Lava
extrusive

Granitic Basaltic

Metamorphic

Slate Schist Gneiss

Quartzite Marble

D-2
Some common symbols on geologic maps. Similar symbols are used in drawings throughout this book.

proximately 36 square miles (93 square kilometers). Each block is subdivided and numbered into *sections* of approximately 1 square mile ($2^6/_{10}$ square kilometers). Within any one section, a system of subdivsion by quarters is traditional.

As an example of how this system works, we could describe an area as located in the NE$^1/_4$, NW$^1/_4$, Sec. 20, T. 10 N., R. 5 W. Translating, the area is in the northeast quarter of the northwest quarter of section 20, 10 townships north and 5 ranges west of the intersection of the arbitrary baselines in the area.

GEOLOGIC MAPS

Geologic maps convey the geologist's interpretation of the geologic features of any one area. The map may be highly detailed and specialized in areas where rock is clearly ex-

	Period	Epoch	Symbol	Color
Cenozoic era				
	Tertiary	Pliocene	Tpl	
		Miocene	Tm	
		Oligocene	To	Yellow – brown
		Eocene	Te	
		Paleocene	Tp	
Mesozoic era				
Paleozoic era	Permian		P	Light blue
	Pennsylvanian		IP	Blue
	Mississippian		M	Blue
	Devonian		D	Blue – gray
	Silurian		S	Purple
	Ordovician		O	Red – purple
	Cambrian		€	Orange

D-3
Colors and symbols used to separate rock units of different ages on geologic maps. Although not used within the text, the names of the subdivisions of each era and the subdivisions of each of the periods within the Cenozoic era are given here to assist in interpretation of geologic maps.

posed, or it may be quite generalized in areas of substantial regolith. The map may be of the regolith itself and may ignore the underlying bedrock.

Other kinds of maps describe the occurrence of groundwater, karst areas, economic ore deposits, gravel resources, landslide danger, quarrying ease, slope stability and form, or any of a host of other kinds of geologic information.

Most geologic maps, however, record the geologist's impression of the nature and attitude of the bedrock. Any geologic map, then, reflects the state of current geologic knowledge; any map is an interpretation— an interpretation that presumably is closer to reality as amount of exposed rock increases.

Geologic maps are made in many ways, but they all involve a geologist walking over the area, carefully noting the kinds of rock, soils, fossils, structures, attitudes, and stratigraphic relations among rocks. Such "on-the-ground" analysis is often supplemented by aerial photography and various types of imagery from airplanes and space satellites. Geologic maps of Mars are an example of what can be done without having actually placed a geologist there.

Additionally, the geologist plots all the observations on a field map, which is further refined by detailed study of the rocks in the laboratory and by detailed analysis of fossils, minerals, and structural information. Also, the geologist may measure and describe stratified rocks in many places in the area to be mapped and work out the correlation of these rocks. Most geologic maps have built into them many hours of laboratory work by many people and a lot of hiking and careful observing of the details of the earth's surface.

A synthesis of all the information available allows the geologist to draw the map using colors and symbols to describe both the age and rock types of the area (see Figures D-2 and D-3).

Typically, the map also contains an explanation area that illustrates what each symbol means and artificially "stacks" the geologic units in correct age sequence; the oldest unit is on the bottom of the stack, or column. Symbols are used in this geologic column to indicate the rock type characteristic of each unit. Some examples are given in Figure D-2; similar symbols are used throughout the drawings in this textbook.

Whatever the purpose of a map, it is finally an attempt to convey quickly a mass of information in a highly visual form. Its success depends on the skill of the geologist, the extent of exposure, the complexity of the geologic situation, and the combined skill of many artists, editors, and printers.

Appendix E
Measurement Conversion

For many years Americans have been used to stating measurements in the English system. As we join the rest of the world in using the metric system, a few words of explanation will be helpful.

The basic unit of *length* measurement in the metric system is the *meter*, a unit approximately equal to 1.1 yards. By using various **prefixes** *common to the entire metric system of measurement*, the basic unit can be expressed in terms of multiples of tens or tenths. A few of the common prefixes are listed.

*kilo*meter = 1000 meters
*centi*meter = $\frac{1}{100}$ of a meter
*milli*meter = $\frac{1}{1000}$ of a meter
*micro*meter = $\frac{1}{1000000}$ of a meter

In the same way, the basic unit of mass is the *gram*, a unit approximately equal to $\frac{1}{28}$ of an ounce. One *kilo*gram is thus 1000 grams and is *very* approximately equal to 2 pounds.

Approximate conversion factors for various classes of measurement follow.

When you know:	You can find:	If you multiply by:
Length		
inches	millimeters	25
feet	centimeters	30
yards	meters	0.9
miles	kilometers	1.6
millimeters	inches	0.04
centimeters	inches	0.4
meters	yards	1.1
kilometers	miles	0.6
Area		
square inches	square centimeters	6.5
square feet	square meters	0.09
square yards	square meters	0.8
square miles	square kilometers	2.6
acre	square *yards*	4840
square centimeters	square inches	0.16
square meters	square yards	1.2
square kilometers	square miles	0.4
Volume		
cubic inches	cubic centimeters	16.4
cubic feet	cubic meters	0.03
cubic yard	cubic meters	0.76
cubic mile	cubic kilometers	4
cubic centimeters	cubic inches	0.06
cubic meters	cubic feet	35.3
cubic kilometers	cubic miles	0.24
liters	gallons	0.25
Mass		
ounces	grams	28
pounds	kilograms	0.45
tons (2000 pounds)	metric ton (1000 kilograms)	0.9
grams	ounces	0.035
kilograms	pounds	2.2
metric tons (1000 kilograms)	ton (short ton) (2000 pounds)	1.1
Miscellaneous Conversions		
gram per cubic centimeter (*density*)	pounds per cubic foot	62.43
watt (*power*)	Btu per minute	0.057
gallons of *oil*	barrels	42
gallon (*volume*)	liters	3.78
miles per hour (*velocity*)	kilometers per hour	1.6
miles per hour	inches per second	17.6
kilometers per hour	centimeters per second	27.8

When you know:	You can find:	If you multiply by:
bar (*pressure*)	atmosphere (14.7 pounds per square inch)	0.987
kilometer of average rock	kilograms per square centimeter	265
kilogram per square centimeter	pounds per square inch	14.22
degrees Fahrenheit (*temperature*)	degrees Celsius	5/9 (after *subtracting* 32)
degrees Celsius	degrees Fahrenheit	9/5 (then *add* 32)

CLASSIFICATION OF LIFE

Biologic classification dates from the Swedish naturalist Carolus Linnaeus, who established a system for naming life in the eighteenth century. In this system, the categories of life are arranged in a hierarchy that expresses levels of biologic relationship. A *species* is a group of life forms so alike that they can interbreed. A *genus* (pl. *genera*) is a group of species so closely related that they share a common ancestry, but members of two separate genera cannot interbreed. A *family* is a group of related genera, while an *order* is a group of related families. A group of related orders is called a *class,* and a group of related classes is called a *phylum* (pl. *phyla*). A *kingdom* is a group of related phyla.

A human being is classified as follows:

KINGDOM: Animalia

  PHYLUM: Chordata

    CLASS: Mammalia

      ORDER: Primates

        FAMILY: Hominidae

          GENUS: Homo

            SPECIES: sapiens

The classification that follows is highly simplified and emphasizes the life forms that are described in this textbook. For a more complete classification of living forms, see any biology textbook.

KINGDOM PROKARYOTA: All prokaryotic life lacking a well-defined nucleus. Includes bacteria and blue-green algae

KINGDOM PROTISTA: Eukaryotic single-celled organisms, either solitary or colonial. Includes yellow-green and golden-brown algae, diatoms, coccoliths, amoeba, paramecium, etc.

KINGDOM PLANTAE: Includes all true plants

PHYLUM PSILOPHYTA: Extinct, leafless, rootless plants

PHYLUM LYCOPODOPHTA: Includes scale trees (Lycopsids) of the Paleozoic

PHYLUM EQUISETOPHYTA: Horsetails and scouring rushes and sphenopsids such as *Calamites* (Late Paleozoic)

PHYLUM POLYPODIOPHYTA: True ferns (Pteropsids)

PHYLUM PINOPHYTA: Gymnosperms ("naked seeds")

CLASS LYGINOPTERIODOP-SIDA: Seed ferns, including *Glossopteris*

CLASS BENNETTITOPSIDA: Cycadeoids

CLASS CYCADOPSIDA: Cycads

CLASS GINKGOOPSIDA: Ginkgoes

CLASS PINOPSIDA: Conifers ("evergreens"); also *Cordaites*

PHYLUM MAGNOLIOPHYTA: All flowering plants ("angiosperms")

KINGDOM ANIMALIA: Includes all animal life

PHYLUM ARCHAEOCYATHA: Earliest Paleozoic spongelike forms of uncertain affinity

PHYLUM PORIFERA: Sponges

PHYLUM COELENTERATA: Includes all corals and jellyfish

PHYLUM PLATYHELMINTHES: Flatworms. Other worm varieties comprise separate phyla

PHYLUM BRYOZOA: Bryozoans ("moss animals")

PHYLUM BRACHIOPODA: Marine animals with two shell halves

PHYLUM ANNELIDA: Segmented worms

PHYLUM ARTHROPODA: Segmented animals with jointed appendages and chitonous external skeletons

SUBPHYLUM TRILOBITA: All trilobites of the Paleozoic

SUBPHYLUM CHELICERATA: Includes eurypterids, scorpions, spiders, ticks, and mites

SUBPHYLUM CRUSTACEA: Includes lobsters, barnacles, crabs, and ostracods

SUBPHYLUM LABIATA: Includes millipedes, centipedes, and all insects

PHYLUM MOLLUSCA: Soft-bodied, unsegmented animals, usually protected by a shell

CLASS SCAPHOPODA: Tusk shells or scaphopods

CLASS GASTROPODA: Snails

CLASS PELECYPODA: Clams and oysters

CLASS CEPHALOPODA: Marine animals with tentacles, well-developed eyes and central nervous systems, such as squids and octopuses

ORDER NAUTILOIDEA: Nautiloids, both straight and coiled, simple shells

ORDER AMMONOIDEA: More complexly ornamented shells

ORDER BELEMNOIDEA: Belemnites

PHYLUM ECHINODERMATA: Marine animals with spiny, calcareous plates, such as starfish and brittle stars

CLASS ECHINOIDEA: Sea urchins and sand dollars

CLASS BLASTOIDEA: Paleozoic blastoids

CLASS CRINOIDEA: Sea lilies and feather stars

PHYLUM PROTOCHORDATA: Includes graptolites

PHYLUM CHORDATA: Includes animals with central nervous system, including all vertebrates

SUBPHYLUM UROCHORDATA: Sea quirts or tunicates

SUBPHYLUM VERTEBRATA: All animals with backbones

CLASS AGNATHA: Primitive jawless fish ("ostracoderms")

CLASS ACANTHODII: Primitive, spiny jawed fish

CLASS PLACODERMII: Paleozoic jawed, armored fish

CLASS CHONDRICHTHYES: Fish with cartilaginous skeletons, like the shark

CLASS OSTEICHTHYES: Bony-skeleton fish

SUBCLASS ACTINOPTERYGII: Ray-finned fish

SUBCLASS SARCOPTERYGII: Lobe-finned fish, breathe air directly

ORDER CROSSOPTERGII: Amphibian ancestors

ORDER DIPNOI: Lungfish

CLASS AMPHIBIA: Amphibians, including labyrinthodonts

CLASS REPTILIA: Reptiles, scaly skin, amniotic egg

SUBCLASS ANAPSIDA: Mesosaurs, cotylosaurs, and turtles

SUBCLASS SYNAPSIDA: Therapsids and mammallike reptiles

SUBCLASS EURYAPSIDA: Plesiosaurs and icthyosaurs

SUBCLASS DIAPSIDA: Lizards, snakes, tuatara, and all dinosaurs

CLASS AVES: True birds

CLASS MAMMALIA: Warm-blooded, hairy animals, young nursed at mammary glands

SUBCLASS PROTOTHERIA: Egg-laying mammals, such as platypus

SUBCLASS ALLOTHERIA: Multituberculates

SUBCLASS EUTHERIA: Placental mammals. Young fetus develops in uterus with nutrition furnished thru placenta

ORDER INSECTIVORA: Moles and shrews

ORDER CHIROPTERA: Bats

ORDER EDENTATA: Armadillos, tree sloths, glyptodonts, and ground sloths

ORDER RODENTIA: Mice, rats, and beavers

ORDER CETACEA: Whales

ORDER CREODONTA: Carnivorous and extinct

ORDER CARNIVORA: Modern meat eaters, including dogs and cats

ORDER CONDYLARTHA: Ancestral ungulates

ORDER AMBLYPODA: Primitive ungulates

ORDER PERISSO-DACTYLA: Odd-toed hoofed mammals; horses, titanotheres, and chalicotheres

ORDER ARTIODACTYLA: Even-toed hoofed mammals; oreodonts, cattle, and pigs

ORDER PROBOSCIDEA: Elephants, mastodons, and mammoths

ORDER PRIMATES: Monkeys, apes, and humans

Glossary

(Number in parentheses refers to chapter in which term is first used or defined. Some terms are redefined in additional chapters.)

accordant (1) adjective describing topographic features that have a common elevation; for example, accordant stream junctions—two streams that join at a common elevation. Antonym: *discordant*.

aluminosilicates (2) chemical compounds of aluminum, silicon, and oxygen, including amphiboles, some pyroxenes, all micas, and all feldspars and clays.

American Rule (10) a rule that modifies the English Rule by requiring that water pumped from under the land be used *on* the land from which it is taken. Water cannot be transferred from the land if injury to others would occur. Also called the *reasonable use rule*. Compare with *English Rule*.

amniotic egg (13) an egg that has a hard covering is capable of protecting an embryo that is developing within while the egg remains on dry land. First developed by reptiles.

angiosperm (14) large group of plants whose seeds are borne in a flower or fruit, so that the seeds are protected, but require pollinization by insects. Compare with *gymnosperm*.

angular unconformity (13) an erosional surface cut across tilted layers beneath it. Implies that tilting preceded erosion.

anthracite (9) highest rank of coal, developed by metamorphism of lower ranks of coal. Sometimes called "hard coal."

aquifer (10) any geologic unit capable of transmitting water; aquifers must be both porous and permeable.

arête (8) a drainage divide sharpened to a knifelike edge by glacial erosion of valleys on both sides of the *arête*.

artesian well (10) any water well where water rises above the water table when the water table is penetrated by a well.

aseismic fault (6) a break in bedrock along which movement occurs continuously, without earthquakes being generated.

asthenosphere (6) the part of the upper mantle that seems to be semifluid and slows seismic body waves. The asthenosphere marks the base of the *lithosphere*.

atomic number (11) the number of protons within the nucleus of a single atom of an element. Compare with *isotope*.

atomic weight (11) the mass of an element, recorded as compared to some other element, usually oxygen, with an atomic weight of 16. The average relative weight of an element.

azonal soil (4) a soil that, in a vertical exposure, lacks developed soil horizons. Contrast with *zonal soil*.

batholith (3) a body of plutonic rock whose exposed area exceeds 40 square miles (about 100 square kilometers) or a very large mass of plutonic rock, whether exposed or not at the surface.

basement (12) the crust of the earth, beneath sedimentary deposits, which extends to the Mohorovicic discontinuity. Usually basement rocks are Precambrian igneous and metamorphic rocks, but the basement rocks may be of any age and form the platform for overlying veneers of sediments or sedimentary rocks.

bauxite (4) used as both a mineral and rock name to refer to a naturally formed unit of impure aluminum oxide, primarily used as an ore of aluminum. Develops by intense tropical weathering of aluminosilicate-rich rocks.

bedding (5) term used to refer to the layering within sedimentary rocks, made visible by changes in color, texture, mineralogy, or other attributes of the rock. It is the most common sedimentary structure and forms a horizontal to subhorizontal surface when sediment is deposited in water.

bedrock (4) a term applied to any solid rock that underlies unconsolidated material on the surface of the earth.

Benioff zone (7) a zone marked by numerous earthquake foci formed when a plate carrying continental rock overrides an oceanic plate, forcing the oceanic plate under the continental plate. Benioff zones often dip steeply beneath the continents and are zones where seismicity and melting are common. Also called *subduction zones*.

binary fission (12) a form of asexual reproduction by simple division of cell material by a prokaryotic cell.

bituminous coal (8) a black industrial coal of higher rank than *lignite* and lower rank than *anthracite*. Sometimes called "soft coal."

body wave (6) any seismic energy wave that travels through the earth, as compared to *surface waves,* which travel only within the earth's crust.

bombs (volcanic) (3) pyroclastic rock produced by the ejection of viscous lava that cools in flight and is larger than a few inches (centimeters) in its greatest dimension. Bombs may be of any shape.

breccia (5) sharp, angular rock material. When consolidated, the resulting sedimentary rock is also called a breccia. Compare with *conglomerate.*

British thermal unit (Btu) (9) heat energy required to raise 1 pound (about ½ kilogram) of water 1 degree Fahrenheit. Equals 252 calories. Is approximately the heat given off by one kitchen match.

bulk modulus (14) a number that expresses a material's resistance to elastic changes in volume; the "compressibility" of a substance. Compare with *shear modulus.*

caldera (3) a large, basin-shaped volcanic depression that may be formed by collapse, erosion, explosion, or any combination of these three processes.

caliche (4) a loosely defined term for any carbonate-rich layer formed near the surface in an arid or semiarid area. Caliche may include many types of calcium salts and varying amounts of gravel and other soil material. Compare with *hardpan*.

calorie (3) when written with a lowercase c, the term is the quantity of heat required to raise 1 gram ($\frac{3}{100}$ ounce) of water from 15 to 16 degrees Celsius. One Calorie (kilocalorie) equals 1000 calories; 252 calories equals 1 Btu.

carbonation (4) a form of chemical weathering in which weak carbonic acid converts minerals into carbonate or bicarbonate compounds.

Cenozoic era (11) the last 65 million years, during which mammals have been the dominant life form. Cenozoic literally means "modern life."

chemical differentiation (3) any process or group of processes that takes a chemically homogenous medium and separates it into various components of unlike chemistry.

chemical sedimentary rocks (5) a large and varied group of rocks that form by a great variety of chemical processes, including organic processes. This varied group includes essentially all nonclastic sedimentary rocks. Compare with *clastic* rocks.

chemical weathering (4) all forms of weathering that involve chemical changes within rock or mineral matter, usually facilitated on earth by the presence of both heat and water. Compare with *mechanical weathering*.

cinders (3) pyroclastic material ranging from sand- to pebble-sized material. Cinders are usually porous.

cinder cone (3) a volcano made up of cinders; typically the volcano is steep sided and is composed of basaltic cinders with or without associated lava flows.

clastic sedimentary rocks (5) sedimentary rocks composed of cemented fragments. Compare with *chemical sedimentary rock*.

clay (4) a word used to define a clastic fragment smaller than silt, or a sediment or rock largely composed of minerals from the clay group, or a large and diverse group of minerals that are chiefly hydrous aluminosilicates, derived from the chemical weathering of other aluminosilicates.

cleavage (2) a plane of ready breakage in a mineral. A mineral possessing cleavage planes will split along these planes when struck. The term *rock cleavage* defines a similar property characteristic of some rocks. Compare with *fracture*.

coal (9) a name for a group of chemical sedimentary rocks produced by the alteration of partially decayed plant matter in a swampy or bog environment. Varieties of coal include *peat, lignite, bituminous,* and *anthracite*.

color (2) a physical property of a mineral, produced by the selective absorption of part of the light incident on a mineral. For most minerals, the color of various specimens may range widely, and it is not a diagnostic physical property. Compare with *streak*.

competency (8) the *maximum* size particle that a flowing stream can carry at any one time.

composite cone (3) a volcano produced by alternate eruptions of pyroclastics and liquid lava. Most composite cones have a symmetrical appearance and are formed by igneous material of intermediate composition. Synonym: *stratovolcano*.

constancy of interfacial angles, principle of (2) an observation by Steno that for any one mineral species, the angle between the same two mineral faces on any specimen of the same mineral species remains constant.

conglomerate (5) a clastic sedimentary rock composed of rounded pebbles. Compare with *breccia*.

continental drift (7) an idea proposed by Wegener that continents at some time in the geologic past were entirely united as a single supercontinent called *Pangaea* and subsequently broke up and "drifted" across and through the ocean basins to their present location. Compare with *plate tectonics*.

continental glacier (8) a large glacier, unconfined by valley walls, that covers a significant portion of a continent. Also called an *ice sheet*. Continental glaciers cover Greenland and Antarctica today.

continuity, principle of (5, 11) an assertion that layered sedimentary rock, now separated by erosional valleys between two exposures, was once part of a continuous sheet or widespread layer of rock.

continuous reaction, principle of (3) feldspars within a cooling magma continuously react with the surrounding magma and modify their overall composition through time.

convection (7) a process of transfer of heat by upward movement of a heated fluid, accompanied by downward descent of a cooler fluid, which is slightly denser than its heated counterpart. A mechanism for heat transfer in fluid material.

core (6) the central part of the earth, probably composed of an alloy of nickel and iron. The outer core responds to seismic waves as a fluid, while the inner core responds to seismic waves as a solid.

correlate (11) to determine that separated sedimentary layers of either like or unlike composition are of the same age.

correlative rights (10) a law governing water usage; asserts that water that cannot be used to benefit the land under which it lies is available for appropriation and that all landowners must share in a water shortage as a proportion of landownership. Correlative rights may be regarded as a modification of the *American rule* and limits the use of water by the landowner even more stringently.

craton (12) any part of the earth's continental crust that has achieved stability and is no longer being actively deformed. Most cratonic rocks are Precambrian, but cratonic rocks may be of any age. Cratonic rocks form platforms for overlying sedimentary rocks. Synonym: *shield*.

creep (8) gradual movement of unconsolidated or consolidated material downslope under gravitational stress.

cross-bedding (5) bedding that intersects other bedding at some angle. May be produced by water currents or wind.

crosscutting, principle of (11) any geologic unit is younger than the unit it cuts across or affects.

crust (6) the outermost layer of the solid earth, often defined as the layer above the Mohorovicic discontinuity. The crust includes thicker, generally granitic continental crust, and thinner, generally basaltic oceanic crust.

deductive reasoning (1) to infer reasonable consequences from a general principle. See *inductive reasoning*.

deflation (8) erosion by wind action.

dike (3) igneous tabular unit that crosscuts the layering in surrounding rock.

dilatancy (6) a change in volume. Used to refer to events preceding an earthquake, the term implies the slight increase in volume produced when stressed rock begins forming numerous tiny cracks.

dilatancy-diffusion theory (6) an idea that suggests that some earthquakes are preceded by a period of dry dilatancy under stress, followed by inflow of water to fill the tiny cracks, which then diminishes the cohesion of the rock and so weakens it that the rock fails.

dilational wave (6) an energy wave that causes an elastic change in volume of substances through which it passes. A *P-wave* is a dilational seismic wave.

discharge (8) the volume of flow of a stream past a fixed point per unit of time. Expressed as cubic feet per second in the United States, or cubic meters per second elsewhere.

discontinuous reaction principle (3) olivine, pyroxene, and amphibole progressively react with magma and change to a different mineral, which is in equilibrium with the magma at any one time.

distortional wave (6) an energy wave that causes an elastic change in shape of a substance through which it passes. An *S-wave* is a distortional seismic wave. See *dilational wave*.

divergent plate margin (7) the rift margin of a plate produced when a single plate separates into two plates that move away from one another. The divergent margin of a plate is a zone of relative seismic quiet and sediment accumulation on the continental shelf and rise.

dormant volcano (3) a loosely defined term for a volcano that has not erupted within historic time but may still be capable of future eruption. An *extinct* volcano presumably has no potential for future eruption, but criteria for separating dormant and extinct volcanoes are poorly established. An *active* volcano is one that has erupted within historic times and is capable of future eruption; the distinction between active and dormant volcanoes is also based on poorly established criteria.

drainage basin (8) the area whose surface water flows into a single stream or network of coalescing streams.

drainage divide (8) higher ground separating two or more drainage basins.

drift (8) unstratified glacial sediment of any kind.

elastic body (6) a substance that is capable of regaining its original shape after its shape has been temporarily altered. A classic example is a tennis ball.

elastic rebound theory (6) an idea that suggests that earthquakes are due to stress levels exceeding the capacity of a rock to store energy as elastic distortion. The rock fractures suddenly and moves at high velocity to a new site, where its stored elastic energy is zero or nearly zero. Compare with *dilatancy-diffusion* theory.

electron (11) one of the elementary particles of an atom, having a negative electric charge, and a mass $\frac{1}{1837}$ that of a proton. Electrons surround the positively charged nucleus of the atom and largely determine the chemical properties of the atom. Compare with *proton* and *neutron*.

English Rule (10) the oldest form of water law; holds that ownership of water beneath the land is absolute. The owner of the land may do with the water whatsoever the owner chooses, although most courts hold that the owner may not pollute or contaminate the water to the detriment of nearby owners. Compare with *American Rule* or *correlative rights*.

epicenter (6) an imaginary point on the earth's surface above the focus. Compare with *focus*.

era (11) the largest subdivision of geologic time, based on major changes in life forms or major physical events.

erosion (5) a collective name for a group of processes that involve the transport of earth material from one place to another. Most erosive processes move material downslope. Compare with *weathering*.

esker (8) a generally sinuous ridge of stratified sand and gravel deposited by a meltwater stream flowing under a glacier.

eugeosyncline (12) the oceanward part of a geosyncline, usually approximately coinciding with the continental slope and rise. Sometimes called the *eugeocline,* a more modern term. Most often the eugeosyncline is associated with volcanism and deep water sedimentation. Compare with *miogeosyncline*.

eukaryote (12) a cell type found in all life except bacteria and blue-green algae. Eukaryotic cells contain a nucleus and numerous specialized cellular subunits. Compare with *prokaryote*.

faunal assemblage, principle of (5, 11) groups of fossils are unique to a limited interval of time, as each fossil within the group changes or evolves at its own rate. Concept developed independently by Cuvier and Smith.

fault plane or zone (6) a plane or zone along which bedrock shifts with respect to bedrock on the other side of the fault plane or zone. The shift may be accompanied by seismic activity or may be aseismic. See *aseismic fault*.

floodplain (8) a generally flat land surface adjacent to a stream produced by deposition of stream sediment during periods when the stream overflows its banks and moves onto the floodplain.

focus (6) the site or area of first motion along a fault plane or zone. The focus may be on the surface, in which case the *epicenter* and focus coincide, or it may be as deep as 400 miles (640 kilometers) or more. Compare with *epicenter*.

foliated (5) a common structure in metamorphic rocks produced by the parallel or sub-parallel alignment of platy or needlelike minerals formed under pressure. Antonym: *nonfoliated*.

foredeep (6) a submarine trench or down-buckle of the ocean floor. A foredeep usually marks the surface continuation of a subduction zone. Also called an *oceanic trench*. Compare with *subduction zone*.

fossil (5) any evidence of past life, including but not limited to, impressions, tracks, trails, hard parts, and skeletons.

fossil fuel (9) any form of natural hydrocarbon that may be used as fuel. Includes petroleum, natural gas, and coal. All fossil fuels are altered carbohydrates and represent stored solar energy.

fractional crystallization (3) process by which successive crystallization of different minerals in a cooling magma leads to development of separate minerals. See *discontinuous* and *continuous reaction*.

fracture (2) a broken surface whose orientation is random. Term is applied to both rocks and minerals. Compare with *cleavage*.

fumaroles (3) a vent for volcanic gases. See *solfatara*.

geology (1) the term literally means "earth study." The science of the earth, including its ocean basins, continents, life, minerals, rocks, structures, water, ores, fuels, economic resources, physical and chemical properties, and associated astronomic bodies.

geosyncline (7) an elongate or basinlike downwarping of the earth's crust in which sedimentary and volcanic rocks may accumulate to great thicknesses.

glacial erratic (8) a boulder that has been transported a considerable distance from its place of origin by a glacier.

Gondwanaland (7) one scheme of continental drift calls for the reconstruction of the earth's continental mass into two large supercontinents; the southern one was called Gondwanaland.

Gondwana strata (7) the unique assemblage of sedimentary and volcanic rocks, including tillites, which formed in the southern supercontinent prior to its breakup.

graben (6) a downdropped block of the earth's crust, usually produced by tension rifting (faulting) the crust into pieces, allowing a crustal block to sag or subside.

gradient (8) the slope of a streambed, measured in feet (meters) of elevation loss per mile (kilometer) of horizontal distance.

granular disintegration (4) a form of chemical weathering in which the minerals of a rock take on water, swell, and separate from one another.

ground moraine (8) a blanket of glacial deposits, often drift, which covers an area, producing gently rolling topography.

ground motion (6) the observed motion of the earth's surface during an earthquake. Normally the extent (acceleration) of ground motion may be described as a percentage of the "force" (acceleration) of gravity.

groundwater (8, 10) water stored beneath the water table.

Gutenberg discontinuity (6) boundary between mantle and outer core, recognized as surface below which S-waves are absorbed.

gymnosperms (14) a large group of plants that bear their seeds naked in cones; includes all modern conifers. See *angiosperms*.

half-life (11) the length of time required for one-half of the atoms of a radioactive element to change into another product.

hardness (2) the resistance to scratching of a mineral, usually measured on a scale of relative hardness, such as the *Mohs scale*. A hardness test measures the resistance to breakage of the atomic bonds within a mineral; hardness is a diagnostic physical property of minerals.

hardpan (4) an accumulation of soluble minerals in a soil within arid or semiarid areas. See *caliche*.

horizon (soil) (4) one of a distinctive vertical sequence of layers within a zonal soil. The vertical sequence of horizons is generally labeled alphabetically from the surface downward; thus, the A-horizon is one horizon near the surface.

horizontality, original, principle of (5, 11) an assertion that sedimentary deposits are originally deposited as horizontal or subhorizontal layers.

horns (glacial) (8) roughly triangular peaks in map view, produced by the convergence of *arêtes*. See *arête*.

hundred-year flood (8) the discharge that any stream may produce on the average once a century, or the discharge that has a 1 percent chance of occurrence in any single year.

hydration (4) the chemical combination of water with other substances. Water becomes part of the resulting chemical compound.

hydrocarbon (9) an organic chemical compound containing hydrogen and carbon; may contain oxygen. Both oil and coal are hydrocarbons.

hydrolysis (4) the substitution of hydrogen in the water for a metal, which is then removed in solution.

Ice Age (8) For North America, the last 2 million years, during which continental glaciers have advanced and retreated across the land from central Canada. Sometimes called the *Pleistocene epoch*.

igneous (3) an adjective describing rock that formerly was molten.

inclusion, principle of (11) a rock fragment is older than the material that surrounds it.

inductive reasoning (1) the method of logic that seeks generalizations to explain many particular instances.

invertebrate (13) said of any animal that lacks a backbone.

island arc (7) a series of volcanic islands that, in map view, form a curving arc. Island arcs are usually landward from a foredeep.

isostasy (6) a principle of equilibrium that declares that mass excess above the earth's surface must be compensated by mass deficiency beneath the surface in order that the crust be in approximate equilibrium.

isotope (11) all atoms of the same element possess the same number of protons, but may contain different numbers of neutrons. Each of the variants is an isotope. Thus, C^{12}, C^{13}, and C^{14} are isotopes of the element carbon. Each isotope has the same atomic number, but a different atomic weight. See *atomic number* and *atomic weight*.

karst (10) a type of topography formed over soluble rocks, characterized by closed depressions, sinkholes, caves, and underground drainage. First described from a limestone plateau (karst area) in the Dinaric Alps of Yugoslavia.

kettle (8) an approximately circular depression in drift, often containing a lake or swamp. Formed when a piece of glacial ice that is buried in drift melts and allows the drift cover to collapse.

kilowatt-hour (9) a unit of power equivalent to 1000 watts expended in 1 hour. One kilowatt equals approximately $3/4$ horsepower.

kinetic energy (8) the work done by a moving body; equivalent to mass $\times$ velocity^2.

lag gravel (8) gravel and coarse rock debris that remains behind on a surface that has undergone extensive deflation of finer material. Also called *deflation armor* and *desert pavement*.

lahar (3) a mudflow consisting of fine pyroclastic material that occurs on the slopes of a volcano.

Laramide orogeny (14) a time of deformation in the eastern Rocky Mountains that extended from approximately 50 to 100 million years ago. The Laramide orogeny is probably best considered the eastern, later phase of a lengthy time of deformation that generally began in the western United States and moved eastward through time. The earlier events are called the *Nevadian orogeny.*

laterite (4) a type of soil developed by intensive tropical weathering and leaching; all soluble compounds are lost.

lava (3) liquid erupted magma on the earth's surface.

lava flow (3) a landform produced by an extrusion of lava that flows across the earth's surface and cools to rock.

lava plateau (3) an extensive flat area, produced by the deposition of numerous lava flows on top of one another.

Le Chatelier's principle (4) a natural system at equilibrium, when disturbed, will react so as to gain a new state of equilibrium and minimize the disturbance.

lignite (9) a low rank of coal. See *coal.*

liquefaction (6) the temporary transformation of a fluid-filled solid into a liquid due to an abrupt rise in pore fluid pressure caused by a sudden shock or other type of stress.

lithosphere (6) the upper solid portion of the earth that reacts to long-term stress by fracture or folding. The lithosphere rests on the asthenosphere beneath it. See *asthenosphere.*

loess (8) a type of silty soil, produced by deflation of glacial deposits, causing removal of silt-sized particles followed by the deposition of the silt by the wind.

luster (2) the appearance of the surface of a mineral as it reflects light.

maar crater (3) a type of volcanic crater produced when groundwater gains access to the magma source, creating a violent steam eruption.

magma (3) liquid (usually silicate melt plus gases/crystals) beneath the earth's surface. Magma contains dissolved gases, chiefly water vapor, liquid matter and, on partial cooling, some mineral crystals.

magnetism (2) the property of a few minerals whereby they attract iron particles or another magnet to themselves.

mantle (6) the portion of the earth below the Mohorovicic and above the Gutenberg discontinuities, or the portion beneath the earth's crust and above the earth's outer core.

mass wasting (8) a term for *all* of the processes that move material downslope solely under the acceleration of gravity.

mechanical weathering (4) a term for all of the processes that break rock into smaller fragments.

meiosis (12) a form of cell division in which one-half of the number of chromosomes in the original cell are transferred to the new sperm and egg cells.

Mesozoic era (11) the period of time between approximately 65 to 225 million years ago in which reptiles were the dominant animal life form. The early part of the Mesozoic was marked by the breakup of Pangaea.

metamorphism (5) a term for a group of processes that internally reorganize the crystalline structure and/or mineral types of a rock, *while it remains solid,* under the influence of heat and pressure different from those under which the original rock formed.

metamorphism, principle of (11) a metamorphosed rock is older than the agent that metamorphosed it. For example, a baked rock must have been there prior to the baking event.

metazoa (11) a multicellular organism.

mineral (2) a naturally occurring, crystalline, inorganic chemical compound whose chemical composition and physical properties are fixed or vary within narrow limits.

mineraloid (2) a mineral that possesses no crystalline structure or only a poorly developed crystalline structure.

miogeosyncline (12) the part of the geosyncline located next to the craton, approximately coincident with the continental shelf. Sediments received are clean, shallow water sediments. Also called the *miogeocline,* a more modern usage. Compare with *eugeosyncline.*

mitotic cell division (12) the method of cell division in which exact duplication of chromosomes occurs, with one-half of each chromosome distributed to each sperm and egg cell.

Mohorovicic discontinuity (6) the narrow zone beneath the crust characterized by rapid increase in the velocity of seismic waves. The base of the crust.

moraine (8) a pile of drift produced at the margin of a glacier. Moraines mark the maximum extent of glacial advance or the area where two glaciers merged.

mud cracks (5) roughly polygonal fractures produced in drying mud by volume loss as mud dries out.

mudstone (5) a rock composed largely of clay, but lacking the well-defined thin bedding planes characteristic of a shale.

neutron (11) an uncharged elementary atomic particle with a mass nearly equal to that of a proton. An isolated neutron is unstable and decays with a half-life of about 13 minutes into an electron, a proton, and an electrically neutral elementary particle (the neutrino) whose mass is so small it is difficult to detect. See *proton* and *electron.*

Nevadian orogeny (14) a time of deformation during the early and middle Mesozoic in the western United States. Compare with *Laramide orogeny.*

nonfoliated (5) a texture of metamorphic rocks produced when crystals of roughly equant shape are produced during the recrystallization of a rock. Marbles and quartzites are typical nonfoliated metamorphic rocks.

obsidian (13) a natural volcanic glass produced by rapid cooling of silica-rich lava.

oil shale (9) shale of freshwater lake origin that contains organic compounds that are precursors to petroleum.

ore deposit (2) an accumulation of minerals that can be mined and processed to produce a desirable commodity at a profit.

orogeny (13) the process by which structures within mountainous areas are formed; generally includes faulting, folding, igneous activity, and metamorphism. The formation of the mountainous *topography* is a later event than orogeny.

paleomagnetism (7) one of the many scientific specialties within geology that concerns itself with understanding ancient magnetic phenomena and products.

paleontology (5) the study of past life forms and the history of life.

Paleozoic era (11) the period of time stretching from approximately 225 to 570 million years ago. Some geologists add the Eocambrian period to the Paleozoic, which would make the era extend back to about 800 million years. This is a modern but controversial usage. The beginning of the Paleozoic era coincides with the development of metazoan life, and the skeleton and hard parts. The development of the backbone and of both plant and animal life on the continents occurred during this era.

Pangaea (7) Wegener proposed this name for the hypothetical supercontinent that formed at the end of the Paleozoic era. Other reconstructions have believed there were two smaller continental agglomerations, the northern one called *Laurasia* and the southern one called *Gondwanaland.*

peat (9) the lowest rank of coal. Slightly altered, partially decayed plant material, often quarried from bogs.

pedalfers (4) all soils in which leaching is moderate but neither excessive (the *laterites*) or nearly lacking (the *pedocals*). See those terms for contrasts.

pediment (8) a gently sloping bedrock surface at the front of a mountainous mass in a desert area. The pediment is commonly veneered with a thin gravel deposit, and it grades laterally into an alluvial fan deposit downslope. Its origin is controversial.

pedocal (4) a soil containing an excess of soluble components. Compare with *pedalfer.*

permeability (10) the percentage of interconnected pores in natural materials, or the ease of passage of fluids through material.

phytoplankton (12) marine unicellular plants, deriving their energy from photosynthesis.

placers (4) an alluvial deposit containing heavy particles of commercial value.

plate tectonics theory (7) an idea that proposes that the earth's lithosphere is subdivided into a mosaic of plates that are in motion relative to one another. See *lithosphere* and *continental drift.*

plutonic (3) igneous material that has cooled slowly beneath the earth's surface, or igneous activity at depth.

pluvial lake (8) a lake formed during a period of exceptionally heavy rainfall. Usually applied to lakes formed during the Ice Age, but distant from the glacial margin.

porphyritic (3) an adjective that states that an igneous rock texture is composed of two distinctly contrasting grain sizes.

potential energy (8) the form of mechanical energy possessed by a body because of its position. If the elevation of a body is raised, it is gaining potential energy. Compare with *kinetic energy.*

power (9) the *rate* at which work is done. Common units of power are the watt and the horsepower. One horsepower equals 746 watts.

Precambrian era (11) all geologic time before the Paleozoic era. Numerous subdivisions of Precambrian time have been proposed, but there is no internationally agreed on standard for subdivision. This textbook uses Precambrian era as the term for all time prior to the Paleozoic era.

prior appropriation doctrine (10) a concept of water rights unique to the western United States; holds that the right to water is a function of seniority of use. "First in sight is first in right." During a time of water shortage, more recent users may be rationed or forbidden to use water, while those who have used the water resource for some time may proceed unimpaired.

porous (10) an adjective describing any material containing pores. Compare with *permeability*. Porosity is percent pore space in material.

prokaryote (12) cells that lack nuclear membranes. Include bacteria and blue-green algae. All other cells have a defined nucleus. Compare with *eukaryote*.

proton (11) an elementary atomic particle with a single positive charge and a mass approximately 1847 times that of the electron. The number of protons in the nucleus of an atom is the *atomic number* of the element.

P-wave (6) a seismic wave whose energy travels by elastic compression of the earth. The P-wave is a body wave and travels at the greatest wave velocity, causing vibration of particles parallel its wave path.

pyroclastic (3) a sedimentary rock composed of fragments of igneous material that have been blown into the air and settled to form layers of pyroclastic material. In some rock classifications, pyroclastics are treated as volcanic rocks; in others, they are classed as sedimentary rocks. They are, of course, both.

quicksand (8) sand saturated with water; has little or no capacity to support weight. Quicksand is a dense liquid that may become solid by draining or freezing.

radioactive decay (11) spontaneous transformation of one element to another or one isotope to another accompanied by emission of subatomic particles.

radioactivity (11) emission of alpha and beta particles and gamma rays, plus heat energy, as a result of radioactive decay.

radiometric dating (11) calculating the chronologic age of a specimen by any method that is based on decay rates of radioactive elements.

rain shadow desert (8) an arid area in the lee of a major mountain mass, which precipitates moisture on its windward side.

recrystallization (5) a group of processes that reorganize the chemical components of minerals *while they remain solid crystals* and form new minerals more stable at elevated pressures and temperatures. See *metamorphism*.

reflection (6) the bouncing back of light rays as they strike a solid surface is the most familiar example, but any type of energy wave, including seismic energy, may be reflected from a bounding surface.

refraction (6) a change in direction and speed of an energy wave as it passes from one medium to another of different density.

regolith (4) a term for all unconsolidated material that overlies bedrock. It includes any form of rock debris, organic accumulations, and soils. Compare with *bedrock*.

regression of the sea (13) locally, a drop in sea level. Regionally, an offlap of the sea caused by the elevation of the land surface rising or by the seafloor dropping. One theory holds that worldwide regressions of the sea follow periods of slow spreading rates in the oceanic spreading centers.

Richter magnitude (6) a measure of the ground motion produced by an earthquake. The *intensity* of an earthquake, in contrast, is a measure of the damage produced. The Richter magnitude scale is exponential; $M = 6$ means 10 times the amplitude of ground motion as $M = 5$, and 100 times the amplitude of ground motion of $M = 4$.

rift zone (6) an extensive fracture in the crust, produced by crustal tension. The block(s) between the rift zone may drop downward, forming a *graben*. The oceanic ridges of the world's ocean basin are the most extensive rift zones on earth. See *graben* and *spreading center*.

riparian rule (doctrine) (10) a system of water law that allows the landowner, adjacent to any surface water source, to divert the water to the use of the landowner, provided that the water is returned to the waterway, undiminished in quality or quantity. It is the typical surface water law of the eastern United States. Compare with *prior appropriation doctrine,* the surface water law of the more arid west.

ripple marks (5) a common sedimentary structure produced by wind or water currents flowing over loose sediment. The structure consists of alternate peaks and valleys and is commonly preserved in consolidated sedimentary rock.

rock cleavage (5) planes of easy parting naturally developed in rock whose minerals are strongly aligned, or *foliated*.

rock cycle (5) a concept that envisages all rocks forming from alteration of other rocks as a response to changed environments.

root wedging (4) a type of mechanical weathering in which growing roots wedge and fracture rocks that surround them.

sandstone (5) a clastic sedimentary rock composed of consolidated, sand-sized grains.

schistosity (5) parallel alignment of micaceous minerals in a medium-grade metamorphic rock. Texture is produced by total recrystallization of rock under elevated pressure, temperature, and shearing stress.

scientific method (2) a method of reasoning that assumes that things naturally together can be understood in a rational world. Scientific reasoning searches for repetitive relations in the natural world and seeks to understand the connections between all parts of the world.

seafloor spreading (7) a theory that proposes that seafloor is created at oceanic ridges and is consumed at foredeeps, subduction zones, or Benioff zones by remelting. As basaltic seafloor is formed at the oceanic ridge, it moves away from the ridge, displaced by younger seafloor.

sediment (5) unconsolidated particles of rocks and minerals.

sedimentary rocks (5) all rocks formed on the earth's surface by organic and inorganic means at low temperature and pressure.

sedimentary structures (5) a large-scale feature in a sedimentary rock formed either before, during, or after consolidation. An example is a ripple mark.

seiches (6) an oscillation of the water surface of a lake or bay, produced by sudden winds or earthquakes.

seismic creep (6) the movement of bedrock, broken by fractures, such that the slow movement along the fracture produces frequent, minor earthquakes.

seismogram (6) the written record of earth movement produced by a seismograph.

seismograph (6) an instrument that records ground motion during an earthquake.

seismologist (6) a geologist whose professional speciality is the study of the causes and effects of earthquakes.

seismology (6) the science of earthquake study.

sequence (13) a packet or group of cratonic deposits, bounded both above and below by widespread, regional unconformities.

shadow zone (6) a zone on the surface of the earth where no earthquake energy is received because of absorption of S-waves and refraction of P-waves by the outer core.

shale (5) a clastic sedimentary rock, composed mostly of clay minerals, with well-defined thin, laminar bedding.

shear modulus (6) ratio of shearing stress to change in shape produced by that stress. Also called the *modulus of rigidity*. A measure of the natural *resistance* of any substance to change in shape. The shear modulus for a gas or fluid is zero.

shear wave (6) an energy wave that travels by temporarily changing the shape of the material through which it travels. The S-wave, a seismic wave, is a shear wave. A shear wave can only travel through a solid whose resistance to change in shape (its shear modulus) is appreciable; therefore shear waves cannot travel through gases or liquids.

shield (12) synonym for craton. See *craton*.

shield volcano (3) a volcano produced when fairly fluid lava erupts, forming a cone whose sides slope very gently. The term comes from a supposed resemblance of these volcanoes to an ancient soldier's shield turned upside down on the earth.

silicate (2) any chemical compound composed of the two elements, silicon and oxygen, which are the most abundant elements on the earth's surface. Most common minerals are silicates or *aluminosilicates*.

sill (3) a tabular igneous intrusion that is roughly parallel to the layering of the enclosing rock.

sinkhole (10) a depression on the earth's surface, produced by the collapse of a cavern roof. Sinkholes are common in regions of *karst* topography. See *karst*.

slaty cleavage (5) a type of cleavage produced in low-grade metamorphic rocks, particularly slates. Much, but probably not all, slaty cleavage is produced when muddy sediment is dewatered, with consequent alignment of the mineral grains.

snow line (8) the elevation above which snow remains year around.

soil (4) a loosely defined term. In this textbook, the term is restricted to natural accumulations of sediment (the azonal soils) or highly modified regolith (the zonal soils), but the term is often used to mean just about anything that is not solid rock.

solfatara (3) synonym for fumarole. See *fumarole*.

solifluction (8) a type of mass wasting unique to subarctic climates, where the thawed upper layer of otherwise permanently frozen regolith may move downslope as a mudflow during the summer season.

specific gravity (2) the ratio of a unit volume of a substance to the same volume of water. It is numerically equal to *density*, which is mass per unit volume.

spreading center (7) an oceanic ridge along which lava is extruded, displacing earlier lava laterally along the seafloor. Many spreading centers are coincident with the rift zone in the central part of an oceanic ridge. See *rift zone*.

spring (10) water flow produced where the earth's surface intersects the water table, allowing groundwater to flow out.

stratigraphy (5) the science of study of stratified sedimentary rock and its fossils.

stratovolcano (3) synonym for composite cone. See *composite cone*.

streak (2) the color of the powdered mineral as it is rubbed off on a streak plate. The streak of a mineral may or may not be the same as the color of the solid mineral.

stress (6) force per unit area, as in pounds per square inch (kilograms per square centimeter). Often confused with *strain,* the deformation produced by stress.

subduction (zone) (7) an area where seafloor is forced downward and remelted or consumed. Coincident with a *foredeep,* the surface expression of a subduction zone. Synonym: *Benioff zone*.

superposition, principle of (5, 11) unless the sedimentary pile is completely overturned, older rocks underlie younger rocks.

surface faulting (6) displacement of the earth's surface along a visible fracture or fault zone during an earthquake. Not all earthquakes produce surface faulting.

surface wave (6) a seismic energy wave that travels only in the crust and does not penetrate the earth's interior. Compare with *body wave*.

S-wave (6) shear wave or secondary wave. A type of seismic wave that displaces particles perpendicular to the direction of wave travel. Synonym: *shear wave*.

symmetry (2) the concept of symmetry recognizes the symmetrical distribution of faces, edges, and corners of a crystal about certain planes and lines of reference as an indication of the ordered internal arrangement of a crystal.

talus (8) rock fragments lying at the base of a slope. An accumulation or apron of these fragments is called a *talus slope*. Synonym: *rubble*.

taste (2) a physical property of some minerals that yields a distinctive taste when touched to one's tongue.

temporary baselevel (8) the elevation below which a stream cannot erode, until the temporary baselevel itself is lowered. For many streams, the temporary baselevel is the elevation of the next lower stream or a lake.

time scale, geologic (11) a system of division of all geologic time into eras, periods, and epochs, based on biologic and physical events (see Appendix D).

transform faults (7) a specific class of faults that transforms the spreading motion of a spreading center into sliding motion along a fault connecting two offset spreading centers.

transgression (13) sea moves onto the land, due to submergence of the continent or increase in oceanic volume. See *regression* for contrast.

tsunami (3) a seismic sea wave produced by deformation and offset of the ocean basin floor. Seismic sea waves travel at high speed in deep water, but slow down and reach extreme wave heights in shallow water.

uniformity, principle of (1, 5) the principle used by Lyell to describe a concept originated by Hutton. In its broadest form, the principle of uniformity asserts that past geologic events can be explained in terms of the processes operating today. A modern understanding of uniformity does not insist that rates or duration of processes in the past are necessarily similar to those operating today. A modern restatement of the principle might well be that "the present is *one* key to the past."

ultimate baselevel (8) elevation of sea level. The elevation below which streams cannot erode the continents, although both glaciers and submarine currents may erode below sea level.

unconformity (13) an erosional interval of time preserved as an eroded surface in rocks.

valley glacier (8) a glacier whose margins are confined by valley walls or stream divides. Compare with *continental glacier*. Valley glaciers are sometimes called *alpine glaciers*. Valley glaciers generally roughen the previous topography over which they pass, while continental glaciers generally smooth and round the topography over which they pass.

velocity (8) the rate of flow. Stream velocity is measured in feet per second (meters per second).

volcanic neck (3) the erosional remnant of the feeder pipe of a volcano.

volcanic rock (3) rock produced by the freezing of igneous material placed on the earth's surface.

water table (10) the zone below which the pores in material are totally filled with water. The line that divides the saturated from the unsaturated zone of the regolith.

wave velocity (6) the speed of *advance* of the waveform. Wave velocity is independent of the velocity of particle *vibration* in the substance transmitting the wave.

weathering (4) a term for a large group of processes that alter solid rock in contact with the atmosphere, the hydrosphere, and the biosphere.

weathering zone (4) the area within the uppermost part of the regolith where weathering is an active process.

zonal soil group (4) one of two major groups of soils, distinguished by the presence in a vertical exposure of separate soil horizons. See *horizon*. Zonal soils form due to both leaching and deposition of soluble material within the entire weathering zone; they represent a kind of chemical differentiation of an originally roughly homogenous parent material.

Index

Playfair, John, 282
    glaciation, ancient, 283
Plutonic, *see* Rocks, igneous
Polar wandering, 209-210, 218
    apparent, 218
Precambrian era, 386-387, 395-429, **569**
    atmosphere, 400, 406
    earth origin, 397
    mineral wealth, 422-424
    oceans, 400
    oldest rock, 415
    primitive life, 402-406
    rocks, 424-425
Prokaryotes, 403, **570**

Quicksand, 252

Radioactivity, 378, 540, **570**
    half-life, 380-381, **565**
Radiolaria, 458, 511
Radiometric dating, 379, 381, **570**
    beryllium-10, 382
    carbon-14, 381
    fission track, 385
    isochron, 383-384
    meteoritic, 397
    potassium-argon, 383
    uranium-lead, 382-383
Reasoning:
    deductive, 11, **562**
    inductive, 11, **566**
    scientific method, 18, 101, 529
Regolith, 101, **570**
Regressive rock sequence, 437, **570**
    Cenozoic, 496-497
    and continental assembly, 472
    and worldwide climates, 472
Reptiles, 460, 511
    amniotic egg, 460, 480, **559**
    dinosaurs, *see* Dinosaurs
    thecodonts, 481, 487
    therapsids, 480, 488, 512
Richter scale, *see* Magnitude, ground motion
Rift, 188, 224, 232, 468, **570**
Ripple marks, 122, 124, **571**
Risk:
    seismic, 158, 165-167
    volcanic, 81
Rock cycle, 142-144, **571**
Rocks, 54, 543-547
    igneous, 59, 65, **566**
        classification, 68
        minerals, 63

plutonic, 65, 118, **569**
    texture, 67
    volcanic, 57
metamorphic, 118, 130
    banded iron formation, 415
    foliated, 135, 564, **571**
    non-foliated, 133, **568**
    origin, 134-136
    types, 130-136
    oldest, 415
sedimentary, 11, 103, 401, **571**
    classification, 118-122
    clastic vs. chemical, 119, **561**
    environments, 117
    exposure area vs. rock age, 118
    percent exposure, 117
    sediment, 116
    stratified, 130
    structures, 123, **560, 562**
    textures, 122
    type through time, 401
Running water, 258
    baselevel, 259-264
    cutting vs. mass wasting, 263
    in deserts, 274
    energy, 259

Schistosity, origin of, 134, 137, **571**
Science, 10, 13
    as ordering process, 101-102
    development of, 529-530
    development of humans, 521-523
    development of inquiry, 141
Scientific method, 18, 101-102, **571**
    in mineral identification, 20, 23
    self-correcting model, 411
Seafloor spreading, 221, **571**
    and age of ocean floors, 226-228
    convection in mantle, 223
    and mantle plumes, 504-506
    plate consumption, 236
    rate of, 227, 470
    spreading centers, 221, 231, **572**
    and transgressive sequences, 470
Sediment, **570**
Sedimentary rocks, *see* Rock, sedimentary
Seismic sea waves, 55-56
Seismographs, 162, 163, **571**
    epicenter location, 187
    seismograms, 163, **571**
    strong-motion, 163
Sequences, cratonic, 438-439, 470, **572**
Shadow zone, 184, **572**

prediction of eruption, 84-85
primitive, 416
relation to batholiths, 67
at spreading centers, 231
worldwide distribution, 57
Warm-bloodedness, 486-487
Water, 329-355
  groundwater, 331-335, **565**
  hard, 341
  and karst, 347
  law, 348
  porosity underground, 333, **569, 570**
  problems, 341
  quality, 342-344
  recovery, 339-341
  running, *see* Running water; Surface water
  surface, 331
  table, 333, 335
  treatment, 339-341
  use, 335-339
  wells, 340-341
  see also Law, water
Waterpower, 320
Water table, 331, 333, 335, **574**
  declining, 344-347

karst, 347
perched, 335, **573**
regional, 335
Weathering, 92
  acid rain, 99
  chemical, 97, **561, 574**
    acidity, 99
    carbonation, **561**
    controls on, 97
    desert varnish, 107, 276
    hydrolysis, 99, **566**
    solution, 100
  controls on, 93, 97
  mechanical, 93, **567, 574**
    crystal growth, 96
    frost wedging, 94
    granular disintegration, 96
    root wedging, 105, **571**
    unloading, 94
    volume change, 95
Wegener, Alfred, 12, 201-215, 273. *See also*
    Continental drift
Wells, 312, 340
  oil, 312-313
  water, 340-341, 344, **559**

74

Principal Islands of
HAWAII
SCALE 1:7,500,000

ALASKA
SCALE 1:12,000,000

U.S. DEPARTMENT OF THE INTERIOR
GEOLOGICAL SURVEY